Jar

James Herriot (a pseudonym) grew up in [illegible] s a veterinary surgeon at Glasgow Veterinary College. Shortly afterwards he took up a position as an assistant in a North Yorkshire practice where he remained for the rest of his life, with the exception of his wartime service in the RAF.

James Herriot's interests extended beyond writing and veterinary work to music, and dog-walking in the Dales. He was married, with a son who is also a veterinary surgeon and a daughter who is a doctor.

Britain's best loved vet died in 1995.

Also by James Herriot in Pan

Vet in Harness
Vets Might Fly
Vet in a Spin

and

The Lord God Made them All

and

All Creatures Great and Small
All Things Bright and Beautiful
All Things Wise and Wonderful
(Omnibus editions)

James Herriot's Dog Stories

JAMES HERRIOT

If Only They Could Talk

It Shouldn't Happen to a Vet

Let Sleeping Vets Lie

Every Living Thing

PAN BOOKS
IN ASSOCIATION WITH MICHAEL JOSEPH

If Only They Could Talk first published 1970 by Michael Joseph Ltd
and first published by Pan Books 1973 in association with Michael Joseph Ltd.
It Shouldn't Happen to a Vet first published 1972 by Michael Joseph Ltd
and first published by Pan Books 1973 in association with Michael Joseph Ltd.
Let Sleeping Vets Lie first published 1973 by Michael Joseph Ltd
and first published by Pan Books 1974 in association with Michael Joseph Ltd.
Every Living Thing first published 1992 by Michael Joseph Ltd
and first published by Pan Books 1993

This combined edition published 1995 by Pan Books
an imprint of Macmillan General Books
25 Eccleston Place, London SW1W 9NF
and Basingstoke
in association with Michael Joseph Ltd.

Associated companies throughout the world

ISBN 0 330 34597 4

1 3 5 7 9 8 6 4 2

A CIP catalogue record for this book is available from the British Library

Printed and bound in Great Britain by
Cox & Wyman Ltd, Reading, Berkshire

If Only They Could Talk

To

EDDIE STRAITON

with gratitude and affection

CHAPTER ONE

They didn't say anything about this in the books, I thought, as the snow blew in through the gaping doorway and settled on my naked back.

I lay face down on the cobbled floor in a pool of nameless muck, my arm deep inside the straining cow, my feet scrabbling for a toe-hold between the stones. I was stripped to the waist and the snow mingled with the dirt and the dried blood on my body. I could see nothing outside the circle of flickering light thrown by the smoky oil lamp which the farmer held over me.

No, there wasn't a word in the books about searching for your ropes and instruments in the shadows; about trying to keep clean in a half bucket of tepid water; about the cobbles digging into your chest. Nor about the slow numbing of the arms, the creeping paralysis of the muscles as the fingers tried to work against the cow's powerful expulsive efforts.

There was no mention anywhere of the gradual exhaustion, the feeling of futility and the little far-off voice of panic.

My mind went back to that picture in the obstetrics book. A cow standing in the middle of a gleaming floor while a sleek veterinary surgeon in a spotless parturition overall inserted his arm to a polite distance. He was relaxed and smiling, the farmer and his helpers were smiling, even the cow was smiling. There was no dirt or blood or sweat anywhere.

That man in the picture had just finished an excellent lunch and had moved next door to do a bit of calving just for the sheer pleasure of it, as a kind of dessert. He hadn't crawled shivering from his bed at two o'clock in the morning and bumped over twelve miles of frozen snow, staring sleepily ahead till the lonely farm showed in the headlights. He hadn't climbed half a mile of white fell-side to the doorless barn where his patient lay.

I tried to wriggle my way an extra inch inside the cow. The calf's head was back and I was painfully pushing a thin, looped rope towards its lower jaw with my finger tips. All the time my arm was being squeezed between the calf and the bony pelvis. With every straining effort from the cow the pressure became almost unbearable, then she would relax and I would push the rope another inch. I wondered how long I would be able to keep this up. If I didn't snare that jaw soon I would never get the calf away. I groaned, set my teeth and reached forward again.

Another little flurry of snow blew in and I could almost hear the flakes sizzling on my sweating back. There was sweat on my forehead too, and it trickled into my eyes as I pushed.

There is always a time at a bad calving when you begin to wonder if you will ever win the battle. I had reached this stage.

Little speeches began to flit through my brain. 'Perhaps it would be better to slaughter this cow. Her pelvis is so small and narrow that I can't see a calf coming through,' or 'She's a good fat animal and really of the beef type, so don't you think it would pay you better to get the butcher?' or perhaps 'This is a very bad presentation. In a roomy cow it would be simple enough to bring the head round but in this case it is just about impossible.'

Of course, I could have delivered the calf by embryotomy – by passing a wire over the neck and sawing off the head. So many of these occasions ended with the floor strewn with heads, legs, heaps of intestines. There were thick text books devoted to the countless ways you could cut up a calf.

But none of it was any good here, because this calf was alive. At my furthest stretch I had got my finger as far as the commissure of the mouth and had been startled by a twitch of the little creature's tongue. It was unexpected because calves in this position are usually dead, asphyxiated by the acute flexion of the neck and the pressure of the dam's powerful contractions. But this one had a spark of life in it and if it came out it would have to be in one piece.

I went over to my bucket of water, cold now and bloody, and silently soaped my arms. Then I lay down again, feeling the cobbles harder than ever against my chest. I worked my toes between the stones, shook the sweat from my eyes and for the hundredth time thrust an arm that felt like spaghetti into the cow; alongside the little dry legs of the calf, like sandpaper tearing against my flesh, then to the bend in the neck and so to the ear and then, agonizingly, along the side of the face towards the lower jaw which had become my major goal in life.

It was incredible that I had been doing this for nearly two hours; fighting as my strength ebbed to push a little noose round that jaw. I had tried everything else – repelling a leg, gentle traction with a blunt hook in the eye socket, but I was back to the noose.

It had been a miserable session all through. The farmer, Mr Dinsdale, was a long, sad, silent man of few words who always seemed to be expecting the worst to happen. He had a long, sad, silent son with him and the two of them had watched my efforts with deepening gloom.

But worst of all had been Uncle. When I had first entered the hillside barn I had been surprised to see a little bright-eyed old man in a pork pie hat settling down comfortably on a bale of straw. He was filling his pipe and clearly looking forward to the entertainment.

'Now then, young man,' he cried in the nasal twang of the West Riding. 'I'm Mr Dinsdale's brother. I farm over in Listondale.'

I put down my equipment and nodded. 'How do you do? My name is Herriot.'

The old man looked me over, piercingly. 'My vet is Mr Broomfield. Expect you'll have heard of him – everybody knows him, I reckon. Wonderful man, Mr Broomfield, especially at calving. Do you know, I've never seen 'im beat yet.'

I managed a wan smile. Any other time I would have been delighted to hear how good my colleague was, but somehow not now, not now. In fact, the words set a mournful little bell tolling inside me.

'No, I'm afraid I don't know Mr Broomfield,' I said, taking off my jacket and, more reluctantly, peeling my shirt over my head. 'But I haven't been around these parts very long.'

Uncle was aghast. 'You don't know him! Well you're the only one as doesn't. They think the world of him in Listondale, I can tell you.' He lapsed into a shocked silence and applied a match to his pipe. Then he shot a glance at my goose-pimpled torso. 'Strips like a boxer does Mr Broomfield. Never seen such muscles on a man.'

A wave of weakness coursed sluggishly over me. I felt suddenly leaden-footed and inadequate. As I began to lay out my ropes and instruments on a clean towel the old man spoke again.

'And how long have you been qualified, may I ask?'

'Oh, about seven months.'

'Seven months!' Uncle smiled indulgently, tamped down his tobacco and blew out a cloud of rank, blue smoke. 'Well, there's nowt like a bit of experience, I always says. Mr Broomfield's been doing my work now for over ten years and he really knows what he's about. No, you can 'ave your book learning. Give me experience every time.'

I tipped some antiseptic into the bucket and lathered my arms carefully. I knelt behind the cow.

'Mr Broomfield always puts some special lubricating oils on his arms first,' Uncle said, pulling contentedly on his pipe. 'He says you get infection of the womb if you just use soap and water.'

I made my first exploration. It was the burdened moment all vets go through when they first put their hand into a cow. Within seconds I would know whether I would be putting on my jacket in fifteen minutes or whether I had hours of hard labour ahead of me.

I was going to be unlucky this time; it was a nasty presentation. Head back and no room at all; more like being inside an undeveloped heifer than a second calver. And she was bone dry – the 'waters' must have come away from her hours ago. She had been running out on the high fields and had started to calve a week before her time; that was why they had had to bring her into this half-ruined barn. Anyway, it would be a long time before I saw my bed again.

'Well now, what have you found, young man?' Uncle's penetrating voice cut through the silence. 'Head back, eh? You won't have much trouble, then. I've seen Mr Broomfield do 'em like that – he turns calf right round and brings it out back legs first.'

I had heard this sort of nonsense before. A short time in practice had taught me that all farmers were experts with other farmers' live stock. When their own animals were in trouble they tended to rush to the phone for the vet, but with their neighbours' they were confident, knowledgeable and full of helpful advice. And another phenomenon I had observed was that their advice was usually regarded as more valuable than the vet's. Like now, for instance; Uncle was obviously an accepted sage and the Dinsdales listened with deference to everything he said.

'Another way with a job like this,' continued Uncle, 'is to get a few strong chaps with ropes and pull the thing out, head back and all.'

I gasped as I felt my way around. 'I'm afraid it's impossible to turn a calf completely round in this small space. And to pull it out without bringing the head round would certainly break the mother's pelvis.'

The Dinsdales narrowed their eyes. Clearly they thought I was hedging in the face of Uncle's superior knowledge.

And now, two hours later, defeat was just round the corner. I was just about whacked. I had rolled and grovelled on the filthy cobbles while the Dinsdales watched me in morose silence and Uncle kept up a non-stop stream of comment. Uncle, his ruddy face glowing with delight, his little eyes sparkling, hadn't had such a happy night for years. His long trek up the hillside had been repaid a hundredfold. His vitality was undiminished; he had enjoyed every minute.

As I lay there, eyes closed, face stiff with dirt, mouth hanging open, Uncle took his pipe in his hand and leaned forward on his straw bale. 'You're about beat, young man,' he said with deep satisfaction. 'Well, I've never seen Mr Broomfield beat but he's had a lot of experience. And what's more, he's strong, really strong. That's one man you couldn't tire.'

Rage flooded through me like a draught of strong spirit. The right thing to do, of course, would be to get up, tip the bucket of bloody water over Uncle's head, run down the hill and drive away; away from Yorkshire, from Uncle, from the Dinsdales, from this cow.

Instead, I clenched my teeth, braced my legs and pushed with everything I had; and with a sensation of disbelief I felt my noose slide over the sharp little incisor teeth and into the calf's mouth. Gingerly, muttering a prayer, I pulled on the thin rope with my left hand and felt the slipknot tighten. I had hold of that lower jaw.

At last I could start doing something. 'Now hold this rope, Mr Dinsdale, and just keep a gentle tension on it. I'm going to repel the calf and if you pull steadily at the same time, the head ought to come round.'

'What if the rope comes off?' asked Uncle hopefully.

I didn't answer. I put my hand in against the calf's shoulder and began to push against the cow's contractions. I felt the small body moving away from me. 'Now a steady pull, Mr Dinsdale, without jerking.' And to myself, 'Oh God, don't let it slip off.'

The head was coming round. I could feel the neck straightening against my arm, then the ear touched my elbow. I let go the shoulder and grabbed the little muzzle. Keeping the teeth away from the vaginal wall with my hand, I guided the head till it was resting where it should be, on the fore limbs.

Quickly I extended the noose till it reached behind the ears. 'Now pull on the head as she strains.'

'Nay, you should pull on the legs now,' cried Uncle.

'Pull on the bloody head rope, I tell you!' I bellowed at the top of my voice and felt immediately better as Uncle retired, offended, to his bale.

With traction the head was brought out and the rest of the body followed easily. The little animal lay motionless on the cobbles, eyes glassy and unseeing, tongue blue and grossly swollen.

'It'll be dead. Bound to be,' grunted Uncle, returning to the attack.

I cleared the mucus from the mouth, blew hard down the throat and began artificial respiration. After a few pressures on the ribs, the calf gave a gasp and the eyelids flickered. Then it started to inhale and one leg jerked.

Uncle took off his hat and scratched his head in disbelief. 'By gaw, it's alive. I'd have thowt it'd sure to be dead after you'd messed about all that time.' A lot of the fire had gone out of him and his pipe hung down empty from his lips.

'I know what this little fellow wants,' I said. I grasped the calf by its fore legs and pulled it up to its mother's head. The cow was stretched out on her side, her head extended wearily along the rough floor. Her ribs heaved, her eyes were almost closed; she looked past caring about anything. Then she felt the calf's body against her face and there was a transformation; her eyes opened wide and her muzzle began a snuffling exploration of the new object. Her interest grew with every sniff and she struggled on to her chest, nosing and probing all over the calf, rumbling deep in her chest. Then she began to lick him methodically. Nature provides the perfect stimulant massage for a time like this and the little creature arched his back as the coarse papillae on the tongue dragged along his skin. Within a minute he was shaking his head and trying to sit up.

I grinned. This was the bit I liked. The little miracle. I felt it was something that would never grow stale no matter how often I saw it. I cleaned as much of the dried blood and filth from my body as I could, but most of it had caked on my skin and not even my finger nails would move it. It would have to wait for the hot bath at home. Pulling my shirt over my head, I felt as though I had been beaten for a long time with a thick stick. Every muscle ached. My mouth was dried out, my lips almost sticking together.

A long, sad figure hovered near. 'How about a drink?' asked Mr Dinsdale.

I could feel my grimy face cracking into an incredulous smile. A vision of hot tea well laced with whisky swam before me. 'That's very kind of you, Mr Dinsdale, I'd love a drink. It's been a hard two hours.'

'Nay,' said Mr Dinsdale looking at me steadily, 'I meant for the cow.'

I began to babble. 'Oh yes, of course, certainly, by all means give her a drink. She must be very thirsty. It'll do her good. Certainly, certainly, give her a drink.'

I gathered up my tackle and stumbled out of the barn. On the moor it was still dark and a bitter wind whipped over the snow, stinging my eyes. As I plodded down the slope, Uncle's voice, strident and undefeated, reached me for the last time.

'Mr Broomfield doesn't believe in giving a drink after calving. Says it chills the stomach.'

CHAPTER TWO

It was hot in the rickety little bus and I was on the wrong side where the July sun beat on the windows. I shifted uncomfortably inside my best suit and eased a finger inside the constricting white collar. It was a foolish outfit for this weather but a few miles ahead, my prospective employer was waiting for me and I had to make a good impression.

There was a lot hanging on this interview; being a newly

qualified veterinary surgeon in this year of 1937 was like taking out a ticket for the dole queue. Agriculture was depressed by a decade of government neglect, the draught horse which had been the mainstay of the profession was fast disappearing. It was easy to be a prophet of doom when the young men emerging from the colleges after a hard five years' slog were faced by a world indifferent to their enthusiasm and bursting knowledge. There were usually two or three situations vacant in the '*Record*' each week and an average of eighty applicants for each one.

It hadn't seemed true when the letter came from Darrowby in the Yorkshire Dales. Mr Siegfried Farnon MRCVS would like to see me on the Friday afternoon; I was to come to tea and if we were mutually suited I could stay on as assistant. I had grabbed at the lifeline unbelievingly; so many friends who had qualified with me were unemployed or working in shops or as labourers in the shipyards that I had given up hope of any other future for myself.

The driver crashed his gears again as he went into another steep bend. We had been climbing steadily now for the last fifteen miles or so, moving closer to the distant blue swell of the Pennines. I had never been in Yorkshire before but the name had always raised a picture of a county as stodgy and unromantic as its pudding; I was prepared for solid worth, dullness and a total lack of charm. But as the bus groaned its way higher I began to wonder. The formless heights were resolving into high, grassy hills and wide valleys. In the valley bottoms, rivers twisted among the trees and solid grey-stone farmhouses lay among islands of cultivated land which pushed bright green promontories up the hillsides into the dark tide of heather which lapped from the summits.

I had seen the fences and hedges give way to dry stone walls which bordered the roads, enclosed the fields and climbed endlessly over the surrounding fells. The walls were everywhere, countless miles of them, tracing their patterns high on the green uplands.

But as I neared my destination the horror stories kept forcing their way into my mind; the tales brought back to college by veterans hardened and embittered by a few months of practice. Assistants were just little bits of dirt to be starved and worked into the ground by the principals who were heartless and vicious to a man. Dave Stevens, lighting a cigarette with trembling hand: 'Never a night off or a half day. He made me wash the car, dig the garden, mow the lawn, do the family shopping. But when he told me to sweep the chimney I left.' Or Willie Johnstone: 'First job I had to do was pass the stomach tube on a horse. Got it into the trachea instead of the oesophagus. Couple of quick pumps and down went the horse with a hell of a crash – dead as a hammer. That's when I started these grey hairs.' Or that dreadful one they passed around about Fred Pringle. Fred had trocharized a bloated cow and the farmer had been so impressed by the pent up gas hissing from the abdomen that Fred had got carried away and applied his cigarette lighter to the canula. A roaring sheet of flame had swept on to some straw bales and burned the byre to the ground. Fred had taken up a colonial appointment immediately afterwards – Leeward Islands wasn't it?

Oh hell, that one couldn't be true. I cursed my fevered imagination and tried to shut out the crackling of the inferno, the terrified bellowing of the cattle as they were led to safety. No, it couldn't be as bad as that; I rubbed my sweating palms on my knees and tried to concentrate on the man I was going to meet.

Siegfried Farnon. Strange name for a vet in the Yorkshire Dales. Probably a German who had done his training in this country and decided to set up in practice. And it wouldn't have been Farnon in the beginning; probably Farrenen. Yes, Siegfried Farrenen. He was beginning to take shape; short, fat, roly poly type with merry eyes and a bubbling laugh. But at the same time I had trouble with the obtruding image of a hulking, cold-eyed, bristle-skulled Teuton more in keeping with the popular idea of the practice boss.

I realized the bus was clattering along a narrow street which opened on to a square where we stopped. Above the window of an unpretentious grocer shop I read 'Darrowby Co-operative Society'. We had arrived.

I got out and stood beside my battered suitcase, looking about me. There was something unusual and I couldn't put my finger on it at first. Then I realized what it was – the silence. The other passengers had dispersed, the driver had switched off his engine and there was not a sound or a movement anywhere. The only visible sign of life was a group of old men sitting round the clock tower in the centre of the square but they might have been carved from stone.

Darrowby didn't get much space in the guide books but when it was mentioned it was described as a grey little town on the river Darrow with a cobbled market place and little of interest except its two ancient bridges. But when you looked at it, its setting was beautiful on the pebbly river where the houses clustered thickly and straggled unevenly along the lower slopes of Herne Fell. Everywhere in Darrowby, in the streets, through the windows of the houses you could see the Fell rearing its calm, green bulk more than two thousand feet above the huddled roofs.

There was a clarity in the air, a sense of space and airiness that made me feel I had shed something on the plain, twenty miles behind. The confinement of the city, the grime, the smoke – already they seemed to be falling away from me.

Trengate was a quiet street leading off the square and I had my first sight of Skeldale House. I knew it was the right place before I was near enough to read 'S. Farnon MRCVS' on the old fashioned brass plate hanging slightly askew on the iron railings. I knew by the ivy which climbed untidily over the mellow brick to the topmost windows. It was what the letter had said – the only house with ivy; and this could be where I would work for the first time as a veterinary surgeon.

Now that I was here, right on the doorstep, I felt breathless, as though I had been running. If I got the job, this was where

I would find out about myself. There were many things to prove.

But I liked the look of the old house. It was Georgian with a fine, white-painted doorway. The windows, too, were white – wide and graceful on the ground floor and first storey but small and square where they peeped out from under the overhanging tiles far above. The paint was flaking and the mortar looked crumbly between the bricks, but there was a changeless elegance about the place. There was no front garden and only the railings separated the house from the street a few feet away.

I rang the doorbell and instantly the afternoon peace was shattered by a distant baying like a wolf pack in full cry. The upper half of the door was of glass and, as I peered through, a river of dogs poured round the corner of a long passage and dashed itself with frenzied yells against the door. If I hadn't been used to animals I would have turned and run for my life. As it was I stepped back warily and watched the dogs as they appeared, sometimes two at a time, at the top of their leap, eyes glaring, jaws slavering. After a minute or two of this I was able to sort them out and I realized that my first rough count of about fourteen was exaggerated. There were, in fact, five; a huge fawn greyhound who appeared most often as he hadn't so far to jump as the others, a cocker spaniel, a Scottie, a whippet and a tiny, short-legged hunt terrier. This terrier was seldom seen since the glass was rather high for him, but when he did make it he managed to get an even more frantic note into his bark before he disappeared.

I was thinking of ringing the bell again when I saw a large woman in the passage. She rapped out a single word and the noise stopped as if by magic. When she opened the door the ravening pack was slinking round her feet ingratiatingly, showing the whites of their eyes and wagging their tucked-in tails. I had never seen such a servile crew.

'Good afternoon,' I said with my best smile. 'My name is Herriot.'

The woman looked bigger than ever with the door open. She was about sixty but her hair, tightly pulled back from her forehead, was jet black and hardly streaked with grey. She nodded and looked at me with grim benevolence, but she seemed to be waiting for further information. Evidently, the name struck no answering spark.

'Mr Farnon is expecting me. He wrote asking me to come today.'

'Mr Herriot?' she said thoughtfully. 'Surgery is from six to seven o'clock. If you wanted to bring a dog in, that would be your best time.'

'No, no,' I said, hanging on to my smile. 'I'm applying for the position of assistant. Mr Farnon said to come in time for tea.'

'Assistant? Well, now, that's nice.' The lines in her face softened a little. 'I'm Mrs Hall. I keep house for Mr Farnon. He's a bachelor, you know. He never said anything to me about you, but never mind, come in and have a cup of tea. He shouldn't be long before he's back.'

I followed her between whitewashed walls, my feet clattering on the tiles. We turned right at the end into another passage and I was beginning to wonder just how far back the house extended when I was shown into a sunlit room.

It had been built in the grand manner, high-ceilinged and airy with a massive fireplace flanked by arched alcoves. One end was taken up by a french window which gave on a long, high-walled garden. I could see unkempt lawns, a rockery and many fruit trees. A great bank of peonies blazed in the hot sunshine and at the far end, rooks cawed in the branches of a group of tall elms. Above and beyond were the green hills with their climbing walls.

Ordinary looking furniture stood around on a very worn carpet. Hunting prints hung on the walls and books were scattered everywhere, some on shelves in the alcoves but others piled on the floor in the corners. A pewter pint pot occupied a prominent place at one end of the mantelpiece. It was an interesting pot. Cheques and bank notes had been stuffed into it till they bulged out of the top and overflowed on to the hearth beneath. I was studying this with astonishment when Mrs Hall came in with a tea tray.

'I suppose Mr Farnon is out on a case.' I said.

'No, he's gone through to Brawton to visit his mother. I can't really say when he'll be back.' She left me with my tea.

The dogs arranged themselves peacefully around the room and, except for a brief dispute between the Scottie and the cocker spaniel about the occupancy of a deep chair, there was no sign of their previous violent behaviour. They lay regarding me with friendly boredom and, at the same time, fighting a losing battle against sleep. Soon the last nodding head had fallen back and a chorus of heavy breathing filled the room.

But I was unable to relax with them. A feeling of let-down gripped me; I had screwed myself up for an interview and I was left dangling. This was all very odd. Why should anyone write for an assistant, arrange a time to meet him and then go to visit his mother? Another thing – if I was engaged, I would be living in this house, yet the housekeeper had no instructions to prepare a room for me. In fact, she had never even heard of me.

My musings were interrupted by the door bell ringing and the dogs, as if touched by a live wire, leaped screaming into the air and launched themselves in a solid mass through the door. I wished they didn't take their duties so seriously. There was no sign of Mrs Hall so I went out to the front door where the dogs were putting everything into their fierce act.

'Shut up!' I shouted and the din switched itself off. The five dogs cringed abjectly round my ankles, almost walking on their knees. The big greyhound got the best effect by drawing his lips back from his teeth in an apologetic grin.

I opened the door and looked into a round, eager face. Its owner, a plump man in wellington boots leaned confidently against the railings.

'Hello, 'ello, Mr Farnon in?'

'Not at the moment. Can I help you?'

'Aye, give 'im a message when he comes in. Tell 'im Bert Sharpe of Barrow Hills has a cow wot wants borin' out?'

'Boring out?'

'That's right, she's nobbut going on three cylinders.'

'Three cylinders?'

'Aye and if we don't do summat she'll go wrang in 'er ewer, won't she?'

'Very probably.'

'Don't want felon, do we?'

'Certainly not.'

'OK, you'll tell 'im, then. Ta-ta.'

I returned thoughtfully to the sitting-room. It was disconcerting but I had listened to my first case history without understanding a word of it.

I had hardly sat down when the bell rang again. This time I unleashed a frightening yell which froze the dogs when they were still in mid air; they took the point and returned, abashed, to their chairs.

This time it was a solemn gentleman with a straightly adjusted cloth cap resting on his ears, a muffler knotted precisely over his adam's apple and a clay pipe growing from the exact centre of his mouth. He removed the pipe and spoke with a rich, unexpected accent.

'Me name's Mulligan and I want Misther Farnon to make up some midicine for me dog.'

'Oh, what's the trouble with your dog, Mr Mulligan?'

He raised a questioning eyebrow and put a hand to his ear. I tried again with a full blooded shout.

'What's the trouble?'

He looked at me doubtfully for a moment. 'He's womitin', sorr. Womitin' bad.'

I immediately felt on secure ground now and my brain began to seethe with diagnostic procedures. 'How long after eating does he vomit?'

The hand went to the ear again. 'Phwhat's that?'

I leaned close to the side of his head, inflated my lungs and bawled: 'When does he womit – I mean vomit?'

Comprehension spread slowly across Mr Mulligan's face. He gave a gentle smile. 'Oh aye, he's womitin'. Womitin' bad, sorr.'

I didn't feel up to another effort so I told him I would see to it and asked him to call later. He must have been able to lip-read me because he seemed satisfied and walked away.

Back in the sitting-room, I sank into a chair and poured a cup of tea. I had taken one sip when the bell rang again. This time, a wild glare from me was enough to make the dogs cower back in their chairs; I was relieved they had caught on so quickly.

Outside the front door a lovely, red-haired girl was standing. She smiled, showing a lot of very white teeth.

'Good afternoon,' she said in a loud, well-bred voice. 'I am Diana Brompton. Mr Farnon is expecting me for tea.'

I gulped and clung to the door handle. 'He's asked YOU to tea?'

The smile became fixed. 'Yes, that is correct,' she said, spelling the words out carefully, 'He asked me to tea.'

'I'm afraid Mr Farnon isn't at home. I can't say when he'll be back.'

The smile was plucked away. 'Oh,' she said, and she got a lot into the word. 'At any rate, perhaps I could come in.'

'Oh, certainly, do come in. I'm sorry.' I babbled, suddenly conscious that I had been staring, open mouthed at her.

I held open the door and she brushed past me without a word. She knew her way about because, when I got to the first corner, she had disappeared into the room. I tiptoed past the door and broke into a gallop which took me along another thirty yards or so of twisting passage to a huge, stone-flagged kitchen. Mrs Hall was pottering about there and I rushed at her.

'There's a young lady here, a Miss Brompton. She's come to tea, too.' I had to fight an impulse to pluck at her sleeve.

Mrs Hall's face was expressionless. I thought she might have started to wave her arms about, but she didn't even seem surprised.

'You go through and talk to her and I'll bring a few more cakes,' she said.

'But what the heck am I going to talk to her about? How long is Mr Farnon going to be?'

'Oh, just chat to her for a bit. I shouldn't think he'll be very long,' she said calmly.

Slowly, I made my way back to the sitting-room and when I opened the door the girl turned quickly with the makings of another big smile. She made no attempt to hide her disgust when she saw it was only me.

'Mrs Hall thinks he should be back fairly soon. Perhaps you would join me in a cup of tea while you're waiting.'

She gave me a quick glance which raked me from my rumpled hair to my scuffed old shoes. I realized suddenly how grimy and sweaty I was after the long journey. Then she shrugged her shoulders and turned away. The dogs regarded her apathetically. A heavy silence blanketed the room.

I poured a cup of tea and held it out to her. She ignored me and lit a cigarette. This was going to be tough, but I could only try.

I cleared my throat and spoke lightly. 'I've only just arrived myself. I hope to be the new assistant.'

This time she didn't trouble to look round. She just said 'Oh' and again the monosyllable carried a tremendous punch.

'Lovely part of the world, this.' I said, returning to the attack.

'Yes.'

'I've never been in Yorkshire before, but I like what I've seen.'

'Oh.'

'Have you known Mr Farnon very long?'

'Yes.'

'I believe he's quite young – about thirty?'

'Yes.'

'Wonderful weather.'

'Yes.'

I kept at it with courage and tenacity for about five minutes, hunting for something original or witty, but finally, Miss Brompton, instead of answering, took the cigarette from her mouth, turned towards me and gave me a long, blank stare. I knew that was the end and shrank into silence.

After that, she sat staring out of the french window, pulling deeply at her cigarette, narrowing her eyes as the smoke trickled from her lips. As far as she was concerned, I just wasn't there.

I was able to observe her at will and she was interesting. I had never met a living piece of a society magazine before. Cool, linen dress, expensive-looking cardigan, elegant legs and the glorious red hair falling on her shoulders.

And yet here was a fascinating thought. She was sitting there positively hungering for a little fat German vet. This Farnon must have something.

The tableau was finally broken up when Miss Brompton jumped to her feet. She hurled her cigarette savagely into the fireplace and marched from the room.

Wearily, I got out of my chair. My head began to ache as I shuffled through the french window into the garden. I flopped down among the knee deep grass on the lawn and rested my back against a towering acacia tree. Where the devil was Farnon? Was he really expecting me or had somebody played a horrible practical joke on me? I felt suddenly cold. I had spent my last few pounds getting here and if there was some mistake I was in trouble.

But, looking around me, I began to feel better. The sunshine beat back from the high old walls, bees droned among the bright masses of flowers. A gentle breeze stirred the withered blooms of a magnificent wistaria which almost covered the back of the house. There was peace here.

I leaned my head against the bark and closed my eyes. I

could see Herr Farrenen, looking just as I had imagined him, standing over me. He wore a shocked expression.

'Wass is dis you haff done?' he spluttered, his fat jowls quivering with rage. 'You kom to my house under false pretences, you insult Fraulein Brompton, you trink my tea, you eat my food. Vat else you do, hein? Maybe you steal my spoons. You talk about assistant but I vant no assistant. Is best I telephone the police.'

Herr Farrenen seized the phone in a pudgy hand. Even in my dream, I wondered how the man could use such a completely corny accent. I heard the thick voice saying 'Hello, hello.'

And I opened my eyes. Somebody was saying 'Hello', but it wasn't Herr Farrenen. A tall, thin man was leaning against the wall, his hands in his pockets. Something seemed to be amusing him. As I struggled to my feet, he heaved himself away from the wall and held out his hand. 'Sorry you've had to wait. I'm Siegfried Farnon.'

He was just about the most English looking man I had ever seen. Long, humorous, strong-jawed face. Small, clipped moustache, untidy, sandy hair. He was wearing an old tweed jacket and shapeless flannel trousers. The collar of his check shirt was frayed and the tie carelessly knotted. He looked as though he didn't spend much time in front of a mirror.

Studying him, I began to feel better despite the ache in my neck where it had rested against the tree. I shook my head to get my eyes fully open and tufts of grass fell from my hair. 'There was a Miss Brompton here,' I blurted out. 'She came to tea. I explained you had been called away.'

Farnon looked thoughtful, but not put out. He rubbed his chin slowly. 'Mm, yes – well, never mind. But I do apologize for being out when you arrived. I have a shocking memory and I just forgot.'

It was the most English voice, too.

Farnon gave me a long, searching look, then he grinned. 'Let's go inside. I want to show you round the place.'

CHAPTER THREE

The long offshoot behind the house had been the servants' quarters in grander days. Here, everything was dark and narrow and poky as if in deliberate contrast with the front.

Farnon led me to the first of several doors which opened off a passage where the smell of ether and carbolic hung on the air. 'This,' he said, with a secret gleam in his eye as though he were about to unveil the mysteries of Aladdin's cave, 'is the dispensary.'

The dispensary was an important place in the days before penicillin and the sulphonamides. Rows of gleaming Winchester bottles lined the white walls from floor to ceiling. I savoured the familiar names: Sweet Spirits of Nitre, Tincture of Camphor, Chlorodyne, Formalin, Salammoniac, Hexamine, Sugar of Lead, Linimentum Album, Perchloride of Mercury, Red Blister. The lines of labels were comforting.

I was an initiate among old friends. I had painfully accumulated their lore, ferreting out their secrets over the years. I knew their origins, actions and uses, and their maddeningly varied dosage. The examiner's voice— 'And what is the dose for the horse? – and the cow? – and the sheep? – and the pig? – and the dog? – and the cat?'

These shelves held the vets' entire armoury against disease and, on a bench under the window, I could see the instruments for compounding them; the graduated vessels and beakers, the mortars and pestles. And underneath, in an open cupboard, the medicine bottles, piles of corks of all sizes, pill boxes, powder papers.

As we moved around, Farnon's manner became more and more animated. His eyes glittered and he talked rapidly. Often, he reached up and caressed a Winchester on its shelf; or he would lift out a horse ball or an electuary from its box, give it a friendly pat and replace it with tenderness.

'Look at this stuff, Herriot,' he shouted without warning. 'Adrevan! This is the remedy, par excellence, for red worms in horses. A bit expensive, mind you – ten bob a packet. And these gentian violet pessaries. If you shove one of these into a cow's uterus after a dirty cleansing, it turns the discharges a very pretty colour. Really looks as though it's doing something. And have you seen this trick?'

He placed a few crystals of resublimated iodine on a glass dish and added a drop of turpentine. Nothing happened for a second then a dense cloud of purple smoke rolled heavily to the ceiling. He gave a great bellow of laughter at my startled face.

'Like witchcraft, isn't it? I use it for wounds in horses' feet. The chemical reaction drives the iodine deep into the tissues.'

'It does?'

'Well, I don't know, but that's the theory, and anyway, you must admit it looks wonderful. Impresses the toughest client.'

Some of the bottles on the shelves fell short of the ethical standards I had learned in college. Like the one labelled 'Colic Drench' and featuring a floridly drawn picture of a horse rolling in agony. The animal's face was turned outwards and wore an expression of very human anguish. Another bore the legend 'Universal Cattle Medicine' in ornate script – 'A Sovereign Remedy for coughs, chills, scours, pneumonia, milk fever, gargett and all forms of indigestion.' At the bottom of the label, in flaring black capitals was the assurance, 'Never Fails to Give Relief'.

Farnon had something to say about most of the drugs. Each one had its place in his five years' experience of practice; they all had their fascination, their individual mystique. Many of the bottles were beautifully shaped, with heavy glass stoppers and their Latin names cut deeply into their sides; names familiar to physicians for centuries, gathering fables through the years.

The two of us stood gazing at the gleaming rows without any idea that it was nearly all useless and that the days of the old medicines were nearly over. Soon they would be hustled into oblivion by the headlong rush of the new discoveries and they would never return.

'This is where we keep the instruments.' Farnon showed me into another little room. The small animal equipment lay on green baize shelves, very neat and impressively clean. Hypodermic syringes, whelping forceps, tooth scalers, probes, searchers, and, in a place of prominence, an ophthalmoscope.

Farnon lifted it lovingly from its black box. 'My latest purchase,' he murmured, stroking its smooth shaft. 'Wonderful thing. Here, have a peep at my retina.'

I switched on the bulb and gazed with interest at the glistening, coloured tapestry in the depths of his eye. 'Very pretty. I could write you a certificate of soundness.'

He laughed and thumped my shoulder. 'Good, I'm glad to hear it. I always fancied I had a touch of cataract in that one.'

He began to show me the large animal instruments which hung from hooks on the walls. Docking and firing irons, bloodless castrators, emasculators, casting ropes and hobbles, calving ropes and hooks. A new, silvery embryotome hung in the place of honour, but many of the instruments, like the drugs, were museum pieces. Particularly the blood stick and fleam, a relic of medieval times, but still used to bring the rich blood spouting into a bucket.

'You still can't beat it for laminitis,' Farnon declared seriously.

We finished up in the operating room with its bare white walls, high table, oxygen and ether anaesthetic outfit and a small sterilizer.

'Not much small animal work in this district.' Farnon smoothed the table with his palm. 'But I'm trying to encourage it. It makes a pleasant change from lying on your belly in a cow house. The thing is, we've got to do the job right. The old castor oil and prussic acid doctrine is no good at all. You probably know that a lot of the old hands won't look at a dog or a cat, but the profession has got to change its ideas.'

He went over to a cupboard in the corner and opened the door. I could see glass shelves with a few scalpels, artery forceps, suture needles and bottles of catgut in spirit. He took out his handkerchief and flicked at an auroscope before closing the doors carefully.

'Well, what do you think of it all?' he asked as he went out into the passage.

'Great,' I replied. 'You've got just about everything you need here. I'm really impressed.'

He seemed to swell visibly. The thin cheeks flushed and he hummed softly to himself. Then he burst loudly into song in a shaky baritone, keeping time with our steps as we marched along.

Back in the sitting-room, I told him about Bert Sharpe. 'Something about boring out a cow which was going on three cylinders. He talked about her ewer and felon – I didn't quite get it.'

Farnon laughed. 'I think I can translate. He wants a Hudson's operation doing on a blocked teat. Ewer is the udder and felon the local term for mastitis.'

'Well, thanks. And there was a deaf Irishman, a Mr Mulligan . . .'

'Wait a minute.' Farnon held up a hand. 'Let me guess – womitin'?'

'Aye, womitin' bad, sorr.'

'Right, I'll put up another pint of bismuth carb for him. I'm in favour of long range treatment for this dog. He looks like an airedale but he's as big as a donkey and has a moody disposition. He's had Joe Mulligan on the floor a few times – just gets him down and worries him when he's got nothing better to do. But Joe loves him.'

'How about the womitin'?'

'Doesn't mean a thing. Natural reaction from eating every bit of rubbish he finds. Well, we'd better get out to Sharpe's.

And there are one or two other visits – how about coming with me and I'll show you a bit of the district.'

Outside the house, Farnon motioned me towards a battered Hillman and, as I moved round to the passenger's side, I shot a startled glance at the treadless tyres, the rusty bodywork, the almost opaque windscreen with its network of fine cracks. What I didn't notice was that the passenger seat was not fixed to the floor but stood freely on its sledge-like runners. I dropped into it and went over backwards, finishing with my head on the rear seat and my feet against the roof. Farnon helped me up, apologizing with great charm, and we set off.

Once clear of the market place, the road dipped quite suddenly and we could see all of the Dale stretching away from us in the evening sunshine. The outlines of the great hills were softened in the gentle light and a broken streak of silver showed where the Darrow wandered on the valley floor.

Farnon was an unorthodox driver. Apparently captivated by the scene, he drove slowly down the hill, elbows resting on the wheel, his chin cupped in his hands. At the bottom of the hill he came out of his reverie and spurted to seventy miles an hour. The old car rocked crazily along the narrow road and my movable seat slewed from side to side as I jammed my feet against the floor boards.

Then he slammed on the brakes, pointed out some pedigree Shorthorns in a field and jolted away again. He never looked at the road in front; all his attention was on the countryside around and behind him. It was that last bit that worried me, because he spent a lot of time driving fast and looking over his shoulder at the same time.

We left the road at last and made our way up a gated lane. My years of seeing practice had taught me to hop in and out very smartly as students were regarded primarily as gate-opening machines. Farnon, however, thanked me gravely every time and once I got over my surprise I found it refreshing.

We drew up in a farmyard. 'Lame horse here,' Farnon said.

A strapping Clydesdale gelding was brought out and we watched attentively as the farmer trotted him up and down.

'Which leg do you make it?' my colleague asked. 'Near fore? Yes, I think so, too. Like to examine it?'

I put my hand on the foot, feeling how much hotter it was than the other. I called for a hammer and tapped the wall of the hoof. The horse flinched, raised the foot and held it trembling for a few seconds before replacing it carefully on the ground. 'Looks like pus in the foot to me.'

'I'll bet you're right,' Farnon said. 'They call it gravel around here, by the way. What do you suggest we do about it?'

'Open up the sole and evacuate the pus.'

'Right.' He held out a hoof knife. 'I'll watch your technique.'

With the uncomfortable feeling that I was on trial, I took the knife, lifted the foot and tucked it between my knees. I knew what I had to do – find the dark mark on the sole where the infection had entered and follow it down till I reached the pus. I scraped away the caked dirt and found not one, but several marks. After more tapping to find the painful area I selected a likely spot and started to cut.

The horn seemed as hard as marble and only the thinnest little shaving came away with each twist of the knife. The horse, too, appeared to appreciate having his sore foot lifted off the ground and gratefully leaned his full weight on my back. He hadn't been so comfortable all day. I groaned and dug him in the ribs with my elbow and, though it made him change his position for a second, he was soon leaning on again.

The mark was growing fainter and, after a final gouge with the knife, it disappeared altogether. I swore quietly and started on another mark. With my back at breaking point and the sweat trickling into my eyes, I knew that if this one petered out, too, I would have to let the foot go and take a rest. And with Farnon's eye on me I didn't want to do that.

Agonizingly, I hacked away and, as the hole deepened, my knees began an uncontrollable trembling. The horse rested happily, his fifteen hundredweight cradled by this thoughtful human. I was wondering how it would look when I finally fell flat on my face when, under the knife blade, I saw a thin spurt of pus followed by a steady trickle.

'There it goes,' the farmer grunted. 'He'll get relief now.'

I enlarged the drainage hole and dropped the foot. It took me a long time to straighten up and when I stepped back, my shirt clung to my back.

'Well done, Herriot.' Farnon took the knife from me and slipped it into his pocket. 'It just isn't funny when the horn is as hard as that.'

He gave the horse a shot of tetanus antitoxin then turned to the farmer. 'I wonder if you'd hold up the foot for a second while I disinfect the cavity.' The stocky little man gripped the foot between his knees and looked down with interest as Farnon filled the hole with iodine crystals and added some turpentine. Then he disappeared behind a billowing purple curtain.

I watched, fascinated, as the thick pall mounted and spread. I could locate the little man only by the spluttering noises from somewhere in the middle.

As the smoke began to clear, a pair of round, startled eyes came into view. 'By Gaw, Mr Farnon, I wondered what the 'ell had happened for a minute,' the farmer said between coughs. He looked down again at the blackened hole in the hoof and spoke reverently: 'It's wonderful what science can do nowadays.'

We did two more visits, one to a calf with a cut leg which I stitched, dressed and bandaged, then to the cow with the blocked teat.

Mr Sharpe was waiting, still looking eager. He led us into the byre and Farnon gestured towards the cow. 'See what you can make of it.'

I squatted down and palpated the teat, feeling the mass of thickened tissue half way up. It would have to be broken down by a Hudson's instrument and I began to work the thin metal spiral up the teat. One second later, I was sitting gasping in the dung channel with the neat imprint of a cloven hoof on my shirt front, just over the solar plexus.

It was embarrassing, but there was nothing I could do but sit there fighting for breath, my mouth opening and shutting like a stranded fish.

Mr Sharpe held his hand over his mouth, his innate politeness at war with his natural amusement at seeing the vet come to grief. 'I'm sorry, young man, but I owt to 'ave told you that this is a very friendly cow. She allus likes to shake hands.' Then, overcome by his own wit, he rested his forehead on the cow's back and went into a long paroxysm of silent mirth.

I took my time to recover, then rose with dignity from the channel. With Mr Sharpe holding the nose and Farnon lifting up the tail, I managed to get the instrument past the fibrous mass and by a few downward tugs I cleared the obstruction; but, though the precautions cramped the cow's style a little, she still got in several telling blows on my arms and legs.

When it was over, the farmer grasped the teat and sent a long white jet frothing on the floor. 'Capital! She's going on four cylinders now!'

CHAPTER FOUR

'We'll go home a different way.' Farnon leaned over the driving wheel and wiped the cracked windscreen with his sleeve. 'Over the Brenkstone Pass and down Sildale. It's not much further and I'd like you to see it.'

We took a steep, winding road, climbing higher and still higher with the hillside falling away sheer to a dark ravine where a rocky stream rushed headlong to the gentler country below. On the top, we got out of the car. In the summer dusk, a wild panorama of tumbling fells and peaks rolled away and lost itself in the crimson and gold ribbons of the Western sky. To the East, a black mountain overhung us, menacing in its naked black bulk. Huge, square-cut boulders littered the lower slopes.

I whistled softly as I looked around. This was different from the friendly hill country I had seen on the approach to Darrowby.

Farnon turned towards me. 'Yes, one of the wildest spots in England. A fearsome place in winter. I've known this pass to be blocked for weeks on end.'

I pulled the clean air deeply into my lungs. Nothing stirred in the vastness, but a curlew cried faintly and I could just hear the distant roar of the torrent a thousand feet below.

It was dark when we got into the car and started the long descent into Sildale. The valley was a shapeless blur but points of light showed where the lonely farms clung to the hillsides.

We came to a silent village and Farnon applied his brakes violently. I tobogganed effortlessly across the floor on my mobile seat and collided with the windscreen. My head made a ringing sound against the glass but Farnon didn't seem to notice. 'There's a grand little pub here. Let's go in and have a beer.'

The pub was something new to me. It was, simply, a large kitchen, square and stone-flagged. An enormous fireplace and an old black cooking range took up one end. A kettle stood on the hearth and a single large log hissed and crackled, filling the room with its resinous scent.

About a dozen men sat on the high-backed settles which lined the walls. In front of them, rows of pint mugs rested on oak tables which were fissured and twisted with age.

There was a silence as we went in. Then somebody said 'Now then, Mr Farnon,' not enthusiastically, but politely, and this brought some friendly grunts and nods from the company. They were mostly farmers or farm workers taking their pleasure without fuss or excitement. Most were burnt red by the sun and some of the younger ones were tieless, muscular necks and chests showing through the open shirt fronts. Soft murmurs and clicks rose from a peaceful domino game in the corner.

Farnon guided me to a seat, ordered two beers and turned to face me. 'Well, you can have this job if you want it. Four quid a week and full board. OK?'

The suddenness struck me silent. I was in. And four pounds a week! I remembered the pathetic entries in the *Record*. 'Veterinary surgeon, fully experienced, will work for keep.' The BVMA had had to put pressure on the editor to stop him printing these cries from the heart. It hadn't looked so good to see members of the profession offering their services free. Four pounds a week was affluence.

'Thank you,' I said, trying hard not to look triumphant. 'I accept.'

'Good.' Farnon took a hasty gulp at his beer. 'Let me tell you about the practice. I bought it a year ago from an old man of eighty. Still practising, mind you, a real tough old character. But he'd got past getting up in the middle of the night, which isn't surprising. And, of course, in lots of other ways he had let things slide – hanging on to all the old ideas. Some of those ancient instruments in the surgery were his. One way and another, there was hardly any practice left and I'm trying to work it up again now. There's very little profit in it so far, but if we stick in for a few years, I'm confident we'll have a good business. The farmers are pleased to see a younger man taking over and they welcome new treatments and operations. But I'm having to educate them out of the three and sixpenny consulting fee the old chap used to charge and it's been a hard slog. These Dalesmen are wonderful people and you'll like them, but they don't like parting with their brass unless you can prove they are getting something in return.'

He talked on enthusiastically of his plans for the future, the drinks kept coming and the atmosphere in the pub thawed steadily. The place filled up as the regulars from the village streamed in, the noise and heat increased and by near closing time I had got separated from my colleague and was in the middle of a laughing group I seemed to have known for years.

But there was one odd character who swam repeatedly into my field of vision. An elderly little man with a soiled white panama perched above a smooth, brown, time-worn face like an old boot. He was dodging round the edge of the group, beckoning and winking.

I could see there was something on his mind, so I broke away and allowed myself to be led to a seat in the corner. The old man sat opposite me, rested his hands and chin on the handle of his walking stick and regarded me from under drooping eyelids.

'Now then, young man, ah've summat to tell thee. Ah've been among beasts all me life and I'm going to tell tha summat.'

My toes began to curl. I had been caught this way before. Early in my college career I had discovered that all the older inhabitants of the agricultural world seemed to have the idea that they had something priceless to impart. And it usually took a long time. I looked around me in alarm but I was trapped. The old man shuffled his chair closer and began to talk in a conspiratorial whisper. Gusts of beery breath hit my face from six inches range.

There was nothing new about the old man's tale – just the usual recital of miraculous cures he had wrought, infallible remedies known only to himself and many little sidetracks about how unscrupulous people had tried in vain to worm his secrets from him. He paused only to take expert pulls at his pint pot; his tiny frame seemed to be able to accommodate a surprising amount of beer.

But he was enjoying himself and I let him ramble on. In fact I encouraged him by expressing amazement and admiration at his feats.

The little man had never had such an audience. He was a retired smallholder and it had been years since anybody had shown him the appreciation he deserved. His face wore a lopsided leer and his swimmy eyes were alight with friendship. But suddenly he became serious and sat up straight.

'Now, afore ye go, young man, I'm going to tell thee summat nobody knows but me. Ah could've made a lot o' money out o' this. Folks 'ave been after me for years to tell 'em but I never 'ave.'

He lowered the level in his glass by several inches then narrowed his eyes to slits. 'It's the cure for mallenders and sallenders in 'osses.'

I started up in my chair as though the roof had begun to fall in. 'You can't mean it,' I gasped. 'Not mallenders and sallenders.'

The old man looked smug. 'Ah, but ah do mean it. All you have to do is rub on this salve of mine and the 'oss walks away sound. He's better by that!' His voice rose to a thin shout and he made a violent gesture with his arm which swept his nearly empty glass to the floor.

I gave a low, incredulous whistle and ordered another pint. 'And you're really going to tell me the name of this salve?' I whispered.

'I am, young man, but only on one condition. Tha must tell no one. Tha must keep it to thaself, then nobody'll know but thee and me.' He effortlessly tipped half of his fresh pint down his throat. 'Just thee and me, lad.'

'All right, I promise you. I'll not tell a soul. Now what is this wonderful stuff?'

The old man looked furtively round the crowded room. Then he took a deep breath, laid his hand on my shoulder and put his lips close to my ear. He hiccuped once, solemnly, and spoke in a hoarse whisper. 'Marshmallow ointment.'

I grasped his hand and wrung it silently. The old man, deeply moved, spilled most of his final half pint down his chin.

But Farnon was making signals from the door. It was time to go. We surged out with our new friends, making a little island of noise and light in the quiet village street. A tow-haired young fellow in shirt sleeves opened the car door with natural courtesy and, waving a final goodnight, I plunged in. This time, the seat went over quicker than usual and I hurtled backwards, coming to rest with my head among some Wellingtons and my knees tucked underneath my chin.

A row of surprised faces peered in at me through the back window, but soon, willing hands were helping me up and the trick seat was placed upright on its rockers again. I wondered how long it had been like that and if my employer had ever thought of having it fixed.

We roared off into the darkness and I looked back at the waving group. I could see the little man, his panama gleaming like new in the light from the doorway. He was holding his finger to his lips.

CHAPTER FIVE

The past five years had been leading up to one moment and it hadn't arrived yet. I had been in Darrowby for twenty-four hours now and I still hadn't been to a visit on my own.

Another day had passed in going around with Farnon. It was a funny thing, but, for a man who seemed careless, forgetful and a few other things, Farnon was frustratingly cautious about launching his new assistant.

We had been over into Lidderdale today and I had met more of the clients – friendly, polite farmers who received me pleasantly and wished me success. But working under Farnon's supervision was like being back at college with the professor's eye on me. I felt strongly that my professional career would not start until I, James Herriot, went out and attended a sick animal, unaided and unobserved.

However, the time couldn't be very far away now. Farnon had gone off to Brawton to see his mother again. A devoted son, I thought wonderingly. And he had said he would be back late, so the old lady must keep unusual hours. But never mind about that – what mattered was that I was in charge.

I sat in an armchair with a frayed loose cover and looked out through the french windows at the shadows thrown by the evening sun across the shaggy lawn. I had the feeling that I would be doing a lot of this.

I wondered idly what my first call would be. Probably an anticlimax after the years of waiting. Something like a coughing calf or a pig with constipation. And maybe that would be no bad thing – to start with something I could easily put right. I was in the middle of these comfortable musings when the telephone exploded out in the passage. The insistent clamour sounded abnormally loud in the empty house. I lifted the receiver.

'Is that Mr Farnon?' It was a deep voice with a harsh edge to it. Not a local accent; possibly a trace of the South West.

'No, I'm sorry, he's out. This is his assistant.'

'When will he be back?'

'Not till late, I'm afraid. Can I do anything for you?'

'I don't know whether you can do anything for me or not.' The voice took on a hectoring tone. 'I am Mr Soames, Lord Hulton's farm manager. I have a valuable hunting horse with colic. Do you know anything about colic?'

I felt my hackles rising. 'I am a veterinary surgeon, so I think I should know something about it.'

There was a long pause, and the voice barked again. 'Well, I reckon you'll have to do. In any case, I know the injection the horse wants. Bring some arecoline with you. Mr Farnon uses it. And for God's sake, don't be all night getting here. How long will you be?'

'I'm leaving now.'

'Right.'

I heard the receiver bang down onto its rest. My face felt hot as I walked away from the phone. So my first case wasn't going to be a formality. Colics were tricky things and I had an aggressive know-all called Soames thrown in for good measure.

On the eight mile journey to the case, I re-read from memory the great classic, Caulton Reeks' Common Colics of the Horse.

I had gone through it so often in my final year that I could recite stretches of it like poetry. The well-thumbed pages hovered in front of me, phantom-like, as I drove.

This would probably be a mild impaction or a bit of spasm. Might have had a change of food or too much rich grass. Yes, that would be it; most colics were like that. A quick shot of arecoline and maybe some chlorodyne to relieve the discomfort and all would be well. My mind went back to the cases I had met while seeing practice. The horse standing quietly except that it occasionally eased a hind leg or looked round at its side. There was nothing to it, really.

I was elaborating this happy picture when I arrived. I drove into a spotless, gravelled yard surrounded on three sides by substantial loose boxes. A man was standing there, a broad-shouldered, thick-set figure, very trim in check cap and jacket, well-cut breeches and shiny leggings.

The car drew up about thirty yards away and, as I got out, the man slowly and deliberately turned his back on me. I walked across the yard, taking my time, waiting for the other to turn round, but he stood motionless, hands in pockets, looking in the other direction.

I stopped a few feet away but still the man did not turn. After a long time, and when I had got tired of looking at the back, I spoke.

'Mr Soames?'

At first the man did not move, then he turned very slowly. He had a thick, red neck, a ruddy face and small, fiery eyes. He made no answer but looked me over carefully from head to foot, taking in the worn raincoat, my youth, my air of inexperience. When he had completed his examination he looked away again.

'Yes, I am Mr Soames.' He stressed the 'Mr' as though it meant a lot to him. 'I am a very great friend of Mr Farnon.'

'My name is Herriot.'

Soames didn't appear to have heard. 'Yes, a clever man is Mr Farnon. We are great friends.'

'I understand you have a horse with colic.' I wished my voice didn't sound so high and unsteady.

Soames' gaze was still directed somewhere into the sky. He whistled a little tune softly to himself before replying. 'In there,' he said, jerking his head in the direction of one of the boxes. 'One of his lordship's best hunters. In need of expert assistance, I think.' He put a bit of emphasis on the 'expert'.

I opened the door and went inside. And I stopped as though I had walked into a wall. It was a very large box, deeply bedded with peat moss. A bay horse was staggering round and round the perimeter where he had worn a deep path in the peat. He was lathered in sweat from nose to tail, his nostrils were dilated and his eyes stared blankly in front of him. His head rolled about at every step and, through his clenched teeth, gobbets of foam dripped to the floor. A rank steam rose from his body as though he had been galloping.

My mouth had gone dry. I found it difficult to speak and when I did, it was almost in a whisper. 'How long has he been like this?'

'Oh, he started with a bit of belly ache this morning. I've been giving him black draughts all day, or at least this fellow has. I wouldn't be surprised if he's made a bloody mess of it like he does everything.'

I saw that there was somebody standing in the shadows in the corner; a large, fat man with a head collar in his hand.

'Oh, I got the draughts down him, right enough, Mr Soames, but they haven't done 'im no good.' The big man looked scared.

'You call yourself a horseman,' Soames said, 'but I should have done the damn job myself. I reckon he'd have been better by now.'

'It would take more than a black draught to help him,' I said. 'This is no ordinary colic.'

'What the hell is it, then?'

'Well, I can't say till I've examined him, but severe, continuous pain like that could mean a torsion – a twisted bowel.'

'Twisted bowel, my foot! He's got a bit of belly ache, that's all. He hasn't passed anything all day and he wants something to shift him. Have you got the arecoline with you?'

'If this is a torsion, arecoline would be the worst thing you could give him. He's in agony now, but that would drive him mad. It acts by contracting the muscles of the intestines.'

'God dammit,' snarled Soames. 'Don't start giving me a bloody lecture. Are you going to start doing something for the horse or aren't you?'

I turned to the big man in the corner. 'Slip on that head collar and I'll examine him.'

With the collar on, the horse was brought to a halt. He stood there, trembling and groaning as I passed a hand between ribs and elbows, feeling for the pulse. It was as bad as it could be – a racing, thready beat. I everted an eyelid with my fingers; the mucous membrane was a dark, brick red. The thermometer showed a temperature of a hundred and three.

I looked across the box at Soames. 'Could I have a bucket of hot water, soap and a towel, please?'

'What the devil for? You've done nothing yet and you want to have a wash?'

'I want to make a rectal examination. Will you please bring me the water?'

'God help us, I've never seen anything like this.' Soames passed a hand wearily over his eyes then swung round on the big man. 'Well, come on, don't stand around there. Get him his water and we'll maybe get something done.'

When the water came, I soaped my arm and gently inserted it into the animal's rectum. I could feel plainly the displacement of the small intestine on the left side and a tense, tympanitic mass which should not have been there. As I touched it, the horse shuddered and groaned again.

As I washed and dried my arms, my heart pounded. What was I to do? What could I say?

Soames was stamping in and out of the box, muttering to himself as the pain maddened animal writhed and twisted. 'Hold the bloody thing,' he bellowed at the horseman who was gripping the head collar. 'What the bloody hell are you playing at?'

The big man said nothing. He was in no way to blame but he just stared back stolidly at Soames.

I took a deep breath. 'Everything points to the one thing. I'm convinced this horse has a torsion.'

'All right then, have it your own way. He's got a torsion. Only for God's sake do something, will you? Are we going to stand in here all night?'

'There's nothing anybody can do. There is no cure for this. The important thing is to put him out of his pain as quickly as possible.'

Soames screwed up his face. 'No cure? Put him out of his pain? What rubbish is this you're talking? Just what are you getting at?'

I took a hold on myself. 'I suggest you let me put him down immediately.'

'What do you mean?' Soames' mouth fell open.

'I mean that I should shoot him now, straight away. I have a humane killer in the car.'

Soames looked as if he was going to explode. 'Shoot him! Are you stark raving mad? Do you know how much that horse is worth?'

'It makes no difference what he's worth, Mr Soames. He has been going through hell all day and he's dying now. You should have called me out long ago. He might live a few hours more but the end would be the same. And he's in dreadful pain, continuous pain.'

Soames sunk his head in his hands. 'Oh God, why did this have to happen to me? His lordship is on holiday or I'd call him out to try to make you see some sense. I tell you, if your boss had been here he'd have given that horse an injection and put him right in half an hour. Look here, can't we wait till Mr Farnon gets back tonight and let him have a look at him?'

Something in me leaped gladly at the idea. Give a shot of morphine and get away out of it. Leave the responsibility to somebody else. It would be easy. I looked again at the horse. He had recommenced his blind circling of the box, stumbling round and round in a despairing attempt to leave his agony behind. As I watched, he raised his lolling head and gave a little whinny. It was a desolate, uncomprehending, frantic sound and it was enough for me.

I strode quickly out and got the killer from the car. 'Steady his head,' I said to the big man and placed the muzzle between the glazing eyes. There was a sharp crack and the horse's legs buckled. He thudded down on the peat and lay still.

I turned to Soames who was staring at the body in disbelief. 'Mr Farnon will come round in the morning and carry out a post mortem. I'd like Lord Hulton to have my diagnosis confirmed.'

I put on my jacket and went out to the car. As I started the engine, Soames opened the door and pushed his head in. He spoke quietly but his voice was furious. 'I'm going to inform his lordship about this night's work. And Mr Farnon too. I'll let him know what kind of an assistant he's landed himself with. And let me tell you this. You'll be proved wrong at that post mortem tomorrow and then I'm going to sue you.' He banged the door shut and walked away.

Back at the surgery, I decided to wait up for my boss and I sat there trying to rid myself of the feeling that I had blasted my career before it had got started. Yet, looking back, I knew I couldn't have done anything else. No matter how many times I went over the ground, the conclusion was always the same.

It was 1 AM before Farnon got back. His evening with his mother had stimulated him. His thin cheeks were flushed and he smelt pleasantly of gin. I was surprised to see that he was wearing evening dress and though the dinner jacket was of old-fashioned cut and hung in loose folds on his bony frame, he still managed to look like an ambassador.

He listened in silence as I told him about the horse. He was about to comment when the phone rang. 'A late one,' he whispered, then 'Oh, it's you, Mr Soames.' He nodded at me and settled down in his chair. He was a long time saying 'Yes' and 'No' and 'I see', then he sat up decisively and began to speak.

'Thank you for ringing, Mr Soames, and it seems as though Mr Herriot did the only possible thing in the circumstances. No, I cannot agree. It would have been cruel to leave him. One of our duties is to prevent suffering. Well, I'm sorry you feel like that, but I consider Mr Herriot to be a highly capable veterinary surgeon. If I had been there I have no doubt I'd have done the same thing. Goodnight, Mr Soames, I'll see you in the morning.'

I felt so much better that I almost launched into a speech of gratitude, but in the end, all I said was 'Thanks'.

Farnon reached up into the glass-fronted cupboard above the mantelpiece and pulled out a bottle of whisky. He carelessly slopped out half a tumblerful and pushed it at me. He gave himself a similar measure and fell back into the armchair.

He took a deep swallow, stared for a few seconds at the amber fluid in the glass then looked up with a smile. 'Well, you certainly got chucked in at the deep end tonight, my boy. Your first case! And it had to be Soames, too.'

'Do you know him very well?'

'Oh, I know all about him. A nasty piece of work and enough to put anybody off their stroke. Believe me, he's no friend of mine. In fact, rumour has it that he's a bit of a crook. They say he's been feathering his nest for a long time at his lordship's expense. He'll slip up one day, I expect.'

The neat whisky burned a fiery path down to my stomach but I felt I needed it. 'I wouldn't like too many sessions like tonight's, but I don't suppose veterinary practice is like that all the time.'

'Well, not quite,' Farnon replied, 'but you never know what's in store for you. It's a funny profession, ours, you know. It offers unparalleled opportunities for making a chump of yourself.'

'But I expect a lot depends on your ability.'

'To a certain extent. It helps to be good at the job, of course, but even if you're a positive genius humiliation and ridicule are lurking just round the corner. I once got an eminent horse specialist along here to do a rig operation and the horse stopped breathing halfway through. The sight of that man dancing frantically on his patient's ribs taught me a great truth – that I was going to look just as big a fool at fairly regular intervals throughout my career.'

I laughed. 'Then I might as well resign myself to it right at the beginning.'

'That's the idea. Animals are unpredictable things so our whole life is unpredictable. It's a long tale of little triumphs and disasters and you've got to really like it to stick it. Tonight it was Soames, but another night it'll be something else. One thing, you never get bored. Here, have some more whisky.'

I drank the whisky and then some more and we talked. It seemed no time at all before the dark bulk of the acacia tree began to emerge from the grey light beyond the french window, a blackbird tried a few tentative pipes and Farnon was regretfully shaking the last drops from the bottle into his glass.

He yawned, jerked the knot out of his black tie and looked at his watch. 'Well, five o'clock. Who would have thought it? But I'm glad we had a drink together – only right to celebrate your first case. It was a right one, wasn't it?'

CHAPTER SIX

Two and a half hours sleep was a meagre ration but I made a point of being up by seven thirty and downstairs, shaved and scrubbed, by eight.

But I breakfasted alone. Mrs Hall, impassively placing scrambled eggs before me, told me that my employer had left some time ago to do the PM on Lord Hulton's horse. I wondered if he had bothered to go to bed at all.

I was busy with the last of the toast when Farnon burst into the room. I was getting used to his entrances and hardly jumped at all as he wrenched at the door handle and almost leaped into the middle of the carpet. He looked rosy and in excellent spirits.

'Anything left in that coffee pot? I'll join you for a cup.' He crashed down on a protesting chair. 'Well, you've nothing to worry about. The PM showed a classical torsion. Several loops of bowel involved – black and tympanitic. I'm glad you put the poor beggar down straight away.'

'Did you see my friend Soames?'

'Oh, he was there, of course. He tried to get in a few digs about you but I quietened him. I just pointed out that he had delayed far too long in sending for us and that Lord Hulton wasn't going to be too pleased when he heard how his horse had suffered. I left him chewing over that.'

The news did a lot to lighten my outlook. I went over to the desk and got the day book. 'Here are this morning's calls. What would you like me to do?'

Farnon picked out a round of visits, scribbled the list on a scrap of paper and handed it over. 'Here you are,' he said, 'A few nice, trouble-free cases to get yourself worked in.'

I was turning to leave when he called me back. 'Oh, there's one other thing I'd like you to do. My young brother is hitching from Edinburgh today. He's at the Veterinary College there and the term finished yesterday. When he gets within striking distance he'll probably give us a ring. I wonder if you'd slip out and pick him up?'

'Certainly. Glad to.'

'His name is Tristan, by the way.'

'Tristan?'

'Yes. Oh, I should have told you. You must have wondered about my own queer name. It was my father. Great Wagnerian. It nearly ruled his life. It was music all the time – mainly Wagner.'

'I'm a bit partial myself.'

'Ah well, yes, but you didn't get it morning noon and night like we did. And then to be stuck with a name like Siegfried. Anyway, it could have been worse – Wotan, for instance.'

'Or Pogner.'

Farnon looked startled. 'By golly, you're right. I'd forgotten about old Pogner. I suppose I've a lot to be thankful for.'

It was late afternoon before the expected call came. The voice at the other end was uncannily familiar.

'This is Tristan Farnon.'

'Gosh, you sound just like your brother.'

A pleasant laugh answered me. 'Everybody says that – oh, that's very good of you. I'd be glad of a lift. I'm at the Holly Tree Café on the Great North Road.'

After the voice I had been expecting to find a younger edition of my employer but the small, boyish-faced figure sitting on a rucksack could hardly have been less like him. He got up, pushed back the dark hair from his forehead and held out his hand. The smile was charming.

'Had much walking to do?' I asked.

'Oh, a fair bit, but I needed the exercise. We had a roughish end of term party last night.' He opened the car door and threw the rucksack into the back. As I started the engine he settled himself in the passenger seat as though it were a luxurious armchair, pulled out a paper packet of Woodbines, lit one with tender concentration and gulped the smoke down blissfully. He produced the *Daily Mirror* from a side pocket and shook it open with a sigh of utter content. The smoke, which had been gone a long time, began to wisp from his nose and mouth.

I turned West off the great highway and the rumble of traffic faded rapidly behind us. I glanced round at Tristan. 'You'll have just finished exams?' I said.

'Yes, pathology and parasitology.'

I almost broke one of my steadfast rules by asking him if he had passed, but stopped myself in time. It is a chancy business. But in any case, there was no shortage of conversation. Tristan had something to say about most of the news items and now and then he read out an extract and discussed it with me. I felt a growing conviction that I was in the presence of a quicker and livelier mind than my own. It seemed no time at all before we pulled up outside Skeldale House.

Siegfried was out when we arrived and it was early evening when he returned. He came in through the french window, gave me a friendly greeting and threw himself into an armchair. He had begun to talk about one of his cases when Tristan walked in.

The atmosphere in the room changed as though somebody had clicked a switch. Siegfried's smile became sardonic and he gave his brother a long, appraising look. He grunted a 'hello', then reached up and began to run his finger along the titles of the books in the alcove. He seemed absorbed in this for a few minutes and I could feel the tension building up. Tristan's expression had changed remarkably; his face had gone completely deadpan but his eyes were wary.

Siegfried finally located the book he was looking for, took it down from the shelf and began to leaf through it unhurriedly. Then, without looking up, he said quietly: 'Well, how did the exams go?'

Tristan swallowed carefully and took a deep breath. 'Did all right in parasitology,' he replied in a flat monotone.

Siegfried didn't appear to have heard. He had found something interesting in his book and settled back to read. He took his time over it, then put the book back on the shelf. He began again the business of going along the titles; still with his back to his brother, he spoke again in the same soft voice.

'How about pathology?'

Tristan was on the edge of his chair now, as if ready to make a run for it. His eyes darted from his brother to the book shelves and back again. 'Didn't get it,' he said tonelessly.

There was no reaction from Siegfried. He kept up his patient search for his book, occasionally pulling a volume out, glancing at it and replacing it carefully. Then he gave up the hunt, lay back in the chair with his arms dangling almost to the floor and looked at Tristan. 'So you failed pathology,' he said conversationally.

I was surprised to hear myself babbling with an edge of hysteria in my voice. 'Well now that's pretty good you know. It puts him in the final year and he'll be able to sit path. at Christmas. He won't lose any time that way and, after all, it's a tough subject.'

Siegfried turned a cold eye on me. 'So you think it's pretty good, do you?' There was a pause and a long silence which was broken by a totally unexpected bellow as he rounded on his brother. 'Well, I don't! I think it is bloody awful! It's a damned disgrace, that's what it is. What the hell have you been doing all this term, anyway? Boozing, I should think, chasing women, spending my money, anything but working. And now you've got the bloody nerve to walk in here and tell me you've failed pathology. You're lazy, that's your trouble, isn't it? You're bloody bone idle!'

He was almost unrecognizable. His face was darkly flushed and his eyes glared. He yelled wildly again at his brother. 'But I've had enough this time. I'm sick of you. I'm not going to work my fingers to the bloody bone to keep you up there idling your time away. This is the end. You're sacked, do you hear me. Sacked once and for all. So get out of here – I don't want to see you around any more. Go on, get out!'

Tristan, who had preserved an air of injured dignity throughout, withdrew quietly.

Writhing with embarrassment, I looked at Siegfried. He was showing the strain of the interview. His complexion had gone blotchy; he muttered to himself and drummed his fingers on the arm of the chair.

I was aghast at having to witness this break-up and I was grateful when Siegfried sent me on a call and I was able to get out of the room.

It was nearly dark when I got back and I drove round to the back lane and into the yard at the foot of the garden. The creaking of the garage doors disturbed the rooks in the great elms which overhung the buildings. Far up in the darkness there was a faint fluttering, a muffled cawing then silence. As I stood listening, I became aware of a figure in the gloom, standing by the yard door, looking down the garden. As the face turned towards me I saw it was Tristan.

Again, I felt embarrassed. It was an unfortunate intrusion when the poor fellow had come up here to brood alone. 'Sorry about the way things turned out,' I said awkwardly.

The tip of the cigarette glowed brightly as Tristan took a long pull. 'No, no, that's all right. Could have been a lot worse, you know.'

'Worse? Well, it's bad enough, isn't it? What are you going to do?'

'Do? What do you mean?'

'Well, you've been kicked out, haven't you? Where are you going to sleep tonight?'

'I can see you don't understand,' Tristan said. He took his cigarette from his mouth and I saw the gleam of very white teeth as he smiled. 'You needn't worry. I'm sleeping here and I'll be down to breakfast in the morning.'

'But how about your brother?'

'Siegfried? Oh, he'll have forgotten all about it by then.'

'Are you sure?'

'Dead sure. He's always sacking me and he always forgets. Anyway, things turned out very well. The only tricky bit back there was getting him to swallow that bit about the parasitology.'

I stared at the shadowy form by my side. Again, there was a rustling as the rooks stirred in the tall trees then settled into silence.

'The parasitology?'

'Yes. If you think back, all I said was that I had done all right. I wasn't any more specific than that.'

'Then you mean . . .?'

Tristan laughed softly and thumped my shoulder.

'That's right, I didn't get parasitology. I failed in both. But don't worry, I'll pass them at Christmas.'

CHAPTER SEVEN

I huddled deeper in the blankets as the strident brreeng-brreeng, brreeng-brreeng of the telphone echoed through the old house.

It was three weeks since Tristan's arrival and life at Skeldale House had settled into a fairly regular pattern. Every day began much the same with the phone ringing between seven and eight o'clock after the farmers had had the first look at their stock.

There was only one phone in the house. It rested on a ledge in the tiled passage downstairs. Siegfried had impressed on me that I shouldn't get out of bed for these early calls. He had delegated the job to Tristan; the responsibility would be good for him. Siegfried had been emphatic about it.

I listened to the ringing. It went on and on – it seemed to get louder. There was neither sound nor movement from Tristan's room and I waited for the next move in the daily drama. It came, as always, with a door crashing back on its hinges, then

Siegfried rushed out on to the landing and bounded down the stairs three at a time.

A long silence followed and I could picture him shivering in the draughty passage, his bare feet freezing on the tiles as he listened to the farmer's leisurely account of the animal's symptoms. Then the ting of the phone in its rest and the mad pounding of feet on the stairs as Siegfried made a dash for his brother's room.

Next a wrenching sound as the door was flung open, then a yell of rage. I detected a note of triumph; it meant Tristan had been caught in bed – a definite victory for Siegfried and he didn't have many victories. Usually, Tristan exploited his quick-dressing technique and confronted his brother fully dressed. It gave him a psychological advantage to be knotting his tie when Siegfried was still in pyjamas.

But this morning Tristan had overplayed his hand; trying to snatch the extra few seconds he was caught between the sheets. I listened to the shouts. 'Why didn't you answer the bloody phone like I told you? Don't tell me you're deaf as well as idle! Come on, out of it, out, out!'

But I knew Tristan would make a quick come-back. When he was caught in bed he usually scored a few points by being halfway through his breakfast before his brother came in.

Later, I watched Siegfried's face as he entered the dining-room and saw Tristan munching his toast happily, his *Daily Mirror* balanced against the coffee pot. It was as if he had felt a sudden twinge of toothache.

It all made for a strained atmosphere and I was relieved when I was able to escape to collect my things for the morning round. Down the narrow passage with its familiar, exciting smell of ether and carbolic and out into the high-walled garden which led to the yard where the cars were kept.

It was the same every morning but, to me, there was always the feeling of surprise. When I stepped out into the sun-shine and the scent of flowers it was as though I was doing it for the first time. The clear air held a breath of the nearby moorland; after being buried in a city for five years it was difficult to take it all in.

I never hurried over this part. There could be an urgent case waiting but I still took my time. Along the narrow part between the ivy-covered wall and the long offshoot of the house where the wistaria climbed, pushing its tendrils and its withered blooms into the very rooms. Then past the rockery where the garden widened to the lawn, unkempt and lost looking but lending coolness and softness to the weathered brick. Around its borders flowers blazed in untidy profusion, battling with a jungle of weeds.

And so to the rose garden, then an asparagus bed whose fleshy fingers had grown into tall fronds. Further on were strawberries and raspberries. Fruit trees were everywhere, their branches dangling low over the path. Peaches, pears, cherries and plums were trained against the South wall where they fought for a place with wild-growing rambler roses.

Bees were at work among the flowers and the song of blackbirds and thrushes competed with the cawing of the rooks high up in the elms.

Life was full for me. There were so many things to find out and a lot I had to prove to myself. The days were quick and challenging and they pressed on me with their very newness. But it all stopped here in the garden. Everything seemed to have stopped here a long time ago. I looked back before going through the door into the yard and it was like suddenly coming across a picture in an old book; the empty, wild garden and the tall, silent house beyond. I could never quite believe it was there and that I was a part of it.

And the feeling was heightened when I went into the yard. It was square and cobbled and the grass grew in thick tufts between the stones. Buildings took up two sides; the two garages, once coach houses, a stable and saddle room, a loose box and a pig sty. Against the free wall a rusty iron pump hung over a stone water trough.

Above the stable was a hay loft and over one of the garages

a dovecot. And there was old Boardman. He, too, seemed to have been left behind from grander days, hobbling round on his lame leg, doing nothing in particular.

He grunted good morning from his cubby hole where he kept a few tools and garden implements. Above his head his reminders of the war looked down; a row of coloured prints of Bruce Bairnsfather cartoons. He had stuck them up when he came home in 1918 and there they were still, dusty and curled at the edges but still speaking to him of Kaiser Bill and the shell holes and muddy trenches.

Boardman washed a car sometimes or did a little work in the garden, but he was content to earn a pound or two and get back to his yard. He spent a lot of time in the saddle room, just sitting. Sometimes he looked round the empty hooks where the harness used to hang and then he would make a rubbing movement with his fist against his palm.

He often talked to me of the great days. 'I can see t'owd doctor now, standing on top step waiting for his carriage to come round. Big, smart looking feller he was. Allus wore a top hat and frock coat, and I can remember him when I was a lad, standing there, pulling on 'is gloves and giving his hat a tilt while he waited.'

Boardman's features seemed to soften and a light came into his eyes as though he were talking more to himself than to me. 'The old house was different then. A housekeeper and six servants there were and everything just so. And a full time gardener. There weren't a blade of grass out of place in them days and the flowers all in rows and the trees pruned, tidy-like. And this yard – it were t'owd doctor's favourite spot. He'd come and look over t' door at me sitting here polishing the harness and pass time o' day, quiet like. He were a real gentleman but you couldn't cross 'im. A few specks o' dust anywhere down here and he'd go nearly mad.

'But the war finished it all. Everybody's rushing about now. They don't care about them things now. They've no time, no time at all.'

He would look round in disbelief at the overgrown cobbles, the peeling garage doors hanging crazily on their hinges. At the empty stable and the pump from which no water flowed.

He was always friendly with me in an absent way, but with Siegfried he seemed to step back into his former character, holding himself up smartly and saying 'Very good, sir,' and saluting repeatedly with one finger. It was as though he recognized something there – something of the strength and authority of t'owd doctor – and reached out eagerly towards the lost days.

'Morning, Boardman,' I said, as I opened the garage door. 'How are you today?'

'Oh, middlin' lad, just middlin'.' He limped across and watched me get the starting handle and begin the next part of the daily routine. The car allotted to me was a tiny Austin of an almost forgotten vintage and one of Boardman's voluntary duties was towing it off when it wouldn't start. But this morning, surprisingly, the engine coughed into life after six turns.

As I drove round the corner of the back lane, I had the feeling, as I did every morning, that this was where things really got started. The problems and pressures of my job were waiting for me out there and at the moment I seemed to have plenty.

I had arrived in the Dales, I felt, at a bad time. The farmers, after a generation of neglect, had seen the coming of a prophet, the wonderful new vet, Mr Farnon. He appeared like a comet, trailing his new ideas in his wake. He was able, energetic and charming and they received him as a maiden would a lover. And now, at the height of the honeymoon, I had to push my way into the act, and I just wasn't wanted.

I was beginning to get used to the questions. 'Where's Mr Farnon?' – 'Is he ill or something?' – 'I expected Mr Farnon.' It was a bit daunting to watch their faces fall when they saw me walking on to their farms. Usually they looked past me hopefully and some even went and peered into the car to see if the man they really wanted was hiding in there.

And it was uphill work examining an animal when its owner

was chafing in the background, wishing with all his heart that I was somebody else.

But I had to admit they were fair. I got no effusive welcomes and when I started to tell them what I thought about the case they listened with open scepticism, but I found that if I got my jacket off and really worked at the job they began to thaw a little. And they were hospitable. Even though they were disappointed at having me they asked me into their homes. 'Come in and have a bit o' dinner,' was a phrase I heard nearly every day. Sometimes I was glad to accept and I ate some memorable meals with them.

Often, too, they would slip half a dozen eggs or a pound of butter into the car as I was leaving. This hospitality was traditional in the Dales and I knew they would probably do the same for any visitor, but it showed the core of friendliness which lay under the often unsmiling surface of these people and it helped.

I was beginning to learn about the farmers and what I found I liked. They had a toughness and a philosophical attitude which was new to me. Misfortunes which would make the city dweller want to bang his head against a wall were shrugged off with 'Aye, well, these things happen.'

It looked like being another hot day and I wound down the car windows as far as they would go. I was on my way to do a tuberculin test; the national scheme was beginning to make its first impact in the Dales and the more progressive farmers were asking for survey tests.

And this was no ordinary herd. Mr Copfield's Galloway cattle were famous in their way. Siegfried had told me about them. 'The toughest lot in this practice. There's eighty-five of them and none has ever been tied up. In fact, they've scarcely been touched by hand. They live out on the fells, they calve and rear their calves outside. It isn't often anybody goes near them so they're practically wild animals.'

'What do you do when there's anything wrong with them?' I had asked.

'Well, you have to depend on Frank and George – they're the two Copfield sons. They've been reared with those cattle since they were babies – started tackling the little calves as soon as they could walk, then worked up to the big ones. They're about as tough as the Galloways.'

Copfield's place was one of the bleak ones. Looking across the sparse pastures to the bald heights with their spreading smudges of heather it was easy to see why the farmer had chosen a breed hardier than the local shorthorns. But this morning the grim outlines were softened by the sunshine and there was a desert peace in the endless greens and browns.

Frank and George were not as I expected. The durable men who helped me in my daily jobs tended to be dark and lean with stringy muscles but the Copfields were golden haired and smooth skinned. They were good looking young men about my own age and their massive necks and wide spread of shoulder made their heads look small. Neither of them was tall but they looked formidable with their shirt sleeves rolled high to reveal wrestlers' arms and their thick legs encased in cloth gaiters. Both wore clogs.

The cattle had been herded into the buildings and they just about filled all the available accommodation. There were about twenty-five in a long passage down the side of the fold yard; I could see the ragged line of heads above the rails, the steam rising from their bodies. Twenty more occupied an old stable and two lots of twenty milled about in large loose boxes.

I looked at the black, untamed animals and they looked back at me, their reddish eyes glinting through the rough fringe of hair which fell over their faces. They kept up a menacing, bad-tempered swishing with their tails.

It wasn't going to be easy to get an intradermal injection into every one of them. I turned to Frank.

'Can you catch these beggars?' I asked.

'We'll 'ave a bloody good try,' he replied calmly, throwing a halter over his shoulder. He and his brother lit cigarettes before climbing into the passage where the biggest beasts were packed. I followed them and soon found that the tales I had heard about the Galloways hadn't been exaggerated. If I approached them from the front they came at me with their great hairy heads and if I went behind them they kicked me as a matter of course.

But the brothers amazed me. One of them would drop a halter on a beast, get his fingers into its nose and then be carried away as the animal took off like a rocket. They were thrown about like dolls but they never let go; their fair heads bobbed about incongruously among the black backs; and the thing that fascinated me was that through all the contortions the cigarettes dangled undisturbed.

The heat increased till it was like an oven in the buildings and the animals, their bowels highly fluid with their grass diet, ejected greenish-brown muck like non-stop geysers.

The affair was conducted in the spirit of a game with encouragement shouted to the man in action: 'Thou 'as 'im, Frank.' 'Sniggle 'im, George.' In moments of stress the brothers cursed softly and without heat: 'Get off ma bloody foot, thou awd bitch.' They both stopped work and laughed with sincere appreciation when a cow slashed me across the face with her sodden tail; and another little turn which was well received was when I was filling my syringe with both arms raised and a bullock, backing in alarm from the halter, crashed its craggy behind into my midriff. The wind shot out of me in a sharp hiccup, then the animal decided to turn round in the narrow passage, squashing me like a fly against the railings. I was pop-eyed as it scrambled round; I wondered whether the creaking was coming from my ribs or the wood behind me.

We finished up with the smallest calves and they were just about the most difficult to handle. The shaggy little creatures kicked, bucked, sprang into the air, ran through our legs and even hurtled straight up the walls. Often the brothers had to throw themselves on top of them and bear them to the ground before I could inject them and when the calves felt the needle they stuck out their tongues and bawled deafeningly; outside, the anxious mothers bellowed back in chorus.

It was midday when I reeled out of the buildings. I seemed to have been a month in there, in the suffocating heat, the continuous din, the fusillade of muck.

Frank and George produced a bucket of water and a scrubbing brush and gave me a rough clean-up before I left. A mile from the farm I drove off the unfenced road, got out of the car and dropped down on the cool fell-side. Throwing wide my arms I wriggled my shoulders and my sweat-soaked shirt into the tough grass and let the sweet breeze play over me. With the sun on my face I looked through half closed eyes at the hazy-blue sky.

My ribs ached and I could feel the bruises of a dozen kicks on my legs. I knew I didn't smell so good either. I closed my eyes and grinned at the ridiculous thought that I had been conducting a diagnostic investigation for tuberculosis back there. A strange way to carry out a scientific procedure; a strange way, in fact, to earn a living.

But then I might have been in an office with the windows tight shut against the petrol fumes and the traffic noise, the desk light shining on the columns of figures, my bowler hat hanging on the wall.

Lazily I opened my eyes again and watched a cloud shadow riding over the face of the green hill across the valley. No, no ... I wasn't complaining.

CHAPTER EIGHT

I hardly noticed the passage of the weeks as I rattled along the moorland roads on my daily rounds; but the district was beginning to take shape, the people to emerge as separate personalities. Most days I had a puncture. The tyres were through to the canvas on all wheels; it surprised me that they took me anywhere at all.

One of the few refinements on the car was a rusty 'sunshine roof'. It grated dismally when I slid it back, but most of the time I kept it open and the windows too, and I drove in my shirt sleeves with the delicious air swirling about me. On wet days it didn't help much to close the roof because the rain dripped through the joints and formed pools on my lap and the passenger seat.

I developed great skill in zig-zagging round puddles. To drive through was a mistake as the muddy water fountained up through the gaps in the floor boards.

But it was a fine Summer and long days in the open gave me a tan which rivalled the farmers'. Even mending a puncture was no penance on the high, unfenced roads with the wheeling curlews for company and the wind bringing the scents of flowers and trees up from the valleys. And I could find other excuses to get out and sit on the crisp grass and look out over the airy roof of Yorkshire. It was like taking time out of life. Time to get things into perspective and assess my progress. Everything was so different that it confused me. This countryside after years of city streets, the sense of release from exams and study, the job with its daily challenge. And then there was my boss.

Siegfried Farnon charged round the practice with fierce energy from dawn till dark and I often wondered what drove him on. It wasn't money because he treated it with scant respect. When the bills were paid, the cash went into the pint pot on the mantelpiece and he grabbed handfuls when he wanted it. I never saw him take out a wallet, but his pockets bulged with loose silver and balled-up notes. When he pulled out a thermometer they flew around him in a cloud.

After a week or two of headlong rush he would disappear; maybe for the evening, maybe overnight and often without saying where he was going. Mrs Hall would serve a meal for two, but when she saw I was eating alone she would remove the food without comment.

He dashed off the list of calls each morning with such speed that I was quite often sent hurrying off to the wrong farm or to do the wrong thing. When I told him later of my embarrassment he would laugh heartily.

There was one time when he got involved himself. I had just taken a call from a Mr Heaton of Bronsett about doing a PM on a dead sheep.

'I'd like you to come with me, James,' Siegfried said. 'Things are quiet this morning and I believe they teach you blokes a pretty hot post mortem procedure. I want to see you in action.'

We drove into the village of Bronsett and Siegfried swung the car left into a gated lane.

'Where are you going?' I said. 'Heaton's is at the other end of the village.'

'But you said Seaton's.'

'No, I assure you . . .'

'Look, James, I was right by you when you were talking to the man. I distinctly heard you say the name.'

I opened my mouth to argue further but the car was hurtling down the lane and Siegfried's jaw was jutting. I decided to let him find out for himself.

We arrived outside the farmhouse with a screaming of brakes. Siegfried had left his seat and was rummaging in the boot before the car had stopped shuddering. 'Hell!' he shouted. 'No post mortem knife. Never mind, I'll borrow something from the house.' He slammed down the lid and bustled over to the door.

The farmer's wife answered and Siegfried beamed on her. 'Good morning to you, Mrs Seaton, have you a carving knife?'

The good lady raised her eyebrows. 'What was that you said?'

'A carving knife, Mrs Seaton, a carving knife, and a good sharp one, please.'

'You want a carving knife?'

'Yes, that's right, a carving knife!' Siegfried cried, his scanty store of patience beginning to run out. 'And I wonder if you'd mind hurrying. I haven't much time.'

The bewildered woman withdrew to the kitchen and I could hear whispering and muttering. Children's heads peeped out at intervals to get a quick look at Siegfried stamping irritably on the step. After some delay, one of the daughters advanced timidly, holding out a long, dangerous-looking knife.

Siegfried snatched it from her hand and ran his thumb up and down the edge. 'This is no damn good!' he shouted in exasperation. 'Don't you understand I want something really sharp. Fetch me a steel.'

The girl fled back into the kitchen and there was a low rumble of voices. It was some minutes before another young girl was pushed round the door. She inched her way up to Siegfried, gave him the steel at arm's length and dashed back to safety.

Siegfried prided himself on his skill at sharpening a knife. It was something he enjoyed doing. As he stropped the knife on the steel, he warmed to his work and finally burst into song. There was no sound from the kitchen, only the ring of steel on steel backed by the tuneless singing; there were silent intervals when he carefully tested the edge, then the noise would start again.

When he had completed the job to his satisfaction he peered inside the door. 'Where is your husband?' he called.

There was no reply so he strode into the kitchen, waving the gleaming blade in front of him. I followed him and saw Mrs Seaton and her daughters cowering in the far corner, staring at Siegfried with large, frightened eyes.

He made a sweeping gesture at them with the knife. 'Well, come on, I can get started now!'

'Started what?' the mother whispered, holding her family close to her.

'I want to PM this sheep. You have a dead sheep, haven't you?'

Explanations and apologies followed.

Later, Siegfried remonstrated gravely with me for sending him to the wrong farm.

'You'll have to be a bit more careful in future, James,' he said seriously. 'Creates a very bad impression, that sort of thing.'

Another thing about my new life which interested me was the regular traffic of women through Skeldale House. They were all upper class, mostly beautiful and they had one thing in common – eagerness. They came for drinks, for tea, to dinner, but the real reason was to gaze at Siegfried like parched travellers in the desert sighting an oasis.

I found it damaging to my own ego when their eyes passed over me without recognition or interest and fastened themselves hungrily on my colleague. I wasn't envious, but I was puzzled. I used to study him furtively, trying to fathom the secret of his appeal. Looking at the worn jacket hanging from the thin shoulders, the frayed shirt collar and anonymous tie, I had to conclude that clothes had nothing to do with it.

There was something attractive in the long, bony face and humorous blue eyes, but a lot of the time he was so haggard and sunken-cheeked that I wondered if he was ill.

I often spotted Diana Brompton in the queue and at these times I had to fight down an impulse to dive under the sofa. She was difficult to recognize as the brassy beauty of that afternoon as she looked up meltingly at Siegfried, hanging on his words, giggling like a schoolgirl.

I used to grow cold at the thought that Siegfried might pick her out of the mob and marry her. It worried me a lot because I knew I would have to leave just when I was beginning to enjoy everything about Darrowby.

But Siegfried showed no sign of marrying any of them and the procession continued hopefully. I finally got used to it and stopped worrying.

* * *

I got used, too, to my employer's violent changes of front. There was one morning when Siegfried came down to breakfast, rubbing a hand wearily over red-rimmed eyes.

'Out at 4 AM,' he groaned, buttering his toast listlessly. 'And I don't like to have to say this, James, but it's all your fault.'

'My fault?' I said, startled.

'Yes, lad, your fault. This was a cow with a mild impaction of the rumen. The farmer had been mucking about with it himself for days; a pint of linseed oil one day, a bit of bicarb and ginger the next, and at four o'clock in the morning he decides it is time to call the vet. When I pointed out it could have waited a few hours more he said Mr Herriot told him never to hesitate to ring – he'd come out any hour of the day or night.'

He tapped the top of his egg as though the effort was almost too much for him. 'Well, it's all very well being conscientious and all that, but if a thing has waited several days it can wait till morning. You're spoiling these chaps, James, and I'm getting the backwash of it. I'm sick and tired of being dragged out of my bed for trifles.'

'I'm truly sorry, Siegfried. I honestly had no wish to do that to you. Maybe it's just my inexperience. If I didn't go out, I'd be worried the animal might die. If I left it till morning and it died, how would I feel?'

'That's all right,' snapped Siegfried. 'There's nothing like a dead animal to bring them to their senses. They'll call us out a bit earlier next time.'

I absorbed this bit of advice and tried to act on it. A week later, Siegfried said he wanted a word with me.

'James, I know you won't mind my saying this, but old Sumner was complaining to me today. He says he rang you the other night and you refused to come out to his cow. He's a good client, you know, and a very nice fellow, but he was quite shirty about it. We don't want to lose a chap like that.'

'But it was just a chronic mastitis,' I said. 'A bit of thickening in the milk, that's all. He'd been dosing it himself for nearly a week with some quack remedy. The cow was eating all right, so I thought it would be quite safe to leave it till next day.'

Siegfried put a hand on my shoulder and an excessively patient look spread over his face. I steeled myself. I didn't mind his impatience; I was used to it and could stand it. But the patience was hard to take.

'James,' he said in a gentle voice, 'there is one fundamental rule in our job which transcends all others, and I'll tell you what it is. YOU MUST ATTEND. That is it and it ought to be written on your soul in letters of fire.' He raised a portentous forefinger. 'YOU MUST ATTEND. Always remember that, James; it is the basis of everything. No matter what the circumstances, whether it be wet or fine, night or day, if a client calls you out, you must go; and go cheerfully. You say this didn't sound like an urgent case. Well, after all, you have only the owner's description to guide you and he is not equipped with the knowledge to decide whether it is urgent or not. No, lad, you have to go. Even if they have been treating the animal themselves, it may have taken a turn for the worse. And don't forget,' wagging the finger solmenly 'the animal may die.'

'But I thought you said there was nothing like a dead animal to bring them to their senses,' I said querulously.

'What's that?' barked Siegfried, utterly astonished. 'Never heard such rubbish. Let's have no more of it. Just remember – YOU MUST ATTEND.'

Sometimes he would give me advice on how to live. As when he found me hunched over the phone which I had just crashed down; I was staring at the wall, swearing softly to myself.

Siegfried smiled whimsically. 'Now what is it, James?'

'I've just had a torrid ten minutes with Rolston. You remember that outbreak of calf pneumonia? Well, I spent hours with those calves, poured expensive drugs into them. There wasn't a single death. And now he's complaining about his bill. Not a word of thanks. Hell, there's no justice.'

Siegfried walked over and put his arm round my shoulders. He was wearing his patient look again. 'My dear chap,' he coo'd. 'Just look at you. Red in the face, all tensed up. You mustn't let yourself get upset like this; you must try to relax. Why do you think professional men are cracking up all over the country with coronaries and ulcers? Just because they allow themselves to get all steamed up over piffling little things like you are doing now. Yes, yes, I know these things are annoying, but you've got to take them in your stride. Keep calm, James, calm. It just isn't worth it – I mean, it will all be the same in a hundred years.'

He delivered the sermon with a serene smile, patting my shoulder reassuringly like a psychiatrist soothing a violent patient.

I was writing a label on a jar of red blister a few days later when Siegfried catapulted into the room. He must have kicked the door open because it flew back viciously against the rubber stop and rebounded almost into his face. He rushed over to the desk where I was sitting and began to pound on it with the flat of his hand. His eyes glared wildly from a flushed face.

'I've just come from that bloody swine Holt!' he shouted.

'Ned Holt, you mean?'

'Yes, that's who I mean, damn him!'

I was surprised. Mr Holt was a little man who worked on the roads for the county council. He kept four cows as a sideline and had never been known to pay a veterinary bill; but he was a cheerful character and Siegfried had rendered his unpaid services over the years without objection.

'One of your favourites, isn't he?' I said.

'Was, by God, was,' Siegfried snarled. 'I've been treating Muriel for him. You know, the big red cow second from the far end of his byre. She's had recurrent tympany – coming in from the field every night badly blown – and I'd tried about everything. Nothing did any good. Then it struck me that it might be actinobacillosis of the reticulum. I shot some sodium iodide into the vein and when I saw her today the difference was incredible – she was standing there, chewing her cud, right as rain. I was just patting myself on the back for a smart piece of diagnosis, and do you know what Holt said? He said he knew she'd be better today because last night he gave her half a pound of epsom salts in a bran mash. That was what had cured her.'

Siegfried took some empty cartons and bottles from his pockets and hurled them savagely into the wastepaper basket. He began to shout again.

'Do you know, for the past fortnight I've puzzled and worried and damn nearly dreamt about that cow. Now I've found the cause of the trouble, applied the most modern treatment and the animal has recovered. And what happens? Does the owner express his grateful thanks for my skill? Does he hell – the entire credit goes to the half pound of epsom salts. What I did was a pure waste of time.'

He dealt the desk another sickening blow.

'But I frightened him, James,' he said, his eyes staring, 'By God, I frightened him. When he made that crack about the salts, I yelled out "You bugger!" and made a grab for him. I think I would have strangled him, but he shot into the house and stayed there. I didn't see him again.'

Siegfried threw himself into a chair and began to churn his hair about. 'Epsom salts!' he groaned. 'Oh God, it makes you despair.'

I thought of telling him to relax and pointing out that it would all be the same in a hundred years, but my employer still had an empty serum bottle dangling from one hand. I discarded the idea.

Then there came the day when Siegfried decided to have my car rebored. It had been using a steady two pints of oil a day and he hadn't thought this excessive, but when it got to half a gallon a day he felt something ought to be done. What probably decided him was a farmer on market day saying he always knew when the young vet was coming because he could see the cloud of blue smoke miles away.

When the tiny Austin came back from the garage, Siegfried fussed round it like an old hen. 'Come over here, James,' he called. 'I want to talk to you.'

I saw he was looking patient again and braced myself.

'James,' he said, pacing round the battered vehicle, whisking specks from the paintwork. 'You see this car?'

I nodded.

'Well, it has been rebored, James, rebored at great expense, and that's what I want to talk to you about. You now have in your possession what nounts to a new car.' With an effort he unfastened the catch and the bonnet creaked open in a shower of rust and dirt. He pointed down at the engine, black and oily, with unrelated pieces of flex a..d rubber tubing hanging around it like garlands. 'You have a piece of fine mechanism here and I want you to treat it with respect. I've seen you belting along like a maniac and it won't do. You've got to nurse this machine for the next two or three thousand miles; thirty miles an hour is quite fast enough. I think it's a crime the way some people abuse a new engine – they should be locked up – so remember, lad, no flogging or I'll be down on you.'

He closed the bonnet with care, gave the cracked windscreen a polish with the cuff of his coat and left.

These strong words made such an impression on me that I crawled round the visits all day almost at walking pace.

The same night, I was getting ready for bed when Siegfried came in. He had two farm lads with him and they both wore silly grins. A powerful smell of beer filled the room.

Siegfried spoke with dignity, slurring his words only slightly. 'James, I met these gentlemen in the Black Bull this evening. We have had several excellent games of dominoes but unfortunately they have missed the last bus. Will you kindly bring the Austin round and I will run them home.'

I drove the car to the front of the house and the farm lads piled in, one in the front, the other in the back. I looked at

Siegfried lowering himself unsteadily into the driving seat and decided to go along. I got into the back.

The two young men lived in a farm far up on the North Moors and, three miles out of the town, we left the main road and our headlights picked out a strip of track twisting along the dark hillside.

Siegfried was in a hurry. He kept his foot on the boards, the note of the engine rose to a tortured scream and the little car hurtled on into the blackness. Hanging on grimly, I leaned forward so that I could shout into my employer's ear. 'Remember this is the car which has just been rebored,' I bellowed above the din.

Siegfried looked round with an indulgent smile. 'Yes, yes, I remember, James. What are you fussing about?' As he spoke, the car shot off the road and bounded over the grass at sixty miles an hour. We all bounced around like corks till he found his way back. Unperturbed, he carried on at the same speed. The silly grins had left the lads' faces and they sat rigid in their seats. Nobody said anything.

The passengers were unloaded at a silent farmhouse and the return journey began. Since it was downhill all the way, Siegfried found he could go even faster. The car leaped and bumped over the uneven surface with its engine whining. We made several brief but tense visits to the surrounding moors, but we got home.

It was a month later that Siegfried had occasion to take his assistant to task once more. 'James, my boy,' he said sorrowfully, 'you are a grand chap, but by God, you're hard on cars. Look at this Austin. Newly rebored a short time ago, in tip top condition, and look at it now – drinking oil. I don't know how you did it in the time. You're a real terror.'

CHAPTER NINE

'First, please,' I called as I looked into the waiting room. There was an old lady with a cat in a cardboard box, two small boys trying to keep hold of a rabbit, and somebody I didn't recognize at first. Then I remembered – it was Soames.

When it was his turn, he came into the surgery but he was a vastly different character from the one I knew. He wore an ingratiating smile. His head bobbed up and down as he spoke. He radiated anxiety to please. And the most interesting thing was that his right eye was puffed and closed and surrounded by an extensive area of bluish-black flesh.

'I hope you don't mind my coming to see you, Mr Herriot,' he said. 'The fact is I have resigned my position with his lordship and am looking for another post. I was wondering if you and Mr Farnon would put in a word for me if you heard of anything.'

I was too astonished at the transformation to say much. I replied that we would do what we could and Soames thanked me effusively and bowed himself out.

I turned to Siegfried after he had gone. 'Well, what do you make of that?'

'Oh, I know all about it.' Siegfried looked at me with a wry smile. 'Remember I told you he was working one or two shady sidelines up there – selling a few bags of corn or a hundredweight of fertilizer here and there. It all mounted up. But it didn't last; he got a bit careless and he was out on his ear before he knew what had happened.'

'And how about the lovely black eye?'

'Oh, he got that from Tommy. You must have seen Tommy when you were there. He's the horseman.'

My mind went back to that uncomfortable night and to the

quiet man holding the horse's head. 'I remember him – big fat chap.'

'Yes, he's a big lad and I'd hate to have him punch me in the eye. Soames gave him a hell of a life and as soon as Tommy heard about the sacking he paid a visit just to settle the score.'

I was now comfortably settled into the way of life in Skeldale House. At first I wondered where Tristan fitted into the set up. Was he supposed to be seeing practice, having a holiday, working or what? But it soon became clear that he was a factotum who dispensed and delivered medicines, washed the cars, answered the phone and even, in an emergency, went to a case.

At least, that was how Siegfried saw him and he had a repertoire of tricks aimed at keeping him on his toes. Like returning unexpectedly or bursting into a room in the hope of catching him doing nothing. He never seemed to notice the obvious fact that the college vacation was over and Tristan should have been back there. I came to the conclusion over the next few months that Tristan must have had some flexible arrangement with the college authorities because, for a student, he seemed to spend a surprising amount of time at home.

He interpreted his role rather differently from his brother and, while resident in Darrowby, he devoted a considerable amount of his acute intelligence to the cause of doing as little as possible. Tristan did, in fact, spend much of his time sleeping in a chair. When he was left behind to dispense when we went out on our rounds he followed an unvarying procedure. He half filled a sixteen ounce bottle with water, added a few drachms of chlorodyne and a little epicacuanha, pushed the cork in and took it through to the sitting-room to stand by his favourite chair. It was a wonderful chair for his purpose; old fashioned and high backed with wings to support the head.

He would get out his *Daily Mirror*, light a Woodbine and settle down till sleep overcame him. If Siegfried rushed in on him he grabbed the bottle and started to shake it madly, inspecting the contents at intervals. Then he went through to the dispensary, filled up the bottle and labelled it.

It was a sound, workable system but it had one big snag. He never knew whether it was Siegfried or not when the door opened and often I walked in and found him half lying in his chair, staring up with startled, sleep-blurred eyes while he agitated his bottle.

Most evenings found him sitting on a high stool at the bar counter of the Drovers' Arms, conversing effortlessly with the barmaid. At other times he would be out with one of the young nurses from the local hospital which he seemed to regard as an agency to provide him with female company. All in all, he managed to lead a fairly full life.

Saturday night, 10.30 PM and I was writing up my visits when the phone rang. I swore, crossed my fingers and lifted the receiver.

'Hello, Herriot speaking.'

'Oh, it's you is it,' growled a dour voice in broadest Yorkshire. 'Well, ah want Mr Farnon.'

'I'm sorry, Mr Farnon is out. Can I help you?'

'Well, I 'ope so, but I'd far raither 'ave your boss. This is Sims of Beal Close.'

(Oh no, please no, not Beal Close on a Saturday night. Miles up in the hills at the end of a rough lane with about eight gates.)

'Yes, Mr Sims, and what is the trouble?'

'Ah'll tell you, there is some trouble an' all. I 'ave a grand big show 'oss here. All of seventeen hands. He's cut 'isself badly on the hind leg, just above the hock. I want him stitched immediately.'

(Glory be! Above the hock! What a charming place to have to stitch a horse. Unless he's very quiet, this is going to be a real picnic.)

'How big is the wound, Mr Sims?'

'Big? It's a gurt big thing about a foot long and bleedin'

like 'ell. And this 'oss is as wick as an eel. Could kick a fly's eye out. Ah can't get near 'im nohow. Goes straight up wall when he sees anybody. By gaw, I tell you I had 'im to t'blacksmith t'other day and feller was dead scared of 'im. Twiltin' gurt 'oss 'e is.'

(Damn you, Mr Sims, damn Beal Close and damn your twiltin' gurt 'oss.)

'Well, I'll be along straight away. Try to have some men handy just in case we have to throw him.'

'Throw 'im? Throw 'im? You'd never throw this 'oss. He'd kill yer first. Anyways, I 'ave no men here so you'll have to manage on your own. Ah know Mr Farnon wouldn't want a lot of men to help 'im.'

(Oh lovely, lovely. This is going to be one for the diary.)

'Very well, I'm leaving now, Mr Sims.'

'Oh, ah nearly forgot. My road got washed away in the floods yesterday. You'll 'ave to walk the last mile and a half. So get a move on and don't keep me waiting all night.'

(This is just a bit much.)

'Look here, Mr Sims, I don't like your tone. I said I would leave now and I will get there just as soon as I can.'

'You don't like ma tone, eh? Well, ah don't like useless young apprentices practising on my good stock, so ah don't want no cheek from you. You know nowt about t'damn job, any road.'

(That finally does it.)

'Now just listen to me, Sims. If it wasn't for the sake of the horse I'd refuse to come out at all. Who do you think you are, anyway? If you ever try to speak to me like that again . . .'

'Now, now, Jim, get a grip on yourself. Take it easy old boy. You'll burst a blood vessel if you go on like this.'

'Who the devil . . .?'

'Ah, ah, Jim, calm yourself now. That temper of yours, you know. You'll really have to watch it.'

'Tristan! Where the hell are you speaking from?'

'The kiosk outside the Drovers. Five pints inside me and feeling a bit puckish. Thought I'd give you a ring.'

'By God, I'll murder you one of these days if you don't stop this game. It's putting years on me. Now and again isn't so bad, but this is the third time this week.'

'Ah, but this was by far the best, Jim. It was really wonderful. When you started drawing yourself up to your full height – it nearly killed me. Oh God, I wish you could have heard yourself.' He trailed off into helpless laughter.

And then my feeble attempts at retaliation; creeping, trembling, into some lonely phone box.

'Is that young Mr Farnon?' in a guttural croak. 'Well, this is Tilson of High Woods. Ah want you to come out here immediately I 'ave a terrible case of . . .'

'Excuse me for interrupting, Jim, but is there something the matter with your tonsils? Oh, good. Well, go on with what you were saying, old lad. Sounds very interesting.'

There was only one time when I was not on the receiving end. It was Tuesday – my half day – and at 11.30 AM a call came in. An eversion of the uterus in a cow. This is the tough job in country practice and I felt the usual chill.

It happens when the cow, after calving, continues to strain until it pushes the entire uterus out and it hangs down as far as the animal's hocks. It is a vast organ and desperately difficult to replace, mainly because the cow, having once got rid of it, doesn't want it back. And in a straightforward contest between man and beast the odds were very much on the cow.

The old practitioners, in an effort to even things up a bit, used to sling the cow up by its hind limbs and the more inventive among them came up with all sorts of contraptions like the uterine valise which was supposed to squeeze the organ into smaller bulk. But the result was usually the same – hours of back-breaking work.

The introduction of the epidural anaesthetic made everything easier by removing sensation from the uterus and preventing the cow from straining but, for all that, the words 'calf bed out' coming over the line were guaranteed to wipe the smile off any vet's face.

I decided to take Tristan in case I needed a few pounds of extra push. He came along but showed little enthusiasm for the idea. He showed still less when he saw the patient, a very fat shorthorn lying, quite unconcerned, in her stall. Behind her, a bloody mass of uterus, afterbirth, muck and straw spilled over into the channel.

She wasn't at all keen to get up, but after we had done a bit of shouting and pushing at her shoulder she rose to her feet, looking bored.

The epidural space was difficult to find among the rolls of fat and I wasn't sure if I had injected all the anaesthetic into the right place. I removed the afterbirth, cleaned the uterus and placed it on a clean sheet held by the farmer and his brother. They were frail men and it was all they could do to keep the sheet level. I wouldn't be able to count on them to help me much.

I nodded to Tristan; we stripped off our shirts, tied clean sacks round our waists and gathered the uterus in our arms.

It was badly engorged and swollen and it took us just an hour to get it back. There was a long spell at the beginning when we made no progress at all and the whole idea of pushing the enormous organ through a small hole seemed ludicrous, like trying to thread a needle with a sausage. Then there was a few minutes when we thought we were doing famously only to find we were feeding the thing down through a tear in the sheet, (Siegfried once told me he had spent half a morning trying to stuff a uterus up a cow's rectum. What really worried him, he said, was that he nearly succeeded) and at the end when hope was fading, there was the blissful moment when the whole thing began to slip inside and incredibly disappeared from sight.

Somewhere halfway through we both took a breather at

the same time and stood panting, our faces almost touching. Tristan's cheeks were prettily patterned where a spouting artery had sprayed him; I was able to look deep into his eyes and I read there a deep distaste for the whole business.

Lathering myself in the bucket and feeling the ache in my shoulders and back, I looked over at Tristan. He was pulling his shirt over his head as though it cost him the last of his strength. The cow, chewing contentedly at a mouthful of hay, had come best out of the affair.

Out in the car, Tristan groaned. 'I'm sure that sort of thing isn't good for me. I feel as though I've been run over by a steam roller. Hell, what a life this is at times.'

After lunch I rose from the table. 'I'm off to Brawton now, Triss, and I think I'd better mention that you may not have seen the last of that cow. These bad cases sometimes recur and there's a chance that little lot may come out again. If it does, it's all yours because Siegfried won't be back for hours and nothing is going to stop me having my half day.'

For once Tristan's sense of humour failed him. He became haggard, he seemed to age suddenly. 'Oh God,' he moaned, 'don't even talk about it. I'm all in – another session like that would kill me. And on my own! It would be the end of me, I tell you.'

'Ah well,' I said sadistically, 'try not to worry. It may never happen.'

It was when I saw the phone box about ten miles along the Brawton road that the thought struck me. I slowed down and got out of the car. 'I wonder,' I muttered, 'I wonder if I could do it just once.'

Inside the box, inspiration was strong in me. I wrapped my handkerchief over the mouthpiece, dialled the practice number and when I heard Tristan on the line I shouted at the top of my voice. 'Are you t'young feller that put our cow's calf bed back this morning?'

'Yes, I'm one of them.' Tension sprang into Tristan's voice. 'Why, is there something wrong?'

'Aye, there is summat wrong,' I bawled. 'She's putten it out again.'

'Out again? Out again? All of it?' He was almost screaming.

'Aye, it's a terrible mess. Pourin' blood and about twice size it was this morning. You'll 'ave some job with 'er.'

There was a long silence and I wondered if he had fainted. Then I heard him again, hoarse but resolute. 'Very well, I'll come straight away.'

There was another pause then he spoke again almost in a whisper. 'Is it out completely?'

I broke down then. There was a wistful quality about the words which defeated me; a hint of a wild hope that the farmer may have been exaggerating and that there might be only a tiny piece peeping out. I began to laugh. I would have liked to toy with my victim a little longer but it was impossible. I laughed louder and took my handkerchief from the mouthpiece so that Tristan could hear me.

I listened for a few seconds to the frenzied swearing at the other end then gently replaced the receiver. It would probably never happen again but it was sweet, very sweet.

CHAPTER TEN

'You want Mr Herriot? Certainly, I'll get him for you.' Siegfried cupped the phone with his hand. 'Come on, James, here's another one prefers you to me.' I glanced at him quickly, but he was smiling. He was pleased.

I thought, as I took the phone, of the tales I had heard of the other kind of boss; the man who couldn't bear to be knocked off his little pedestal. And I thought, too, of the difference a few weeks had made in the farmers' attitude; they didn't look past me now, hoping that Mr Farnon had come with me. They were beginning to accept me, and I liked to think that it wasn't only their hospitable traditions that made them ask me in for a 'bit o' dinner'.

This really meant something, because, with the passage of time, an appreciation of the Dales people had grown in me; a sense of the value of their carefully given friendship. The higher up the country, the more I liked them. At the bottom of the valley, where it widened into the plain, the farmers were like farmers everywhere, but the people grew more interesting as the land heightened, and in the scattered hamlets and isolated farms near the bleak tops I found their characteristics most marked; their simplicity and dignity, their rugged independence and their hospitality.

This Sunday morning it was the Bellerbys and they lived at the top of Halden, a little valley branching off the main Dale. My car bumped and rattled over the last rough mile of an earth road with the tops of boulders sticking up every few yards.

I got out and from where I stood, high at the head, I could see all of the strangely formed cleft in the hills, its steep sides grooved and furrowed by countless streams feeding the boisterous Halden Beck which tumbled over its rocky bed far below. Down there, were trees and some cultivated fields, but immediately behind me the wild country came crowding in on the bowl where the farmhouse lay. Halsten Pike, Alstang, Birnside – the huge fells with their barbarous names were very near.

Up here, the trappings of civilization seemed far away. The farm buildings had been built massively of stone hundreds of years ago with the simple object of sheltering the animals. Those ancient masons were untroubled by regulations about the light and ventilation and the cow byre was gloomy, thick walled, almost windowless. The floor was broken and pitted, and rotting wooden partitions separated the cows from each other.

I went in, groping my way until my eyes grew accustomed to the dim light. There was nobody there but a roan cow had a label tied to its tail. Since this was a common way of communicating with the vet I lifted the tail and read 'Felon, back quarters'.

I pushed the cow over and began to examine the back teats. I was drawing out the stringy, discoloured milk when a voice addressed me from the doorway: 'Oh, it's you, Mr Herriot. I'm right glad you've come to see us this morning. You could do us such a great favour if you would.'

I looked up and saw Ruth Bellerby, a fine looking woman in her late thirties. She was the go-ahead member of the family and had an intelligent, questing mind. She was a great believer in self-improvement for the Dales people.

'I'll be glad to help you if I can, Miss Bellerby. What is it you'd like me to do?'

'Well, Mr Herriot, you know they are putting on the Messiah at Darrowby church this afternoon and we did badly want to go, but it's such a job getting the pony and trap ready and it's so slow. If you could give us a lift down in your car, I know we'd be able to get a ride back. It would be such a help.'

'Of course I'll run you down,' I replied. 'I'll be delighted to do it. I'm going myself as a matter of fact. You don't get many chances to hear good music in Darrowby.'

It was good to have a chance to help these kindly people. I had always marvelled at the Bellerbys. They seemed to me to be survivors from another age and their world had a timeless quality. They were never in a hurry; they rose when it was light, went to bed when they were tired, ate when they were hungry and seldom looked at a clock.

Ruth led the way over to the house. 'There's just mother and dad and me going. Bob's not interested, I'm afraid.'

I was slightly taken aback when I entered the house. The family were just sitting down to Sunday dinner and were still in their working clothes. I stole a look at my watch; a quarter to twelve and the performance started at 2 PM. Oh well, I probably had plenty of time.

'Come on, young man,' said little Mr Bellerby. 'Sit down and have a bit o' dinner.'

It was always a bit tricky refusing these invitations without causing offence, but I pointed out that my own meal would be ready when I got back and it would be hard on Mrs Hall if it were wasted.

They were quick to appreciate this argument and settled down round the scrubbed kitchen table. Mrs Bellerby served a large, round Yorkshire pudding to each of them and poured a pool of gravy into it from a quart size enamel jug. I had had a hard morning and the delicious scent that rose from the gravy as it ran over the golden slabs was a sweet torture. But I consoled myself with the thought that the fact of my sitting there would make them hurry.

The pudding was consumed in leisurely silence, then Bob, an amiable, thick-set youth in his twenties, pushed out his empty plate. He did not say anything, but his mother planked down another pudding on the plate and plied the gravy jug again. His parents and sister watched him benevolently as he methodically demolished the thick, doughy mass.

Next, a tremendous roast appeared from the oven and Mr Bellerby hacked and sawed at it till they all had a heap of thick slices on their plates. Then mountains of mashed potatoes were served from something that looked like a washing-up bowl. Chopped turnip followed and the family went into action again.

There was no sign of haste. They ate calmly and quietly without any small talk. Bob had an extra helping of mashed potatoes.

The Bellerbys were relaxed and happy, but I couldn't say the same about myself. Hunger was tearing fiercely at me and the minutes on my watch were ticking away relentlessly.

There was a decent interval before Mrs Bellerby went over to the old fire oven in the corner, opened the door and pulled forth a great flat baking tin of steaming apple pie. She then proceeded to carve off about a square foot for each of them and deluged it with something like a pint of custard from another towering enamel jug.

The family set to as though they were just beginning the meal and once more a busy silence fell on the group. Bob cleared his plate in effortless style and pushed it wordlessly into the middle of the table. His mother was ready with another great rectangle of pie and another copious libation of custard.

It was going to be a close thing, I thought, but this surely must be the end. They would realize time was getting short and start to change. But, to my consternation, Mrs Bellerby moved slowly over to the fire and put the kettle on, while her husband and Bob pushed their chairs back and stretched out their legs. They both wore corduroy breeches with the lacing undone and on their feet were enormous hobnailed boots. Bob, after a search through his pockets, brought out a battered packet of cigarettes and lay back in a happy coma as his mother put a cup of tea in front of him. Mr Bellerby produced a clasp knife and began to cut up some plug tobacco for his pipe.

As they rearranged themselves round the table and began to slowly sip the hot tea, I found I had started to exhibit all the classical symptoms of tension. Pounding pulse, tighly clenched jaws and the beginnings of a headache.

After a second cup of tea, there were signs of activity. Mr Bellerby rose with a groan, scratched his shirt front and stretched luxuriously. 'Well, young man, we'll just have a bit of a wash and get changed. Bob'll stay and talk to you – he's not coming with us.'

There was a lot of splashing and spluttering in the big stone sink at the far end of the kitchen as they made their ablutions, then they disappeared upstairs. I was greatly relieved to find that it didn't take them long to change. Mr Bellerby was down very soon, transformed in appearance by a stiff and shiny suit of navy blue serge with a faint greenish tinge. His wife and daughter followed soon in a blaze of flowered cotton.

'Ah well, now, here we are. All ready, eh?' There was a note of hysteria in my heartiness. 'Right, then, off we go. After you, ladies.'

But Ruth did not move. She was pulling on a pair of white gloves and looking at her brother sprawled in his chair. 'You know, Bob, you're nowt but a disgrace!' she burst out. 'Here we are going off to hear this lovely music and you're lying there in your muck, not caring. You've no interest in culture at all. You care no more about bettering yourself than one of them bullocks out there.'

Bob stirred uneasily under this sudden attack, but there was more to come.

Ruth stamped her foot. 'Really, it makes my blood boil to look at you. And I know we won't be right out of t'door before you're asleep. Aye, snoring there all afternoon like a pig.' She swung round to Mrs Bellerby. 'Mother! I've made up my mind. I'm not going to leave him snoring here. He's got to come with us!'

I felt the sweat start out on my brow. I began to babble. 'But don't you think, perhaps . . . might be just a little late . . . starts at two o'clock . . . my lunch . . .'

But my words were utterly lost. Ruth had the bit properly between her teeth. 'Get up out of there, Bob! Get up this minute and get dressed!' She shut her mouth tightly and thrust out her lower jaw.

She was too much for Bob. Although an impressive eater, he didn't seem to have much mind of his own. He mumbled sulkily and shuffled over to the sink. He took off his shirt and they all sat down and watched as he lathered his torso with a large block of White Windsor and sluiced his head and neck by working the pump handle by the side of the sink.

The family regarded him happily, pleased that he was coming with them and content in the knowledge that it would be good for him. Ruth watched his splashings with the light of love in her eyes. She kept looking over at me as if to say 'Isn't this grand'.

For my part, I was only just stopping myself from tearing out my hair in great handfuls. A compulsion to leap up and pace the floor, to scream at the top of my voice showed that I was nearing the end of my tether. I fought this feeling by closing my eyes and I must have kept them closed for a long time because, when I opened them, Bob was standing by my side in a suit exactly like his father's.

I could never remember much about that ride to Darrowby. I had only a vague recollection of the car hurtling down the stony track at forty miles an hour. Of myself staring straight ahead with protruding eyes and the family, tightly packed but cheerful, thoroughly enjoying the ride.

Even the imperturbable Mrs Hall was a little tight lipped as I shot into the house at ten to two and out again at two after bolting her good food.

I was late for the Messiah. The music had started as I crept into the church and I ran a gauntlet of disapproving stares. Out of the corner of my eye I saw the Bellerbys sitting very upright, all in a row. It seemed to me that they looked disapproving, too.

CHAPTER ELEVEN

I looked again at the slip of paper where I had written my visits. 'Dean, 3, Thompson's Yard. Old dog ill.'

There were a lot of these 'yards' in Darrowby. They were, in fact, tiny streets, like pictures from a Dickens' novel. Some of them opened off the market place and many more were scattered behind the main thoroughfares in the old part of the town. From the outside you could see only an archway and it was always a surprise to me to go down a narrow passage and come suddenly upon the uneven rows of little houses with no two alike, looking into each other's windows across eight feet of cobbles.

In front of some of the houses a strip of garden had been dug out and marigolds and nasturtiums straggled over the rough stones; but at the far end the houses were in a tumble-down condition and some were abandoned with their windows boarded up.

Number three was down at this end and looked as though it wouldn't be able to hold out much longer.

The flakes of paint quivered on the rotten wood of the door as I knocked; above, the outer wall bulged dangerously on either side of a long crack in the masonry.

A small, white haired man answered. His face, pinched and lined, was enlivened by a pair of cheerful eyes; he wore a much-darned woollen cardigan, patched trousers and slippers.

'I've come to see your dog,' I said, and the old man smiled.

'Oh, I'm glad you've come, sir,' he said. 'I'm getting a bit worried about the old chap. Come inside, please.'

He led me into the tiny living-room. 'I'm alone now, sir. Lost my missus over a year ago. She used to think the world of the old dog.'

The grim evidence of poverty was everywhere. In the worn out lino, the fireless hearth, the dank, musty smell of the place. The wall paper hung away from the damp patches and on the table the old man's solitary dinner was laid; a fragment of bacon, a few fried potatoes and a cup of tea. This was life on the old age pension.

In the corner, on a blanket, lay my patient, a cross-bred labrador. He must have been a big, powerful dog in his time, but the signs of age showed in the white hairs round his muzzle and the pale opacity in the depth of his eyes. He lay quietly and looked at me without hostility.

'Getting on a bit, isn't he, Mr Dean?'

'Aye he is that. Nearly fourteen, but he's been like a pup galloping about until these last few weeks. Wonderful dog for his age, is old Bob and he's never offered to bite anybody in his life. Children can do anything with him. He's my only friend now – I hope you'll soon be able to put him right.'

'Is he off his food, Mr Dean?'

'Yes, clean off, and that's a strange thing because by gum, he could eat. He always sat by me and put his head on my knee at meal times, but he hasn't been doing it lately.'

I looked at the dog with growing uneasiness. The abdomen was grossly distended and I could read the tell-tale symptoms of pain; the catch in the respirations, the retracted commissures of the lips, the anxious, preoccupied expression in the eyes.

When his master spoke, the tail thumped twice on the blankets and a momentary interest showed in the white old eyes; but it quickly disappeared and the blank, inward look returned.

I passed my hand carefully over the dog's abdomen. Ascites was pronounced and the dropsical fluid had gathered till the pressure was intense. 'Come on, old chap,' I said, 'Let's see if we can roll you over.' The dog made no resistance as I eased him slowly on to his other side, but, just as the movement was completed, he whimpered and looked round. The cause of the trouble was now only too easy to find.

I palpated gently. Through the thin muscle of the flank I could feel a hard, corrugated mass; certainly a splenic or hepatic carcinoma, enormous and completely inoperable. I stroked the old dog's head as I tried to collect my thoughts. This wasn't going to be easy.

'Is he going to be ill for long?' the old man asked, and again came the thump, thump of the tail at the sound of the loved voice. 'It's miserable when Bob isn't following me round the house when I'm doing my little jobs.'

'I'm sorry, Mr Dean, but I'm afraid this is something very serious. You see this large swelling. It is caused by an internal growth.'

'You mean ... cancer?' the little man said faintly.

'I'm afraid so, and it has progressed too far for anything to be done. I wish there was something I could do to help him, but there isn't.'

The old man looked bewildered and his lips trembled. 'Then he's going to die?'

I swallowed hard. 'We really can't just leave him to die, can we? He's in some distress now, but it will soon be an awful lot worse. Don't you think it would be kindest to put him to sleep? After all, he's had a good, long innings.' I always aimed at a brisk, matter-of-fact approach, but the old clichés had an empty ring.

The old man was silent, then he said, 'Just a minute,' and slowly and painfully knelt down by the side of the dog. He did not speak, but ran his hand again and again over the grey old muzzle and the ears, while the tail thump, thump, thumped on the floor.

He knelt there a long time while I stood in the cheerless room, my eyes taking in the faded pictures on the walls, the frayed, grimy curtains, the broken-springed arm chair.

At length the old man struggled to his feet and gulped once or twice. Without looking at me, he said huskily, 'All right, will you do it now?'

I filled the syringe and said the things I always said. 'You needn't worry, this is absolutely painless. Just an overdose of an anaesthetic. It is really an easy way out for the old fellow.'

The dog did not move as the needle was inserted, and, as the barbiturate began to flow into the vein, the anxious expression left his face and the muscles began to relax. By the time the injection was finished, the breathing had stopped.

'Is that it?' the old man whispered.

'Yes, that's it,' I said. 'He is out of his pain now.'

The old man stood motionless except for the clasping and unclasping of his hands. When he turned to face me his eyes were bright. 'That's right, we couldn't let him suffer, and I'm grateful for what you've done. And now, what do I owe you for your services, sir?'

'Oh, that's all right, Mr Dean,' I said quickly. 'It's nothing – nothing at all. I was passing right by here – it was no trouble.'

The old man was astonished. 'But you can't do that for nothing.'

'Now please say no more about it, Mr Dean. As I told you, I

was passing right by your door.' I said goodbye and went out of the house, through the passage and into the street. In the bustle of people and the bright sunshine, I could still see only the stark, little room, the old man and his dead dog.

As I walked towards my car, I heard a shout behind me. The old man was shuffling excitedly towards me in his slippers. His cheeks were streaked and wet, but he was smiling. In his hand he held a small, brown object.

'You've been very kind, sir. I've got something for you.' He held out the object and I looked at it. It was tattered but just recognizable as a precious relic of a bygone celebration.

'Go on, it's for you,' said the old man. 'Have a cigar.'

CHAPTER TWELVE

It was unfortunate that Siegfried ever had the idea of delegating the book-keeping to his brother, because Skeldale House had been passing through a period of peace and I found it soothing.

For nearly a fortnight there had been hardly a raised voice or an angry word except for one unpleasant interlude when Siegfried had come in and found his brother cycling along the passage. Tristan found all the rage and shouting quite incomprehensible – he had been given the job of setting the table and it was a long way from kitchen to dining-room; it seemed the most natural thing in the world to bring his bike in.

Autumn had come with a sharpness in the air and at nights the log fire burned bright in the big room, sending shadows flickering over the graceful alcoves and up to the high, carved ceiling. It was always a good time when the work of the day was through and the three of us lay back in the shabby arm chairs and stretched our feet out to the blaze.

Tristan was occupied with the *Daily Telegraph* crossword which he did every night. Siegfried was reading and I was dozing. It embarrassed me to be drawn into the crossword; Siegfried could usually make a contribution after a minute's thought but Tristan could have the whole thing worked out while I wrestled with the first clue.

The carpet round our feet was hidden by the dogs, all five of them, draped over each other in heavy-breathing layers and adding to the atmosphere of camaraderie and content.

It seemed to me that a chill breath struck through the comfort of the room as Siegfried spoke. 'Market day tomorrow and the bills have just gone out. They'll be queueing up to give us their money so I want you, Tristan, to devote the entire day to taking it from them. James and I are going to be busy, so you'll be in sole charge. All you have to do is take their cheques, give them a receipt and enter their names in the receipt book. Now do you think you can manage that without making a bloody hash of it?'

I winced. It was the first discordant note for a long time and it struck deep.

'I think I might just about cope with that,' Tristan replied haughtily.

'Good. Let's get to bed then.'

But, next day, it was easy to see that the assignment was right up Tristan's street. Stationed behind the desk, he took in the money in handfuls; and all the time he talked. But he did not talk at random; each character got a personal approach.

With the upright methodist, it was the weather, the price of cows and the activities of the village institute. The raffish type with his cap on one side, exhaling fumes of market ale, got the latest stories which Tristan kept on the backs of envelopes. But with the ladies he rose to his greatest heights. They were on his side from the first because of his innocent, boyish face, and when he turned the full blast of his charm on them their surrender was complete.

I was amazed at the giggles which came from behind the door. I was pleased the lad was doing well. Nothing was going wrong this time.

Tristan was smug at lunch time and cock-a-hoop at tea. Siegfried too, was satisfied with the day's takings which his brother presented in the form of a column of neat figures accurately totalled at the bottom. 'Thank you, Tristan, very efficient.' All was sweetness.

At the end of the day I was in the yard, throwing the used bottles from the boot of my car into a bin. It had been a busy day and I had accumulated a bigger than usual load of empties.

Tristan came panting in from the garden. 'Jim, I've lost the receipt book!'

'Always trying to pull my leg, always joking,' I said, 'Why don't you give your sense of humour a rest some time?' I laughed heartily and sent a liniment bottle crashing among the others.

He plucked at my sleeve. 'I'm not joking, Jim, believe me. I really have lost the bloody thing.' For once, his *sang froid* had deserted him. His eyes were wide, his face pale.

'But it can't just have disappeared,' I said. 'It's bound to turn up.'

'It'll never turn up.' Tristan wrung his hands and did a bit of pacing on the cobbles. 'Do you know I've spent about two hours searching for it. I've ransacked the house. It's gone, I tell you.'

'But it doesn't matter, does it? You'll have transferred all the names into the ledger.'

'That's just it. I haven't. I was going to do it tonight.'

'So that means that all the farmers who have been handing you money today are going to get the same bill next month?'

'Looks like it. I can't remember the names of more than two or three of them.'

I sat down heavily on the stone trough. 'Then God help us all, especially you. These Yorkshire lads don't like parting with their brass once, but when you ask them to do it twice – oh, brother!'

Another thought struck me and I said with a touch of cruelty. 'And how about Siegfried. Have you told him yet?'

A spasm crossed Tristan's face. 'No, he's just come in. I'm going to do it now.' He squared his shoulders and strode from the yard.

I decided not to follow him to the house. I didn't feel strong enough for the scene which was bound to follow. Instead, I went out into the back lane and round behind the house to the market place where the lighted entrance of the Drovers' Arms beckoned in the dusk.

I was sitting behind a pint when Tristan came in looking as though somebody had just drained half a gallon of blood from him.

'How did it go?' I asked.

'Oh, the usual, you know. Bit worse this time, maybe. But I can tell you this, Jim. I'm not looking forward to a month from today.'

The receipt book was never found and, a month later, all the bills were sent out again, timed, as usual, to arrive on market day morning.

The practice was quiet that particular day and I had finished my round by mid morning. I didn't go into the house, because through the waiting room window I could see rows of farmers sitting round the walls; they all wore the same offended, self-righteous expression.

I stole away to the market place. When I had time, I enjoyed moving among the stalls which crowded the ancient square. You could buy fruit, fish, second-hand books, cheeses, clothes, in fact nearly everything; but the china stall was my favourite.

It was run by a Jewish gentleman from Leeds – fat, confident, sweating, and with a hypnotic selling technique. I never got tired of watching him. He fascinated me. He was in his best form today, standing in a little clearing surrounded on all sides by heaps of crockery, while beyond, the farmers' wives listened open-mouthed to his oratory.

'Ah'm not good lookin',' he was saying. 'Ah'm not clever,

but by God ah can talk. Ah can talk the hind leg off a donkey. Now look 'ere.' He lifted a cheap cup and held it aloft, but tenderly, gripping it between his thick thumb and forefinger, his little finger daintily outspread. 'Beautiful, isn't it? Now isn't that lovely?' Then he placed it reverently on the palm of his hand and displayed it to the audience. 'Now I tell you ladies, you can buy this self same tea-set in Conners in Bradford for three pounds fifteen. I'm not jokin' nor jestin', it's there and that's the price. But my price, ladies?' and here he fished out an old walking stick with a splintered handle. 'My price for this beautiful tea-set?' He held the stick by its end and brought it crashing down on an empty tea-chest. 'Never mind three pound fifteen.' Crash! 'Never mind three pound.' Crash! 'Never mind two pound.' Crash! 'Never mind thirty bob.' Crash! ''ere, 'ere, come on, who'll give me a quid?' Not a soul moved. 'All right, all right, I can see ah've met me match today. Go on, seventeen and a tanner the lot.' A final devastating crash and the ladies began to make signals and fumble in their handbags. A little man emerged from the back of the stall and started to hand out the tea-sets. The ritual had been observed and everybody was happy.

I was waiting, deeply content, for the next item from the virtuoso when I saw a burly figure in a check cap waving wildly at me from the edge of the crowd. He had his hand inside his jacket and I knew what he was feeling for. I didn't hesitate but dodged quickly behind a stall laden with pig troughs and wire netting. I had gone only a few steps before another farmer hailed me purposefully. He was brandishing an envelope.

I felt trapped, then I saw a way of escape. Rapidly skirting a counter displaying cheap jewellery, I plunged into the doorway of the Drovers' Arms and, avoiding the bar which was full of farmers, slipped into the manager's office. I was safe; this was one place where I was always welcome.

The manager looked up from his desk, but he did not smile. 'Look here,' he said sharply, 'I brought my dog in to see you some time ago and in due course I received an account from you.' I cringed inwardly. 'I paid by return and was extremely surprised this morning to find that another account had been rendered. I have here a receipt signed by . . .'

I couldn't stand any more. 'I'm very sorry, Mr Brooke, but there's been a mistake. I'll put it right. Please accept our apologies.'

This became a familiar refrain over the next few days, but it was Siegfried who had the most unfortunate experience. It was in the bar of his favourite pub, the Black Swan. He was approached by Billy Breckenridge, a friendly, jocular little character, one of Darrowby's worthies. 'Hey, remember that three and six I paid at your surgery? I've had another bill for it.'

Siegfried made a polished apology – he'd had a lot of practice – and bought the man a drink. They parted on good terms.

The pity of it was that Siegfried, who seldom remembered anything, didn't remember this. A month later, also in the Swan, he ran into Billy Breckenridge again. This time, Billy wasn't so jocular. 'Hey, remember that bill you sent me twice? Well, I've had it again.'

Siegfried did his best, but his charm bounced off the little man. He was offended. 'Right, I can see you don't believe I paid your bill. I had a receipt from your brother, but I've lost it.' He brushed aside Siegfried's protestations. 'No, no, there's only one way to settle this. I say I've paid the three and six, you say I haven't. All right, I'll toss you for it.'

Miserably, Siegfried demurred, but Billy was adamant. He produced a penny and, with great dignity, balanced it on his thumbnail. 'OK, you call.'

'Heads,' muttered Siegfried and heads it was. The little man did not change expression. Still dignified, he handed the three and six to Siegfried. 'Perhaps we might be able to consider the matter closed.' He walked out of the bar.

Now there are all kinds of bad memories, but Siegfried's was of the inspired type. He somehow forgot to make a note of this last transaction and, at the end of the month, Billy Brenckenridge received a fourth request for the amount which he had already paid twice. It was about then that Siegfried changed his pub and started going to the Cross Keys.

CHAPTER THIRTEEN

As Autumn wore into Winter and the high tops were streaked with the first snows, the discomforts of practice in the Dales began to make themselves felt.

Driving for hours with frozen feet, climbing to the high barns in biting winds which seared and flattened the wiry hill grass. The interminable stripping off in draughty buildings and the washing of hands and chest in buckets of cold water, using scrubbing soap and often a piece of sacking for a towel.

I really found out the meaning of chapped hands. When there was a rush of work, my hands were never quite dry and the little red fissures crept up almost to my elbows.

This was when some small animal work came as a blessed relief. To step out of the rough, hard routine for a while; to walk into a warm drawing-room instead of a cow house and tackle something less formidable than a horse or a bull. And among all those comfortable drawing-rooms there was none so beguiling as Mrs Pumphrey's.

Mrs Pumphrey was an elderly widow. Her late husband, a beer baron whose breweries and pubs were scattered widely over the broad bosom of Yorkshire, had left her a vast fortune and a beautiful house on the outskirts of Darrowby. Here she lived with a large staff of servants, a gardener, a chauffeur and Tricki Woo. Tricki Woo was a Pekingese and the apple of his mistress' eye.

Standing now in the magnificent doorway, I furtively rubbed the toes of my shoes on the backs of my trousers and blew on my cold hands. I could almost see the deep armchair drawn close to the leaping flames, the tray of cocktail biscuits, the bottle of excellent sherry. Because of the sherry, I was always careful to time my visits for half an hour before lunch.

A maid answered my ring, beaming on me as an honoured guest and led me to the room, crammed with expensive furniture and littered with glossy magazines and the latest novels. Mrs Pumphrey, in the high backed chair by the fire, put down her book with a cry of delight. 'Tricki! Tricki! Here is your uncle Herriot.' I had been made an uncle very early and, sensing the advantages of the relationship, had made no objection.

Tricki, as always, bounded from his cushion, leaped on to the back of a sofa and put his paws on my shoulders. He then licked my face thoroughly before retiring, exhausted. He was soon exhausted because he was given roughly twice the amount of food needed for a dog of his size. And it was the wrong kind of food.

'Oh, Mr Herriot,' Mrs Pumphrey said, looking at her pet anxiously. 'I'm so glad you've come. Tricki has gone flop-bott again.'

This ailment, not to be found in any text book, was her way of describing the symptoms of Tricki's impacted anal glands. When the glands filled up, he showed discomfort by sitting down suddenly in mid walk and his mistress would rush to the phone in great agitation.

'Mr Herriot! Please come, he's going flop-bott again!'

I hoisted the little dog on to a table and, by pressure on the anus with a pad of cotton wool, I evacuated the glands.

It baffled me that the Peke was always so pleased to see me. Any dog who could still like a man who grabbed him and squeezed his bottom hard every time they met had to have an incredibly forgiving nature. But Tricki never showed any resentment; in fact he was an outstandingly equable little animal, bursting with intelligence, and I was genuinely attached to him. It was a pleasure to be his personal physician.

The squeezing over, I lifted my patient from the table, noticing the increased weight, the padding of extra flesh over the ribs. 'You know, Mrs Pumphrey, you're overfeeding him again.

Didn't I tell you to cut out all those pieces of cake and give him more protein?'

'Oh yes, Mr Herriot,' Mrs Pumphrey wailed. 'But what can I do? He's so tired of chicken.'

I shrugged; it was hopeless. I allowed the maid to lead me to the palatial bathroom where I always performed a ritual handwashing after the operation. It was a huge room with a fully stocked dressing table, massive green ware and rows of glass shelves laden with toilet preparations. My private guest towel was laid out next to the slab of expensive soap.

Then I returned to the drawing-room, my sherry glass was filled and I settled down by the fire to listen to Mrs Pumphrey. It couldn't be called a conversation because she did all the talking, but I always found it rewarding.

Mrs Pumphrey was likeable, gave widely to charities and would help anybody in trouble. She was intelligent and amusing and had a lot of waffling charm; but most people have a blind spot and her's was Tricki Woo. The tales she told about her darling ranged far into the realms of fantasy and I waited eagerly for the next instalment.

'Oh Mr Herriot, I have the most exciting news. Tricki has a pen pal! Yes, he wrote a letter to the editor of *Doggy World* enclosing a donation, and told him that even though he was descended from a long line of Chinese emperors, he had decided to come down and mingle freely with the common dogs. He asked the editor to seek out a pen pal for him among the dogs he knew so that they could correspond to their mutual benefit. And for this purpose, Tricki said he would adopt the name of Mr Utterbunkum. And, do you know, he received the most beautiful letter from the editor' (I could imagine the sensible man leaping upon this potential gold mine) 'who said he would like to introduce Bonzo Fotheringham, a lonely Dalmatian who would be delighted to exchange letters with a new friend in Yorkshire.'

I sipped the sherry. Tricki snored on my lap. Mrs Pumphrey went on.

'But I'm so disappointed about the new Summerhouse – you know I got it specially for Tricki so we could sit out together on warm afternoons. It's such a nice little rustic shelter, but he's taken a passionate dislike to it. Simply loathes it – absolutely refuses to go inside. You should see the dreadful expression on his face when he looks at it. And do you know what he called it yesterday? Oh, I hardly dare tell you.' She looked around the room before leaning over and whispering: 'He called it "the bloody hut"!'

The maid struck fresh life into the fire and refilled my glass. The wind hurled a handful of sleet against the window. This, I thought, was the life. I listened for more.

'And did I tell you, Mr Herriot, Tricki had another good win yesterday? You know, I'm sure he must study the racing columns, he's such a tremendous judge of form. Well, he told me to back Canny Lad in the three o'clock at Redcar yesterday and, as usual, it won. He put on a shilling each way and got back nine shillings.'

These bets were always placed in the name of Tricki Woo and I thought with compassion of the reactions of the local bookies. The Darrowby turf accountants were a harassed and fugitive body of men. A board would appear at the end of some alley urging the population to invest with Joe Downs and enjoy perfect security. Joe would live for a few months on a knife edge while he pitted his wits against the knowledgeable citizens, but the end was always the same; a few favourites would win in a row and Joe would be gone in the night, taking his board with him. Once I had asked a local inhabitant about the sudden departure of one of these luckless nomads. He replied unemotionally: 'Oh, we brok 'im.'

Losing a regular flow of shillings to a dog must have been a heavy cross for these unfortunate men to bear.

'I had such a frightening experience last week,' Mrs Pumphrey continued. 'I was sure I would have to call you out. Poor little Tricki – he went completely crackerdog!'

I mentally lined this up with flop-bott among the new canine diseases and asked for more information.

'It was awful. I was terrified. The gardener was throwing rings for Tricki – you know he does this for half an hour every day.' I had witnessed this spectacle several times. Hodgkin, a dour, bent old Yorkshireman who looked as though he hated all dogs and Tricki in particular, had to go out on the lawn every day and throw little rubber rings over and over again. Tricki bounded after them and brought them back, barking madly till the process was repeated. The bitter lines on the old man's face deepened as the game progressed. His lips moved continually, but it was impossible to hear what he was saying.

Mrs Pumphrey went on: 'Well, he was playing his game, and he does adore it so, when suddenly, without warning, he went crackerdog. He forgot all about his rings and began to run around in circles, barking and yelping in such a strange way. Then he fell over on his side and lay like a little dead thing. Do you know, Mr Herriot, I really thought he was dead, he lay so perfectly still. And what hurt me most was that Hodgkin began to laugh. He has been with me for twenty-four years and I have never even seen him smile, and yet, when he looked down at that still form, he broke into a queer, high-pitched cackle. It was horrid. I was just going to rush to the telephone when Tricki got up and walked away – he seemed perfectly normal.'

Hysteria, I thought, brought on by wrong feeding and over-excitement. I put down my glass and fixed Mrs Pumphrey with a severe glare. 'Now look, this is just what I was talking about. If you persist in feeding all that fancy rubbish to Tricki you are going to ruin his health. You really must get him on to a sensible dog diet of one or, at the most, two small meals a day of meat and brown bread or a little biscuit. And nothing in between.'

Mrs Pumphrey shrank into her chair, a picture of abject guilt. 'Oh, please don't speak to me like that. I do try to give him the right things, but it is so difficult. When he begs for his little titbits, I can't refuse him.' She dabbed her eyes with a handkerchief.

But I was unrelenting. 'All right, Mrs Pumphrey, it's up to you, but I warn you that if you go on as you are doing, Tricki will go crackerdog more and more often.'

I left the cosy haven with reluctance, pausing on the gravelled drive to look back at Mrs Pumphrey waving and Tricki, as always, standing against the window, his wide-mouthed face apparently in the middle of a hearty laugh.

Driving home, I mused on the many advantages of being Tricki's uncle. When he went to the seaside he sent me boxes of oak-smoked kippers; and when the tomatoes ripened in his greenhouse, he sent a pound or two every week. Tins of tobacco arrived regularly, sometimes with a photograph carrying a loving inscription.

But it was when the Christmas hamper arrived from Fortnum and Mason's that I decided that I was on a really good thing which should be helped along a bit. Hitherto, I had merely rung up and thanked Mrs Pumphrey for the gifts, and she had been rather cool, pointing out that it was Tricki who had sent the things and he was the one who should be thanked.

With the arrival of the hamper it came to me, blindingly, that I had been guilty of a grave error of tactics. I set myself to compose a letter to Tricki. Avoiding Siegfried's sardonic eye, I thanked my doggy nephew for his Christmas gifts and for all his generosity in the past. I expressed my sincere hopes that the festive fare had not upset his delicate digestion and suggested that if he did experience any discomfort he should have recourse to the black powder his uncle always prescribed. A vague feeling of professional shame was easily swamped by floating visions of kippers, tomatoes and hampers. I addressed the envelope to Master Tricki Pumphrey, Barlby Grange and slipped it into the post box with only a slight feeling of guilt.

On my next visit, Mrs Pumphrey drew me to one side. 'Mr Herriot,' she whispered, 'Tricki adored your charming letter and he will keep it always, but he was very put out about one thing – you addressed it to Master Tricki and he does insist upon Mister. He was dreadfully affronted at first, quite beside himself, but when he saw it was from you he soon recovered his good temper. I can't think why he should have these little prejudices. Perhaps it is because he is an only dog – I do think an only dog develops more prejudices than one from a large family.'

Entering Skeldale House was like returning to a colder world. Siegfried bumped into me in the passage. 'Ah, who have we here? Why I do believe it's dear Uncle Herriot. And what have you been doing, Uncle? Slaving away at Barlby Grange, I expect. Poor fellow, you must be tired out. Do you really think it's worth it, working your fingers to the bone for another hamper?'

CHAPTER FOURTEEN

Looking back, I can scarcely believe we used to spend all those hours in making up medicines. But our drugs didn't come to us in proprietary packages and before we could get out on the road we had to fill our cars with a wide variety of carefully compounded and largely useless remedies.

When Siegfried came upon me that morning I was holding a twelve ounce bottle at eye level while I poured syrup of coccilana into it. Tristan was moodily mixing stomach powders with a mortar and pestle and he stepped up his speed of stroke when he saw his brother's eye on him. He was surrounded by packets of the powder and, further along the bench, were orderly piles of pessaries which he had made by filling cellophane cylinders with boric acid.

Tristan looked industrious; his elbow jogged furiously as he ground away at the ammon carb and nux vomica. Siegfried smiled benevolently.

I smiled too. I felt the strain badly when the brothers were at variance, but I could see that this was going to be one of the happy mornings. There had been a distinct improvement in the atmosphere since Christmas when Tristan had slipped casually back to college and, apparently without having done any work, had re-sat and passed his exams. And there was something else about my boss today; he seemed to glow with inner satisfaction as though he knew for certain that something good was on the way. He came in and closed the door.

'I've got a bit of good news.'

I screwed the cork into the bottle. 'Well, don't keep us in suspense. Let's have it.'

Siegfried looked from one of us to the other. He was almost smirking. 'You remember that bloody awful shambles when Tristan took charge of the bills?'

His brother looked away and began to grind still faster, but Siegfried laid a friendly hand on his shoulder. 'No, don't worry, I'm not going to ask you to do it again. In fact, you'll never have to do it again because, from now on, the job will be done by an expert.' He paused and cleared his throat. 'We're going to have a secretary.'

As we stared blankly at him he went on. 'Yes, I picked her myself and I consider she's perfect.'

'Well, what's she like?' I asked.

Siegfried pursed his lips. 'It's difficult to describe her. But just think – what do we want here? We don't want some flighty young thing hanging about the place. We don't want a pretty little blonde sitting behind that desk powdering her nose and making eyes at everybody.'

'We don't?' Tristan interrupted, plainly puzzled.

'No, we don't!' Siegfried rounded on him. 'She'd be daydreaming about her boy friends half the time and just when we'd got her trained to our ways she'd be running off to get married.'

Tristan still looked unconvinced and it seemed to exasperate his brother. Siegfried's face reddened. 'And there's another thing. How could we have an attractive young girl in here with somebody like you in the house. You'd never leave her alone.'

Tristan was nettled. 'How about you?'

'I'm talking about you, not me!' Siegfried roared. I closed my eyes. The peace hadn't lasted long. I decided to cut in. 'All right, tell us about the new secretary.'

With an effort, he mastered his emotion. 'Well, she's in her fifties and she has retired after thirty years with Green and Moulton in Bradford. She was company secretary there and I've had the most wonderful reference from the firm. They say she is a model of efficiency and that's what we want in this practice – efficiency. We're far too slack. It's just a stroke of luck for us that she decided to come and live in Darrowby. Anyway, you'll be able to meet her in a few minutes – she's coming at ten o'clock this morning.'

The church clock was chiming when the door bell rang. Siegfried hastened out to answer it and led his great discovery into the room in triumph. 'Gentlemen, I want you to meet Miss Harbottle.'

She was a big, high-bosomed woman with a round healthy face and gold-rimmed spectacles. A mass of curls, incongruous and very dark, peeped from under her hat; they looked as if they might be dyed and they didn't go with her severe clothes and brogue shoes.

It occurred to me that we wouldn't have to worry about her rushing off to get married. It wasn't that she was ugly, but she had a jutting chin and an air of effortless command that would send any man running for his life.

I shook hands and was astonished at the power of Miss Harbottle's grip. We looked into each other's eyes and had a friendly trial of strength for a few seconds, then she seemed happy to call it a draw and turned away. Tristan was entirely unprepared and a look of alarm spread over his face as his hand was engulfed; he was released only when his knees started to buckle.

She began a tour of the office while Siegfried hovered behind her, rubbing his hands and looking like a shopwalker with his favourite customer. She paused at the desk, heaped high with in-coming and out-going bills, Ministry of Agriculture forms, circulars from drug firms with here and there stray boxes of pills and tubes of udder ointment.

Stirring distastefully among the mess, she extracted the dog-eared old ledger and held it up between finger and thumb. 'What's this?'

Siegfried trotted forward. 'Oh, that's our ledger. We enter the visits into it from our day book which is here somewhere.' He scrabbled about on the desk. 'Ah, here it is. This is where we write the calls as they come in.'

She studied the two books for a few minutes with an expression of amazement which gave way to a grim humour. 'You gentlemen will have to learn to write if I am going to look after your books. There are three different hands here, but this one is by far the worst. Quite dreadful. Whose is it?'

She pointed to an entry which consisted of a long, broken line with an occasional undulation.

'That's mine, actually,' said Siegfried, shuffling his feet. 'Must have been in a hurry that day.'

'But it's all like that, Mr Farnon. Look here and here and here. It won't do, you know.'

Siegfried put his hands behind his back and hung his head.

'I expect you keep your stationery and envelopes in here.' She pulled open a drawer in the desk. It appeared to be filled entirely with old seed packets, many of which had burst open. A few peas and french beans rolled gently from the top of the heap. The next drawer was crammed tightly with soiled calving ropes which somebody had forgotten to wash. They didn't smell so good and Miss Harbottle drew back hurriedly; but she was not easily deterred and tugged hopefully at the third drawer. It came open with a musical clinking and she looked down on a dusty row of empty pale ale bottles.

She straightened up slowly and spoke patiently. 'And where, may I ask, is your cash box?'

'Well, we just stuff it in there, you know.' Siegfried pointed to the pint pot on the corner of the mantelpiece. 'Haven't got what you'd call a proper cash box, but this does the job all right.'

Miss Harbottle looked at the pot with horror. 'You just stuff . . .' Crumpled cheques and notes peeped over the brim at her; many of their companions had burst out on to the hearth below. 'And you mean to say that you go out and leave that money there day after day?'

'Never seems to come to any harm,' Siegfried replied.

'And how about your petty cash?'

Siegfried gave an uneasy giggle. 'All in there, you know. All cash – petty and otherwise.'

Miss Harbottle's ruddy face had lost some of its colour 'Really, Mr Farnon, this is too bad. I don't know how you have gone on so long like this. I simply do not know. However, I'm confident I will be able to straighten things out very soon. There is obviously nothing complicated about your business – a simple card index system would be the thing for your accounts. The other little things,' – she glanced back unbelieving at the pot – 'I will put right very quickly.'

'Fine, Miss Harbottle, fine.' Siegfried was rubbing his hands harder than ever. 'We'll expect you on Monday morning.'

'Nine o'clock sharp, Mr Farnon.'

After she had gone there was a silence. Tristan had enjoyed her visit and was smiling thoughtfully, but I felt uncertain.

'You know, Siegfried,' I said, 'maybe she is a demon of efficiency but isn't she just a bit tough?'

'Tough?' Siegfried gave a loud, rather cracked laugh. 'Not a bit of it. You leave her to me. I can handle her.'

CHAPTER FIFTEEN

There was little furniture in the dining-room but the noble lines and the very size of the place lent grace to the long sideboard and the modest mahogany table where Tristan and I sat at breakfast.

The single large window was patterned with frost and in the street outside, the footsteps of the passers-by crunched in the crisp snow. I looked up from my boiled egg as a car drew up. There was a stamping in the porch, the outer door banged shut and Siegfried burst into the room. Without a word he made for the fire and hung over it, leaning his elbows on the grey marble mantelpiece. He was muffled almost to the eyes in greatcoat and scarf but what you could see of his face was purplish blue.

He turned a pair of streaming eyes to the table. 'A milk fever up at old Heseltine's. One of the high buildings. God, it was cold up there. I could hardly breathe.'

As he pulled off his gloves and shook his numbed fingers in front of the flames, he darted sidelong glances at his brother. Tristan's chair was nearest the fire and he was enjoying his breakfast as he enjoyed everything, slapping the butter happily on to his toast and whistling as he applied the marmalade. His *Daily Mirror* was balanced against the coffee pot. You could almost see the waves of comfort and contentment coming from him.

Siegfried dragged himself unwillingly from the fire and dropped into a chair. 'I'll just have a cup of coffee, James. Heseltine was very kind – asked me to sit down and have breakfast with him. He gave me a lovely slice of home fed bacon – a bit fat, maybe, but what a flavour! I can taste it now.'

He put down his cup with a clatter. 'You know, there's no

reason why we should have to go to the grocer for our bacon and eggs. There's a perfectly good hen house at the bottom of the garden and a pig sty in the yard with a boiler for the swill. All our household waste could go towards feeding a pig. We'd probably do it quite cheaply.'

He rounded on Tristan who had just lit a Woodbine and was shaking out his *Mirror* with the air of ineffable pleasure which was peculiar to him. 'And it would be a useful job for you. You're not producing much sitting around here on your arse all day. A bit of stock keeping would do you good.'

Tristan put down his paper as though the charm had gone out of it. 'Stock keeping? Well, I feed your mare as it is.' He didn't enjoy looking after Siegfried's new hunter because every time he turned her out to water in the yard she would take a playful kick at him in passing.

Siegfried jumped up. 'I know you do, and it doesn't take all day, does it? It won't kill you to take on the hens and pigs.'

'Pigs?' Tristan looked startled. 'I thought you said pig?'

'Yes, pigs. I've just been thinking. If I buy a litter of weaners we can sell the others and keep one for ourselves. Won't cost a thing that way.'

'Not with free labour, certainly.'

'Labour? Labour? You don't know what it means! Look at you lying back there puffing your head off. You smoke too many of those bloody cigarettes!'

'So do you.'

'Never mind me, I'm talking about you!' Siegfried shouted.

I got up from the table with a sigh. Another day had begun.

When Siegfried got an idea he didn't muck about. Immediate action was his watchword. Within forty-eight hours a litter of ten little pigs had taken up residence in the sty and twelve Light Sussex pullets were pecking about behind the wire of the hen house. He was particularly pleased with the pullets. 'Look at them, James; just on point of lay and a very good strain, too. There'll be just a trickle of eggs at first, but once they get cracking we'll be snowed under. Nothing like a nice fresh egg warm from the nest.'

It was plain from the first that Tristan didn't share his brother's enthusiasm for the hens. I often found him hanging about outside the hen house, looking bored and occasionally throwing bread crusts over the wire. There was no evidence of the regular feeding, the balanced diet recommended by the experts. As egg producers, the hens held no appeal for him, but he did become mildly interested in them as personalities. An odd way of clucking, a peculiarity in gait – these things amused him.

But there were no eggs and as the weeks passed, Siegfried became increasingly irritable. 'Wait till I see the chap that sold me those hens. Damned scoundrel. Good laying strain my foot!' It was pathetic to see him anxiously exploring the empty nesting boxes every morning.

One afternoon, I was going down the garden when Tristan called to me. 'Come over here, Jim. This is something new. I bet you've never seen anything like it before.' He pointed upwards and I saw a group of unusually coloured large birds perched in the branches of the elms. There were more of them in the neighbour's apple trees.

I stared in astonishment. 'You're right, I've never seen anything like them. What are they?'

'Oh, come on,' said Tristan, grinning in delight, 'surely there's something familiar about them. Take another look.'

I peered upwards again. 'No, I've never seen birds as big as that and with such exotic plumage. What is it – a freak migration?'

Tristan gave a shout of laughter. 'They're our hens!'

'How the devil did they get up there?'

'They've left home. Hopped it.'

'But I can only see seven. Where are the rest of them?'

'God knows. Let's have a look over the wall.'

The crumbling mortar gave plenty of toe holds between the bricks and we looked down into the next garden. The other five hens were there, pecking contentedly among some cabbages.

It took a long time to get them all back into the hen house and the tedious business had to be repeated several times a day thereafter. For the hens had clearly grown tired of life under Tristan and decided that they would do better living off the country. They became nomads, ranging ever further afield in their search for sustenance.

At first the neighbours chuckled. They phoned to say their children were rounding up the hens and would we come and get them; but with the passage of time their jocularity wore thin. Finally Siegfried was involved in some painful interviews. His hens, he was told, were an unmitigated nuisance.

It was after one particularly unpleasant session that Siegfried decided that the hens must go. It was a bitter blow and as usual he vented his fury on Tristan. 'I must have been mad to think that any hens under your care would ever lay eggs. But really, isn't it just a bit hard? I give you this simple little job and one would have thought that even you would be hard put to it to make a mess of it. But look at the situation after only three weeks. Not one solitary egg have we seen. The bloody hens are flying about the countryside like pigeons. We are permanently estranged from our neighbours. You've done a thorough job haven't you?' All the frustrated egg producer in Siegfried welled out in his shrill tones.

Tristan's expression registered only wounded virtue, but he was rash enough to try to defend himself. 'You know, I thought there was something queer about those hens from the start,' he muttered.

Siegfried shed the last vestiges of his self control. 'Queer!' he yelled wildly. 'You're the one that's queer, not the poor bloody hens. You're the queerest bugger there is. For God's sake get out – get out of my sight!'

Tristan withdrew with quiet dignity.

It took some time for the last echoes of the poultry venture to die away but after a fortnight, sitting again at the dining-table with Tristan, I felt sure that all was forgotten. So that it was with a strange sense of the workings of fate that I saw Siegfried stride into the room and lean menacingly over his brother. 'You remember those hens, I suppose,' he said almost in a whisper, 'you'll recall that I gave them away to Mrs Dale, that old aged pensioner down Brown's Yard. Well, I've just been speaking to her. She's delighted with them. Gives them a hot mash night and morning and she's collecting ten eggs a day.' His voice rose almost to a scream. 'Ten eggs, do you hear, ten eggs!'

I hurriedly swallowed the last of my tea and excused myself. I trotted along the passage out the back door and up the garden to my car. On the way I passed the empty hen house. It had a forlorn look. It was a long way to the dining-room but I could still hear Siegfried.

CHAPTER SIXTEEN

'Jim! Come over here and look at these little beggars.' Tristan laughed excitedly as he leaned over the door of the pig sty.

I walked across the yard. 'What is it?'

'I've just given them their swill and it's a bit hot. Just look at them!'

The little pigs were seizing the food, dropping it and walking suspiciously round it. Then they would creep up, touch the hot potatoes with their muzzles and leap back in alarm. There was none of the usual meal time slobbering; just a puzzled grunting.

Right from the start Tristan had found the pigs more interesting than the hens which was a good thing because he had to retrieve himself after the poultry disaster. He spent a lot of time in the yard, sometimes feeding or mucking out but more often resting his elbows on the door watching his charges.

As with the hens, he was more interested in their characters than their ability to produce pork or bacon. After he poured the swill into the long trough he always watched, entranced, while the pigs made their first rush. Soon, in the desperate gobbling there would be signs of uneasiness. The tiny animals would begin to glance sideways till their urge to find out what their mates were enjoying so much became unbearable; they would start to change position frantically, climbing over each other's backs and falling into the swill.

Old Boardman was a willing collaborator, but mainly in an advisory capacity. Like all countrymen he considered he knew all about the husbandry and diseases of animals and, it turned out, pigs were his speciality. There were long conferences in the dark room under the Bairnsfather cartoons and the old man grew animated over his descriptions of the vast, beautiful animals he had reared in that very sty.

Tristan listened with respect because he had solid proof of Boardman's expertise in the way he handled the old brick boiler. Tristan could light the thing but it went out if he turned his back on it; but it was docile in Boardman's hands. I often saw Tristan listening wonderingly to the steady blub-blub while the old man rambled on and the delicious scent of cooking pig potatoes drifted over them both.

But no animal converts food more quickly into flesh than a pig and as the weeks passed the little pink creatures changed with alarming speed into ten solid, no-nonsense porkers. Their characters deteriorated, too. They lost all their charm. Meal times stopped being fun and became a battle with the odds growing heavier against Tristan all the time.

I could see that it brought a lot of colour into old Boardman's life and he always dropped whatever he was doing when he saw Tristan scooping the swill from the boiler.

He obviously enjoyed watching the daily contest from his seat on the stone trough. Tristan bracing himself, listening to the pigs squealing at the rattle of the bucket; giving a few fearsome shouts to encourage himself then shooting the bolt and plunging among the grunting, jostling animals; broad, greedy snouts forcing into the bucket, sharp feet grinding his toes, heavy bodies thrusting against his legs.

I couldn't help smiling when I remembered the light-hearted game it used to be. There was no laughter now. Tristan finally took to brandishing a heavy stick at the pigs before he dared to go in. Once inside his only hope of staying on his feet was to clear a little space by beating on the backs.

It was on a market day when the pigs had almost reached bacon weight that I came upon Tristan sprawled in his favourite chair. But there was something unusual about him; he wasn't asleep, no medicine bottle, no Woodbines, no *Daily Mirror*. His arms hung limply over the sides of the chair, his eyes were half closed and sweat glistened on his forehead.

'Jim,' he whispered. 'I've had the most hellish afternoon I've ever had in my life.'

I was alarmed at his appearance. 'What's happened.'

'The pigs,' he croaked. 'They escaped today.'

'Escaped! How the devil could they do that?'

Tristan tugged at his hair. 'It was when I was feeding the mare. I gave her her hay and thought I might as well feed the pigs at the same time. You know what they've been like lately – well, today they went berserk. Soon as I opened the door they charged out in a solid block. Sent me up in the air, bucket and all, then ran over the top of me.' He shuddered and looked up at me wide-eyed. 'I'll tell you this, Jim, when I was lying there on the cobbles, covered with swill and that lot trampling on me, I thought it was all over. But they didn't savage me. They belted out through the yard door at full gallop.'

'The yard door was open then?'

'Too true it was. I would just choose this one day to leave it open.'

Tristan sat up and wrung his hands. 'Well, you know, I thought it was all right at first. You see, they slowed down when they got into the lane and trotted quietly round into the front street with Boardman and I hard on their heels. They formed a group there. Didn't seem to know where to go next. I was sure we were going to be able to head them off, but just then one of them caught sight of itself in Robson's shop window.'

He gave a remarkable impression of a pig staring at its reflection for a few moments then leaping back with a startled grunt.

'Well, that did it, Jim. The bloody animal panicked and shot off into the market place at about fifty miles an hour with the rest after it.'

I gasped. Ten large pigs loose among the packed stalls and market day crowds was difficult even to imagine.

'Oh God, you should have seen it.' Tristan fell back wearily into his chair. 'Women and kids screaming. The stall holders, police and everybody else cursing me. There was a terrific traffic jam too – miles of cars tooting like hell while the policeman on point duty concentrated on browbeating me.' He wiped his brow. 'You know that fast talking merchant on the china stall – well, today I saw him at a loss for words. He was balancing a cup on his palm and in full cry when one of the pigs got its fore feet on his stall and stared him straight in the face. He stopped as if he'd been shot. Any other time it would have been funny but I thought the perishing animal was going to wreck the stall. The counter was beginning to rock when the pig changed its mind and made off.'

'What's the position now?' I asked. 'Have you got them back?'

'I've got nine of them back,' Tristan replied, leaning back and closing his eyes. 'With the help of almost the entire male population of the district I've got nine of them back. The tenth was last seen heading North at a good pace. God knows where it is now. Oh, I didn't tell you – one of them got into the post office. Spent quite some time in there.' He put his hands over his face. 'I'm for it this time, Jim. I'll be in the hands of the law after this lot. There's no doubt about it.'

I leaned over and slapped his leg. 'Oh, I shouldn't worry. I don't suppose there's been any serious damage done.'

Tristan replied with a groan. 'But there's something else. When I finally closed the door after getting the pigs back in their sty I was on the verge of collapse. I was leaning against the wall gasping for breath when I saw the mare had gone. Yes, gone. I'd gone straight out after the pigs and forgot to close her box. I don't know where she is. Boardman said he'd look around – I haven't the strength.'

Tristan lit a trembling Woodbine. 'This is the end, Jim. Siegfried will have no mercy this time.'

As he spoke, the door flew open and his brother rushed in. 'What the hell is going on?' he roared. 'I've just been speaking to the vicar and he says my mare is in his garden eating his wallflowers. He's hopping mad and I don't blame him. Go on, you lazy scoundrel. Don't lie there, get over to the vicarage this instant and bring her back!'

Tristan did not stir. He lay inert, looking up at his brother. His lips moved feebly.

'No,' he said.

'What's that?' Siegfried shouted incredulously. 'Get out of that chair immediately. Go and get that mare!'

'No,' replied Tristan.

I felt a chill of horror. This sort of mutiny was unprecedented. Siegfried had gone very red in the face and I steeled myself for an eruption; but it was Tristan who spoke.

'If you want your mare you can get her yourself.' His voice was quiet with no note of defiance. He had the air of a man to whom the future is of no account.

Even Siegfried could see that this was one time when Tristan had had enough. After glaring down at his brother for a few seconds he turned and walked. He got the mare himself.

Nothing more was said about the incident but the pigs were moved hurriedly to the bacon factory and were never replaced. The stock keeping project was at an end.

CHAPTER SEVENTEEN

When I came in, Miss Harbottle was sitting, head bowed, over the empty cash box; she looked bereaved. It was a new, shiny, black box with the words 'Petty Cash' printed on top in white letters. Inside was a red book with the incomings and outgoings recorded in neat columns. But there was no money.

Miss Harbottle's sturdy shoulders sagged. She listlessly took up the red book between finger and thumb and a lonely sixpence rolled from between its pages and tinkled into the box. 'He's been at it again,' she whispered.

A stealthy footstep sounded in the passage. 'Mr Farnon!' she called out. And to me: 'It's really absurd the way the man always tries to slink past the door.'

Siegfried shuffled in. He was carrying a stomach tube and pump, calcium bottles bulged from his jacket pockets and a bloodless castrator dangled from the other hand.

He smiled cheerfully but I could see he was uncomfortable, not only because of the load he carried, but because of his poor tactical position. Miss Harbottle had arranged her desk across the corner diagonally opposite the door and he had to walk across a long stretch of carpet to reach her. From her point of view it was strategically perfect. From her corner she could see every inch of the big room, into the passage when the door was open and out on to the front street from the window on her left. Nothing escaped her – it was a position of power.

Siegfried looked down at the square figure behind the desk. 'Good morning, Miss Harbottle, can I do anything for you?'

The grey eyes glinted behind the gold-rimmed spectacles. 'You can, indeed, Mr Farnon. You can explain why you have once more emptied my petty cash box.'

'Oh, I'm so sorry. I had to rush through to Brawton last night and I found myself a bit short. There was really nowhere else to turn to.'

'But Mr Farnon, in the two months I have been here, we must have been over this a dozen times. What is the good of my trying to keep an accurate record of the money in the practice if you keep stealing it and spending it?'

'Well, I suppose I got into the habit in the old pint pot days. It wasn't a bad system, really.'

'It wasn't a system at all. It was anarchy. You cannot run a business that way. But I've told you this so many times and each time you have promised to alter your ways. I feel almost at my wits' end.'

'Oh, never mind, Miss Harbottle. Get some more out of the bank and put it in your box. That'll put it right.' Siegfried gathered up the loose coils of the stomach tube from the floor and turned to go, but Miss Harbottle cleared her throat warningly.

'There are one or two other matters. Will you please try to keep your other promise to enter your visits in the book every day and to price them as you do so. Nearly a week has gone by since you wrote anything in. How can I possibly get the bills out on the first of the month? This is most important, but how do you expect me to do it when you impede me like this?'

'Yes, yes, I'm sorry, but I have a string of calls waiting. I really must go.' He was halfway across the floor and the tube was uncoiling itself again when he heard the ominous throat clearing behind him.

'And one more thing, Mr Farnon. I still can't decipher your writing. These medical terms are difficult enough, so please take a little care and don't scribble.'

'Very well, Miss Harbottle.' He quickened his pace through the door and into the passage where, it seemed, was safety and peace. He was clattering thankfully over the tiles when the familiar rumbling reached him. She could project that sound a surprising distance by giving it a bit of extra pressure, and it was a summons which had to be obeyed. I could hear him wearily putting the tube and pump on the floor; the calcium bottles must have been digging into his ribs because I heard them go down too.

He presented himself again before the desk. Miss Harbottle wagged a finger at him. 'While I have you here I'd like to mention another point which troubles me. Look at this day book. You see all these slips sticking out of the pages? They are all queries – there must be scores of them – and I am at a standstill until you clear them for me. When I ask you you never have the time. Can you go over them with me now?'

Siegfried backed away hurriedly. 'No, no, not just now. As I said, I have some urgent calls waiting. I'm very sorry but it will have to be some other time. First chance I get I'll come in and see you.' He felt the door behind him and with a last glance at the massive, disapproving figure behind the desk, he turned and fled.

CHAPTER EIGHTEEN

I could look back now on six months of hard practical experience. I had treated cows, horses, pigs, dogs and cats seven days a week; in the morning, afternoon, evening and through the hours when the world was asleep. I had calved cows and farrowed sows till my arms ached and the skin peeled off. I had been knocked down, trampled on and sprayed liberally with every kind of muck. I had seen a fair cross section of the diseases of animals. And yet a little voice had begun to niggle at the back of my mind; it said I knew nothing, nothing at all.

This was strange, because those six months had been built upon five years of theory; a slow, painful assimilation of thousands of facts and a careful storage of fragments of knowledge like a squirrel with its nuts. Beginning with the study of plants and the lowest forms of life, working up to dissection in the anatomy lab and physiology and the vast, soul-less territory of materia medica. Then pathology which tore down the curtain of ignorance and let me look for the first time into the deep secrets. And parasitology, the teeming other world of the worms and fleas and mange mites. Finally, medicine and surgery, the crystallization of my learning and its application to the everyday troubles of animals.

And there were many others, like physics, chemistry, hygiene; they didn't seem to have missed a thing. Why then should I feel I knew nothing? Why had I begun to feel like an astronomer looking through a telescope at an unknown galaxy? This sensation that I was only groping about on the fringes of limitless space was depressing. It was a funny thing, because everybody else seemed to know all about sick animals. The chap who held the cow's tail, the neighbour from the next farm, men in pubs, jobbing gardeners; they all knew and were free and confident with their advice.

I tried to think back over my life. Was there any time when I had felt this supreme faith in my own knowledge. And then I remembered.

I was back in Scotland, I was seventeen and I was walking under the arch of the Veterinary College into Montrose Street. I had been a student for three days but not until this afternoon had I felt the thrill of fulfilment. Messing about with botany and zoology was all right but this afternoon had been the real thing; I had had my first lecture in animal husbandry.

The subject had been the points of the horse. Professor Grant had hung up a life size picture of a horse and gone over it from nose to tail, indicating the withers, the stifle, the hock, the poll and all the other rich, equine terms. And the professor had been wise; to make his lecture more interesting he kept throwing in little practical points like 'This is where we find curb,' or 'Here is the site for windgalls.' He talked of thoroughpins and sidebones, splints and quittor; things the students wouldn't learn about for another four years, but it brought it all to life.

The words were still spinning in my head as I walked slowly

down the sloping street. This was what I had come for. I felt as though I had undergone an initiation and become a member of an exclusive club. I really knew about horses. And I was wearing a brand new riding mac with all sorts of extra straps and buckles which slapped against my legs as I turned the corner of the hill into busy Newton Road.

I could hardly believe my luck when I saw the horse. It was standing outside the library below Queen's Cross like something left over from another age. It drooped dispiritedly between the shafts of a coal cart which stood like an island in an eddying stream of cars and buses. Pedestrians hurried by, uncaring, but I had the feeling that fortune was smiling on me.

A horse. Not just a picture but a real, genuine horse. Stray words from the lecture floated up into my mind; the pastern, cannon bone, coronet and all those markings – snip, blaze, white sock near hind. I stood on the pavement and examined the animal critically.

I thought it must be obvious to every passer-by that here was a true expert. Not just an inquisitive onlooker but a man who knew and understood all. I felt clothed in a visible aura of horsiness.

I took a few steps up and down, hands deep in the pockets of the new riding mac, eyes probing for possible shoeing faults or curbs or bog spavins. So thorough was my inspection that I worked round to the off side of the horse and stood perilously among the racing traffic.

I glanced around at the people hurrying past. Nobody seemed to care, not even the horse. He was a large one, at least seventeen hands, and he gazed apathetically down the street, easing his hind legs alternatively in a bored manner. I hated to leave him but I had completed my examination and it was time I was on my way. But I felt that I ought to make a gesture before I left; something to communicate to the horse that I understood his problems and that we belonged to the same brotherhood. I stepped briskly forward and patted him on the neck.

Quick as a striking snake, the horse whipped downwards and

seized my shoulder in his great strong teeth. He laid back his ears, rolled his eyes wickedly and hoisted me up, almost off my feet. I hung there helplessly, suspended like a lopsided puppet. I wriggled and kicked but the teeth were clamped immovably in the material of my coat.

There was no doubt about the interest of the passers by now. The grotesque sight of a man hanging from a horse's mouth brought them to a sudden halt and a crowd formed with people looking over each other's shoulders and others fighting at the back to see what was going on.

A horrified old lady was crying: 'Oh, poor boy! Help him, somebody!' Some of the braver characters tried pulling at me but the horse whickered ominously and hung on tighter. Conflicting advice was shouted from all sides. With deep shame I saw two attractive girls in the front row giggling helplessly.

Appalled at the absurdity of my position, I began to thrash about wildly; my shirt collar tightened round my throat; a stream of the horse's saliva trickled down the front of my mac. I could feel myself choking and was giving up hope when a man pushed his way through the crowd.

He was very small. Angry eyes glared from a face blackened by coal dust. Two empty sacks were draped over an arm.

'Whit the hell's this?' he shouted. A dozen replies babbled in the air.

'Can ye no leave the bloody hoarse alone?' he yelled into my face. I made no reply, being pop-eyed, half throttled and in no mood for conversation.

The coalman turned his fury on the horse. 'Drop him, ya big bastard! Go on, let go, drop him!'

Getting no response he dug the animal viciously in the belly with his thumb. The horse took the point at once and released me like an obedient dog dropping a bone. I fell on my knees and ruminated in the gutter for a while till I could breath more easily. As from a great distance I could still hear the little man shouting at me.

After some time I stood up. The coalman was still shouting

and the crowd was listening appreciatively. 'Whit d'ye think you're playing at – keep yer hands off ma bloody hoarse – get the poliss tae ye.'

I looked down at my new mac. The shoulder was chewed to a sodden mass. I felt I must escape and began to edge my way through the crowd. Some of the faces were concerned but most were grinning. Once clear I started to walk away rapidly and as I turned the corner the last faint cry from the coalman reached me.

'Dinna meddle wi' things ye ken nuthin' aboot!'

CHAPTER NINETEEN

I flipped idly through the morning mail. The usual stack of bills, circulars, brightly coloured advertisements for new drugs; after a few months the novelty had worn off and I hardly bothered to read them. I had almost reached the bottom of the pile when I came on something different; an expensive looking envelope in heavy, deckle-edged paper addressed to me personally. I ripped it open and pulled out a gilt coloured card which I scanned quickly. I felt my face redden as I slipped the card into an inside pocket.

Siegfried finished ticking off the visits and looked up. 'What are you looking so guilty about, James? Your past catching up with you. What is it, anyway – a letter from an outraged mother?'

'Go on then,' I said sheepishly, pulling out the card and handing it to him, 'have a good laugh. I suppose you'd find out, anyway.'

Siegfried's face was expressionless as he read the card aloud. 'Tricki requests the pleasure of Uncle Herriot's company on Friday February 5th. Drinks and dancing.' He looked up and spoke seriously. 'Now isn't that nice. You know, that must be one of the most generous Pekingeses in England. Sending you kippers and tomatoes and hampers isn't enough – he has to ask you to his home for a party.'

I grabbed the card and slipped it out of sight. 'All right, all right, I know. But what am I supposed to do?'

'Do? What you do is to sit down right away and get a letter off saying thank you very much, you'll be there on February the fifth. Mrs Pumphrey's parties are famous. Mountains of exotic food, rivers of champagne. Don't miss it whatever you do.'

'Will there be a lot of people there?' I asked, shuffling my feet.

Siegfried struck himself on the forehead with his open hand. 'Of course there'll be a lot of people. What d'you think. Did you expect it would be just you and Tricki? You'd have a few beers together and then you'd dance a slow foxtrot with him? The cream of the county will be there in full regalia but my guess is that there will be no more honoured guest than Uncle Herriot. Why? Because Mrs Pumphrey invited the others but Tricki invited you.'

'OK, OK,' I groaned. 'I'll be on my own and I haven't got a proper evening suit. I don't fancy it.'

Siegfried rose and put a hand on my shoulder. 'My dear chap, don't mess about. Sit down and accept the invitation and then go into Brawton and hire a suit for the night. You won't be on your own for long – the debs will be tramping over each other for a dance with you.' He gave the shoulder a final pat before walking to the door. Before leaving he turned round and his expression was grave. 'And remember for Pete's sake don't write to Mrs Pumphrey. Address your letter to Tricki himself or you're sunk.'

I had a lot of mixed feelings churning around in me when I presented myself at the Pumphrey home on the night of February 5th. A maid let me into the hall and I could see Mrs Pumphrey at the entrance to the ballroom receiving her guests and beyond, an elegant throng standing around with drinks. There was a well bred clamour, a general atmosphere of wealth. I straightened the tie on my hired outfit, took a deep breath and waited.

Mrs Pumphrey was smiling sweetly as she shook hands with the couple in front of me but when she saw me her face became radiant. 'Oh Mr Herriot, how nice of you to come. Tricki was so delighted to have your letter – in fact we really must go in and see him now.' She led me across the hall.

'He's in the morning-room,' she whispered. 'Between ourselves he finds these affairs rather a bore, but he'll be simply furious if I don't take you in for a moment.'

Tricki was curled up in an armchair by the side of a bright fire. When he saw me he jumped on the back of the chair barking in delight, his huge, laughing mouth bisecting his face. I was trying to fend off his attempts to lick my face when I caught sight of two large food bowls on the carpet. One contained about a pound of chopped chicken, the other a mass of crumbled cake.

'Mrs Pumphrey!' I thundered, pointing at the bowls. The poor woman put her hand to her mouth and shrank away from me.

'Oh do forgive me,' she wailed, her face a picture of guilt. 'It's just a special treat because he's alone tonight. And the weather is so cold, too.' She clasped her hands and looked at me abjectly.

'I'll forgive you,' I said sternly, 'If you will remove half the chicken and all the cake.'

Fluttering, like a little girl caught in naughtiness, she did as I said.

I parted regretfully from the little Peke. It had been a busy day and I was sleepy from the hours in the biting cold. The room with its fire and soft lighting looked more inviting than the noisy glitter of the ballroom and I would have preferred to curl up here with Tricki on my knee for an hour or two.

Mrs Pumphrey became brisk. 'Now you must come and meet some of my friends.' We went into the ballroom where light blazed down from three cut glass chandeliers and was reflected dazzlingly from the cream and gold, many-mirrored walls. We moved from group to group as Mrs Pumphrey introduced me and I squirmed in embarrassment as I heard myself described as 'Tricki's dear kind uncle'. But either they were people of superb self control or they were familiar with their hostess's blind spot because the information was received with complete gravity.

Along one wall a five piece orchestra was tuning up; white-jacketed waiters hurried among the guests with trays of food and drinks. Mrs Pumphrey stopped one of the waiters. 'François, some champagne for this gentleman.'

'Yes, Madame.' The waiter proffered his tray.

'No, no, no, not those. One of the big glasses.'

François hurried away and returned with something like a soup plate with a stem. It was brimming with champagne.

'François.'

'Yes, Madame?'

'This is Mr Herriot. I want you to take a good look at him.'

The waiter turned a pair of sad, spaniel eyes on me and drank me in for a few moments.

'I want you to look after him. See that his glass is full and that he has plenty to eat.'

'Certainly, Madame.' He bowed and moved away.

I buried my face in the ice cold champagne and when I looked up, there was François holding out a tray of smoked salmon sandwiches.

It was like that all the evening. François seemed always to be at my elbow, filling up the enormous glass or pushing dainties at me. I found it delightful; the salty snacks brought on a thirst which I quenched with deep draughts of champagne, then I had more snacks which made me thirsty again and François would unfailingly pop up with the magnum.

It was the first time I had had the opportunity of drinking champagne by the pint and it was a rewarding experience. I was quickly aware of a glorious lightness, a heightening of the perceptions. I stopped being overawed by this new world and began to enjoy it. I danced with everybody in sight – sleek young beauties, elderly dowagers and twice with a giggling Mrs Pumphrey.

Or I just talked. And it was witty talk; I repeatedly amazed myself by my lightning shafts. Once I caught sight of myself in the mirror – a distinguished figure, glass in hand, the hired suit hanging on me with quiet grace. It took my breath away.

Eating, drinking, talking, dancing, the evening winged past. When it was time to go and I had my coat on and was shaking hands with Mrs Pumphrey in the hall, François appeared again with a bowl of hot soup. He seemed to be worried lest I grow faint on the journey home.

After the soup, Mrs Pumphrey said: 'And now you must come and say goodnight to Tricki. He'll never forgive you if you don't.' We went into his room and the little dog yawned from the depths of the chair and wagged his tail. Mrs Pumphrey put her hand on my sleeve. 'While you're here, I wonder if you would be so kind as to examine his claws. I've been so worried in case they might be growing too long.'

I lifted up the paws one by one and scrutinized the claws while Tricki lazily licked my hands. 'No, you needn't worry, they're perfectly all right.'

'Thank you so much, I'm so grateful to you. Now you must wash your hands.'

In the familiar bathroom with the sea green basins and the enamelled fishes on the walls and the dressing-table and the bottles on the glass shelves, I looked around as the steaming water ran from the tap. There was my own towel by the basin and the usual new slab of soap – soap that lathered in an instant and gave off an expensive scent. It was the final touch of balm on a gracious evening. It had been a few hours of luxury and light and I carried the memory back with me to Skeldale House.

I got into bed, switched off the light and lay on my back looking up into the darkness. Snatches of music still tinkled about in my head and I was beginning to swim back to the ballroom when the phone rang.

'This is Atkinson of Beck Cottage,' a far away voice said. 'I 'ave a sow 'ere what can't get pigged. She's been on all night. Will you come?'

I looked at the clock as I put down the receiver. It was two AM. I felt numbed. A farrowing right on top of the champagne and the smoked salmon and those little biscuits with the black heaps of caviare. And at Beck Cottage, one of the most primitive smallholdings in the district. It wasn't fair.

Sleepily, I took off my pyjamas and pulled on my shirt. As I reached for the stiff, worn corduroys I used for work, I tried not to look at the hired suit hanging on a corner of the wardrobe.

I groped my way down the long garden to the garage. In the darkness of the yard I closed my eyes and the great chandeliers blazed again, the mirrors flashed and the music played.

It was only two miles out to Beck Cottage. It lay in a hollow and in the winter the place was a sea of mud. I left my car and squelched through the blackness to the door of the house. My knock was unanswered and I moved across to the cluster of buildings opposite and opened the half door into the byre. The warm, sweet bovine smell met me as I peered towards a light showing dimly at the far end where a figure was standing.

I went inside past the shadowy row of cows standing side by side with broken wooden partitions between them and past the mounds of manure piled behind them. Mr Atkinson didn't believe in mucking out too often.

Stumbling over the broken floor, splashing through pools of urine, I arrived at the end where a pen had been made by closing off a corner with a gate. I could just make out the form of a pig, pale in the gloom, lying on her side. There was a scanty bed of straw under her and she lay very still except for the trembling of her flanks. As I watched, she caught her breath and strained for a few seconds then the straining began again.

Mr Atkinson received me without enthusiasm. He was middle-aged, sported a week's growth of beard and wore an ancient hat with a brim which flopped round his ears. He stood hunched against a wall, one hand deep in a ragged pocket, the other holding a bicycle lamp with a fast-failing battery.

'Is this all the light we've got?' I asked.

'Aye, it is,' Mr Atkinson replied, obviously surprised. He looked from the lamp to me with a 'what more does he want?' expression.

'Let's have it, then.' I trained the feeble beam on my patient. 'Just a young pig, isn't she?'

'Aye, nobbut a gilt. Fust litter.'

The pig strained again, shuddered and lay still.

'Something stuck there, I reckon,' I said. 'Will you bring me a bucket of hot water some soap and a towel, please.'

'Haven't got no 'ot water. Fire's out.'

'OK, bring me whatever you've got.'

The farmer clattered away down the byre taking the light with him and, with the darkness, the music came back again. It was a Strauss waltz and I was dancing with Lady Frenswick; she was young and very fair and she laughed as I swung her round. I could see her white shoulders and the diamonds winking at her throat and the wheeling mirrors.

Mr Atkinson came shuffling back and dumped a bucket of water on the floor. I dipped a finger in the water; it was ice cold. And the bucket had seen many hard years – I would have to watch my arms on that jagged rim.

Quickly stripping off jacket and shirt, I sucked in my breath as a villainous draught blew through a crack on to my back.

'Soap, please,' I said through clenched teeth.

'In t'bucket.'

I plunged an arm into the water, shivered, and felt my way round till I found a roundish object about the size of a golf ball. I pulled it out and examined it; it was hard and smooth and speckled like a pebble from the sea shore and, optimistically, I began to rub it between my hands and up my arms, waiting for the lather to form. But the soap was impervious; it yielded nothing.

I discarded the idea of asking for another piece in case this would be construed as another complaint. Instead, I borrowed the light and tracked down the byre into the yard, the mud sucking at my Wellingtons, goose pimples rearing on my chest. I searched around in the car boot, listening to my teeth chattering, till I came on a jar of antiseptic lubricating cream.

Back in the pen, I smeared the cream on my arm, knelt behind the pig and gently inserted my hand into the vagina. I moved my hand forward and as wrist and elbow disappeared inside the pig I was forced to roll over on my side. The stones were cold and wet but I forgot my discomfort when my fingers touched something; it was a tiny tail. Almost a transverse presentation, biggish piglet stuck like a cork in a bottle.

Using one finger, I worked the hind legs back until I was able to grasp them and draw the piglet out. 'This is the one that's been causing the trouble. He's dead, I'm afraid – been squashed in there too long. But there could be some live ones still inside. I'll have another feel.'

I greased my arm and got down again. Just inside the os uteri, almost at arm's length, I found another piglet and I was feeling at the face when a set of minute but very sharp teeth sank into my finger.

I yelped and looked up at the farmer from my stony bed. 'This one's alive, anyway. I'll soon have him out.'

But the piglet had other ideas. He showed no desire to leave his warm haven and every time I got hold of his slippery little foot between my fingers he jerked it away. After a minute or two of this game I felt a cramping in my arm. I relaxed and lay back, my head resting on the cobbles, my arm still inside the pig. I closed my eyes and immediately I was back in the ballroom, in the warmth and the brilliant light. I was holding out my immense glass while François poured from the magnum; then I was dancing, close to the orchestra this time and the leader, beating time with one hand, turned round and smiled into my face; smiled and bowed as though he had been looking for me all his life.

I smiled back but the bandleader's face dissolved and there was only Mr Atkinson looking down at me expressionlessly, his unshaven jaw and shaggy eyebrows thrown into sinister relief by the light striking up from the bicycle lamp.

I shook myself and raised my cheek from the floor. This wouldn't do. Falling asleep on the job; either I was very tired or there was still some champagne in me. I reached again and grasped the foot firmly between two fingers and this time, despite his struggles, the piglet was hauled out into the world. Once arrived, he seemed to accept the situation and tottered round philosophically to his mother's udder.

'She's not helping at all,' I said. 'Been on so long that's she's exhausted. I'm going to give her an injection.'

Another numbing expedition through the mud to the car, a shot of pituitrin into the gilt's thigh and within minutes the action began with powerful contractions of the uterus. There was no obstruction now and soon a wriggling pink piglet was deposited in the straw; then quite quickly another and another.

'Coming off the assembly line now, all right,' I said. Mr Atkinson grunted.

Eight piglets had been born and the light from the lamp had almost given out when a dark mass of afterbirth welled from the gilt's vulva.

I rubbed my cold arms. 'Well, I should say that's the lot now.' I felt suddenly chilled; I couldn't say how long I had been standing there looking at the wonder that never grew stale; the little pigs struggling on to their legs and making their way unguided to the long double row of teats; the mother with her first family easing herself over to expose as much as possible of her udder to the hungry mouths.

Better get dressed quickly. I had another try at the marble-like soap but it defeated me as easily as the first time. I wondered how long it had been in the family. Down my right side my cheek and ribs were caked with dirt and mucus. I did my best to scrape some off with my finger nails then I swilled myself down with the cold water from the bucket.

'Have you a towel there?' I gasped.

Mr Atkinson wordlessly handed me a sack. Its edges were stiff with old manure and it smelled musty from the meal it had long since contained. I took it and began to rub my chest and as the sour grains of the meal powdered my skin, the last bubbles of champagne left me, drifted up through the gaps in the tiles and burst sadly in the darkness beyond.

I dragged my shirt over my gritty back, feeling a sense of coming back to my own world. I buttoned my coat, picked up the syringe and the bottle of pituitrin and climbed out of the pen. I had a last look before I left. The bicycle lamp was shedding its final faint glow and I had to lean over the gate to see the row of little pigs sucking busily, utterly absorbed. The gilt carefully shifted her position and grunted. It was a grunt of deep content.

Yes, I was back and it was all right. I drove through the mud and up the hill where I had to get out to open a gate and the wind, with the cold, clean smell of the frosty grass in it caught at my face. I stood for a while looking across the dark fields, thinking of the night which was ending now. My mind went back to my schooldays and an old gentleman talking to the class about careers. He had said: 'If you decide to become a veterinary surgeon you will never grow rich but you will have a life of endless interest and variety.'

I laughed aloud in the darkness and as I got into the car I was still chuckling. That old chap certainly wasn't kidding. Variety. That was it – variety.

CHAPTER TWENTY

As I checked my list of calls it occurred to me that, this time, Siegfried didn't look so much like a schoolboy as he faced Miss Harbottle. For one thing, he hadn't marched straight in and stood in front of the desk; that was disastrous and he always looked beaten before he started. Instead, he had veered off over the last few yards till he stood with his back to the window. This way she had to turn her head slightly to face him and besides, he had the light at his back.

He thrust his hands into his pockets and leaned back against the window frame. He was wearing his patient look, his eyes were kind and his face was illumined by an almost saintly smile. Miss Harbottle's eyes narrowed.

'I just wanted a word with you, Miss Harbottle. One or two little points I'd like to discuss. First, about your petty cash box. It's a nice box and I think you were quite right to institute it, but I think you would be the first to agree that the main function of a cash box is to have cash in it.' He gave a light laugh. 'Now last night I had a few dogs in the surgery and the owners wanted to pay on the spot. I had no change and went for some to your box – it was quite empty. I had to say I would send them a bill, and that isn't good business, is it Miss Harbottle? It didn't look good, so I really must ask you to keep some cash in your cash box.'

Miss Harbottle's eyes widened incredulously. 'But Mr Farnon, you removed the entire contents to go to the hunt ball at...'

Siegfried held up a hand and his smile took on an unearthly quality. 'Please hear me out. There is another very small thing I want to bring to your attention. It is now the tenth day of the month and the accounts have not gone out. Now this is a very undesirable state of affairs and there are several points to consider here.'

'But Mr Farnon . . .!'

'Just one moment, Miss Harbottle, till I explain this to you. It is a known fact that farmers pay their bills more readily if they receive them on the first of the month. And there is another, even more important factor.' The beautiful smile left his face and was replaced by an expression of sorrowing gravity. 'Have you ever stopped to work out just how much interest the practice is losing on all the money lying out there because you are late in sending out the accounts.'

'Mr Farnon . . .!'

'I am almost finished, Miss Harbottle, and, believe me, it grieves me to have to speak like this. But the fact is, I can't afford to lose money in this way.' He spread out his hands in a gesture of charming frankness. 'So if you will just apply yourself to this little matter I'm sure all will be well.'

'But will you tell me how I can possibly send the accounts when you refuse to write up the . . .'

'In conclusion, Miss Harbottle, let me say this. I have been very satisfied with your progress since you joined us, and I am sure that with time you will tighten up on those little points I have just mentioned.' A certain roguishness crept into his smile and he put his head on one side. Miss Harbottle's strong fingers closed tightly round a heavy ebony ruler.

'Efficiency,' he said, crinkling his eyes. 'That's what we must have – efficiency.'

CHAPTER TWENTY-ONE

I dropped the suture needle into the tray and stepped back to survey the finished job. 'Well though I say it myself, that looks rather nice.'

Tristan leaned over the unconscious dog and examined the

neat incision with its row of regular stitches. 'Very pretty indeed, my boy. Couldn't have done better myself.'

The big black labrador lay peacefully on the table, his tongue lolling, his eyes glazed and unseeing. He had been brought in with an ugly growth over his ribs and I had decided that it was a simple lipoma, quite benign and very suitable for surgery. And so it had turned out. The tumour had come away with almost ridiculous ease, round, intact and shining, like a hard boiled egg from its shell. No haemorrhage, no fear of recurrence.

The unsightly swelling had been replaced by this tidy scar which would be invisible in a few weeks. I was pleased.

'We'd better keep him here till he comes round,' I said. 'Give me a hand to get him on to these blankets.' We made the dog comfortable in front of an electric stove and I left to start my morning round.

It was during lunch that we first heard the strange sound. It was something between a moan and a howl, starting quite softly but rising to a piercing pitch before shuddering back down the scale to silence.

Siegfried looked up, startled, from his soup. 'What in God's name is that?'

'Must be that dog I operated on this morning,' I replied. 'The odd one does that coming out of barbiturates. I expect he'll stop soon.'

Siegfried looked at me doubtfully. 'Well, I hope so – I could soon get tired of that. Gives me the creeps.'

We went through and looked at the dog. Pulse strong, respirations deep and regular, mucous membranes a good colour. He was still stretched out, immobile, and the only sign of returning consciousness was the howl which seemed to have settled down into a groove of one every ten seconds.

'Yes, he's perfectly all right,' Siegfried said. 'But what a bloody noise! Let's get out of here.'

Lunch was finished hastily and in silence except for the ceaseless background wailing. Siegfried had scarcely swallowed his last mouthful before he was on his feet. 'Well, I must fly. Got a lot on this afternoon. Tristan, I think it would be a good idea to bring that dog through to the sitting-room and put him by the fire. Then you could stay by him and keep an eye on him.'

Tristan was stunned. 'You mean I have to stay in the same room as that noise all afternoon?'

'Yes, I mean just that. We can't send him home as he is and I don't want anything to happen to him. He needs care and attention.'

'Maybe you'd like me to hold his paw or perhaps wheel him round the market place?'

'Don't give me any of your bloody cheek. You stay with the dog and that's an order!'

Tristan and I stretchered the heavy animal along the passage on the blankets, then I had to leave for the afternoon round. I paused and looked back at the big black form by the fire and Tristan crouched miserably in his chair. The noise was overpowering. I closed the door hurriedly.

It was dark when I got back and the old house hung over me, black and silent against the frosty sky. Silent, that is, except for the howling which still echoed along the passage and filtered eerily into the deserted street.

I glanced at my watch as I slammed the car door. It was six o'clock, so Tristan had had four hours of it. I ran up the steps and along the passage and when I opened the sitting-room door the noise jarred in my head. Tristan was standing with his back to me, looking through the french window into the darkness of the garden. His hands were deep in his pockets; tufts of cotton wool drooped from his ears.

'Well, how is it going?' I asked.

There was no reply so I walked over and tapped him on the shoulder. The effect was spectacular. Tristan leaped into the air and corkscrewed round. His face was ashen and he was trembling violently.

'God help us, Jim, you nearly killed me there. I can't hear a damn thing through these ear plugs – except the dog, of course. Nothing keeps that out.'

I knelt by the labrador and examined him. The dog's condition was excellent but, except for a faint eye reflex there was no sign that he was regaining consciousness. And all the time there were the piercing, evenly spaced howls.

'He's taking a hell of a time to come out of it,' I said. 'Has he been like this all afternoon?'

'Yes, just like that. Not one bit different. And don't waste any sympathy on him, the yowling devil. He's as happy as a sandboy down by the fire – doesn't know a thing about it. But how about me? My nerves are about shot to bits listening to him hour after hour. Much more of it and you'll have to give me a shot too.' He ran a shaking hand through his hair and a twitching started in his cheek.

I took his arm. 'Well, come through and eat. You'll feel better after some food.' I led him unresisting into the dining-room.

Siegfried was in excellent form over the meal. He seemed to be in a mood of exhilaration and monopolized the conversation but he did not once refer to the shrill obligato from the other room. There was no doubt, however, that it was still getting through to Tristan.

As they were leaving the room, Siegfried put his hand on my shoulder. 'Remember we've got that meeting in Brawton tonight, James. Old Reeves on diseases of sheep – he's usually very good. Pity you can't come too, Tristan, but I'm afraid you'll have to stay with the dog till he comes round.'

Tristan flinched as if he had been struck. 'Oh not another session with that bloody animal! He's driving me mad!'

'I'm afraid there's nothing else for it. James or I could have taken over tonight but we have to show up at this meeting. It would look bad if we missed it.'

Tristan stumbled back into the room and I put on my coat. As I went out into the street I paused for a moment and listened. The dog was still howling.

The meeting was a success. It was held in one of Brawton's lush hotels and, as usual, the best part was the get together of the vets in the bar afterwards. It was infinitely soothing to hear the other man's problems and mistakes – especially the mistakes.

It amused me to look round the crowded room and try to guess what the little knots of men were talking about. That man over there, bent double and slashing away at the air with one hand – he was castrating a colt in the standing position. And the one with his arm out at full stretch, his fingers working busily at nothing – almost certainly foaling a mare; probably correcting a carpal flexion. And doing it effortlessly too. Veterinary surgery was a childishly simple matter in a warm bar with a few drinks inside you.

It was eleven o'clock before we all got into our cars and headed for our own particular niche in Yorkshire – some to the big industrial towns of the West Riding, others to the seaside places of the East coast and Siegfried and I hurrying thankfully back on the narrow road which twisted between its stone walls into the Northern Pennines.

I thought guiltily that for the last few hours I had completely forgotten about Tristan and his vigil. Still, it must have been better tonight. The dog would surely have quietened down by now. But, jumping from the car in Darrowby, I froze in mid stride as a thin wail came out faintly from Skeldale House. This was incredible; it was after midnight and the dog was still at it. And what of Tristan? I hated to think what kind of shape he'd be in. Almost fearfully I turned the knob on the sitting-room door.

Tristan's chair made a little island in a sea of empty beer bottles. An upturned crate lay against the wall and Tristan was sitting very upright and looking solemn. I picked my way over the debris.

'Well, has it been rough, Triss? How do you feel now?'

'Could be worse, old lad, could be worse. Soon as you'd gone I slipped over to the Drovers for a crate of pint Magnets. Made all the difference. After three or four the dog stopped worrying me – matter of fact, I've been yowling back at him for hours now. We've had quite an interesting evening. Anyway, he's coming out now. Look at him.'

The big dog had his head up and there was recognition in his eyes. The howling had stopped. I went over and patted him and the long black tail jerked in a fair attempt at a wag.

'That's better, old boy,' I said. 'But you'd better behave yourself now. You've given your uncle Tristan one hell of a day.'

The labrador responded immediately by struggling to his feet. He took a few swaying steps and collapsed among the bottles.

Siegfried appeared in the doorway and looked distastefully at Tristan, still very upright and wearing a judicial expression, and at the dog scrabbling among the bottles. 'What an infernal mess! Surely you can do a little job without making an orgy out of it.'

At the sound of his voice the labrador staggered up and, in a flush of over confidence, tried to run towards him, wagging his tail unsteadily. He didn't get very far and went down in a heap, sending an empty Magnet rolling gently up to Siegfried's feet.

Siegfried bent over and stroked the shining black head. 'Nice friendly animal that. I should think he's a grand dog when he's got his senses about him. He'll be normal in the morning, but the problem is what to do with him now. We can't leave him staggering about down here – he could break a leg.' He glanced at Tristan who had not moved a muscle. He was sitting up straighter than ever; stiff and motionless like a Prussian general. 'You know, I think the best thing would be for you to take him up to your room tonight. Now we've got him so far, we don't want him to hurt himself. Yes, that's it, he can spend the night with you.'

'Thank you, thank you very much indeed,' Tristan said in a flat voice, still looking straight to his front.

Siegfried looked at him narrowly for a moment, then turned away. 'Right then, clear away this rubbish and let's get to bed.'

My bedroom and Tristan's were connected by a door. Mine was the main room, huge, square, with a high ceiling, pillared fireplace and graceful alcoves like the ones downstairs. I always felt a little like a duke lying there.

Tristan's had been the old dressing-room and was long and narrow with his small bed crouching at one end as if trying to hide. There were no carpets on the smooth, varnished boards so I laid the dog on a heap of blankets and talked down soothingly at Tristan's wan face on the pillow.

'He's quiet now – sleeping like a baby and looks as though he's going to stay that way. You'll be able to have a well earned rest now.'

I went back to my own room, undressed quickly and got into bed. I went to sleep immediately and I couldn't tell just when the noises started next door, but I came suddenly wide awake with an angry yell ringing in my ears. Then there was a slithering and a bump followed by another distracted cry from Tristan.

I quailed at the idea of going into the dressing-room – there was nothing I could do, anyway – so I huddled closer into the sheets and listened. I kept sliding into a half sleep then starting into wakefulness at more bumping and shouting came through the wall.

After about two hours the noises began to change. The labrador seemed to have gained mastery over his legs and was marching up and down the room, his claws making a regular tck-a-tck, tck-a-tck, tck-a-tck on the wooden floor. It went on and on, interminably. At intervals, Tristan's voice, hoarse now, burst out. 'Stop it, for Christ's sake! Sit down, you bloody dog!'

I must have fallen into a deeper sleep because when I awoke the room was grey with the cold light of morning. I rolled on to my back and listened. I could still hear the tck-a-tck of the claws but it had become irregular as though the labrador was strolling about instead of blundering blindly from one end of the room to the other. There was no sound from Tristan.

I got out of bed, shivering as the icy air of the room gripped me, and pulled on my shirt and trousers. Tiptoeing across the floor, I opened the connecting door and was almost floored as two large feet were planted on my chest. The labrador was delighted to see me and appeared to be thoroughly at home. His fine brown eyes shone with intelligence and well-being and he showed rows of glittering teeth and a flawlessly pink tongue in a wide, panting grin. Far below, the tail lashed ecstatically.

'Well, you're all right, chum,' I said. 'Let's have a look at that wound.' I removed the horny paws from my chest and explored the line of stitches over the ribs. No swelling, no pain, no reaction at all.

'Lovely!' I cried. 'Beautiful. You're as good as new again.' I gave the dog a playful slap on the rump which sent him into a transport of joy. He leaped all over me, clawing and licking.

I was fighting him off when I heard a dismal groan from the bed. In the dim light Tristan looked ghastly. He was lying on his back, both hands clutching the quilt and there was a wild look in his eyes. 'Not a wink of sleep, Jim,' he whispered. 'Not a bloody wink. He's got a wonderful sense of humour, my brother, making me spend the night with this animal. It'll really make his day when he hears what I've been through. Just watch him – I'll bet you anything you like he'll look pleased.'

Later, over breakfast, Siegfried heard the details of his brother's harrowing night and was very sympathetic. He condoled with him at length and apologized for all the trouble the dog had given him. But Tristan was right. He did look pleased.

CHAPTER TWENTY-TWO

As I came into the operating room I saw that Siegfried had a patient on the table. He was thoughtfully stroking the head of an elderly and rather woebegone border terrier.

'James,' he said, 'I want you to take this little dog through to Grier.'

'Grier?'

'Vet at Brawton. He was treating the case before the owner moved into our district. I've seen it a couple of times – stones in the bladder. It needs an immediate operation and I think I'd better let Grier do it. He's a touchy devil and I don't want to stand on his toes.'

'Oh, I think I've heard of him,' I said.

'Probably you have. A cantankerous Aberdonian. Since he practises in a fashionable town he gets quite a few students and he gives them hell. That sort of thing gets around.' He lifted the terrier from the table and handed him to me. 'The sooner you get through there the better. You can see the op and bring the dog back here afterwards. But watch yourself – don't rub Grier the wrong way or he'll take it out of you somehow.'

At my first sight of Angus Grier I thought immediately of whisky. He was about fifty and something had to be responsible for the fleshy, mottled cheeks, the swimmy eyes and the pattern of purple veins which chased each other over his prominent nose. He wore a permanently insulted expression.

He didn't waste any charm on me; a nod and a grunt and he grabbed the dog from my arms. Then he stabbed a finger at a slight, fairish youth in a white coat. 'That's Clinton – final year student. Do ye no' think there's some pansy lookin' buggers coming in to this profession?'

During the operation he niggled constantly at the young man and, in an attempt to create a diversion, I asked when he was going back to college.

'Beginning of next week,' he replied.

'Aye, but he's awa hame tomorrow,' Grier rasped. 'Wasting his time when he could be gettin' good experience here.'

The student blushed. 'Well, I've been seeing practice for over a month and I felt I ought to spend a couple of days with my mother before the term starts.'

'Oh, I ken, I ken. You're all the same – canna stay away from the titty.'

The operation was uneventful and as Grier inserted the last stitch he looked up at me. 'You'll no' want to take the dog back till he's out of the anaesthetic. I've got a case to visit – you can come with me to pass the time.'

We didn't have what you could call a conversation in the car. It was a monologue; a long recital of wrongs suffered at the hands of wicked clients and predatory colleagues. The story I liked best was about a retired admiral who had asked Grier to examine his horse for soundness. Grier said the animal had a bad heart and was not fit to ride, whereupon the admiral flew into a fury and got another vet to examine the horse. The second vet said there was nothing the matter with the heart and passed the animal sound.

The admiral wrote Grier a letter and told him what he thought of him in fairly ripe quarter-deck language. Having got this out of his system he felt refreshed and went out for a ride during which, in the middle of a full gallop the horse fell down dead and rolled on the admiral who sustained a compound fracture of the leg and a crushed pelvis.

'Man,' said Grier with deep sincerity, 'Man, I was awfu' glad.'

We drew up in a particularly dirty farmyard and Grier turned to me. 'I've got a cow tae cleanse here.'

'Right,' I said, 'fine.' I settled down in my seat and took out my pipe. Grier paused, halfway out of the car. 'Are you no' coming to give me a hand?'

I couldn't understand him. 'Cleansing' of cows is simply the removal of retained afterbirth and is a one man job.

'Well, there isn't much I can do is there?' I said. 'And my Wellingtons and coat are back in my car. I didn't realize it was a farm visit – I'd probably get messed up for nothing.'

I knew immediately that I'd said the wrong thing. The toad-skin jowls flushed darker and he gave me a malevolent glance before turning away; but halfway across the yard he stopped and stood for a few moments in thought before coming back to the car. 'I've just remembered. I've got something here you can put on. You might as well come in with me – you'll be able to pass me a pessary when I want one.'

It sounded nutty to me, but I got out of the car and went round to the back. Grier was fishing out a large wooden box from his boot.

'Here, ye can put this on. It's a calving outfit I got a bit ago. I haven't used it much because I found it a mite heavy, but it'll keep ye grand and clean.'

I looked in the box and saw a suit of thick, black, shining rubber. I lifted out the jacket; it bristled with zip fasteners and press studs and felt as heavy as lead. The trousers were even more weighty, with many clips and fasteners. The whole thing was a most imposing creation, obviously designed by somebody who had never seen a cow calved and having the disadvantage that anybody wearing it would be pretty well immobilized.

I studied Grier's face for a moment but the watery eyes told me nothing. I began to take off my jacket – it was crazy but I didn't want to offend the man.

And, in truth, Grier seemed anxious to get me into the suit because he was holding it up in a helpful manner. It was a two man operation. First the gleaming trousers were pulled on and zipped up fore and aft, then it was the turn of the jacket, a wonderful piece of work, fitting tightly round the waist and possessing short sleeves about six inches long with powerful elastic gripping my biceps.

Before I could get it on I had to roll my shirt sleeves to the shoulder, then Grier, heaving and straining, worked me into it. I could hear the zips squeaking into place, the final one being at the back of my neck to close a high, stiff collar which held my head in an attitude of supplication, my chin pointing at the sky.

Grier's heart really seemed to be in his work and, for the final touch, he produced a black rubber skull cap. I shrank away from the thing and began to mouth such objections as the collar would allow, but Grier insisted. 'Stand still a wee minute longer. We might as well do the job right.'

When he had finished he stood back admiringly. I must have been a grotesque sight, sheathed from head to foot in gleaming black, my arms, bare to the shoulders, sticking out almost at right angles. Grier appeared well satisfied. 'Well, come on, it's time we got on wi' the job.' He turned and hurried towards the byre; I plodded ponderously after him like an automaton.

Our arrival in the byre caused a sensation. There were present the farmer, two cowmen and a little girl. The men's cheerful greeting froze on their lips as the menacing figure paced slowly, deliberately in. The little girl burst into tears and ran outside.

'Cleansing' is a dirty, smelly job for the operator and a bore for the onlooker who may have to stand around for twenty minutes without being able to see anything. But this was one time the spectators were not bored. Grier was working away inside the cow and mumbling about the weather, but the men weren't listening; they never took their eyes away from me as I stood rigid, like a suit of armour against the wall. They studied each part of the outfit in turn, wonderingly. I knew what they were thinking. Just what was going to happen when this formidable unknown finally went into action. Anybody dressed like that must have some tremendous task ahead of him.

The intense pressure of the collar against my larynx kept me entirely out of any conversation and this must have added to my air of mystery. I began to sweat inside the suit.

The little girl had plucked up courage and brought her brothers and sisters to look at me. I could see the row of little heads peeping round the door and, screwing my head round painfully, I tried to give them a reassuring smile; but the heads disappeared and I heard their feet clattering across the yard.

I couldn't say how long I stood there, but Grier at last finished his job and called out, 'All right, I'm ready for you now.' The atmosphere became suddenly electric. The men straightened up and stared at me with slightly open mouths. This was the moment they had been waiting for.

I pushed myself away from the wall and did a right turn with some difficulty before heading for the tin of pessaries. It was only a few yards away but it seemed a long way as I approached it like a robot, head in the air, arms extended stiffly on either side. When I arrived at the tin I met a fresh difficulty; I could not bend. After a few contortions I got my hand into the tin, then had to take the paper off the pessary with one hand; a new purgatory. The men watched in fascinated silence.

Having removed the paper, I did a careful about turn and paced back along the byre with measured tread. When I came level with the cow I extended my arm stiffly to Grier who took the pessary and inserted it in the uterus.

I then took up my old position against the wall while my colleague cleaned himself down. I glanced down my nose at the men; their expressions had changed to open disbelief. Surely the mystery man's assignment was tougher than that – he couldn't be wearing that outfit just to hand over a pessary. But when Grier started the complicated business of snapping open the studs and sliding the zips they realized the show was over; and fast on the feeling of let-down came amusement.

As I tried to rub some life back into my swollen arms which had been strangulated by the elastic sleeves, I was surrounded by grinning faces. They could hardly wait, I imagined, to get round to the local that night to tell the tale. Pulling together the shreds of my dignity, I put on my jacket and got into the car. Grier stayed to say a few words to the men, but he wasn't holding their attention; it was all on me, huddling in the seat. They couldn't believe I was true.

Back at the surgery the border terrier was coming out of the anaesthetic. He raised his head and tried bravely to wag his tail when he saw me. I wrapped him in a blanket, gathered him up and was preparing to leave when I saw Grier through the partly open door of a small store room. He had the wooden box on a table and he was lifting out the rubber suit, but there was something peculiar about the way he was doing it; the man seemed to be afflicted by a kind of rigor – his body shook and jerked, the mottled face was strangely contorted and a half stifled wailing issued from his lips.

I stared in amazement. I would have said it was impossible, yet it was happening right in front of me. There was not a shadow of a doubt about it – Angus Grier was laughing.

CHAPTER TWENTY-THREE

Milk fever is one of the straightforward conditions, but, looking down into the beck in the dreary dawn light, I realized that this was one of its more bizarre manifestations. The illness had struck immediately after calving and the cow had slithered down the muddy bank into the water. She was unconscious when I arrived, her hindquarters completely submerged, the head resting on a shelf of rock. Her calf, sodden and pathetic in the driving rain, trembled by her side.

Dan Cooper's eyes were anxious as we made our way down. 'I doubt we're too late. She's dead, isn't she? I can't see her breathing.'

'Pretty far gone, I'm afraid,' I replied, 'but I think there's still life there. If I can get some calcium into her vein she might still come round.'

'Damn, I 'ope so,' Dan grunted. 'She's one of my best milkers. It allus happens to the good 'uns.'

'It does with milk fever, anyway. Here, hold these bottles for me.' I pulled out the syringe box and selected a wide-bored needle. My fingers, numb with the special kind of cold you felt in the early morning with your circulation sluggish and your stomach empty, could hardly hold it. The water was deeper than I thought and it was over my Wellington tops at the first stride. Gasping, I bent down and dug my thumb into the jugular furrow at the base of the neck. The vein came up and as I pushed the needle in, the blood ran warm and dark over my hand. I fumbled the flutter valve from my pocket, pushed a bottle into the cup end and inserted the other end into the needle. The calcium began to flow into the vein.

Standing there in the icy beck, holding the bottle aloft with bloody fingers and feeling the rain working its way inside my collar, I tried to keep out the black thoughts; about all those people I knew who were still in bed and would only leave it when their alarm clocks rang; and they would read their papers over breakfast and drive out to their cosy banks or insurance offices. Maybe I should have been a doctor – they treated their patients in nice, warm bedrooms.

I pulled the needle from the vein and threw the empty bottle on to the bank. There was no response to the injection. I took the other bottle and began to run more calcium under the skin. Might as well go through the motions, futile though it seemed now. It was when I was rubbing away the subcutaneous injection that I noticed the eyelids quiver.

A quick ripple of relief and excitement went through me. I looked up at the farmer and laughed. 'She's still with us, Dan.' I flicked her ear and her eyes opened wide. 'We'll wait a few minutes and then try to roll her on to her chest.'

Within a quarter of an hour she was beginning to toss her head about and I knew it was time. I caught hold of her horns and pulled while Dan and his tall son pushed at her shoulder. We made slow progress but after several concerted heaves the cow took over herself and settled on her chest. Immediately everything looked rosier; when a cow is lying on her side she always has the look of death on her.

I was pretty sure then that she would recover, but I couldn't go away and leave her lying in the beck. Milk fever cows can stay down for days on end but I had the feeling this one would be up soon. I decided to stick it out a bit longer.

She didn't seem to relish her situation in the peaty water and began to make determined efforts to rise, but it was another half hour and my teeth were chattering uncontrollably before she finally staggered to her feet.

'Well, that's a licker!' Dan said. 'Ah never thought she'd stand again. Must be good stuff you gave her.'

'It's a bit quicker than the old bicycle pump,' I laughed. The spectacular effects of intravenous calcium were still enough of a novelty to intrigue me. For generations, cows with milk fever had just died. Then inflation of the udder had saved many; but the calcium was the thing – when they got up within an hour like this one, I always felt like a successful conjurer.

We guided the cow up the bank and at the top, the full force of the wind and rain struck us. The house was only a hundred yards away and we battled towards it, Dan and his son leading, holding the calf in a sack slung between them. The tiny animal swung to and fro, screwing up its eyes against the hard world it had entered. Close behind followed the anxious mother, still rocky on her legs but doing her best to poke her muzzle into the sack. I squelched along in the rear.

We left the cow knee deep in straw in a warm shed, licking her calf vigorously. In the porch of the house, the others dutifully pulled off their Wellingtons; I did the same, pouring about a pint of beck water from each boot. Mrs Cooper had the reputation of being a firebrand who exercised an iron rule over Dan and her family, but from my previous contacts with her I had the feeling that Dan didn't do so badly.

I thought so again as I saw her, square built but comely, plaiting a little girl's pigtails in readiness for school. A crackling fire was mirrored in the gleaming brass of the hearth and above the clean farmhouse smell there was a hint of home-cured bacon just beginning to fry.

Mrs Cooper sent Dan and the boy scurrying upstairs to change their socks then she turned a calm gaze on me as I dripped on her linoleum. She shook her head as though I were a naughty child.

'All right, off with the socks,' she rapped out. 'And your coat, and roll up your trousers, and sit down here, and dry your hair with this.' A clean towel landed on my lap and Mrs Cooper bent over me. 'Don't you ever think of wearing a hat?'

'Not keen on them, I'm afraid,' I mumbled, and she shook her head again.

She poured hot water from a kettle into a large bowl and added mustard from a pound tin. 'Here, stick your feet in this.'

I had obeyed all her commands with alacrity and I gave an involuntary yelp as I made contact with the bubbling mixture. At this, she shot a fierce glance at me and I took care to keep my feet in the bowl. I was sitting, teeth clenched, enveloped in steam, when she pushed a pint pot of tea into my hand.

It was old fashioned treatment but effective. By the time I was halfway down the pint pot I felt as though I were being consumed by fire. The river bed chill was a dream which vanished completely as Mrs Cooper topped up my bowl with another scalding quart from the kettle.

Next, she grabbed chair and bowl and swivelled me round till I was sitting at the table, still with my feet in the water. Dan and the children were already at their breakfast and in front of me was a plate with two eggs, a rough cut piece of bacon and several sausages. I had learned enough of Dales ways to keep quiet at meals; when I first came to the district I had thought it incumbent on me to provide light conversation in return for their hospitality but the questioning glances they exchanged with each other silenced me effectively.

So this morning, I attacked the food without preamble, but the first mouthful almost made me break my new found rule. It was the first time I had tasted a home made Yorkshire sausage and it was an effort to restrain the cries of congratulation which would have been natural in other circles. But Mrs Cooper had been watching me out of the corner of her eye and she must have noticed my rapt expression. Casually, she rose, brought over the frying pan and rolled a few more links on to my plate.

'Killed a pig last week,' she said, pulling open the pantry door. I could see the dishes heaped with chopped meat, spare rib, liver, the rows of pies with the jelly gleaming on their pale gold crusts.

I finished my meal, pulled on a thick pair of socks borrowed from Dan and my dry shoes. I was about to leave when Mrs Cooper tucked a parcel under my arm. I knew it contained further samples from the pantry but her eyes dared me to say much about it. I muttered a few words of thanks and went out to the car.

The church clock was chiming a quarter past nine when I pulled up outside Skeldale House. I felt good – warm, full of superb food and with the satisfying memory of the cow's quick recovery. And there was my parcel on the back seat; it was always a stroke of luck to land on a farm after a pig killing and there was usually a gift from the hospitable farmers, but these sausages were something I would never forget.

I took the surgery steps at a jump and trotted along the passage, but as I rounded the corner my progress was halted. Siegfried was standing there, rigid, his back pressed against the wall. Over his shoulder dangled a long, flexible, leather probang. Between us was the half open door of the office with Miss Harbottle clearly visible at her desk.

I waved cheerfully. 'Hello, hello, off to a choke?'

Siegfried's face twisted in anguish and he held up a warning hand. Then he began to creep past the door, balancing on the balls of his feet like a tightrope walker. He was beyond the door and the tense lines of his body had begun to relax when the brass end of the swinging probang clattered against the wall and, as if in reply came the familiar rumble from Miss Harbottle's corner. Siegfried gave me a single despairing glance then, shoulders drooping, he went slowly into the room.

Watching him go, I thought wonderingly of how things had built up since the secretary's arrival. It was naked war now and it gave life an added interest to observe the tactics of the two sides.

At the beginning it seemed that Siegfried must run out an easy winner. He was the employer; he held the reins and it appeared that Miss Harbottle would be helpless in the face of his obstructive strategy. But Miss Harbottle was a fighter and a resourceful one and it was impossible not to admire the way she made use of the weapons at her command.

In fact, over the past week the tide had been running in her favour. She had been playing Siegfried like an expert fisherman with a salmon; bringing him repeatedly back to her desk to answer footling questions. Her throat clearing had developed into an angry bark which could penetrate the full extent of the house. And she had a new weapon; she had taken to writing Siegfried's clerical idiocies on slips of paper; mis-spellings, errors in addition, wrong entries – they were all faithfully copied down.

Miss Harbottle used these slips as ammunition. She never brought one out when things were slack and her employer was hanging about the surgery. She saved them until he was under pressure, then she would push a slip under his nose and say 'How about this?'

She always kept an expressionless face at these times and it was impossible to say how much pleasure it gave her to see him cower back like a whipped animal. But the end was unvarying – mumbled explanations and apologies from Siegfried and Miss Harbottle, radiating self-righteousness, correcting the entry.

As Siegfried went into the room I watched through the partly open door. I knew my morning round was waiting but I was impelled by morbid curiosity. Miss Harbottle, looking brisk and businesslike, was tapping an entry in the book with her pen while Siegfried shuffled his feet and muttered replies. He made several vain attempts to escape and, as the time passed, I could see he was nearing breaking point. His teeth were clenched and his eyes had started to bulge.

The phone rang and the secretary answered it. Her employer was making again for the door when she called happily, 'Colonel Brent for you.' Like a man in a dream he turned back. The Colonel, a racehorse owner, had been a thorn in our flesh for a long time with his complaints and his continual questioning and probing; a call from him was always liable to send up the blood pressure.

I could see it was that way this morning. The minutes ticked away and Siegfried's face got redder. He made his replies in a choked voice which finally rose almost to a shout. At the end he crashed the receiver down and leaned on the desk, breathing heavily.

Then, as I watched, unbelieving, Miss Harbottle began to open the drawer where she kept her slips. She fished one out, coughed and held it in Siegfried's face.

'How about this?' she asked.

I resisted the impulse to close my eyes and stared in horror. For a few seconds nothing happened and there was a tense interval while Siegfried stood quite motionless. Then his face seemed to break up and with a scything sweep of his arm he snatched the slip from the secretary's hand and began to tear at it with fierce intensity. He didn't say a word but as he tore, he leaned forward over the desk and his glaring eyes approached ever nearer to Miss Harbottle who slowly edged her chair back till it was jammed against the wall.

It was a weird picture. Miss Harbottle straining back, her mouth slightly open, her tinted curls bobbing in alarm, and Siegfried, his ravaged features close to hers, still tearing with insane vigour at the piece of paper. The scene ended when

Siegfried, putting every ounce of his strength into an action like a javelin thrower, hurled the torn up slip at the waste paper basket. It fell in a gentle shower, like confetti, in and around the basket and Siegfried, still without speaking, wrapped his probang around him and strode from the room.

In the kitchen, Mrs Hall opened the parcel and extracted a pie, a chunk of liver and a cluster of the exquisite sausages. She turned a quizzical eye on me. 'You look kind of pleased with yourself this morning, Mr Herriot.'

I leaned back against the oak dresser. 'Yes, Mrs Hall, I've just been thinking. It must be very nice to be the principal of a practice but, you know, it's not such a bad life being an assistant.'

CHAPTER TWENTY-FOUR

The day had started badly. Tristan had been trapped by his brother at 4 AM returning from the Bellringers' Outing.

This function took place annually when a bus load of the bellringers of all the local churches made a trip to Morecambe. They spent very little time on the beach, however, and when they weren't working their way from one pub to another, they were attacking the crates of beer they had brought with them.

When they rolled into Darrowby in the small hours most of the occupants of the bus were unconscious. Tristan, an honoured guest of the party, had been tipped out in the back lane behind Skeldale House. He waved weakly as the bus moved away, but drew no response from the unseeing faces at the windows. Lurching down the garden path, he was horrified to see a light in Siegfried's room. Escape was impossible and, when asked to explain where he had been, he made a series of attempts to articulate 'Bellringers' Outing' without success.

Siegfried, seeing he was wasting his time, had saved his

wrath till breakfast time. That was when Tristan told me the story – just before his brother came into the dining-room and started on him.

But, as usual, it seemed to take more out of Siegfried who went off on his rounds glowering and hoarse from shouting. Ten minutes after he had gone I found Tristan closeted cheerfully in Boardman's cubby hole, Boardman listening to some fresh material from the backs of the envelopes and sniggering appreciatively.

The old man had cheered up greatly since Tristan came home and the two of them spent a lot of time in the gloom where the light from the tiny window picked out the rows of rusting tools, the Bairnsfather cartoons looking down from the wall. The place was usually kept locked and visitors were not encouraged; but Tristan was always welcome.

Often, when I was passing by, I would peep in and see Tristan patiently pulling at a Woodbine while Boardman rambled on. 'We was six weeks up the line. The French was on our right and the Jocks on our left ...' or 'Poor old Fred – one minute 'e was standing by me and next 'e was gone. Never found as much as a trouser button ...'

This morning, Tristan hailed me boisterously and I marvelled again at his resilience and his power to bend like a willow before the winds of misfortune and spring back unscathed. He held up two tickets.

'Village dance tonight, Jim, and I can guarantee it. Some of my harem from the hospital are going, so I'll see you're all right. And that's not all – look here.' He went into the saddle room, lifted out a loose board and produced a bottle of sherry. 'We'll be able to have a toothful between dances.'

I didn't ask where the tickets or the sherry had come from. I liked the village dances. The packed hall with the three piece band at one end – piano, scraping fiddle and drums – and at the other end, the older ladies looking after the refreshments. Glasses of milk, mounds of sandwiches, ham, home-made brawn, trifles heaped high with cream.

That evening, Tristan came out with me on my last visit and in the car the talk was all about the dance. The case was simple enough – a cow with an infected eye – but the farm was in a village high up the dale, and when we finished, it was dusk. I felt good, and everything seemed to stand out, clear and meaningful. The single, empty, grey stone street, the last red streaks in the sky, the dark purple of the enclosing fells. There was no wind, but a soft breath came from the quiet moors, sweet and fresh and full of promise. Among the houses, the thrilling smell of wood smoke was everywhere.

When we got back to the surgery, Siegfried was out but there was a note for Tristan propped up on the mantelpiece. It said simply: 'Tristan. Go home. Siegfried.'

This had happened before, everything in Skeldale House being in short supply, especially beds and blankets. When unexpected visitors arrived, Tristan was packed off to stay with his mother in Brawton. Normally he would board a train without comment, but tonight was different.

'Good God,' he said. 'Somebody must be coming for the night and, of course, I'm the one who's just expected to disappear. It's a nice bloody carry on, I must say! And isn't that a charming letter! It doesn't matter if I've made any private arrangements. Oh no! There's no question of asking me if it's convenient to leave. It's just "Tristan, go home." Polite and thoughtful, isn't it?'

It was unusual for him to get worked up like this. I spoke soothingly. 'Look, Triss. Maybe we'd better just skip this dance. There'll be others.'

Tristan clenched his fists. 'Why should I let him push me around like this?' he fumed. 'I'm a person, am I not? I have my own life to lead and I tell you I am not going to Brawton tonight. I've arranged to go to a dance and I am damn well going to a dance.'

This was fighting talk but I felt a twinge of alarm. 'Wait a minute. What about Siegfried? What's he going to say when he comes in and finds you still here?'

'To hell with Siegfried!' said Tristan. So I left it at that.

Siegfried came home when we were upstairs, changing. I was first down and found him sitting by the fire, reading. I said nothing but sat down and waited for the explosion.

After a few minutes, Tristan came in. He had chosen with care among his limited wardrobe and was resplendent in a dark grey suit; a scrubbed face shone under carefully combed hair; he was wearing a clean collar.

Siegfried flushed as he looked up from his book. 'What the bloody hell are you doing here? I told you to go to Brawton. Joe Ramage is coming tonight.'

'Couldn't go.'

'Why not?'

'No trains.'

'What the hell do you mean, no trains?'

'Just that – no trains.'

The cross talk was bringing on the usual sense of strain in me. The interview was falling into the habitual pattern; Siegfried red faced, exasperated; his brother expressionless, answering in a flat monotone, fighting a defensive battle with the skill of long practice.

Siegfried sank back in his chair, baffled for the moment, but he kept a slit-eyed gaze on his brother. The smart suit, the slicked hair and polished shoes all seemed to irritate him further.

'All right,' he said suddenly, 'it's maybe just as well you are staying. I want you to do a job for me. You can open that haematoma on Charlie Dent's pig's ear.'

This was a bombshell. Charlie Dent's pig's ear was something we didn't talk about.

A few weeks earlier, Siegfried himself had gone to the smallholding halfway along a street on the outskirts of the town to see a pig with a swollen ear. It was an aural haematoma and the only treatment was to lance it, but for some reason, Siegfried had not done the job but had sent me the following day.

I had wondered about it, but not for long. When I climbed into the sty, the biggest sow I had ever seen rose from the straw, gave an explosive bark and rushed at me with its huge mouth gaping. I didn't stop to argue. I made the wall about six inches ahead of the pig and vaulted over into the passage. I stood there, considering the position, looking thoughtfully at the mean little red eyes, the slavering mouth with its long, yellow teeth.

Usually, I paid no attention when pigs barked and grumbled at me but this one really seemed to mean it. As I wondered what the next step would be, the pig gave an angry roar, reared up on its hind legs and tried to get over the wall at me. I made up my mind quickly.

'I'm afraid I haven't got the right instrument with me, Mr Dent. I'll pop back another day and open the ear for you. It's nothing serious – only a small job. Goodbye.'

There the matter had rested, with nobody caring to mention it till now.

Tristan was aghast. 'You mean you want me to go along there tonight. Saturday night? Surely some other time would do? I'm going to a dance.'

Siegfried smiled bitterly from the depths of his chair. 'It has to be done now. That's an order. You can go to your dance afterwards.'

Tristan started to say something, but he knew he had pushed his luck far enough. 'Right,' he said, 'I'll go and do it.'

He left the room with dignity, Siegfried resumed his book, and I stared into the fire, wondering how Tristan was going to handle this one. He was a lad of infinite resource, but he was going to be tested this time.

Within ten minutes he was back. Siegfried looked at him suspiciously. 'Have you opened that ear?'

'No.'

'Why not?'

'Couldn't find the place. You must have given me the wrong address. Number 98, you said.'

'It's number 89 and you know damn well it is. Now get back there and do your job.'

The door closed behind Tristan and again, I waited. Fifteen minutes later it opened again and Tristan reappeared looking faintly triumphant. His brother looked up from his book.

'Done it?'

'No.'

'Why not?'

'The family are all out at the pictures. Saturday night, you know.'

'I don't care a damn where the family are. Just get into that sty and lance that ear. Now get out, and this time I want the job done.'

Again Tristan retreated and a new vigil began. Siegfried did not say a word, but I could feel the tension building up. Twenty minutes passed and Tristan was with us again.

'Have you opened that ear?'

'No.'

'Why not?'

'It's pitch dark in there. How do you expect me to work? I've only got two hands – one for the knife and one for the torch. How can I hold the ear?'

Siegfried had been keeping a tight hold on himself, but now his control snapped. 'Don't give me any more of your bloody excuses,' he shouted, leaping from his chair. 'I don't care how you do it, but, by God, you are going to open that pig's ear tonight or I've finished with you. Now get the hell out of here and don't come back till it's done!'

My heart bled for Tristan. He had been dealt a poor hand and had played his cards with rare skill, but he had nothing left now. He stood silent in the doorway for a few moments, then he turned and walked out.

The next hour was a long one. Siegfried seemed to be enjoying his book and I even tried to read myself; but I got no meaning out of the words and it made my head ache to sit staring at them. It would have helped if I could have paced up and down the carpet but that was pretty well impossible in Siegfried's presence. I had just decided to excuse myself and go out for a walk when I heard the outer door open, then Tristan's footsteps in the passage.

A moment later, the man of destiny entered but the penetrating smell of pig got into the room just ahead of him, and as he walked over to the fire, pungent waves seemed to billow round him. Pig muck was spattered freely over his nice suit, and on his clean collar, his face and hair. There was a great smear of the stuff on the seat of his trousers but despite his ravaged appearance he still maintained his poise.

Siegfried pushed his chair back hurriedly but did not change expression.

'Have you got that ear opened?' he asked quietly.

'Yes.'

Siegfried returned to his book without comment. It seemed that the matter was closed and Tristan, after staring briefly at his brother's bent head, turned and marched from the room. But even after he had gone, the odour of the pigsty hung in the room like a cloud.

Later, in the Drovers', I watched Tristan draining his third pint. He had changed, and if he didn't look as impressive as when he started the evening, at least he was clean and hardly smelt at all. I had said nothing yet, but the old light was returning to his eye. I went over to the bar and ordered my second half and Tristan's fourth pint and, as I set the glasses on the table, I thought that perhaps it was time.

'Well, what happened?'

Tristan took a long, contented pull at his glass and lit a Woodbine. 'Well now, all in all, Jim, it was rather a smooth operation, but I'll start at the beginning. You can imagine me standing all alone outside the sty in the pitch darkness with that bloody great pig grunting and growling on the other side of the wall. I didn't feel so good, I can tell you.

'I shone my torch on the thing's face and it jumped up and ran at me, making a noise like a lion and showing all those dirty yellow teeth. I nearly wrapped it up and came home there and then, but I got to thinking about the dance and all and, on the spur of the moment, I hopped over the wall.

'Two seconds later, I was on my back. It must have charged me but couldn't see enough to get a bite in. I just heard a bark, then a terrific weight against my legs and I was down.

'Well, it's a funny thing, Jim. You know I'm not a violent chap, but as I lay there, all my fears vanished and all I felt was a cold hatred of that bloody animal. I saw it as the cause of all my troubles and before I knew what I was doing I was up on my feet and booting its arse round and round the sty. And, do you know, it showed no fight at all. That pig was a coward at heart.'

I was still puzzled. 'But the ear – how did you manage to open the haematoma?'

'No problem, Jim. That was done for me.'

'You don't mean to say ...'

'Yes,' Tristan said, holding his pint up to the light and studying a small foreign body floating in the depths. 'Yes, it was really very fortunate. In the scuffle in the dark, the pig ran up against the wall and burst the thing itself. Made a beautiful job.'

CHAPTER TWENTY-FIVE

I realized, quite suddenly, that spring had come. It was late March and I had been examining some sheep in a hillside fold. On my way down, in the lee of a small pine wood I leaned my back against a tree and was aware, all at once, of the sunshine, warm on my closed eyelids, the clamour of the larks, the muted sea-sound of the wind in the high branches. And though the snow still lay in long runnels behind the walls and the grass was lifeless and winter-yellowed, there was the feeling of change; almost of liberation, because, unknowing, I had surrounded myself with a carapace against the iron months, the relentless cold.

It wasn't a warm spring but it was dry with sharp winds which fluttered the white heads of the snowdrops and bent the clumps of daffodils on the village greens. In April the roadside banks were bright with the fresh yellow of the primroses.

And in April, too, came the lambing. It came in a great tidal wave, the most vivid and interesting part of the veterinary surgeon's year, the zenith of the annual cycle, and it came as it always does when we were busiest with our other work.

In the spring the livestock were feeling the effects of the long winter. Cows had stood for months in the same few feet of byre and were in dire need of the green grass and the sun on their backs, while their calves had very little resistance to disease. And just when we were wondering how we could cope with the coughs and colds and pneumonias and acetonaemias the wave struck us.

The odd thing is that for about ten months of the year, sheep hardly entered into the scheme of our lives. They were just woolly things on the hills. But for the other two months they almost blotted out everything else.

First came the early troubles, the pregnancy toxaemias, the prolapses. Then the lambings in a concentrated rush followed by the calcium deficiencies, the horrible gangrenous mastitis when the udder turns black and sloughs away; and the diseases which beset the lambs themselves – swayback, pulpy kidney, dysentery. Then the flood slackened, became a trickle and by the end of May had almost dried up. Sheep became woolly things on the hills again.

But in this first year I found a fascination in the work which has remained with me. Lambing, it seemed to me, had all the thrill and interest of calving without the hard labour. It was usually uncomfortable in that it was performed in the open; either in draughty pens improvised from straw bales and gates or more often out in the fields. It didn't seem to occur to the farmers that the ewe might prefer to produce her family in a warm place or that the vet may not enjoy kneeling for an hour in his shirt sleeves in the rain.

But the actual job was as easy as a song. After my experiences in correcting the malpresentations of calves it was delightful to manipulate these tiny creatures. Lambs are usually born in twos or threes and some wonderful mix-ups occur; tangles of heads and legs all trying to be first out and it is the vet's job to sort them around and decide which leg belonged to which head. I revelled in this. It was a pleasant change to be for once stronger and bigger than my patient, but I didn't over-stress this advantage; I have not changed the opinion I formed then that there are just two things to remember in lambing – cleanliness and gentleness.

And the lambs. All young animals are appealing but the lamb has been given an unfair share of charm. The moments come back; of a bitterly cold evening when I had delivered twins on a wind-scoured hillside; the lambs shaking their heads convulsively and within minutes one of them struggling upright and making its way, unsteady, knock-kneed, towards the udder while the other followed resolutely on its knees.

The shepherd, his purpled, weather-roughened face almost hidden by the heavy coat which muffled him to his ears, gave a slow chuckle. 'How the 'ell do they know?'

He had seen it happen thousands of times and he still wondered. So do I.

And another memory of two hundred lambs in a barn on a warm afternoon. We were inoculating them against pulpy kidney and there was no conversation because of the high pitched protests of the lambs and the unremitting deep baa-ing from nearly a hundred ewes milling anxiously around outside. I couldn't conceive how these ewes could ever get their own families sorted out from that mass of almost identical little creatures. It would take hours.

It took about twenty-five seconds. When we had finished injecting we opened the barn doors and the outpouring lambs were met by a concerted rush of distraught mothers. At first the noise was deafening but it died away rapidly to an occasional bleat as the last stray was rounded up. Then, neatly paired off, the flock headed calmly for the field.

Through May and early June my world became softer and warmer. The cold wind dropped and the air, fresh as the sea, carried a faint breath of the thousands of wild flowers which speckled the pastures. At times it seemed unfair that I should be paid for my work; for driving out in the early morning with the fields glittering under the first pale sunshine and the wisps of mist hanging on the high tops.

At Skeldale House the wistaria exploded into a riot of mauve blooms which thrust themselves through the open windows and each morning as I shaved I breathed in the heady fragrance from the long clusters drooping by the side of the mirror. Life was idyllic.

There was only one jarring note; it was the time of the horse. In the thirties there were still quite a lot of horses on the farms though the tractors had already sounded their warning knell. In the farms near the foot of the Dale where there was a fair amount of arable land the rows of stables were half empty but there were still enough horses to make May and June uncomfortable. This was when the castrations were done.

Before that came the foaling and it was a common enough thing to see a mare with her foal either trotting beside her or stretched flat on the ground as its mother nibbled at the grass. Nowadays the sight of a cart mare and foal in a field would make me pull up my car to have another look.

There was all the work connected with the foalings; cleansing the mares, docking the foals' tails, treating the illnesses of the new born – joint ill, retained meconium. It was hard and interesting but as the weather grew warmer the farmers began to think of having the year old colts castrated.

I didn't like the job and since there might be up to a hundred to be done, it cast a shadow over this and many subsequent springs. For generations the operation had been done by casting the colt and tying him up very like a trussed chicken. It was a bit laborious but the animal was under complete restraint and it was possible to concentrate entirely on the job; but at about the time I qualified, standing castration was coming very much to the fore. It consisted simply of applying a twitch to the colt's upper lip, injecting a shot of local anaesthetic into each testicle and going straight ahead. There was no doubt it was a lot quicker.

The obvious disadvantage was that the danger of injury to the operator and his helpers was increased tenfold, but for all that the method rapidly became more popular. A local farmer called Kenny Bright who considered himself an advanced thinker took the step of introducing it to the district. He engaged Major Farley, the horse specialist, to give a demonstration on one of his colts, and a large gathering of farmers came to spectate. Kenny, smug and full of self importance was holding the twitch and beaming round the company as his protégé prepared to disinfect the operation site, but as soon as the Major touched the scrotum with his antiseptic the colt reared and brought a fore foot crashing down on Kenny's head. He was carried away on a gate with his skull fractured and spent a long time in hospital. The other farmers didn't stop laughing for weeks but the example failed to deter them. Standing castration was in.

I said it was quicker. It was when everything went smoothly, but there were other times when the colt kicked or threw himself on top of us or just went generally mad. Out of ten jobs nine would be easy and the tenth would be a rodeo. I don't know how much apprehension this state of affairs built up in other vets but I was undeniably tense on castration mornings.

Of course, one of the reasons was that I was not, am not and never will be a horseman. It is difficult to define the term but I am convinced that horsemen are either born or acquire the talent in early childhood. I knew it was no good my trying to start in my mid twenties. I had the knowledge of equine diseases, I believed I had the ability to treat sick horses efficiently but that power the real horseman had to sooth and quieten and mentally dominate an animal was beyond my reach. I didn't even try to kid myself.

It was unfortunate because there is no doubt horses know. It is quite different with cows; they don't care either way; if a cow feels like kicking you she will kick you; she doesn't give a damn whether you are an expert or not. But horses know.

So on those mornings my morale was never very high as I drove out with my instruments rattling and rolling about on an enamel tray on the back seat. Would he be wild or quiet? How big would he be? I had heard my colleagues airily stating their preference for big horses – the two year olds were far easier, they said, you could get a better grip on the testicles. But there was never any doubt in my own mind. I liked them small; the smaller the better.

One morning when the season was at its height and I had had about enough of the equine race, Siegfried called to me as he was going out. 'James, there's a horse with a tumour on its belly at Wilkinson's of White Cross. Get along and take it off – today if possible but otherwise fix your own time; I'll leave it with you.'

Feeling a little disgruntled at fate having handed me something on top of the seasonal tasks, I boiled up a scalpel, tumour spoons and syringe and put them on my tray with local anaesthetic, iodine and tetanus antitoxin.

I drove to the farm with the tray rattling ominously behind me. That sound always had a connotation of doom for me. I wondered about the horse – maybe it was just a yearling; they did get those little dangling growths sometimes – nanberries, the farmers called them. Over the six miles I managed to build up a comfortable picture of a soft-eyed little colt with pendulous abdomen and over-long hair; it hadn't done well over the winter and was probably full of worms – shaky on its legs with weakness, in fact.

At Wilkinson's all was quiet. The yard was empty except for a lad of about ten who didn't know where the boss was.

'Well, where is the horse?' I asked.

The lad pointed to the stable. 'He's in there.'

I went inside. At one end stood a high, open-topped loose box with a metal grill topping the wooden walls and from within I heard a deep-throated whinnying and snorting followed by a series of tremendous thuds against the sides of the box. A chill crept through me. That was no little colt in there.

I opened the top half door and there, looking down at me was an enormous animal; I hadn't realized horses ever came quite as big as this; a chestnut stallion with a proud arch to his neck and feet like manhole covers. Surging swathes of muscle shone on his shoulders and quarters and when he saw me he laid back his ears, showed the whites of his eyes and lashed out viciously against the wall. A foot long splinter flew high in the air as the great hoof crashed against the boards.

'God almighty,' I breathed and closed the half door hurriedly. I leaned my back against the door and listened to my heart thumping.

I turned to the lad. 'How old is that horse?'

'Over six years, sir.'

I tried a little calm thinking. How did you go about tackling a man-eater like this. I had never seen such a horse – he must weigh over a ton. I shook myself; I hadn't even had a look at the tumour I was supposed to remove. I lifted the latch, opened the door about two inches and peeped inside. I could see it plainly dangling from the belly; probably a papilloma, about the size of a cricket ball, with a lobulated surface which made it look like a little cauliflower. It swung gently from side to side as the horse moved about.

No trouble to take it off. Nice narrow neck to it; a few cc's of local in there and I could twist it off easily with the spoons.

But the snag was obvious. I would have to go under that shining barrel of an abdomen within easy reach of the great feet and stick a needle into those few inches of skin. Not a happy thought.

But I pulled my mind back to practical things; like a bucket of hot water, soap and a towel. And I'd need a good man on the twitch. I began to walk towards the house.

There was no answer to my knock. I tried again; still nothing – there was nobody at home. It seemed the most natural thing in the world to leave everything till another day; the idea of going round the buildings and fields till I found somebody never entered my head.

I almost broke into a gallop on my way to the car, backed it round with the tyres squealing and roared out of the yard.

Siegfried was surprised. 'Nobody there? Well that's a damn funny thing. I'm nearly sure they were expecting you today. But never mind, it's in your hands, James. Give them a ring and fix it up again as soon as possible.'

I found it wonderfully easy to forget about the stallion over the days and weeks that followed; except when my defences were down. At least once a night it thundered through my dreams with gaping nostrils and flying mane and I developed an uncomfortable habit of coming bolt awake at five o'clock in the morning and starting immediately to operate on the horse. On an average, I took that tumour off twenty times before breakfast each morning.

I told myself it would be a lot easier to fix the job up and get it over. What was I waiting for, anyway? Was there a subconscious hope that if I put it off long enough something would happen to get me off the hook? The tumour might fall off or shrink away and disappear, or the horse might drop down dead.

I could have passed the whole thing on to Siegfried – he was good with horses – but my confidence was low enough without that.

All my doubts were resolved one morning when Mr Wilkinson came on the phone. He wasn't in the least upset at the long delay but he made it quite clear that he could wait no longer. 'You see, I want to sell this 'oss, young man, but I can't let him go with that thing on him, can I?'

My journey to Wilkinson's wasn't enlivened by the familiar clatter of the tray on the back seat; it reminded me of the last time when I was wondering what was ahead of me. This time I knew.

Stepping out of the car, I felt almost disembodied. It was like walking a few inches above the ground. I was greeted by a reverberating din from the loose box; the same angry whinneys and splintering crashes I had heard before. I tried to twist my stiff face into a smile as the farmer came over.

'My chaps are getting a halter on him,' he said, but his words were cut short by an enraged squealing from the box and two tremendous blows against the wooden sides. I felt my mouth going dry.

The noise was coming nearer; then the stable doors flew open and the great horse catapulted out into the yard, dragging two big fellows along on the end of the halter shank. The cobbles struck sparks from the men's boots as they slithered about but they were unable to stop the stallion backing and plunging. I imagined I could feel the ground shudder under my feet as the hooves crashed down.

At length, after much manoeuvring, the men got the horse standing with his off side against the wall of the barn. One of them looped the twitch on to the upper lip and tightened it expertly, the other took a firm grip on the halter and turned towards me. 'Ready for you now, sir.'

I pierced the rubber cap on the bottle of cocaine, withdrew the plunger of the syringe and watched the clear fluid flow into the glass barrel. Seven, eight, ten cc's. If I could get that in, the rest would be easy; but my hands were trembling.

Walking up to the horse was like watching an action from a film. It wasn't really me doing this – the whole thing was unreal. The near side eye flickered dangerously at me as I raised my left hand and passed it over the muscles of the neck, down the smooth, quivering flank and along the abdomen till I was able to grasp the tumour. I had the thing in my hand now, the lobulations firm and lumpy under my fingers. I pulled gently downwards, stretching the brown skin joining the growth to the body. I would put the local in there – a few good weals. It wasn't going to be so bad. The stallion laid back his ears and gave a warning whicker.

I took a long, careful breath, brought up the syringe with my right hand, placed the needle against the skin then thrust it in.

The kick was so explosively quick that at first I felt only surprise that such a huge animal could move so swiftly. It was a lightning outward slash that I never even saw and the hoof struck the inside of my right thigh, spinning me round helplessly. When I hit the ground I lay still, feeling only a curious numbness. Then I tried to move and a stab of pain went through my leg.

When I opened my eyes Mr Wilkinson was bending over me. 'Are you all right, Mr Herriot?' The voice was anxious.

'I don't think so.' I was astonished at the matter of fact sound of my own words; but stranger still was the feeling of being at peace with myself for the first time for weeks. I was calm and completely in charge of the situation.

'I'm afraid not, Mr Wilkinson. You'd better put the horse back in his box for now – we'll have a go at him another day – and I wonder if you'd ring Mr Farnon to come and pick me up. I don't think I'll be able to drive.'

My leg wasn't broken but it developed a massive haematoma at the point of impact and then the whole limb blossomed into an unbelievable range of colours from delicate orange to deepest black. I was still hobbling like a Crimean veteran when, a fortnight later, Siegfried and I with a small army of helpers went back and roped the stallion, chloroformed him and removed that little growth.

I have a cavity in the muscle of my thigh to remind me of that day, but some good came out of the incident. I found that the fear is worse than the reality and horse work has never worried me as much since then.

CHAPTER TWENTY-SIX

The first time I saw Phin Calvert was in the street outside the surgery when I was talking to Brigadier Julian Coutts-Browne about his shooting dogs. The Brigadier was almost a stage version of an English aristocrat; immensely tall with a pronounced stoop, hawk features and a high drawling voice. As he spoke, smoke from a narrow cigar trickled from his lips.

I turned my head at the clatter of heavy boots on the pavement. A thick set figure was stumping rapidly towards us, hands tucked behind his braces, ragged jacket pulled wide to display a curving expanse of collarless shirt, wisps of grizzled hair hanging in a fringe beneath a greasy cap. He was smiling widely at nobody in particular and he hummed busily to himself.

The Brigadier glanced at him. 'Morning, Calvert,' he grunted coldly.

Phineas threw up his head in pleased recognition. 'Now then, Charlie, 'ow is ta?' he shouted.

The Brigadier looked as though he had swallowed a swift pint of vinegar. He removed his cigar with a shaking hand and stared after the retreating back. 'Impudent devil,' he muttered.

Looking at Phin, you would never have thought he was a prosperous farmer. I was called to his place a week later and was surprised to find a substantial house and buildings and a fine dairy herd grazing in the fields.

I could hear him even before I got out of the car.

'Hello, 'ello, 'ello! Who's this we've got then? New chap eh? Now we're going to learn summat!' He still had his hands inside his braces and was grinning wider than ever.

'My name is Herriot,' I said.

'Is it now?' Phin cocked his head and surveyed me, then he

turned to three young men standing by. 'Hasn't he a nice smile, lads. He's a real Happy Harry!'

He turned and began to lead the way across the yard. 'Come on, then and we'll see what you're made of. I 'ope you know a bit about calves because I've got some here that are right dowly.'

As he went into the calf house I was hoping I would be able to do something impressive – perhaps use some of the new drugs and sera I had in my car; it was going to take something special to make an impact here.

There were six well grown young animals, almost stirk size, and three of them were behaving very strangely; grinding their teeth, frothing at the mouth and blundering about the pen as though they couldn't see. As I watched, one of them walked straight into the wall and stood with its nose pressed against the stone.

Phin, apparently unconcerned, was humming to himself in a corner. When I started to take my thermometer from its case he burst into a noisy commentary. 'Now what's he doing? Ah, we're off now, get up there!'

The half minute which my thermometer spends in an animal's rectum is usually devoted to hectic thought. But this time I didn't need the time to work out my diagnosis; the blindness made it easy. I began to look round the walls of the calf house; it was dark and I had to get my face close to the stone.

Phin gave tongue again. 'Hey, what's going on? You're as bad as t' calves, nosing about there, dozy like. What d'you think you're lookin' for?'

'Paint, Mr Calvert. I'm nearly sure your calves have got lead poisoning.'

Phin said what all farmers say at this juncture. 'They can't have. I've had calves in here for thirty years and they've never taken any harm before. There's no paint in here, anyway.'

'How about this, then?' I peered into the darkest corner and pulled at a piece of loose board.

'Oh, that's nobbut a bit of wood I nailed down there last week to block up a hole. Came off an old hen house.'

I looked at the twenty year old paint hanging off in the loose flakes which calves find so irresistible. 'This is what's done the damage,' I said. 'Look, you can see the tooth marks where they've been at it.'

Phin studied the board at close quarters and grunted doubtfully. 'All right, what do we do now?'

'First thing is to get this painted board out of here and then give all the calves epsom salts. Have you got any?'

Phin gave a bark of laughter. 'Aye, I've got a bloody great sack full, but can't you do owt better than that? Aren't you going to inject them?'

It was a little embarrassing. The specific antidotes to metal poisoning had not been discovered and the only thing which sometimes did a bit of good was magnesium sulphate which caused the precipitation of insoluble lead sulphate. The homely term for magnesium sulphate is of course, epsom salts.

'No,' I said. 'There's nothing I can inject that will help at all and I can't even guarantee the salts will. But I'd like you to give the calves two heaped tablespoonfuls three times a day.'

'Oh 'ell, you'll skitter the poor buggers to death!'

'Maybe so, but there's nothing else for it,' I said.

Phin took a step towards me so that his face, dark-skinned and deeply wrinkled, was close to mine. The suddenly shrewd, mottled brown eyes regarded me steadily for a few seconds then he turned away quickly. 'Right,' he said. 'Come in and have a drink.'

Phin stumped into the farm kitchen ahead of me, threw back his head and let loose a bellow that shook the windows. 'Mother! Feller 'ere wants a glass o' beer. Come and meet Happy Harry!'

Mrs Calvert appeared with magical speed and put down glasses and bottles. I glanced at the labels – 'Smith's Nutty Brown Ale', and filled my glass. It was a historic moment though I didn't know it then; it was the first of an incredible series of Nutty Browns I was to drink at that table.

Mrs Calvert sat down for a moment, crossed her hands on her lap and smiled encouragingly. 'Can you do anything for the calves, then?' she asked.

Phin butted in before I could reply. 'Oh aye, he can an' all. He's put them on to epsom salts.'

'Epsom salts?'

'That's it, Missis. I said when he came that we'd get summat real smart and scientific like. You can't beat new blood and modern ideas.' Phin sipped his beer gravely.

Over the following days the calves gradually improved and at the end of a fortnight they were all eating normally. The worst one still showed a trace of blindness, but I was confident this too would clear up.

It wasn't long before I saw Phin again. It was early afternoon and I was in the office with Siegfried when the outer door banged and the passage echoed to the clumping of hob nails. I heard a voice raised in song – hi-ti-tiddly-rum-te-tum. Phineas was in our midst once more.

'Well, well, well!' he bawled heartily at Miss Harbottle. 'It's Flossie! And what's my little darlin' doing this fine day?'

There was not a flicker from Miss Harbottle's granite features. She directed an icy stare at the intruder but Phin swung round on Siegfried with a yellow-toothed grin. 'Now, gaffer, 'ow's tricks?'

'Everything's fine, Mr Calvert,' Siegfried replied. 'What can we do for you?'

Phin stabbed a finger at me. 'There's my man. I want him out to my place right sharpish.'

'What's the trouble?' I asked. 'Is it the calves again?'

'Damn, no! Wish it was. It's me good bull. He's puffin' like a bellows – bit like pneumonia but worse than I've known. He's in a 'ell of a state. Looks like he's peggin' out.' For an instant Phin lost his jocularity.

I had heard of this bull; pedigree shorthorn, show winner,

the foundation of his herd. 'I'll be right after you, Mr Calvert. I'll follow you along.'

'Good lad. I'm off, then.' Phin paused at the door, a wild figure, tireless, tattered; baggy trousers ballooning from his ample middle. He turned again to Miss Harbottle and contorted his leathery features into a preposterous leer. 'Ta-ra, Floss!' he cried and was gone.

For a moment the room seemed very empty and quiet except for Miss Harbottle's acid 'Oh, that man! Dreadful! Dreadful!'

I made good time to the farm and found Phin waiting with his three sons. The young men looked gloomy but Phin was still indomitable. 'Here 'e is!' he shouted. 'Happy Harry again. Now we'll be all right.' He even managed a little tune as we crossed to the bull pen but when he looked over the door his head sank on his chest and his hands worked deeper behind his braces.

The bull was standing as though rooted to the middle of the pen. His great rib cage rose and fell with the most laboured respirations I had ever seen. His mouth gaped wide, a bubbling foam hung round his lips and his flaring nostrils; his eyes, almost starting from his head in terror, stared at the wall in front of him. This wasn't pneumonia, it was a frantic battle for breath; and it looked like a losing one.

He didn't move when I inserted my thermometer and though my mind was racing I suspected the half minute wasn't going to be long enough this time. I had expected accelerated breathing, but nothing like this.

'Poor aud beggar,' Phin muttered. 'He's bred me the finest calves I've ever had and he's quiet as a sheep, too. I've seen me little grandchildren walk under 'is belly and he's took no notice. I hate to see him sufferin' like this. If you can't do no good, just tell me and I'll get the gun out.'

I took the thermometer out and read it. One hundred and ten degrees fahrenheit. This was ridiculous; I shook it vigorously and pushed it back into the rectum.

I gave it nearly a minute this time so that I could get in some extra thinking. The second reading said a hundred and ten again and I had an unpleasant conviction that if the thermometer had been a foot long the mercury would still have been jammed against the top.

What in the name of God was this? Could be Anthrax ... must be ... and yet ... I looked over at the row of heads above the half door; they were waiting for me to say something and their silence accentuated the agonized groaning and panting. I looked above the heads to the square of deep blue and a tufted cloud moving across the sun. As it passed, a single dazzling ray made me close my eyes and a faint bell rang in my mind.

'Has he been out today?' I asked.

'Aye, he's been out on the grass on his tether all morning. It was that grand and warm.'

The bell became a triumphant gong. 'Get a hosepipe in here quick. You can rig it to that tap in the yard.'

'A hosepipe? What the 'ell ...?'

'Yes, quick as you can – he's got sunstroke.'

They had the hose fixed in less than a minute. I turned it full on and began to play the jet of cold water all over the huge form – his face and neck, along the ribs, up and down the legs. I kept this up for about five minutes but it seemed a lot longer as I waited for some sign of improvement. I was beginning to think I was on the wrong track when the bull gulped just once.

It was something – he had been unable to swallow his saliva before in his desperate efforts to get the air into his lungs; and I really began to notice a change in the big animal. Surely he was looking just a little less distressed and wasn't the breathing slowing down a bit?

Then the bull shook himself, turned his head and looked at us. There was an awed whisper from one of the young men: 'By gaw, it's working!'

I enjoyed myself after that. I can't think of anything in my working life that has given me more pleasure than standing in that pen directing the life-saving jet and watching the bull savouring it. He liked it on his face best and as I worked my way up from the tail and along the steaming back he would turn his nose full into the water, rocking his head from side to side and blinking blissfully.

Within half an hour he looked almost normal. His chest was still heaving a little but he was in no discomfort. I tried the temperature again. Down to a hundred and five.

'He'll be all right now,' I said, 'but I think one of the lads should keep the water on him for another twenty minutes or so. I'll have to go now.'

'You've time for a drink,' Phin grunted.

In the farm kitchen his bellow of 'Mother' lacked some of its usual timbre. He dropped into a chair and stared into his glass of Nutty Brown. 'Harry,' he said, 'I'll tell you, you've flummoxed me this time.' He sighed and rubbed his chin in apparent disbelief. 'I don't know what the 'ell to say to you.'

It wasn't often that Phin lost his voice, but he found it again very soon at the next meeting of the farmers' discussion group.

A learned and earnest gentleman had been expounding on the advances in veterinary medicine and how the farmers could now expect their stock to be treated as the doctors treated their human patients, with the newest drugs and procedures.

It was too much for Phin. He jumped to his feet and cried: 'Ah think you're talking a lot of rubbish. There's a young feller in Darrowby not long out of college and it doesn't matter what you call 'im out for he uses nowt but epsom salts and cold water.'

CHAPTER TWENTY-SEVEN

It was during one of Siegfried's efficiency drives that Colonel Merrick's cow picked up a wire. The colonel was a personal friend, which made things even more uncomfortable.

Everybody suffered when Siegfried had these spells. They usually came on after he had been reading a technical work or when he had seen a film of some new technical procedure. He would rampage around, calling on the cowering household to stir themselves and be better men. He would be obsessed, for a time, with the craving for perfection.

'We must put on a better show at these operations on the farms. It just isn't good enough to fish out a few old instruments from a bag and start hacking at the animal. We must have cleanliness, asepsis if possible, and an orderly technique.'

So he was jubilant when he diagnosed traumatic reticulitis (foreign body in the second stomach) in the colonel's cow. 'We'll really show old Hubert something. We'll give him a picture of veterinary surgery he'll never forget.'

Tristan and I were pressed into service as assistants, and our arrival at the farm was really impressive. Siegfried led the procession, looking unusually smart in a brand new tweed jacket of which he was very proud. He was a debonair figure as he shook hands with his friend.

The colonel was jovial. 'Hear you're going to operate on my cow. Take out a wire, eh? Like to watch you do it, if it's all right with you.'

'By all means, Hubert, please do. You'll find it very interesting.'

In the byre, Tristan and I had to bustle about. We arranged tables alongside the cow and on these we placed new metal trays with rows of shining, sterilized instruments. Scalpels, directors, probes, artery forceps, hypodermic syringes, suture needles, gut and silk in glass phials, rolls of cotton wool and various bottles of spirit and other antiseptics.

Siegfried fussed around, happy as a schoolboy. He had clever hands and, as a surgeon, he was worth watching. I could read his mind without much trouble. This, he was thinking, was going to be good.

When all was to his liking, he took off his jacket and donned a brilliantly white smock. He handed the jacket to Tristan and almost instantly gave a roar of anger. 'Hey, don't just throw it down on that meal bin! Here, give it to me. I'll find a safe place for it.' He dusted the new garment down tenderly and hung it on a nail on the wall.

Meanwhile, I had shaved and disinfected the operation site on the flank and everything was ready for the local anaesthetic. Siegfried took the syringe and quickly infiltrated the area. 'This is where we go inside, Hubert. I hope you aren't squeamish.'

The colonel beamed. 'Oh, I've seen blood before. You needn't worry, I shan't faint.'

With a bold sweep of the scalpel, Siegfried incised the skin, then the muscles and finally, with delicate care, the glistening peritoneum. The smooth wall of the rumen (the large first stomach) lay exposed.

Siegfried reached for a fresh scalpel and looked for the best place to cut in. But as he poised his knife, the wall of the rumen suddenly bulged out through the skin incision. 'Unusual,' he muttered. 'Probably a bit of rumenal gas.' Unflurried, he gently thrust back the protrusion and prepared again to make his cut; but as he withdrew his hand, the rumen welled out after it, a pinkish mass bigger than a football. Siegfried pushed it back and it shot out again immediately, ballooning to a startling size. This time, he took two hands to the job, pushing and pressing till he forced the thing once more out of sight. He stood for a moment with his hands inside the cow, breathing heavily. Two beads of sweat trickled down his forehead.

Carefully, he withdrew his hands. Nothing happened. It must have settled down. He was reaching back for his knife when, like a live thing, the rumen again came leaping and surging out. It seemed almost as though the entire organ had escaped through the incision – a slippery, gleaming mass rising and swelling till it was level with his eyes.

Siegfried had dropped all pretence of calm and was fighting desperately, both arms round the thing, pressing downwards with all his strength. I hastened forward to help and, as I drew near, he whispered hoarsely: 'What the hell is it?' Clearly, he was wondering if this pulsating heap of tissue was some part of the bovine anatomy he had never even heard of.

Silently, we fought the mass down till it was level with the skin. The colonel was watching intently. He hadn't expected the operation to be so interesting. His eyebrows were slightly raised.

'It must be gas that's doing this,' panted Siegfried. 'Pass me the knife and stand back.'

He inserted the knife into the rumen and cut sharply downwards. I was glad I had moved away because, through the incision shot a high pressure jet of semi-liquid stomach contents – a greenish-brown, foul-smelling cascade which erupted from the depths of the cow as from an invisible pump.

The first direct hit was on Siegfried's face. He couldn't release his hold of the rumen or it would have slipped back into the abdomen and contaminated the peritoneum. So he hung on to each side of the opening while the evil torrent poured onto his hair, down his neck and all over his lovely white smock.

Now and then, the steady stream would be varied by a sudden explosion which sent the fermenting broth spouting viciously over everything in the immediate vicinity. Within a minute, the trays with their gleaming instruments were thoroughly covered. The tidy rows of swabs, the snowy tufts of cotton wool disappeared without trace, but it was the unkindest cut of all when a particular powerful jet sent a liberal spray over the new jacket hanging on the wall. Siegfried's face was too obscured for me to detect any change of expression but at this disaster, I saw real anguish in his eyes.

The colonel's eyebrows were now raised to the maximum and his mouth hung open as he gazed in disbelief at the chaotic scene. Siegfried, still hanging grimly on, was the centre of it all, paddling about in a reeking swamp which came halfway up his Wellington boots. He looked like a Fiji Islander with his hair stiffened and frizzled and his eyes rolling whitely in the brown face.

Eventually, the flood slowed to a trickle and stopped. I was able to hold the lips of the wound while Siegfried inserted his arm and felt his way to the reticulum. I watched him as he groped inside the honeycombed organ far out of sight against the diaphragm. A satisfied grunt told me he had located the piercing wire and within seconds he had removed it.

Tristan had been frantically salvaging and washing suture materials and soon the incision in the rumen was stitched. Siegfried's heroic stand had not been in vain; there was no contamination of the peritoneum.

Silently and neatly, he secured the skin and muscles with retention sutures and swabbed round the wound. Everything looked fine. The cow seemed unperturbed; under the anaesthetic she had known nothing of the titanic struggle with her insides. In fact, freed from the discomfort of the transfixing wire, she appeared already to be feeling better.

It took quite a time to tidy up the mess and the most difficult job was to make Siegfried presentable. We did our best by swilling him down with buckets of water while, all the time, he scraped sadly at his new jacket with a flat stick. It didn't make much difference.

The colonel was hearty and full of congratulations. 'Come in, my dear chap. Come in and have a drink.' But the invitation had a hollow ring and he took care to stand at least ten feet away from his friend.

Siegfried threw his bedraggled jacket over his shoulder. 'No thank you, Hubert. It's most kind of you, but we must be off.' He went out of the byre. 'I think you'll find the cow will be eating in a day or two. I'll be back in a fortnight to take out the stitches.'

In the confined space of the car, Tristan and I were unable to get as far away from him as we could have liked. Even with our heads stuck out of the windows it was still pretty bad.

Siegfried drove for a mile or two in silence, then he turned to me and his streaked features broke into a grin. There was something indomitable about him. 'You never know what's round the corner in this game, my boys, but just think of this – that operation was a success.'

CHAPTER TWENTY-EIGHT

There were three of us in the cheerless yard, Isaac Cranford, Jeff Mallock and myself. The only one who looked at ease was Mallock and it was fitting that it should be so, since he was, in a manner of speaking, the host. He owned the knacker yard and he looked on benignly as we peered into the carcass of the cow he had just opened.

In Darrowby the name Mallock had a ring of doom. It was the graveyard of livestock, of farmers' ambitions, of veterinary surgeons' hopes. If ever an animal was very ill somebody was bound to say: 'I reckon she'll be off to Mallock's afore long,' or 'Jeff Mallock'll have 'er in t' finish.' And the premises fitted perfectly into the picture; a group of drab, red-brick buildings standing a few fields back from the road with a stumpy chimney from which rolled endlessly a dolorous black smoke.

It didn't pay to approach Mallock's too closely unless you had a strong stomach, so the place was avoided by the townspeople, but if you ventured up the lane and peeped through the sliding metal doors you could look in on a nightmare world.

Dead animals lay everywhere. Most of them were dismembered and great chunks of meat hung on hooks, but here and there you could see a bloated sheep or a greenish, swollen pig which not even Jeff could bring himself to open.

Skulls and dry bones were piled to the roof in places and brown mounds of meat stood in the corners. The smell was bad at any time but when Jeff was boiling up the carcasses it was indescribable. The Mallock family bungalow stood in the middle of the buildings and strangers could be pardoned if they expected a collection of wizened gnomes to dwell there. But Jeff was a pink-faced, cherubic man in his forties, his wife plump, smiling and comely. Their family ranged from a positively beautiful girl of nineteen down to a robust five year old boy. There were eight young Mallocks and they had spent their lifetimes playing among tuberculous lungs and a vast spectrum of bacteria from Salmonella to Anthrax. They were the healthiest children in the district.

It was said in the pubs that Jeff was one of the richest men in the town but the locals, as they supped their beer, had to admit that he earned his money. At any hour of the day or night he would rattle out into the country in his ramshackle lorry, winch on a carcass, bring it back to the yard and cut it up. A dog food dealer came twice a week from Brawton with a van and bought the fresh meat. The rest of the stuff Jeff shovelled into his boiler to make the meat meal which was in great demand for mixing in pig and poultry rations. The bones went for making fertilizer, the hides to the tanner and the nameless odds and ends were collected by a wild-eyed individual known only as the 'ket feller'. Sometimes, for a bit of variety, Jeff would make long slabs of strange-smelling soap which found a brisk sale for scrubbing shop floors. Yes, people said, there was no doubt Jeff did all right. But, by gaw, he earned it.

My contacts with Mallock were fairly frequent. A knacker's yard had a useful function for a vet. It served as a crude post mortem room, a place where he could check on his diagnosis in fatal cases; and on occasions where he had been completely baffled, the mysteries would be revealed under Jeff's knife.

Often, of course, farmers would send in an animal which I had been treating and ask Jeff to tell them 'what had been wrong wi't' and this was where a certain amount of friction arose. Because Jeff was placed in a position of power and seldom resisted the temptation to wield it. Although he could neither read nor write, he was a man of great professional pride; he didn't like to be called a knacker man but preferred 'fell-monger'. He considered in his heart that, after twenty odd years of cutting up diseased animals he knew more than any vet alive, and it made things rather awkward that the farming community unhesitatingly agreed with him.

It never failed to spoil my day if a farmer called in at the surgery and told me that, once more, Jeff Mallock had confounded my diagnosis. 'Hey, remember that cow you were treating for magnesium deficiency? She never did no good and ah sent 'er into Mallocks. Well, you know what was really the matter wi' 'er? Worm i' the tail. Jeff said if you'd nobbut cut tail off, that cow would have gotten up and walked away.' It was no good arguing or saying there was no such thing as worm in the tail. Jeff knew – that was all about it.

If only Jeff had taken his priceless opportunities to acquire a commonsense knowledge it wouldn't have been so bad. But instead, he had built up a weird pathology of his own and backed it up by black magic remedies gleaned from his contacts with the more primitive members of the farming community. His four stock diseases were Stagnation of t'lungs, Black Rot, Gastric Ulsters and Golf Stones. It was a quartet which made the vets tremble for miles around.

Another cross which the vets had to bear was his unique gift of being able to take one look at a dead animal on a farm and pronounce immediately on the cause of death. The farmers, awe-struck by his powers, were always asking me why I couldn't do it. But I was unable to dislike the man. He would have had to be more than human to resist the chance to be important and there was no malice in his actions. Still, it made things uncomfortable at times and I liked to be on the spot myself whenever possible. Especially when Isaac Cranford was involved.

Cranford was a hard man, a man who had cast his life in a mould of iron austerity. A sharp bargainer, a win-at-all-cost character and, in a region where thrift was general, he was noted for meanness. He farmed some of the best land in the lower Dale, his Shorthorns won prizes regularly at the shows but he was nobody's friend. Mr Bateson, his neighbour to the North, summed it up: 'That feller 'ud skin a flea for its hide.' Mr Dickon, his neighbour to the South, put it differently: 'If he gets haud on a pound note, by gaw it's a prisoner.'

This morning's meeting had had its origin the previous day. A phone call mid afternoon from Mr Cranford. 'I've had a cow struck by lightning. She's laid dead in the field.'

I was surprised. 'Lightning? Are you sure? We haven't had a storm today.'

'Maybe you haven't, but we have 'ere.'

'Mmm, all right, I'll come and have a look at her.'

Driving to the farm, I couldn't work up much enthusiasm for the impending interview. This lightning business could be a bit of a headache. All farmers were insured against lightning stroke – it was usually part of their fire policy – and after a severe thunder storm it was common enough for the vets' phones to start ringing with requests to examine dead beasts.

The insurance companies were reasonable about it. If they received a certificate from the vet that he believed lightning to be the cause of death they would usually pay up without fuss. In cases of doubt they would ask for a post mortem or a second opinion from another practitioner. The difficulty was that there are no diagnostic post mortem features to go on; occasionally a bruising of the tissues under the skin, but very little else. The happiest situation was when the beast was found with the tell-tale scorch marks running from an ear down the leg to earth into the ground. Often the animal would be found under a tree which itself had obviously been blasted and torn by lightning. Diagnosis was easy then.

Ninety-nine per cent of the farmers were looking only for a square deal and if their vet found some other clear cause of death they would accept his verdict philosophically. But the odd one could be very difficult.

I had heard Siegfried tell of one old chap who had called him out to verify a lightning death. The long scorch marks on the carcass were absolutely classical and Siegfried, viewing them, had been almost lyrical. 'Beautiful, Charlie, beautiful, I've never seen more typical marks. But there's just one thing.' He put an arm round the old man's shoulder. 'What a great pity you let the candle grease fall on the skin.'

The old man looked closer and thumped a fist into his palm. 'Dang it, you're right, maister! Ah've mucked t'job up. And ah took pains ower it an' all – been on for dang near an hour.' He walked away muttering. He showed no embarrassment, only disgust at his own technological shortcomings.

But this, I thought, as the stone walls flipped past the car windows, would be very different. Cranford was in the habit of getting his own way, right or wrong, and if he didn't get it today there would be trouble.

I drove through the farm gate and along a neat tarmac road across the single field. Mr Cranford was standing motionless in the middle of the yard and I was struck, not for the first time, by the man's resemblance to a big, hungry bird. The hunched narrow shoulders, the forward-thrust, sharp-beaked face, the dark overcoat hanging loosely on the bony frame. I wouldn't have been surprised if he had spread his wings and flapped his way on to the byre roof. Instead, he nodded impatiently at me and began to hasten with short, tripping steps to a field at the back of the house.

It was a large field and the dead cow lay almost in the centre. There were no trees, no hedges, not even a small bush. My hopeful picture of the body under a stricken tree melted immediately, leaving an anxious void.

We stopped beside the cow and Mr Cranford was the first to speak. 'Bound to be lightning. Can't be owt else. Nasty storm, then this good beast dropping down dead.'

I looked at the grass around the big Shorthorn. It had been churned and torn out, leaving patches of bare earth. 'But it hasn't exactly dropped down, has it? It died in convulsions – you can see where its feet have kicked out the grass.'

'All right then, it 'ad a convulsion, but it was lightning that caused it.' Mr Cranford had fierce little eyes and they darted flitting glances at my shirt collar, macintosh belt, Wellingtons. He never could quite bring himself to look anybody in the eye.

'I doubt it, Mr Cranford. One of the signs of lightning stroke is that the beast has fallen without a struggle. Some of them even have grass in their mouths.'

'Oh, I know all about that,' Cranford snapped, his thin face flushing. 'I've been among livestock for half a century and this isn't the first beast I've seen that's been struck. They're not all t'same, you know.'

'Oh, I realize that, but, you see, this death could have been caused by so many things.'

'What sort o' things?'

'Well, Anthrax for a start, magnesium deficiency, heart trouble – there's quite a list. I really think we ought to do a post mortem to make sure.'

'Now see here, are you saying I'm trying to do summat I shouldn't?'

'Not at all. I'm only saying we should make sure before I write a certificate. We can go and see her opened at Mallock's and, believe me, if there's no other obvious cause of death you'll get the benefit of the doubt. The insurance people are pretty good about it.'

Mr Cranford's predatory features sank lower into his coat collar. He dug his hands viciously into his pockets. 'I've had vitneries at these jobs afore. Proper, experienced vitneries, too.' The little eyes flashed in the direction of my left ear.

'They've never messed about like this. What's the use of going to all that trouble? Why do you have to be so damn particular?'

Why indeed, I thought. Why make an enemy of this man? He wielded a lot of power in the district. Prominent in the local Farmers' Union, a member of every agricultural committee for miles around. He was a wealthy, successful man and, if people didn't like him they respected his knowledge and listened to him. He could do a young vet a lot of harm. Why not write the certificate and go home? This is to certify that I have examined that above mentioned animal and, in my opinion, lightning stroke was the cause of death. It would be easy and Cranford would be mollified. It would be the end of the whole thing. Why antagonize this dangerous character for nothing? Maybe it really was lightning, anyway.

I turned to face Mr Cranford, trying in vain to look into his eyes that always veered away at the last moment. 'I'm sorry, but I feel we ought to have a look inside this cow. I'll ring Mallock and ask him to pick her up and we can see her in the morning. I'll meet you there at ten o'clock. Will that be all right?'

'Reckon it'll have to be,' Cranford spat out. 'It's a piece o' nonsense, but I suppose I've got to humour you. But just let me remind you – this was a good cow, worth all of eighty pounds. I can't afford to lose that amount of money. I want my rights.'

'I'm sure you'll get them, Mr Cranford. And before I have her moved I'd better take a blood film to eliminate Anthrax.'

The farmer had been under a mounting load of pressure. As a pillar of the methodist chapel his range of language was restricted, so he vented his pent up feelings by kicking out savagely at the carcass. His toe made contact with the unyielding backbone and he hopped around on one leg for a few seconds. Then he limped off towards the house.

I was alone as I nicked the dead ear with my knife and drew a film of blood across a couple of glass slides. It hadn't been a happy session and the one tomorrow didn't hold out much more promise. I enclosed the blood films carefully in a card-board box and set off for Skeldale House to examine them under the microscope.

So it wasn't a particularly cheerful group which assembled at the knacker yard the following morning. Even Jeff, though he preserved his usual Buddha-like expression, was, in fact, deeply offended. The account he had given me when I first arrived at the yard was fragmentary, but I could piece the scene together. Jeff, leaping from his lorry at Cranford's, sweeping the carcass with a piercing glance and making his brilliant spot diagnosis. 'Stagnation o' t'lungs. I can allus tell by the look in their eyes and the way their hair lies along t'back.' Waiting confidently for the wondering gasps, the congratulatory speeches which always followed his tour de force.

Then Mr Cranford, almost dancing with rage. 'Shut your big, stupid mouth, Mallock, tha knows nowt about it. This cow was struck by lightning and you'd better remember that.'

And now, bending my head over the carcass, I couldn't find a clue anyway. No sign of bruising when the skin was removed. The internal organs clean and normal.

I straightened up and pushed my fingers through my hair. The boiler bubbled softly, puffing out odoriferous wisps into the already highly charged atmosphere. Two dogs licked busily at a pile of meat meal.

Then a chill of horror struck through me. The dogs had competition. A little boy with golden curls was pushing a fore-finger into the heap, inserting it in his mouth and sucking with rapt enjoyment.

'Look at that!' I quavered.

The knacker man's face lit up with paternal pride. 'Aye,' he said happily. 'It isn't only the four-legged 'uns wot likes my meal. Wonderful stuff – full of nourishment!'

His good humour completely restored, he struck a match

and began to puff appreciatively at a short pipe which was thickly encrusted with evidence of his grisly trade.

I dragged my attention back to the job in hand. 'Cut into the heart, will you, Jeff,' I said.

Jeff deftly sliced the big organ from top to bottom and I knew immediately that my search was over. The auricles and ventricles were almost completely occluded by a cauliflower-like mass growing from the valves. Verrucose endocarditis, common in pigs but seldom seen in cattle.

'There's what killed your cow, Mr Cranford,' I said.

Cranford aimed his nose at the heart. 'Fiddlesticks! You're not telling me them little things could kill a beast like that.'

'They're not so little. Big enough to stop the flow of blood. I'm sorry, but there's no doubt about it – your cow died of heart failure.'

'And how about lightning?'

'No sign of it, I'm afraid. You can see for yourself.'

'And what about my eighty pounds?'

'I'm truly sorry about that, but it doesn't alter the facts.'

'Facts! What facts? I've come along this morning and you've shown me nowt to make me change my opinion.'

'Well, there's nothing more I can say. It's a clear cut case.'

Mr Cranford stiffened in his perching stance. He held his hands against the front of his coat and the fingers and thumbs rubbed together unceasingly as though fondling the beloved bank notes which were slipping away from him. His face, sunk deeper in his collar, appeared still sharper in outline.

Then he turned to me and made a ghastly attempt to smile. And his eyes, trained on my lapels, tried valiantly to inch their way upwards. There was a fleeting instance when they met my gaze before flickering away in alarm.

He drew me to one side and addressed himself to my larynx. There was a wheedling note in the hoarse whisper.

'Now look here, Mr Herriot, we're both men of the world. You know as well as I do that the insurance company can afford this loss a lot better nor me. So why can't you just say it is lightning?'

'Even though I think it isn't?'

'Well, what the hangment does it matter? You can say it is, can't you? Nobody's going to know.'

I scratched my head. 'But what would bother me, Mr Cranford, is that I would know.'

'You would know?' The farmer was mystified.

'That's right. And it's no good – I can't give you a certificate for this cow and that's the end of it.'

Dismay, disbelief, frustration chased across Mr Cranford's features. 'Well, I'll tell you this. I'm not leaving the matter here. I'm going to see your boss about you.' He swung round and pointed at the cow. 'There's no sign of disease there. Trying to tell me it's all due to little things in the heart. You don't know your job – you don't even know what them things are!'

Jeff Mallock removed his unspeakable pipe from his mouth. 'But ah know. It's what ah said. Stagnation o' t'lungs is caused by milk from milk vein getting back into the body. Finally it gets to t'heart and then it's over wi't. Them's milk clots you're looking at.'

Cranford rounded on him. 'Shut up, you great gumph! You're as bad as this feller here. It was lightning killed my good cow. Lightning!' He was almost screaming. Then he controlled himself and spoke quietly to me. 'You'll hear more of this, Mr Knowledge, and I'll just tell you one thing. You'll never walk on my farm again.' He turned and hurried away with his quick-stepping gait.

I said good morning to Jeff and climbed wearily into my car. Well, everything had worked out just great. If only vetting just consisted of treating sick animals. But it didn't. There were so many other things. I started the engine and drove away.

CHAPTER TWENTY-NINE

It didn't take Mr Cranford long to make good his threat. He called at the surgery shortly after lunch the following day and Siegfried and I, enjoying a post prandial cigarette in the sitting-room, heard the jangle of the door bell. We didn't get up, because most of the farmers walked in after ringing.

The dogs, however, went into their usual routine. They had had a long run on the high moor that morning and had just finished licking out their dinner bowls. Tired and distended, they had collapsed in a snoring heap around Siegfried's feet. There was nothing they wanted more than ten minutes' peace but, dedicated as they were to their self appointed role of fierce guardians of the house, they did not hesitate. They leaped, baying, from the rug and hurled themselves into the passage.

People often wondered why Siegfried kept five dogs. Not only kept them but took them everywhere with him. Driving on his rounds it was difficult to see him at all among the shaggy heads and waving tails; and anybody approaching the car would recoil in terror from the savage barking and the bared fangs and glaring eyes framed in the windows.

'I cannot for the life of me understand,' Siegfried would declare, thumping his fist on his knee, 'why people keep dogs as pets. A dog should have a useful function. Let it be used for farm work, for shooting, for guiding; but why anybody should keep the things just hanging around the place beats me.'

It was a pronouncement he was continually making, often through a screen of flapping ears and lolling tongues as he sat in his car. His listener would look wonderingly from the huge greyhound to the tiny terrier, from the spaniel to the whippet to the Scottie; but nobody ever asked Siegfried why he kept his own dogs.

I judged that the pack fell upon Mr Cranford about the bend

of the passage and many a lesser man would have fled; but I could hear him fighting his way doggedly forward. When he came through the sitting-room door he had removed his hat and was beating the dogs off with it. It wasn't a wise move and the barking rose to a higher pitch. The man's eyes stared and his lips moved continuously, but nothing came through.

Siegfried, courteous as ever, rose and indicated a chair. His lips, too, were moving, no doubt in a few gracious words of welcome. Mr Cranford flapped his black coat, swooped across the carpet and perched. The dogs sat in a ring round him and yelled up into his face. Usually they collapsed after their exhausting performance but there was something in the look or smell of Mr Cranford that they didn't like.

Siegfried leaned back in his chair, put his fingers together and assumed a judicial expression. Now and again he nodded understandingly or narrowed his eyes as if taking an interesting point. Practically nothing could be heard from Mr Cranford but occasionally a word or phrase penetrated.

'... have a serious complaint to make ...'

'... doesn't know his job ...'

'... can't afford ... not a rich man ...'

'... these danged dogs ...'

'... won't have 'im again ...'

'... down dog, get by ...'

'... nowt but robbery ...'

Siegfried, completely relaxed and apparently oblivious of the din, listened attentively but as the minutes passed I could see the strain beginning to tell on Mr Cranford. His eyes began to start from their sockets and the veins corded on his scrawny neck as he tried to get his message across. Finally it was too much for him; he jumped up and a leaping brown tide bore him to the door. He gave a last defiant cry, lashed out again with his hat and was gone.

Pushing open the dispensary door a few weeks later, I found my boss mixing an ointment. He was working with great care, turning and returning the glutinous mass on a marble slab.

'What's this you're doing?' I asked.

Siegfried threw down his spatula and straightened his back. 'Ointment for a boar.' He looked past me at Tristan who had just come in. 'And I don't know why the hell I'm doing it when some people are sitting around on their backsides.' He indicated the spatula. 'Right, Tristan, you can have a go. When you've finished your cigarette, that is.'

His expression softened as Tristan hastily nipped out his Woodbine and began to work away on the slab. 'Pretty stiff concoction, that. Takes a bit of mixing,' Siegfried said with satisfaction, looking at his brother's bent head. 'The back of my neck was beginning to ache with it.'

He turned to me. 'By the way, you'll be interested to hear it's for your old friend Cranford. For that prize boar of his. It's got a nasty sore across its back and he's worried to death about it. Wins him a lot of money at the shows and a blemish there would be disastrous.'

'Cranford's still with us, then.'

'Yes, it's a funny thing, but we can't get rid of him. I don't like losing clients but I'd gladly make an exception of this chap. He won't have you near the place after that lightning job and he makes it very clear he doesn't think much of me either. Tells me I never do his beasts any good – says it would have been a lot better if he'd never called me. And moans like hell when he gets his bill. He's more bother than he's worth and on top of everything he gives me the creeps. But he won't leave – he damn well won't leave.'

'He knows which side his bread's buttered,' I said. 'He gets first rate service and the moaning is part of the system to keep the bills down.'

'Maybe you're right, but I wish there was a simple way to get rid of him.' He tapped Tristan on the shoulder. 'All right, don't strain yourself. That'll do. Put it into this ointment box and label it: "Apply liberally to the boar's back three times daily, working it well in with the fingers." And post it to Mr

Cranford. And while you're on, will you post this faeces sample to the laboratory at Leeds to test for Johne's disease.' He held out a treacle tin brimming with foul-smelling, liquid diarrhoea.

It was a common thing to collect such samples and send them away for Johne's tests, worm counts, etc, and there was always one thing all the samples had in common – they were very large. All that was needed for the tests was a couple of teaspoonfuls but the farmers were lavish in their quantities. They seemed pleasantly surprised that all the vet wanted was a bit of muck from the dung channel; they threw aside their natural caution and shovelled the stuff up cheerfully into the biggest container they could find. They brushed aside all protests; 'take plenty, we've lots of it' was their attitude.

Tristan took hold of the tin gingerly and began to look along the shelves. 'We don't seem to have any of those little glass sample jars.'

'That's right, we're out of them,' said Siegfried. 'I meant to order some more. But never mind – shove the lid on that tin and press it down tight, then parcel it up well in brown paper. It'll travel to the lab all right.'

It took only three days for Mr Cranford's name to come up again. Siegfried was opening the morning mail, throwing the circulars to one side and making a pile of the bills and receipts when he became suddenly very still. He had frozen over a letter on blue notepaper and he sat like a statue till he read it through. At length he raised his head; his face was expressionless. 'James, this is just about the most vitriolic letter I have ever read. It's from Cranford. He's finished with us for good and all and is considering taking legal action against us.'

'What have we done this time?' I asked.

'He accuses us of grossly insulting him and endangering the health of his boar. He says we sent him a treacle tin full of cow shit with instructions to rub it on the boar's back three times daily.'

Tristan, who had been sitting with his eyes half closed, became fully awake. He rose unhurriedly and began to make his way towards the door. His hand was on the knob when his brother's voice thundered out.

'Tristan! Come back here! Sit down – I think we have something to talk about.'

Tristan looked up resolutely, waiting for the storm to break, but Siegfried was unexpectedly calm. His voice was gentle.

'So you've done it again. When will I ever learn that I can't trust you to carry out the simplest task. It wasn't much to ask, was it? Two little parcels to post – hardly a tough assignment. But you managed to botch it. You got the labels wrong, didn't you?'

Tristan wriggled in his chair. 'I'm sorry, I can't think how . . .'

Siegfried held up his hand. 'Oh, don't worry. Your usual luck has come to your aid. With anybody else this bloomer would be catastrophic but with Cranford – it's like divine providence.' He paused for a moment and a dreamy expression crept into his eyes. 'The label said to work it well in with the fingers, I seem to recall. And Mr Cranford says he opened the package at the breakfast table . . . Yes, Tristan, I think you have found the way. This, I do believe, has done it.'

I said, 'But how about the legal action?'

'Oh, I think we can forget about that. Mr Cranford has a great sense of his own dignity. Just think how it would sound in court.' He crumpled the letter and dropped it into the waste paper basket. 'Well, let's get on with some work.'

He led the way out and stopped abruptly in the passage. He turned to face us. 'There's another thing, of course. I wonder how the lab is making out, testing that ointment for Johne's disease?'

CHAPTER THIRTY

I was really worried about Tricki this time. I had pulled up my car when I saw him in the street with his mistress and I was shocked at his appearance. He had become hugely fat, like a bloated sausage with a leg at each corner. His eyes, bloodshot and rheumy, stared straight ahead and his tongue lolled from his jaws.

Mrs Pumphrey hastened to explain. 'He was so listless, Mr Herriot. He seemed to have no energy. I thought he must be suffering from malnutrition, so I have been giving him some little extras between meals to build him up. Some calf's foot jelly and malt and cod liver oil and a bowl of Horlick's at night to make him sleep – nothing much really.'

'And did you cut down on the sweet things as I told you?'

'Oh, I did for a bit, but he seemed to be so weak. I had to relent. He does love cream cakes and chocolates so. I can't bear to refuse him.'

I looked down again at the little dog. That was the trouble. Tricki's only fault was greed. He had never been known to refuse food; he would tackle a meal at any hour of the day or night. And I wondered about all the things Mrs Pumphrey hadn't mentioned; the pâté on thin biscuits, the fudge, the rich trifles – Tricki loved them all.

'Are you giving him plenty of exercise?'

'Well, he has his little walks with me as you can see, but Hodgkin has been down with lumbago, so there has been no ring-throwing lately.'

I tried to sound severe. 'Now I really mean this. If you don't cut his food right down and give him more exercise he is going to be really ill. You must harden your heart and keep him on a very strict diet.'

Mrs Pumphrey wrung her hands. 'Oh I will, Mr Herriot. I'm sure you are right, but it is so difficult, so very difficult.' She set off, head down, along the road, as if determined to put the new regime into practice immediately.

I watched their progress with growing concern. Tricki was tottering along in his little tweed coat; he had a whole wardrobe of these coats – warm tweed or tartan ones for the cold weather and macintoshes for the wet days. He struggled on, drooping in his harness. I thought it wouldn't be long before I heard from Mrs Pumphrey.

The expected call came within a few days. Mrs Pumphrey was distraught. Tricki would eat nothing. Refused even his favourite dishes; and besides, he had bouts of vomiting. He spent all his time lying on a rug, panting. Didn't go for walks, didn't want to do anything.

I had made my plans in advance. The only way was to get Tricki out of the house for a period. I suggested that he be hospitalized for about a fortnight to be kept under observation.

The poor lady almost swooned. She had never been separated from her darling before; she was sure he would pine and die if he did not see her every day.

But I took a firm line. Tricki was very ill and this was the only way to save him; in fact, I thought it best to take him without delay and, followed by Mrs Pumphrey's wailings, I marched out to the car carrying the little dog wrapped in a blanket.

The entire staff was roused and maids rushed in and out bringing his day bed, his night bed, favourite cushions, toys and rubber rings, breakfast bowl, lunch bowl, supper bowl. Realizing that my car would never hold all the stuff, I started to drive away. As I moved off, Mrs Pumphrey, with a despairing cry, threw an armful of the little coats through the window. I looked in the mirror before I turned the corner of the drive; everybody was in tears.

Out on the road, I glanced down at the pathetic little animal gasping on the seat by my side. I patted the head and Tricki made a brave effort to wag his tail. 'Poor old lad,' I said. 'You haven't a kick in you but I think I know a cure for you.'

At the surgery, the household dogs surged round me. Tricki looked down at the noisy pack with dull eyes and, when put down, lay motionless on the carpet. The other dogs, after sniffing round him for a few seconds, decided he was an uninteresting object and ignored him.

I made up a bed for him in a warm loose box next to the one where the other dogs slept. For two days I kept an eye on him, giving him no food but plenty of water. At the end of the second day he started to show some interest in his surroundings and on the third he began to whimper when he heard the dogs in the yard.

When I opened the door, Tricki trotted out and was immediately engulfed by Joe the greyhound and his friends. After rolling him over and thoroughly inspecting him, the dogs moved off down the garden. Tricki followed them, rolling slightly with his surplus fat but obviously intrigued.

Later that day, I was present at feeding time. I watched while Tristan slopped the food into the bowls. There was the usual headlong rush followed by the sounds of high-speed eating; every dog knew that if he fell behind the others he was liable to have some competition for the last part of his meal.

When they had finished, Tricki took a walk round the shining bowls, licking casually inside one or two of them. Next day, an extra bowl was put out for him and I was pleased to see him jostling his way towards it.

From then on, his progress was rapid. He had no medicinal treatment of any kind but all day he ran about with the dogs, joining in their friendly scrimmages. He discovered the joys of being bowled over, trampled on and squashed every few minutes. He became an accepted member of the gang, an unlikely, silky little object among the shaggy crew, fighting like a tiger for his share at meal times and hunting rats in the old hen house at night. He had never had such a time in his life.

All the while, Mrs Pumphrey hovered anxiously in the background, ringing a dozen times a day for the latest bulletins. I dodged the questions about whether his cushions were being turned regularly or his correct coat worn according to the weather; but I was able to tell her that the little fellow was out of danger and convalescing rapidly.

The word 'convalescing' seemed to do something to Mrs Pumphrey. She started to bring round fresh eggs, two dozen at a time, to build up Tricki's strength. For a happy period there were two eggs each for breakfast, but when the bottles of sherry began to arrive, the real possibilities of the situation began to dawn on the household.

It was the same delicious vintage that I knew so well and it was to enrich Tricki's blood. Lunch became a ceremonial occasion with two glasses before and several during the meal. Siegfried and Tristan took turns at proposing Tricki's health and the standard of speechmaking improved daily. As the sponsor, I was always called upon to reply.

We could hardly believe it when the brandy came. Two bottles of Cordon Bleu, intended to put a final edge on Tricki's constitution. Siegfried dug out some balloon glasses belonging to his mother. I had never seen them before, but for a few nights they saw constant service as the fine spirit was rolled around, inhaled and reverently drunk.

They were days of deep content, starting well with the extra egg in the morning, bolstered up and sustained by the midday sherry and finishing luxuriously round the fire with the brandy.

It was a temptation to keep Tricki on as a permanent guest, but I knew Mrs Pumphrey was suffering and after a fortnight, felt compelled to phone and tell her that the little dog had recovered and was awaiting collection.

Within minutes, about thirty feet of gleaming black metal drew up outside the surgery. The chauffeur opened the door and I could just make out the figure of Mrs Pumphrey almost lost in the interior. Her hands were tightly clasped in front of her; her lips trembled. 'Oh, Mr Herriot, do tell me the truth. Is he really better?'

'Yes, he's fine. There's no need for you to get out of the car – I'll go and fetch him.'

I walked through the house into the garden. A mass of dogs was hurtling round and round the lawn and in their midst, ears flapping, tail waving, was the little golden figure of Tricki. In two weeks he had been transformed into a lithe, hard-muscled animal; he was keeping up well with the pack, stretching out in great bounds, his chest almost brushing the ground.

I carried him back along the passage to the front of the house. The chauffeur was still holding the car door open and when Tricki saw his mistress he took off from my arms in a tremendous leap and sailed into Mrs Pumphrey's lap. She gave a startled 'Ooh!' and then had to defend herself as he swarmed over her, licking her face and barking.

During the excitement, I helped the chauffeur to bring out the beds, toys, cushions, coats and bowls, none of which had been used. As the car moved away, Mrs Pumphrey leaned out of the window. Tears shone in her eyes. Her lips trembled.

'Oh, Mr Herriot,' she cried. 'How can I ever thank you? This is a triumph of surgery!'

CHAPTER THIRTY-ONE

I came suddenly and violently awake, my heart thudding and pounding in time with the insistent summons of the telephone. These bedside phones were undoubtedly an improvement on the old system when you had to gallop downstairs and stand shivering with your bare feet on the tiles of the passage; but this explosion a few inches from your ear in the small hours when the body was weak and the resistance low was shattering. I felt sure it couldn't be good for me.

The voice at the other end was offensively cheerful. 'I have a mare on foaling. She doesn't seem to be getting on wi' t'job. Reckon foal must be laid wrong – can you come and give me a hand?'

My stomach contracted to a tight ball. This was just a little bit too much; once out of bed in the middle of the night was bad enough, but twice was unfair, in fact it was sheer cruelty. I had had a hard day and had been glad to crawl between the sheets at midnight. I had been hauled out at one o'clock to a damned awkward calving and hadn't got back till nearly three. What was the time now? Three fifteen. Good God, I had only had a few minutes sleep. And a foaling! Twice as difficult as a calving as a rule. What a life! What a bloody awful life!

I muttered into the receiver, 'Right, Mr Dixon, I'll come straight away' and shuffled across the room, yawning and stretching, feeling the ache in my shoulders and arms. I looked down at the pile of clothing in the chair; I had taken them off, put them on again, taken them off already tonight and something in me rebelled at the thought of putting them on yet again. With a weary grunt I took my macintosh from the back of the door and donned it over my pyjamas, went downstairs to where my Wellingtons stood outside the dispensary door and stuck my feet into them. It was a warm night, what was the point of getting dressed up; I'd only have to strip off again at the farm.

I opened the back door and trailed slowly down the long garden, my tired mind only faintly aware of the fragrance that came from the darkness. I reached the yard at the bottom, opened the double doors into the lane and got the car out of the garage. In the silent town the buildings glowed whitely as the headlights swept across the shuttered shop fronts, the tight-drawn curtains. Everybody was asleep. Everybody except me, James Herriot, creeping sore and exhausted towards another spell of hard labour. Why the hell had I ever decided to become a country vet? I must have been crazy to pick a job where you worked seven days a week and through the night as well. Sometimes I felt as though the practice was a malignant, living entity; testing me, trying me out; putting the pressure on more and more to see just when at what point I would drop down dead.

It was a completely unconscious reaction which hoisted me from my bath of self pity and left me dripping on the brink, regarding the immediate future with a return of some of my natural optimism. For one thing, Dixon's place was down at the foot of the Dale just off the main road and they had that unusual luxury, electric light in the buildings. And I couldn't be all that tired; not at the age of twenty-four with all my faculties unimpaired. I'd take a bit of killing yet.

I smiled to myself and relapsed into the state of half suspended animation which was normal to me at these times; a sleepy blanketing of all the senses except those required for the job in hand. Many times over the past months I had got out of bed, driven far into the country, done my job efficiently and returned to bed without ever having been fully awake.

I was right about Dixon's. The graceful Clydesdale mare was in a well-lit loose box and I laid out my ropes and instruments with a feeling of deep thankfulness. As I tipped antiseptic into the steaming bucket I watched the mare straining and paddling her limbs. The effort produced nothing; there were no feet protruding from the vulva. There was almost certainly a malpresentation.

Still thinking hard, I removed my macintosh and was jerked out of my reverie by a shout of laughter from the farmer. 'God 'elp us, what's this, the Fol-de-rols?'

I looked down at my pyjamas which were pale blue with an arresting broad stripe. 'This, Mr Dixon,' I replied with dignity, 'is my night attire. I didn't bother to dress.'

'Oh, I see now.' The farmer's eyes glinted impishly. 'I'm sorry, but I thought I'd got the wrong chap for a second. I saw a feller just like you at Blackpool last year – same suit exactly, but he 'ad a stripy top hat too and a stick. Did a champion little dance.'

'Can't oblige you, I'm afraid,' I said with a wan smile. 'I'm just not in the mood right now.'

I stripped off, noting with interest the deep red grooves caused by the calf's teeth a couple of hours ago. Those teeth had been like razors, peeling off neat little rolls of skin every time I pushed my arm past them.

The mare trembled as I felt my way inside her. Nothing, nothing, then just a tail and the pelvic bones and the body and hind legs disappearing away beyond my reach. Breech presentation; easy in the cow for a man who knew his job but tricky in the mare because of the tremendous length of the foal's legs.

It took me a sweating, panting half hour with ropes and a blunt hook on the end of a flexible cane to bring the first leg round. The second leg came more easily and the mare seemed to know there was no obstruction now. She gave a great heave and the foal shot out onto the straw with myself, arms around its body, sprawling on top of it. To my delight I felt the small form jerking convulsively; I had felt no movement while I was working and had decided that it was dead, but the foal was very much alive, shaking its head and snorting out the placental fluid it had inhaled during its delayed entry.

When I had finished towelling myself I turned to see the farmer with an abnormally straight face, holding out my colourful jacket like a valet. 'Allow me, sir,' he said gravely.

'OK, OK,' I laughed, 'I'll get properly dressed next time.' As I was putting my things in the car boot the farmer carelessly threw a parcel on to the back seat.

'Bit o' butter for you,' he muttered. When I started the engine he bent level with the window. 'I think a bit about that mare and I've been badly wanting a foal out of her. Thank ye lad, thank ye very much.'

He waved as I moved away and I heard his parting cry. 'You did all right for a Kentucky Minstrel!'

I leaned back in my seat and peered through heavy lids at the empty road unwinding in the pale morning light. The sun had come up – a dark crimson ball hanging low over the misted fields. I felt utterly content, warm with the memory of the foal trying to struggle on to its knees, its absurdly long legs still out of control. Grand that the little beggar had been alive after all – there was something desolate about delivering a lifeless creature.

The Dixon farm was in the low country where the Dale widened out and gave on to the great plain of York. I had to cross a loop of the busy road which connected the West Riding with the industrial North East. A thin tendril of smoke rose from the chimney of the all night transport café which stood there and as I slowed down to take the corner a faint but piercing smell of cooking found its way into the car; the merest breath but rich in the imagery of fried sausages and beans and tomatoes and chips.

God, I was starving. I looked at my watch; five fifteen, I wouldn't be eating for a long time yet. I turned in among the lorries on the broad strip of tarmac.

Hastening towards the still lighted building I decided that I wouldn't be greedy. Nothing spectacular, just a nice sandwich. I had been here a few times before and the sandwiches were very good; and I deserved some nourishment after my hard night.

I stepped into the warm interior where groups of lorry drivers sat behind mounded plates, but as I crossed the floor the busy clatter died and was replaced by a tense silence. A fat man in a leather jacket sat transfixed, a loaded fork halfway to his mouth, while his neighbour, gripping a huge mug of tea in an oily hand stared with bulging eyes at my ensemble.

It occurred to me then that bright red striped pyjamas and Wellingtons might seem a little unusual in those surroundings and I hastily buttoned my macintosh which had been billowing behind me. Even closed, it was on the short side and at least a foot of pyjama leg showed above my boots.

Resolutely I strode over to the counter. An expressionless blonde bulging out of a dirty white overall on the breast pocket of which was inscribed 'Dora' regarded me blankly.

'A ham sandwich and a cup of Bovril, please,' I said huskily. As the blonde put a teaspoonful of Bovril into a cup and filled it with a hissing jet of hot water I was uncomfortably aware of the silence behind me and of the battery of eyes focused on my legs. On my right I could just see the leather jacketed man. He filled his mouth and chewed reflectively for a few moments.

'Takes all kinds, don't it Ernest,' he said in a judicial tone.

'Does indeed, Kenneth, does indeed,' replied his companion.

'Would you say, Ernest, that this is what the Yorkshire country gentleman is wearing this spring?'

'Could be, Kenneth, could be.'

Listening to the titters from the rear, I concluded that these two were the accepted café wags. Best to eat up quickly and get out. Dora pushed the thickly meated sandwich across the counter and spoke with all the animation of a sleep walker. 'That'll be a shillin'.'

I slipped my hand inside my coat and encountered the pocketless flannelette beneath. God almighty, my money was in my trousers back in Darrowby! A wave of sickly horror flooded me as I began a frantic, meaningless search through my macintosh.

I looked wildly at the blonde and saw her slip the sandwich under the counter. 'Look, I've come out without any money. I've been in here before – do you know who I am?'

Dora gave a single bored shake of her head.

'Well, never mind,' I babbled, 'I'll pop in with the money next time I'm passing.'

Dora's expression did not alter but she raised one eyebrow fractionally; she made no effort to retrieve the sandwich from its hiding place.

Escape was the only thing in my mind now. Desperately I sipped at the scalding fluid.

Kenneth pushed back his plate and began to pick his teeth with a match. 'Ernest,' he said as though coming to a weighty conclusion. 'It's my opinion that this 'ere gentleman is eccentric.'

'Eccentric?' Ernest sniggered into his tea. 'Bloody daft, more like.'

'Ah, but not so daft, Ernest. Not daft enough to pay for 'is grub.'

'You 'ave a point there, Kenneth, a definite point.'

'You bet I have. He's enjoying a nice cup of Bovril on the house and if 'e hadn't mistimed his fumble he'd be at the sandwich too. Dora moved a bit sharpish for 'im there – another five seconds and he'd have had 'is choppers in the ham.'

'True, true,' muttered Ernest, seemingly content with his role of straight man.

Kenneth put away his match, sucked his teeth noisily and leaned back. 'There's another possibility we 'aven't considered. He could be on the run.'

'Escaped convict, you mean, Kenneth.'

'I do, Ernest, I do indeed.'

'But them fellers allus have arrows on their uniforms.'

'Ah, some of 'em do. But I 'eard somewhere that some of the prisons is going in for stripes now.'

I had had enough. Tipping the last searing drops of Bovril down my throat I made headlong for the door. As I stepped out into the early sunshine Kenneth's final pronouncement reached me.

'Prob'ly got away from a working party. Look at them Wellingtons . . .'

POSTSCRIPT

I remember it was an afternoon when the sun blazed. I filled my car with Siegfried's dogs and drove to where an old mine track climbed green and inviting on the side of a steep gill. We walked a mile or two on the smooth turf then turned off and headed straight up the hillside through the hot bracken scent and the hum of flies to the very top where the wind was sweet and welcome and you could see nearly all of the Dale laid out there beneath; nearly all of it from the head where the great bare hills stood on the edge of the wild right down to the rich plain, chequered and hazy, at the foot.

I was sitting in the heather with the dogs in an expectant ring when the Dales smell came up on the breeze, the fragrance which the wind stole from the miles of warm grass and the shy flowers of the moorland. It had met me when I first stepped off the bus at Darrowby a year ago. And I realized that I had worked my way through the full cycle: I had travelled that magical first time round.

And it had all happened down there. Many of the farms in the practice were visible from where I sat; splashes of grey stone with their livestock, motionless dots from this distance, scattered in the fields around them. They were unrecognizable as the battle grounds of the past year, the scenes of my first struggles where everything had happened from heady success to abject failure.

There were people down there who thought I was a pretty fair vet, some who regarded me as an amiable idiot, a few who were convinced I was a genius and one or two who would set their dogs on me if I put a foot inside their gates.

All this in a year. What would be the position in thirty years? Well, as it turned out, very much the same.

And what of the animals around whom the whole little

drama revolves? It is a pity they cannot talk because it would be charming to have their views. There are a few things I would like to know. What do they think of their widely varying lives? What do they think of us? And do they manage to get a laugh out of it all?

It Shouldn't Happen To A Vet

To

DONALD and BRIAN SINCLAIR

Still my friends

CHAPTER ONE

I could see that Mr Handshaw didn't believe a word I was saying. He looked down at his cow and his mouth tightened into a stubborn line.

'Broken pelvis? You're trying to tell me she'll never get up n'more? Why, look at her chewing her cud! I'll tell you this, young man – me dad would've soon got her up if he'd been alive today.'

I had been a veterinary surgeon for a year now and I had learned a few things. One of them was that farmers weren't easy men to convince – especially Yorkshire Dalesmen.

And that bit about his dad. Mr Handshaw was in his fifties and I suppose there was something touching about his faith in his late father's skill and judgement. But I could have done very nicely without it.

It had acted as an additional irritant in a case in which I felt I had troubles enough. Because there are few things which get more deeply under a vet's skin than a cow which won't get up. To the layman it may seem strange that an animal can be apparently cured of its original ailment and yet be unable to rise from the floor, but it happens. And it can be appreciated that a completely recumbent milk cow has no future.

The case had started when my boss, Siegfried Farnon, who owned the practice in the little Dales market town of Darrowby, sent me to a milk fever. This suddenly occurring calcium deficiency attacks high yielding animals just after calving and causes collapse and progressive coma. When I first saw Mr Handshaw's cow she was stretched out motionless on her side, and I had to look carefully to make sure she wasn't dead.

But I got out my bottles of calcium with an airy confidence because I had been lucky enough to qualify just about the time when the profession had finally got on top of this hitherto fatal condition. The breakthrough had come many years earlier with inflation of the udder and I still carried a little blowing-up outfit around with me (the farmers used bicycle pumps), but with the advent of calcium therapy one could bask in a cheap glory by jerking an animal back from imminent death within minutes. The skill required was minimal but it looked very very good.

By the time I had injected the two bottles – one into the vein, the other under the skin – and Mr Handshaw had helped me roll the cow on to her chest the improvement was already obvious; she was looking about her and shaking her head as if wondering where she had been for the last few hours. I felt sure that if I had had the time to hang about for a bit I could see her on her feet. But other jobs were waiting.

'Give me a ring if she isn't up by dinner time,' I said, but it was a formality. I was pretty sure I wouldn't be seeing her again.

When the farmer rang at midday to say she was still down it was just a pinprick. Some cases needed an extra bottle – it would be all right. I went out and injected her again.

I wasn't really worried when I learned she hadn't got up the following day, but Mr Handshaw, hands deep in pockets, shoulders hunched as he stood over his cow, was grievously disappointed at my lack of success.

'It's time t'awd bitch was up. She's doin' no good laid there. Surely there's summat you can do. I poured a bottle of water into her lug this morning but even that hasn't shifted her.'

'You what?'

'Poured some cold water down her lug 'ole. Me dad used to get 'em up that way and he was a very clever man with stock was me dad.'

'I've no doubt he was,' I said primly. 'But I really think another injection is more likely to help her.'

The farmer watched glumly as I ran yet another bottle of calcium under the skin. The procedure had lost its magic for him.

As I put the apparatus away I did my best to be hearty. 'I shouldn't worry. A lot of them stay down for a day or two –

you'll probably find her walking about in the morning.'

The phone rang just before breakfast and my stomach contracted sharply as I heard Mr Handshaw's voice. It was heavy with gloom. 'Well, she's no different. Lyin' there eating her 'ead off, but never offers to rise. What are you going to do now?'

What indeed, I thought as I drove out to the farm. The cow had been down for forty-eight hours now – I didn't like it a bit.

The farmer went into the attack immediately. 'Me dad allus used to say they had a worm in the tail when they stayed down like this. He said if you cut tail end off it did the trick.'

My spirits sagged lower. I had had trouble with this myth before. The insidious thing was that the people who still practised this relic of barbarism could often claim that it worked because, after the end of the tail had been chopped off, the pain of the stump touching the ground forced many a sulky cow to scramble to her feet.

'There's no such thing as worm in the tail, Mr Handshaw,' I said. 'And don't you think it's a cruel business, cutting off a cow's tail? I hear the RSPCA had a man in court last week over a job like that.'

The farmer narrowed his eyes. Clearly he thought I was hedging. 'Well, if you won't do that, what the hangment are you going to do? We've got to get this cow up somehow.'

I took a deep breath. 'Well, I'm sure she's got over the milk fever because she's eating well and looks quite happy. It must be a touch of posterior paralysis that's keeping her down. There's no point in giving her any more calcium so I'm going to try this stimulant injection.' I filled the syringe with a feeling of doom. I hadn't a scrap of faith in the stimulant injection but I just couldn't do nothing. I was scraping the barrel out now.

I was turning to go when Mr Handshaw called after me. 'Hey, Mister, I remember summat else me dad used to do. Shout in their lugs. He got many a cow up that way. I'm not very strong in the voice – how about you having a go?'

It was a bit late to stand on my dignity. I went over to the animal and seized her by the ear. Inflating my lungs to the utmost I bent down and bawled wildly into the hairy depths. The cow stopped chewing for a moment and looked at me inquiringly, then her eyes drooped and she returned contentedly to her cudding. 'We'll give her another day,' I said wearily. 'And if she's still down tomorrow we'll have a go at lifting her. Could you get a few of the neighbours to give us a hand?'

Driving round my other cases that day I felt tied up inside with sheer frustration. Damn and blast the thing! What the hell was keeping her down? And what else could I do? This was 1938 and my resources were limited. Thirty years later there are still milk fever cows which won't get up but the vet has a much wider armoury if the calcium has failed to do the job. The excellent Bagshaw hoist which clamps on to the pelvis and raises the animal in a natural manner, the phosphorus injections, even the electric goad which administers a swift shock when applied to the rump and sends many a comfortably ensconced cow leaping to her feet with an offended bellow.

As I expected, the following day brought no change and as I got out of the car in Mr Handshaw's yard I was surrounded by a group of his neighbours. They were in festive mood, grinning, confident, full of helpful advice as farmers always are with somebody else's animals.

There was much laughter and legpulling as we drew sacks under the cow's body and a flood of weird suggestions to which I tried to close my ears. When we all finally gave a concerted heave and lifted her up, the result was predictable; she just hung there placidly with her legs dangling whilst her owner leaned against the wall watching us with deepening gloom.

After a lot of puffing and grunting we lowered the inert body and everybody looked at me for the next move. I was hunting round desperately in my mind when Mr Handshaw piped up again.

'Me dad used to say a strange dog would allus get a cow up.'

There were murmurs of assent from the assembled farmers

and immediate offers of dogs. I tried to point out that one would be enough but my authority had dwindled and anyway everybody seemed anxious to demonstrate their dogs' cow-raising potential. There was a sudden excited exodus and even Mr Smedley the village shopkeeper pedalled off at frantic speed for his border terrier. It seemed only minutes before the byre was alive with snapping, snarling curs but the cow ignored them all except to wave her horns warningly at the ones which came too close.

The flash-point came when Mr Handshaw's own dog came in from the fields where he had been helping to round up the sheep. He was a skinny, hard-bitten little creature with lightning reflexes and a short temper. He stalked, stiff-legged and bristling, into the byre, took a single astounded look at the pack of foreigners on his territory and flew into action with silent venom.

Within seconds the finest dog fight I had ever seen was in full swing and I stood back and surveyed the scene with a feeling of being completely superfluous. The yells of the farmers rose above the enraged yapping and growling. One intrepid man leaped into the mêlée and reappeared with a tiny Jack Russell hanging on determinedly to the heel of his wellington boot. Mr Reynolds of Clover Hill was rubbing the cow's tail between two short sticks and shouting 'Cush! Cush!' and as I watched helplessly a total stranger tugged at my sleeve and whispered: 'Hasta tried a teaspoonful of Jeyes' Fluid in a pint of old beer every two hours?'

It seemed to me that all the forces of black magic had broken through and were engulfing me and that my slender resources of science had no chance of shoring up the dyke. I don't know how I heard the creaking sound above the din – probably because I was bending low over Mr Reynolds in an attempt to persuade him to desist from his tail rubbing. But at that moment the cow shifted her position slightly and I distinctly heard it. It came from the pelvis.

It took me some time to attract attention – I think everybody had forgotten I was there – but finally the dogs were separated and secured with innumerable lengths of binder twine, everybody stopped shouting, Mr Reynolds was pulled away from the tail and I had the stage.

I addressed myself to Mr Handshaw. 'Would you get me a bucket of hot water, some soap and a towel, please.'

He trailed off, grumbling, as though he didn't expect much from the new gambit. My stock was definitely low.

I stripped off my jacket, soaped my arms and pushed a hand into the cow's rectum until I felt the hard bone of the pubis. Gripping it through the wall of the rectum I looked up at my audience. 'Will two of you get hold of the hook bones and rock the cow gently from side to side.'

Yes, there it was again, no mistake about it. I could both hear and feel it – a looseness, a faint creaking, almost a grating.

I got up and washed my arm. 'Well, I know why your cow won't get up – she has a broken pelvis. Probably did it during the first night when she was staggering about with the milk fever. I should think the nerves are damaged too. It's hopeless, I'm afraid.' Even though I was dispensing bad news it was a relief to come up with something rational.

Mr Handshaw stared at me. 'Hopeless? How's that?'

'I'm sorry,' I said, 'but that's how it is. The only thing you can do is get her off to the butcher. She has no power in her hind legs. She'll never get up again.'

That was when Mr Handshaw really blew his top and started a lengthy speech. He wasn't really unpleasant or abusive but firmly pointed out my shortcomings and bemoaned again the tragic fact that his dad was not there to put everything right. The other farmers stood in a wide-eyed ring, enjoying every word.

At the end of it I took myself off. There was nothing more I could do and anyway Mr Handshaw would have to come round to my way of thinking. Time would prove me right.

I thought of that cow as soon as I awoke next morning. It hadn't been a happy episode but at least I did feel a certain peace in the knowledge that there were no more doubts. I knew what was wrong, I knew that there was no hope. There was nothing more to worry about.

I was surprised when I heard Mr Handshaw's voice on the phone so soon. I had thought it would take him two or three days to realize he was wrong.

'Is that Mr Herriot? Aye, well, good mornin' to you. I'm just ringing to tell you that me cow's up on her legs and doing fine.'

I gripped the receiver tightly with both hands.

'What? What's that you say?'

'I said me cow's up. Found her walking about byre this morning, fit as a fiddle. You'd think there'd never been owt the matter with her.' He paused for a few moments then spoke with grave deliberation like a disapproving schoolmaster. 'And you stood there and looked at me and said she'd never get up n'more.'

'But . . . but . . .'

'Ah, you're wondering how I did it? Well, I just happened to remember another old trick of me dad's. I went round to t'butcher and got a fresh-killed sheep skin and put it on her back. Had her up in no time – you'll 'ave to come round and see her. Wonderful man was me dad.'

Blindly I made my way into the dining-room. I had to consult my boss about this. Siegfried's sleep had been broken by a 3 AM calving and he looked a lot older than his thirty-odd years. He listened in silence as he finished his breakfast then pushed away his plate and poured a last cup of coffee. 'Hard luck, James. The old sheep skin, eh? Funny thing – you've been in the Dales over a year now and never come across that one. Suppose it must be going out of fashion a bit now but you know it has a grain of sense behind it like a lot of these old remedies. You can imagine there's a lot of heat generated under a fresh sheep skin and it acts like a great hot poultice on the back – really tickles them up after a while, and if a cow is lying there out of sheer cussedness she'll often get up just to get rid of it.'

'But damn it, how about the broken pelvis? I tell you it was creaking and wobbling all over the place!'

'Well, James, you're not the first to have been caught that way. Sometimes the pelvic ligaments don't tighten up for a few days after calving and you get this effect.'

'Oh God,' I moaned, staring down at the table cloth. 'What a bloody mess I've made of the whole thing.'

'Oh, you haven't really.' Siegfried lit a cigarette and leaned back in his chair. 'That old cow was probably toying with the idea of getting up for a walk just when old Handshaw dumped the skin on her back. She could just as easily have done it after one of your injections and then you'd have got credit. Don't you remember what I told you when you first came here? There's a very fine dividing line between looking a real smart vet on the one hand and an immortal fool on the other. This sort of thing happens to us all, so forget it, James.'

But forgetting wasn't so easy. That cow became a celebrity in the district. Mr Handshaw showed her with pride to the postman, the policeman, corn merchants, lorry drivers, fertilizer salesmen, Ministry of Agriculture officials and they all told me about it frequently with pleased smiles. Mr Handshaw's speech was always the same, delivered, they said, in ringing, triumphant tones:

'There's the cow that Mr Herriot said would never get up n'more!'

I'm sure there was no malice behind the farmer's actions. He had put one over on the young clever-pants vet and nobody could blame him for preening himself a little. And in a way I did that cow a good turn; I considerably extended her life span because Mr Handshaw kept her long beyond her normal working period just as an exhibit. Years after she had stopped giving more than a couple of gallons of milk a day she was still grazing happily in the field by the roadside.

She had one curiously upturned horn and was easy to recognize. I often pulled up my car and looked wistfully over the wall at the cow that would never get up n'more.

CHAPTER TWO

Siegfried came away from the telephone; his face was expressionless. 'That was Mrs Pumphrey. She wants you to see her pig.'

'Peke, you mean,' I said.

'No, pig. She has a six-week-old pig she wants you to examine for soundness.'

I laughed sheepishly. My relations with the elderly widow's Peke was a touchy subject. 'All right, all right, don't start again. What did she really want? Is Tricki Woo's bottom playing him up again?'

'James,' said Siegfried gravely. 'It is unlike you to doubt my word in this way. I will repeat the message from Mrs Pumphrey and then I shall expect you to act upon it immediately and without further question. The lady informed me that she has become the owner of a six-week-old piglet and she wants the animal thoroughly vetted. You know how I feel about these examinations and I don't want the job scamped in any way. I should pay particular attention to its wind – have it well galloped round a paddock before you get your stethoscope on it and for heaven's sake don't miss anything obvious like curbs or ringbones. I think I'd take its height while you're about it; you'll find the measuring stick in ...'

His words trailed on as I hurried down the passage. This was a bit baffling; I usually had a bit of leg-pulling to stand ever since I became Tricki the Peke's adopted uncle and received regular presents and letters and signed photographs from him, but Siegfried wasn't in the habit of flogging the joke to this extent. The idea of Mrs Pumphrey with a pig was unthinkable; there was no room in her elegant establishment for livestock. Oh, he must have got it wrong somehow.

But he hadn't. Mrs Pumphrey received me with a joyful cry. 'Oh, Mr Herriot, isn't it wonderful! I have the most darling little pig. I was visiting some cousins who are farmers and I picked him out. He will be such company for Tricki – you know how I worry about his being an only dog.'

I shook my head vigorously in bewilderment as I crossed the oak-panelled hall. My visits here were usually associated with a degree of fantasy but I was beginning to feel out of my depth.

'You mean you actually have this pig in the house?'

'But of course.' Mrs Pumphrey looked surprised. 'He's in the kitchen. Come and see him.'

I had been in this kitchen a few times and had been almost awestruck by its shining spotlessness; the laboratory look of the tiled walls and floors, the gleaming surfaces of sink unit, cooker, refrigerator. Today, a cardboard box occupied one corner and inside I could see a tiny pig; standing on his hind legs, his forefeet resting on the rim, he was looking round him appreciatively at his new surroundings.

The elderly cook had her back to us and did not look round when we entered; she was chopping carrots and hurling them into a saucepan with, I thought, unnecessary vigour.

'Isn't he adorable!' Mrs Pumphrey bent over and tickled the little head. 'It's so exciting having a pig of my very own! Mr Herriot, I have decided to call him Nugent.'

I swallowed. 'Nugent?' The cook's broad back froze into immobility.

'Yes, after my great uncle Nugent. He was a little pink man with tiny eyes and a snub nose. The resemblance is striking.'

'I see,' I said, and the cook started her splashing again.

For a few moments I was at a loss; the ethical professional man in me rebelled at the absurdity of examining this obviously healthy little creature. In fact I was on the point of saying that he looked perfectly all right to me when Mrs Pumphrey spoke.

'Come now, Nugent,' she said, 'You must be a good boy and let your Uncle Herriot look at you.'

That did it. Stifling my finer feelings I seized the string-like tail and held Nugent almost upside down as I took his temperature. I then solemnly auscultated his heart and lungs, peered into his eyes, ran my fingers over his limbs and flexed his joints.

The cook's back radiated stiff disapproval but I carried on doggedly. Having a canine nephew, I had found, carried incalculable advantages; it wasn't only the frequent gifts – and I could still taste the glorious kippers Tricki had posted to me from Whitby – it was the vein of softness in my rough life, the sherry before lunch, the warmth and luxury of Mrs Pumphrey's fireside. The way I saw it, if a piggy nephew of the same type had been thrown in my path then Uncle Herriot was going to be the last man to interfere with the inscrutable workings of fate.

The examination over, I turned to Mrs Pumphrey who was anxiously awaiting the verdict. 'Sound in all respects,' I said briskly. 'In fact you've got a very fine pig there. But there's just one thing – he can't live in the house.'

For the first time the cook turned towards me and I read a mute appeal in her face. I could sympathize with her because the excretions of the pig are peculiarly volatile and even such a minute specimen as Nugent had already added his own faint pungency to the atmosphere in the kitchen.

Mrs Pumphrey was appalled at the idea at first but when I assured her that he wouldn't catch pneumonia and in fact would be happier and healthier outside, she gave way.

An agricultural joiner was employed to build a palatial sty in a corner of the garden; it had a warm sleeping apartment on raised boards and an outside run. I saw Nugent installed in it, curled up blissfully in a bed of clean straw. His trough was filled twice daily with the best meal and he was never short of an extra titbit such as a juicy carrot or some cabbage leaves. Every day he was allowed out to play and spent a boisterous hour frisking round the garden with Tricki.

In short, Nugent had it made, but it couldn't have happened to a nicer pig; because, though most of his species have an unsuspected strain of friendliness, this was developed in Nugent to an extraordinary degree. He just liked people and over the next few months his character flowered under the constant personal contact with humans.

I often saw him strolling companionably in the garden with Mrs Pumphrey and in his pen he spent much of the time standing upright with his cloven feet against the wire netting, waiting eagerly for his next visitor. Pigs grow quickly and he soon left the pink baby stage behind, but his charm was undiminished. His chief delight was to have his back scratched; he would grunt deeply, screwing up his eyes in ecstasy, then gradually his legs would start to buckle until finally he toppled over on his side.

Nugent's existence was sunny and there was only one cloud in the sky; old Hodgkin, the gardener, whose attitude to domestic pets had been permanently soured by having to throw rubber rings for Tricki every day, now found himself appointed personal valet to a pig. It was his duty to feed and bed down Nugent and to supervise his play periods. The idea of doing all this for a pig who was never ever going to be converted into pork pies must have been nearly insupportable for the old countryman; the harsh lines on his face deepened whenever he took hold of the meal bucket.

On the first of my professional visits to his charge he greeted me gloomily with 'Hasta come to see Nudist?' I knew Hodgkin well enough to realize the impossibility of any whimsical word-play; it was a genuine attempt to grasp the name and throughout my nephew's long career he remained 'Nudist' to the old man.

There is one memory of Nugent which I treasure. The telephone rang one day just after lunch; it was Mrs Pumphrey and I knew by the stricken voice that something momentous had happened; it was the same voice which had described Tricki Woo's unique symptoms of flop-bott and crackerdog.

'Oh, Mr Herriot, thank heavens you are in. It's Nugent! I'm afraid he's terribly ill.'

'Really? I'm sorry to hear that. What's he doing?'

There was a silence at the other end except for gasping breathing then Mrs Pumphrey spoke again. 'Well, he can't manage ... well ...' she was obviously confused. 'Not properly.'

'That's strange,' I said. 'Is he eating all right?'

'I think so but ...' then she suddenly blurted out: 'Oh, Mr Herriot, I'm so terribly worried! I've heard of men being dreadfully ill ... just like this. It's a gland, isn't it?'

'Oh, you needn't worry about that. Pigs don't have that trouble and anyway, I think four months is a bit young for hypertrophy of the prostate.'

'Oh, I'm so glad, but something is ... stopping it. You will come, won't you!'

'I'm leaving now.'

I had quite a long wait outside Nugent's pen. He had grown into a chunky little porker and grunted amiably as he surveyed me through the netting. Clearly he expected some sort of game and, growing impatient, he performed a few stiff-legged little gallops up and down the run.

I had almost decided that my visit was fruitless when Mrs Pumphrey, who had been pacing up and down, wringing her hands, stopped dead and pointed a shaking finger at the pig.

'Oh God,' she breathed. 'There! There! There it is now!' All the colour had drained from her face leaving her deathly pale. 'Oh, it's awful! I can't look any longer.' With a moan she turned away and buried her face in her hands.

I scrutinized Nugent closely. He had halted in mid gallop and was contentedly relieving himself by means of the intermittent spurting jets of the normal male pig.

I turned to Mrs Pumphrey. 'I really can't see anything wrong there.'

'But he's ... he's ...' she still didn't dare to look. 'He's doing it in ... in fits and starts!'

I had had considerable practice at keeping a straight face in Mrs Pumphrey's presence and it stood me in good stead now.

'But they all do it that way, Mrs Pumphrey.'

She half turned and looked tremblingly out of the corner of her eye at Nugent. 'You mean ... all boy pigs ...?'

'Every single boy pig I have ever known has done it like that.'

'Oh ... Oh ... how odd, how very odd.' The poor lady fanned herself with her handkerchief. Her colour had come back in a positive flood.

To cover her confusion I became very business-like. 'Yes, yes indeed. Lots of people make the same mistake, I assure you. Ah well, I suppose I'd better be on my way now – it's been nice to see the little fellow looking so well and happy.'

Nugent enjoyed a long and happy life and more than fulfilled my expectations of him; he was every bit as generous as Tricki with his presents and, as with the little Peke, I was able to salve my conscience with the knowledge that I was really fond of him. As always, Siegfried's sardonic attitude made things a little uncomfortable; I had suffered in the past when I got the signed photographs from the little dog – but I never dared let him see the one from the pig.

CHAPTER THREE

Angus Grier MRCVS was never pretty to look at, but the sight of him propped up in bed, his mottled, pop-eyed face scowling above a pink quilted bed jacket was enough to daunt the bravest. Especially at eight in the morning when I usually had the first of my daily audiences with him.

'You're late again,' he said, his voice grating. 'Can ye no' get out of your bed in the morning? I've told you till I'm tired that I want ye out on the road by eight o'clock.'

As I mumbled apologies he tugged fretfully at the counterpane and looked me up and down with deepening distaste. 'And another thing, that's a terrible pair o' breeches you're wearing. If you must wear breeches to your work, for heaven's sake go and get a pair made at a proper tailor. There's nae cut about those things at all – they're not fit to be worn by a veterinary surgeon.'

The knife really went in then. I was attached to those breeches. I had paid thirty shillings for them at the Army and Navy Stores and cherished a private conviction that they gave me a certain air. And Grier's attack on them was all the more wounding when I considered that the man was almost certainly getting my services free; Siegfried, I felt sure, would wave aside any offers of payment.

I had been here a week and it seemed like a lifetime. Somewhere, far back, I knew, there had been a brighter, happier existence but the memory was growing dim. Siegfried had been sincerely apologetic that morning back in Darrowby.

'James, I have a letter here from Grier of Brawton. It seems he was castrating a colt and the thing threw itself on top of him; he has a couple of cracked ribs. Apparently his assistant walked out on him recently, so there's nobody to run his practice. He wants me to send you along there for a week or two.'

'Oh no! There's a mistake somewhere. He doesn't like me.'

'He doesn't like anybody. But there's no mistake, it's down here – and honestly, what can I do?'

'But the only time I met him he worked me into a horrible rubber suit and made me look a right chump.'

Siegfried smiled sadly. 'I remember, James, I remember. He's a mean old devil and I hate to do this to you, but I can't turn him down, can I?'

At the time I couldn't believe it. The whole idea was unreal. But it was real enough now as I stood at the foot of Grier's bed listening to him ranting away. He was at me again.

'Another thing – my wife tells me you didna eat your porridge. Did you not like it?'

I shuffled my feet. 'Oh yes, it was very nice. I just didn't feel hungry this morning.' I had pushed the tasteless mass about with my spoon and done my best with it but it had defeated me in the end.

'There's something wrong with a man that canna eat his good food.' Grier peered at me suspiciously then held out a slip of paper. 'Here's a list of your visits for this morning. There's a good few so you'll no' have to waste your time getting round. This one here of Adamson's of Grenton – a prolapse of the cervix in a cow. What would you do about that, think ye?'

I put my hand in my pocket, got hold of my pipe then dropped it back again. Grier didn't like smoking.

'Well, I'd give her an epidural anaesthetic, replace the prolapse and fasten it in with retention sutures through the vulva.'

'Havers, man, havers!' snorted Grier. 'What a lot of twaddle. There's no need for a' that. It'll just be constipation that's doing it. Push the thing back, build the cow up with some boards under her hind feet and put her on to linseed oil for a few days.'

'Surely it'll come out again if I don't stitch it in?' I said.

'Na, na, na, not at all,' Grier cried angrily. 'Just you do as I tell you now. I ken more about this than you.'

He probably did. He should, anyway – he had been qualified for thirty years and I was starting my second. I looked at him glowering from his pillow and pondered for a moment on the strange fact of our uncomfortable relationship. A Yorkshireman listening to the two outlandish accents – Grier's rasping Aberdeen, my glottal Clydeside – might have expected that some sort of rapport would exist between us, if only on national grounds. But there was none.

'Right, just as you say.' I left the room and went downstairs to gather up my equipment.

As I set off on the round I had the same feeling as every morning – relief at getting out of the house. I had had to go flat out all week to get through the work but I had enjoyed it. Farmers are nearly always prepared to make allowances for a young man's inexperience and Grier's clients had treated me kindly, but I still had to come back to that joyless establishment for meals and it was becoming more and more wearing.

Mrs Grier bothered me just as much as her husband. She was a tight-lipped woman of amazing thinness and she kept a spartan board in which soggy porridge figured prominently. It was porridge for breakfast, porridge for supper and, in between, a miserable procession of watery stews, anaemic mince and nameless soups. Nothing she cooked ever tasted of anything. Angus Grier had come to Yorkshire thirty years ago, a penniless Scot just like myself, and acquired a lucrative practice by the classical expedient of marrying the boss's daughter; so he got a good living handed to him on a plate, but he also got Mrs Grier.

It seemed to me that she felt she was still in charge – probably because she had always lived in this house with its memories of her father who had built up the practice. Other people would seem like interlopers and I could understand how she felt; after all, she was childless, she didn't have much of a life and she had Angus Grier for a husband. I could feel sorry for her.

But that didn't help because I just couldn't get her out of

my hair; she hung over my every move like a disapproving spectre. When I came back from a round she was always there with a barrage of questions. 'Where have you been all this time?' or 'I wondered wherever you'd got to, were you lost?' or 'There's an urgent case waiting. Why are you always so slow?' Maybe she thought I'd nipped into a cinema for an hour or two.

There was a pretty full small animal surgery every night and she had a nasty habit of lurking just outside the door so that she could listen to what I was saying to the clients. She really came into her own in the dispensary where she watched me narrowly, criticizing my prescriptions and constantly pulling me up for being extravagant with the drugs. 'You're putting in far too much chlorodyne – don't you know it's very expensive?'

I developed a deep sympathy for the assistant who had fled without warning; jobs were hard to come by and young graduates would stand nearly anything just to be at work, but I realized that there had been no other choice for that shadowy figure.

Adamson's place was a small-holding on the edge of the town and maybe it was because I had just been looking at Grier but by contrast the farmer's lined, patient face and friendly eyes seemed extraordinarily warming and attractive. A ragged khaki smock hung loosely on his gaunt frame as he shook hands with me.

'Now then, we've got a new man today, have we?' He looked me over for a second or two. 'And by the look of you you're pretty fresh to t'job.'

'That's right,' I replied. 'But I'm learning fast.'

Mr Adamson smiled. 'Don't worry about that, lad. I believe in new blood and new ideas – it's what we want in farming. We've stood still too long at this game. Come into t'byre and I'll show you the cow.'

There were about a dozen cows, not the usual Shorthorns but Ayrshires, and they were obviously well kept and healthy. My patient was easy to pick out by the football-sized rose-pink protrusion of the vaginal wall and the corrugated uterine cervix. But the farmer had wasted no time in calling for assistance; the mass was clean and undamaged.

He watched me attentively as I swabbed the prolapse with antiseptic and pushed it back out of sight, then he helped me build a platform with soil and planks for the cow's hind feet. When we had finished she was standing on a slope with her tail higher than her head.

'And you say that if I give her linseed oil for a few days that thing won't come out again?'

'That's the idea,' I said. 'Be sure to keep her built up like this.'

'I will, young man, and thank you very much. I'm sure you've done a good job for me and I'll look forward to seeing you again.'

Back in the car, I groaned to myself. Good job! How the hell could that thing stay in without stitches? But I had to do as I was told and Grier, even if he was unpleasant, wasn't a complete fool. Maybe he was right. I put it out of my mind and got on with the other visits.

It was less than a week later at the breakfast table and I was prodding at the inevitable porridge when Grier, who had ventured downstairs, barked suddenly at me.

'I've got a card here frae Adamson. He says he's not satisfied with your work. We'd better get out there this morning and see what's wrong. I dinna like these complaints.' His normal expression of being perpetually offended deepened and the big pale eyes swam and brimmed till I was sure he was going to weep in his porridge.

At the farm, Mr Adamson led us into the byre. 'Well, what do you think of that, young man?'

I looked at the prolapse and my stomach lurched. The innocuous-looking pink projection had been transformed into a great bloated purple mass. It was caked with filth and an ugly wound ran down one side of it.

'It didn't stay in very long, did it?' the farmer said quietly.

I was too ashamed to speak. This was a dreadful thing to do to a good cow. I felt my face reddening, but luckily I had my employer with me; he would be able to explain everything. I turned towards Grier who snuffled, mumbled, blinked his eyes rapidly but didn't say anything.

The farmer went on. 'And you see she's damaged it. Must have caught it on something. I'll tell you I don't like the look of it.'

It was against this decent man's nature to be unpleasant, but he was upset all right. 'Maybe it would be better if you would take the job on this time, Mr Grier,' he said.

Grier, who still had not uttered an intelligible word, now sprang into action. He clipped the hair over the base of the spine, inserted an epidural anaesthetic, washed and disinfected the mass and, with an effort, pushed it back to its place. Then he fastened it in with several strong retention sutures with little one-inch lengths of rubber tubing to stop them cutting into the flesh. The finished job looked neat and workmanlike.

The farmer took me gently by the shoulder. 'Now that's something like. You can see it's not going to come out again now, can't you? Why didn't you do something like that when you came before?'

I turned again to Grier, but this time he was seized by a violent fit of coughing. I continued to stare at him but when he still said nothing I turned and walked out of the byre.

'No hard feelings, though, young man,' Mr Adamson called after me. 'I reckon we've all got to learn and there's no substitute for experience. That's so, Mr Grier, isn't it?'

'Aye, och aye, that's right enough. Aye, aye, rightly so, rightly so, there's no doubt aboot that,' Grier mumbled. We got into the car.

I settled down and waited for some explanation from him. I was interested to know just what he would say. But the blue-veined nose pointed straight ahead and the bulging eyes fixed themselves blankly on the road ahead of us.

We drove back to the surgery in silence.

CHAPTER FOUR

It wasn't long before Grier had to return to bed; he began to groan a lot and hold his injured ribs and soon he was re-installed upstairs with the pillows at his back and the little pink jacket buttoned to the neck. Whisky was the only thing that gave him relief from his pain and the level of his bedside bottle went down with remarkable speed.

Life resumed its dreary pattern. Mrs Grier was usually around when I had to report to her husband; beyond the bedroom door there would be a lot of whispering which stopped as soon as I entered. I would receive my instructions while Mrs Grier fussed round the bed tucking things in, patting her husband's brow with a folded handkerchief and all the time darting little glances of dislike at me. Immediately I got outside the door the whispering started again.

It was quite late one evening – about ten o'clock – when the call from Mrs Mallard came in. Her dog had a bone in its throat and would Mr Grier come at once. I was starting to say that he was ill and I was doing his work but it was too late; there was a click as the receiver went down at the other end.

Grier reacted to the news by going into a sort of trance; his chin sank on his chest and he sat immobile for nearly a minute while he gave the matter careful thought. Then he straightened up suddenly and stabbed a finger at me.

'It'll not be a bone in its throat. It'll only be a touch of pharyngitis making it cough.'

I was surprised at his confidence. 'Don't you think I'd better take some long forceps just in case?'

'Na, na, I've told ye now. There'll be no bone, so go down and put up some of the syrup of squills and ipecacuanha mixture. That's all it'll want. And another thing – if ye can't find anything wrong don't say so. Tell the lady it's pharyngitis and how to treat it – you have to justify your visit, ye ken.'

I felt a little bewildered as I filled a four ounce bottle in the dispensary, but I took a few pairs of forceps with me too; I had lost a bit of faith in Grier's long-range diagnosis.

I was surprised when Mrs Mallard opened the door of the smart semi-detached house. For some reason I had been expecting an old lady, and here was a striking-looking blonde woman of about forty with her hair piled high in glamorous layers as was the fashion at that time. And I hadn't expected the long ballroom dress in shimmering green, the enormous swaying earrings, the heavily made up face.

Mrs Mallard seemed surprised too. She stared blankly at me till I explained the position. 'I've come to see your dog – I'm Mr Grier's locum. He's ill at the moment, I'm afraid.'

It took a fair time for the information to get through because she still stood on the doorstep as if she didn't know what I was talking about; then she came to life and opened the door wide. 'Oh yes, of course, I'm sorry, do come in.' I walked past her through an almost palpable wall of perfume and into a room on the left of the hall. The perfume was even stronger in here but it was in keeping with the single, pink-tinted lamp which shed a dim but rosy light on the wide divan drawn close to the flickering fire. Somewhere in the shadows a radiogram was softly pouring out 'Body and Soul'.

There was no sign of my patient and Mrs Mallard looked at me irresolutely, fingering one of her earrings.

'Do you want me to see him in here?' I asked.

'Oh yes, certainly.' She became brisk and opened a door at the end of the room. Immediately a little West Highland Terrier bounded across the carpet and hurled himself at me with a woof of delight. He tried his best to lick my face by a series of mighty springs and this might have gone on for quite a long time had I not caught him in mid air.

Mrs Mallard smiled nervously. 'He seems a lot better now,' she said.

I flopped down on the divan still with the little dog in my arms and prised open his jaws. Even in that dim light it was obvious that there was nothing in his throat. I gently slid my forefinger over the back of his tongue and the terrier made no protest as I explored his gullet. Then I dropped him down on the carpet and took his temperature – normal.

'Well, Mrs Mallard,' I said, 'there is certainly no bone in his throat and he has no fever.' I was about to add that the dog seemed perfectly fit to me when I remembered Grier's parting admonition – I had to justify my visit.

I cleared my throat. 'It's just possible, though, that he has a little pharyngitis which has been making him cough or retch.' I opened the terrier's mouth again. 'As you see, the back of his throat is rather inflamed. He may have got a mild infection in there or perhaps swallowed some irritant. I have some medicine in the car which will soon put him right.' Realizing I was beginning to gabble, I brought my speech to a close.

Mrs Mallard hung on every word, peering anxiously into the little dog's mouth and nodding her head rapidly. 'Oh yes, I do see,' she said. 'Thank you so much. What a good thing I sent for you!'

On the following evening I was halfway through a busy surgery when a fat man in a particularly vivid tweed jacket bustled in and deposited a sad-eyed Basset Hound on the table.

'Shaking his head about a bit,' he boomed. 'Think he must have a touch of canker.'

I got an auroscope from the instrument cupboard and had begun to examine the ear when the fat man started again.

'I see you were out our way last night. I live next door to Mrs Mallard.'

'Oh yes,' I said peering down the lighted metal tube. 'That's right, I was.'

The man drummed his fingers on the table for a moment. 'Aye, that dog must have a lot of ailments. The vet's car seems always to be outside the house.'

'Really, I shouldn't have thought so. Seemed a healthy little thing to me.' I finished examining one ear and started on the other.

'Well, it's just as I say,' said the man. 'The poor creature's always in trouble and it's funny how often it happens at night.'

I looked up quickly. There was something odd in the way he said that. He looked at me for a moment with a kind of wide-eyed innocence, then his whole face creased into a knowing leer.

I stared at him 'You can't mean . . .'

'Not with that ugly old devil, you mean, eh? Takes a bit of reckoning up, doesn't it?' The eyes in the big red face twinkled with amusement.

I dropped the auroscope on the table with a clatter and my arms fell by my sides.

'Don't look like that, lad!' shouted the fat man, giving me a playful punch in the chest. 'It's a rum old world, you know!'

But it wasn't just the thought of Grier that was filling me with horror; it was the picture of myself in that harem atmosphere pontificating about pharyngitis against a background of 'Body and Soul' to a woman who knew I was talking rubbish.

In another two days Angus Grier was out of bed and apparently recovered; also, a replacement assistant had been engaged and was due to take up his post immediately. I was free to go.

Having said I would leave first thing in the morning I was out of the house by 6.30 AM in order to make Darrowby by breakfast. I wasn't going to face any more of that porridge.

As I drove west across the Plain of York I began to catch glimpses over the hedge tops and between the trees of the long spine of the Pennines lifting into the morning sky; they were pale violet at this distance and still hazy in the early sunshine but they beckoned to me. And later, when the little car pulled harder against the rising ground and the trees became fewer and the hedges gave way to the clean limestone walls I had the feeling I always had of the world opening out, of shackles falling away. And there, at last, was Darrowby sleeping under the familiar bulk of Herne Fell and beyond, the great green folds of the Dales.

Nothing stirred as I rattled across the cobbled market place then down the quiet street to Skeldale House with the ivy hanging in untidy profusion from its old bricks and 'Siegfried Farnon MRCVS' on the lopsided brass plate.

I think I would have galloped along the passage beyond the glass door but I had to fight my way through the family dogs, all five of them, who surged around me, leaping and barking in delight.

I almost collided with the formidable bulk of Mrs Hall who was carrying the coffee-pot out of the dining-room. 'You're back then,' she said and I could see she was really pleased because she almost smiled. 'Well, go in and get sat down. I've got a bit of home-cured in the pan for you.'

My hand was on the door when I heard the brothers' voices inside. Tristan was mumbling something and Siegfried was in full cry. 'Where the hell were you last night, anyway? I heard you banging about at three o'clock in the morning and your room stinks like a brewery. God, I wish you could see yourself – eyes like piss-holes in the snow!'

Smiling to myself, I pushed open the door, I went over to Tristan who stared up in surprise as I seized his hand and began to pump it; he looked as boyishly innocent as ever except for the eyes which, though a little sunken, still held their old gleam. Then I approached Siegfried at the head of the table. Obviously startled at my formal entry, he had choked in mid-chew; he reddened, tears coursed down his thin cheeks and the small sandy moustache quivered. Nevertheless, he rose from his chair, inclined his head and extended his hand with the grace of a marquis.

'Welcome, James,' he spluttered, spraying me lightly with toast crumbs. 'Welcome home.'

CHAPTER FIVE

I had been away for only two weeks but it was enough to bring it home to me afresh that working in the high country had something for me that was missing elsewhere. My first visit took me up on one of the narrow, unfenced roads which join Sildale and Cosdale and when I had ground my way to the top in bottom gear I did what I so often did – pulled the car on to the roadside turf and got out.

That quotation about not having time to stand and stare has never applied to me. I seem to have spent a good part of my life – probably too much – in just standing and staring and I was at it again this morning. From up here you could see away over the Plain of York to the sprawl of the Hambleton Hills forty miles to the east, while behind me, the ragged miles of moorland rolled away, dipping and rising over the flat fell-top. In my year at Darrowby I must have stood here scores of times and the view across the plain always looked different; sometimes in the winter the low country was a dark trough between the snow-covered Pennines and the distant white gleam of the Hambletons, and in April the rain squalls drifted in slow, heavy veils across the great green and brown dappled expanse. There was a day, too, when I stood in brilliant sunshine looking down over miles of thick fog like a rippling layer of cotton wool with dark tufts of trees and hilltops pushing through here and there.

But today the endless patchwork of fields slumbered in the sun, and the air, even on the hill, was heavy with the scents of summer. There must be people working among the farms down there, I knew, but I couldn't see a living soul; and the peace which I always found in the silence and the emptiness of the moors filled me utterly.

At these times I often seemed to stand outside myself, calmly assessing my progress. It was easy to flick back over the years – right back to the time I had decided to become a veterinary surgeon. I could remember the very moment. I was thirteen and I was reading an article about careers for boys in the Meccano Magazine and as I read, I felt a surging conviction that this was for me. And yet what was it based upon? Only that I liked dogs and cats and didn't care much for the idea of an office life; it seemed a frail basis on which to build a career. I knew nothing about agriculture or about farm animals and though, during the years in college, I learned about these things I could see only one future for myself; I was going to be a small animal surgeon. This lasted right up to the time I qualified – a kind of vision of treating people's pets in my own animal hospital where everything would be not just modern but revolutionary. The fully equipped operating theatre, laboratory and X-ray room; they had all stayed crystal clear in my mind until I had graduated MRCVS.

How on earth, then, did I come to be sitting on a high Yorkshire moor in shirt sleeves and wellingtons, smelling vaguely of cows?

The change in my outlook had come quite quickly – in fact almost immediately after my arrival in Darrowby. The job had been a godsend in those days of high unemployment, but only, I had thought, a stepping-stone to my real ambition. But everything had switched round, almost in a flash.

Maybe it was something to do with the incredible sweetness of the air which still took me by surprise when I stepped out into the old wild garden at Skeldale House every morning. Or perhaps the daily piquancy of life in the graceful old house with my gifted but mercurial boss, Siegfried, and his reluctant student brother, Tristan. Or it could be that it was just the realization that treating cows and pigs and sheep and horses had a fascination I had never even suspected; and this brought with it a new concept of myself as a tiny wheel in the great machine of British agriculture. There was a kind of solid satisfaction in that.

Probably it was because I hadn't dreamed there was a place like the Dales. I hadn't thought it possible that I could spend all my days in a high, clean-blown land where the scent of grass or trees was never far away; and where even in the driving rain of winter I could snuff the air and find the freshness of growing things hidden somewhere in the cold clasp of the wind.

Anyway, it had all changed for me and my work consisted now of driving from farm to farm across the roof of England with a growing conviction that I was a privileged person.

I got back into the car and looked at my list of visits; it was good to be back and the day passed quickly. It was about seven o'clock in the evening, when I thought I had finished, that I had a call from Terry Watson, a young farm worker who kept two cows of his own. One of them, he said, had summer mastitis. Mid-July was a bit early for this but in the later summer months we saw literally hundreds of these cases; in fact a lot of the farmers called it 'August Bag'. It was an unpleasant condition because it was just about incurable and usually resulted in the cow losing a quarter (the area of the udder which supplies each teat with milk) and sometimes even her life.

Terry Watson's cow looked very sick. She had limped in from the field at milking time, swinging her right hind leg wide to keep it away from the painful udder, and now she stood trembling in her stall, her eyes staring anxiously in front of her. I drew gently at the affected teat and, instead of milk, a stream of dark, foul-smelling serum spurted into the tin can I was holding.

'No mistaking that stink, Terry,' I said. 'It's the real summer type all right.' I felt my way over the hot, swollen quarter and the cow lifted her leg quickly as I touched the tender tissue. 'Pretty hard, too. It looks bad, I'm afraid.'

Terry's face was grim as he ran his hand along the cow's back. He was in his early twenties, had a wife and a small baby and was one of the breed who was prepared to labour all day for somebody else and then come home and start work on his own few stock. His two cows, his few pigs and hens made a big difference to somebody who had to live on thirty shillings a week.

'Ah can't understand it,' he muttered. 'It's usually dry cows that get it and this 'un's still giving two gallons a day. I'd have been on with tar if only she'd been dry.' (The farmers used to dab the teats of the dry cows with Stockholm tar to keep off the flies which were blamed for carrying the infection.)

'No, I'm afraid all cows can get it, especially the ones that are beginning to dry off.' I pulled the thermometer from the rectum – it said a hundred and six.

'What's going to happen, then? Can you do owt for her?'

'I'll do what I can, Terry. I'll give her an injection and

you must strip the teat out as often as you can, but you know as well as I do that it's a poor outlook with these jobs.'

'Aye, ah know all about it.' He watched me gloomily as I injected the Coryne pyogenes toxoid into the cow's neck. (Even now we are still doing this for summer mastitis because it is a sad fact none of the modern range of antibiotics has much effect on it.) 'She'll lose her quarter, won't she, and maybe she'll even peg out?'

I tried to be cheerful. 'Well, I don't think she'll die, and even if the quarter goes she'll make it up on the other three.' But there was the feeling of helplessness I always had when I could do little about something which mattered a great deal. Because I knew what a blow this was to the young man; a three-teated cow has lost a lot of her market value and this was about the best outcome I could see. I didn't like to think about the possibility of the animal dying.

'Look, is there nowt at all I can do myself? Is the job a bad 'un do you think?' Terry Watson's thin cheeks were pale and as I looked at the slender figure with the slightly stooping shoulders I thought, not for the first time, that he didn't look robust enough for his hard trade.

'I can't guarantee anything,' I said. 'But the cases that do best are the ones that get the most stripping. So work away at it this evening – every half hour if you can manage it. That rubbish in her quarter can't do any harm if you draw it out as soon as it is formed. And I think you ought to bathe the udder with warm water and massage it well.'

'What'll I rub it with?'

'Oh, it doesn't matter what you use. The main thing is to move the tissue about so that you can get more of that stinking stuff out. Vaseline would do nicely.'

'Ah've got a bowl of goose grease.'

'OK use that.' I reflected that there must be a bowl of goose grease on most farms; it was the all-purpose lubricant and liniment for man and beast.

Terry seemed relieved at the opportunity to do something. He fished out an old bucket, tucked the milking stool between his legs and crouched down against the cow. He looked up at me with a strangely defiant expression. 'Right,' he said. 'I'm startin' now.'

As it happened, I was called out early the next morning to a milk fever and on the way home I decided to look in at the Watsons' cottage. It was about eight o'clock and when I entered the little two-stall shed, Terry was in the same position as I had left him on the previous night. He was pulling at the infected teat, eyes closed, cheek resting against the cow's flank. He started as though roused from sleep when I spoke.

'Hello, you're having another go, I see.'

The cow looked round, too, at my words and I saw immediately, with a thrill of pleasure that she was immeasurably improved. She had lost her blank stare and was looking at me with the casual interest of the healthy bovine and best of all, her jaws were moving with that slow, regular, lateral grind that every vet loves to see.

'My God, Terry, she looks a lot better. She isn't like the same cow!'

The young man seemed to have difficulty in keeping his eyes open but he smiled. 'Aye, and come and have a look at this end.' He rose slowly from the stool, straightened his back a little bit at a time and leaned his elbow on the cow's rump.

I bent down by the udder, feeling carefully for the painful swelling of last night, but my hand came up against a smooth, yielding surface and, in disbelief, I kneaded the tissue between my fingers. The animal showed no sign of discomfort. With a feeling of bewilderment I drew on the teat with thumb and forefinger; the quarter was nearly empty but I did manage to squeeze a single jet of pure white milk on to my palm.

'What's going on here, Terry? You must have switched cows on me. You're having me on, aren't you?'

'Nay, guvnor,' the young man said with his slow smile. 'It's same cow all right – she's better, that's all.'

'But it's impossible! What the devil have you done to her?'

'Just what you told me to do. Rub and strip.'

I scratched my head. 'But she's back to normal. I've never seen anything like it.'

'Aye, I know you haven't.' It was a woman's voice and I turned and saw young Mrs Watson standing at the door holding her baby. 'You've never seen a man that would rub and strip a cow right round the clock, have you?'

'Round the clock?' I said.

She looked at her husband with a mixture of concern and exasperation. 'Yes, he's been there on that stool since you left last night. Never been to bed, never been in for a meal. I've been bringing him bits and pieces and cups of tea. Great fool – it's enough to kill anybody.'

I looked at Terry and my eyes moved from the pallid face over the thin, slightly swaying body to the nearly empty bowl of goose grease at his feet. 'Good Lord, man,' I said. 'You've done the impossible but you must be about all in. Anyway, your cow is as good as new – you don't need to do another thing to her, so you can go in and have a bit of rest.'

'Nay, I can't do that.' He shook his head and straightened his shoulders. 'I've got me work to go to and I'm late as it is.'

CHAPTER SIX

I couldn't help feeling just a little bit smug as I squeezed the bright red rubber ball out through the incision in the dog's stomach. We got enough small animal work in Darrowby to make a pleasant break from our normal life around the farms but not enough to make us blasé. No doubt the man with an intensive town practice looks on a gastrotomy as a fairly routine and unexciting event but as I watched the little red ball roll along the table and bounce on the surgery floor a glow of achievement filled me.

The big, lolloping Red Setter pup had been brought in that

morning; his mistress said that he had been trembling, miserable and occasionally vomiting for two days – ever since their little girl's ball had mysteriously disappeared. Diagnosis had not been difficult.

I inverted the lips of the stomach wound and began to close it with a continuous suture. I was feeling pleasantly relaxed unlike Tristan who had been unable to light a Woodbine because of the ether which bubbled in the glass bottle behind him and out through the anaesthetic mask which he held over the dog's face; he stared moodily down at the patient and the fingers of his free hand drummed on the table.

But it was soon my turn to be tense because the door of the operating room burst open and Siegfried strode in. I don't know why it was but whenever Siegfried watched me do anything I started to go to pieces; great waves seemed to billow from him – impatience, frustration, criticism, irritation. I could feel the waves buffeting me now although my employer's face was expressionless; he was standing quietly at the end of the table but as the minutes passed I had the growing impression of a volcano on the bubble. The eruption came when I began to stitch the deep layer of the abdominal muscle. I was pulling a length of catgut from a glass jar when I heard a sharp intake of breath.

'God help us, James,' cried Siegfried. 'Stop pulling at that bloody gut! Do you know how much that stuff costs per foot? Well it's a good job you don't or you'd faint dead away. And that expensive dusting powder you've been chucking about – there must be about half a pound of it inside that dog right now.' He paused and breathed heavily for a few moments. 'Another thing, if you want to swab, a little bit of cotton wool is enough – you don't need a square foot at a time like you've been using. Here, give me the needle. Let me show you.'

He hastily scrubbed his hands and took over. First he took a minute pinch of the iodoform powder and sprinkled it daintily into the wound rather like an old lady feeding her goldfish, then he cut off a tiny piece of gut and inserted a continuous suture in the muscle; he had hardly left himself enough to tie the knot at the end and it was touch and go, but he just made it after a few moments of intense concentration.

This process was repeated about ten times as he closed the skin wound with interrupted silk sutures, his nose almost touching the patient as he laboriously tied off each little short end with forceps. When he had finished he was slightly pop-eyed.

'Right, turn off the ether, Tristan,' he said as he pulled off half an inch of wool and primly wiped the wound down.

He turned to me and smiled gently. With dismay I saw that his patient look was spreading over his face. 'James, please don't misunderstand me. You've made a grand job of this dog but you've got to keep one eye on the economic side of things. I know it doesn't matter a hoot to you just now but some day, no doubt, you'll have your own practice and then you'll realize some of the worries I have on my shoulders.' He patted my arm and I steeled myself as he put his head on one side and a hint of roguishness crept into his smile.

'After all, James, you'll agree it is desirable to make some sort of profit in the end.'

It was a week later and I was kneeling on the neck of a sleeping colt in the middle of a field, the sun was hot on the back of my neck as I looked down at the peacefully closed eyes, the narrow face disappearing into the canvas chloroform muzzle. I tipped a few more drops of the anaesthetic on the sponge and screwed the cap on to the bottle. He had had about enough now.

I couldn't count the number of times Siegfried and I have enacted this scene; the horse on his grassy bed, my employer cutting away at one end while I watched the head. Siegfried was a unique combination of born horseman and dexterous surgeon with which I couldn't compete, so I had inevitably developed into an anaesthetist. We liked to do the operations in the open; it was cleaner and if the horse was wild he stood less chance of injuring himself. We just hoped for a fine morning and today we were lucky. In the early haze I looked over the countless buttercups; the field was filled with them and it was like sitting in a shimmering yellow ocean. Their pollen had powdered my shoes and the neck of the horse beneath me.

Everything had gone off more or less as it usually did. I had gone into the box with the colt, buckled on the muzzle underneath his head collar then walked him quietly out to a soft, level spot in the field. I left a man at the head holding a long shank on the head collar and poured the first half ounce of chloroform on to the sponge, watching the colt snuffling and shaking his head at the strange scent. As the man walked him slowly round I kept adding a little more chloroform till the colt began to stagger and sway; this stage always took a few minutes and I waited confidently for Siegfried's little speech which always came about now. I was not disappointed.

'He isn't going to go down, you know, James. Don't you think we should tie a foreleg up?'

I adopted my usual policy of feigning deafness and a few seconds later the colt gave a final lurch and collapsed on his side. Siegfried, released from his enforced inactivity, sprang into action. 'Sit on his head!' he yelled. 'Get a rope on that upper hind leg and pull it forward! Bring me that bucket of water over here! Come on – move!'

It was a violent transition. Just moments ago, peace and silence and now men scurrying in all directions, bumping into each other, urged on by Siegfried's cries.

Thirty years later I am still dropping horses for Siegfried and he is still saying 'He isn't going to go down, James.'

These days I mostly use an intravenous injection of Thiopentone and it puts a horse out in about ten seconds. It doesn't give Siegfried much time to say his piece but he usually gets it in somewhere between the seventh and tenth seconds.

This morning's case was an injury. But it was a pretty dramatic one, justifying general anaesthetic to repair it. The colt, bred from a fine hunter mare, had been galloping round his paddock and had felt the urge to visit the outside world. He had chosen the only sharp fence post to try to jump over and had been impaled between the forelegs; in his efforts to escape he had caused so much damage in the breast region that it looked like something from a butcher's shop with the skin extensively lacerated and the big sternal muscles hanging out, chopped through as though by a cleaver.

'Roll him on his back,' said Siegfried. 'That's better.' He took a probe from the tray which lay on the grass near by and carefully explored the wound. 'No damage to the bone,' he grunted, still peering into the depths. Then he took a pair of forceps and fished out all the loose debris he could find before turning to me.

'It's just a big stitching job. You can carry on if you like.'

As we changed places it occurred to me that he was disappointed it was not something more interesting. I couldn't see him asking me to take over in a rig operation or something like that. Then, as I picked up the needle, my mind clicked back to that gastrotomy on the dog. Maybe I was on trial for my wasteful ways. This time I would be on my guard.

I threaded the needle with a minute length of gut, took a bite at the severed muscle and, with an effort, stitched it back into place. But it was a laborious business tying the little short ends – it was taking me at least three times as long as it should. However, I stuck to it doggedly. I had been warned and I didn't want another lecture.

I had put in half a dozen sutures in this way when I began to feel the waves. My employer was kneeling close to me on the horse's neck and the foaming breakers of disapproval were crashing into me from close range. I held out for another two sutures then Siegfried exploded in a fierce whisper.

'What the hell are you playing at, James?'

'Well, just stitching. What do you mean?'

'But why are you buggering about with those little bits of gut? We'll be here all bloody day!'

I fumbled another knot into the muscle. 'For reasons of economy,' I whispered back virtuously.

Siegfried leaped from the neck as though the horse had bitten him. 'I can't stand any more of this! Here, let me have a go.'

He strode over to the tray, selected a needle and caught

hold of the free end of the catgut protruding from the jar. With a scything sweep of his arm he pulled forth an enormous coil of gut, setting the bobbin inside the jar whirring wildly like a salmon reel with a big fish on the line. He returned to the horse, stumbling slightly as the gut caught round his ankles and began to stitch. It wasn't easy because even at the full stretch of his arm he was unable to pull the suture tight and had to keep getting up and down; by the time he had tacked the muscles back into their original positions he was puffing and I could see a faint dew of perspiration on his forehead.

'Drop of blood seeping from somewhere down there,' he muttered and visited the tray again where he tore savagely at a huge roll of cotton wool. Trailing untidy white streamers over the buttercups he returned and swabbed out the wound with one corner of the mass.

Back to the tray again. 'Just a touch of powder before I stitch the skin,' he said lightly and seized a two pound carton. He poised for a moment over the wound then began to dispense the powder with extravagant jerks of the wrist. A considerable amount did go into the wound but much more floated over other parts of the horse, over me, over the buttercups, and a particularly wayward flick obscured the sweating face of the man on the foot rope. When he had finished coughing he looked very like Coco the clown.

Siegfried completed the closure of the skin, using several yards of silk, and when he stood back and surveyed the tidy result I could see he was in excellent humour.

'Well now, that's fine. A young horse like that will heal in no time. Shouldn't be surprised if it doesn't even leave a mark.'

He came over and addressed me as I washed the instruments in the bucket. 'Sorry I pushed you out like that, James, but honestly I couldn't think what had come over you – you were like an old hen. You know it looks bad trying to work with piddling little amounts of materials. One has to operate with a certain ... well ... panache, if I can put it that way, and you just can't do that if you stint yourself.'

I finished washing the instruments, dried them off and laid

them on the enamel tray. Then I lifted the tray and set off for the gate at the end of the field. Siegfried, walking alongside me, laid his hand on my shoulder. 'Mind you, don't think I'm blaming you, James. It's probably your Scottish upbringing. And don't misunderstand me, this same upbringing has inculcated in you so many of the qualities I admire – integrity, industry, loyalty. But I'm sure you will be the first to admit,' and here he stopped and wagged a finger at me 'that you Scots sometimes overdo the thrift.' He gave a light laugh. 'So remember, James, don't be too – er – canny when you are operating.'

I measured him up. If I dropped the tray quickly I felt sure I could fell him with a right hook.

Siegfried went on. 'But I know I don't have to ramble on at you, James. You always pay attention to what I say, don't you?'

I tucked the tray under my arm and set off again. 'Yes,' I replied. 'I do. Every single time.'

CHAPTER SEVEN

'I can see you like pigs,' said Mr Worley as I edged my way into the pen.

'You can?'

'Oh yes, I can always tell. As soon as you went in there nice and quiet and scratched Queenie's back and spoke to her I said "There's a young man as likes pigs".'

'Oh good. Well, as a matter of fact you're absolutely right. I do like pigs.' I had, in truth, been creeping very cautiously past Queenie, wondering just how she was going to react. She was a huge animal and sows with litters can be very hostile to strangers. When I had come into the building she had got up from where she was suckling her piglets and eyed me with a non-committal grunt, reminding me of the number of times I had left a pig pen a lot quicker than I had gone in. A big, barking, gaping-mouthed sow has always been able to make me move very smartly.

Now that I was right inside the narrow pen, Queenie seemed to have accepted me. She grunted again, but peaceably, then carefully collapsed on the straw and exposed her udder to the eager little mouths. When she was in this position I was able to examine her foot.

'Aye, that's the one,' Mr Worley said anxiously. 'She could hardly hobble when she got up this morning.'

There didn't seem to be much wrong. A flap of the horn of one claw was a bit overgrown and was rubbing on the sensitive sole, but we didn't usually get called out for little things like that. I cut away the overgrown part and dressed the sore place with our multi-purpose ointment, ung pini sedativum, while all the time Mr Worley knelt by Queenie's head and patted her and sort of crooned into her ear. I couldn't make out the words he used – maybe it was pig language because the sow really seemed to be answering him with little soft grunts. Anyway, it worked better than an anaesthetic and everybody was happy including the long row of piglets working busily at the double line of teats.

'Right, Mr Worley.' I straightened up and handed him the jar of ung pini. 'Keep rubbing in a little of that twice a day and I think she'll be sound in no time.'

'Thank ye, thank ye, I'm very grateful.' He shook my hand vigorously as though I had saved the animal's life. 'I'm very glad to meet you for the first time, Mr Herriot. I've known Mr Farnon for a year or two, of course, and I think a bit about him. Loves pigs does that man, loves them. And his young brother's been here once or twice – I reckon he's fond of pigs, too.'

'Devoted to them, Mr Worley.'

'Ah yes, I thought so. I can always tell.' He regarded me for a while with a moist eye, then smiled, well satisfied.

We went out into what was really the back yard of an inn. Because Mr Worley wasn't a regular farmer, he was the landlord of the Langthorpe Falls Hotel and his precious livestock were crammed into what had once been the stables and coach houses of the inn. They were all Tamworths and whichever door you opened you found yourself staring into the eyes of ginger-haired pigs; there were a few porkers and the odd one being fattened for bacon but Mr Worley's pride was his sows. He had six of them – Queenie, Princess, Ruby, Marigold, Delilah and Primrose.

For years expert farmers had been assuring Mr Worley that he'd never do any good with his sows. If you were going in for breeding, they said, you had to have proper premises; it wasn't a bit of use shoving sows into converted buildings like his. And for years Mr Worley's sows had responded by producing litters of unprecedented size and raising them with tender care. They were all good mothers and didn't savage their families or crush them clumsily under their bodies so it turned out with uncanny regularity that at the end of eight weeks Mr Worley had around twelve chunky weaners to take to market.

It must have spoiled the farmers' beer – none of them could equal that, and the pill was all the more bitter because the landlord had come from the industrial West Riding – Halifax, I think it was – a frail, short-sighted little retired newsagent with no agricultural background. By all the laws he just didn't have a chance.

Leaving the yard we came on to the quiet loop of road where my car was parked. Just beyond, the road dipped steeply into a tree-lined ravine where the Darrow hurled itself over a great broken shelf of rock in its passage to the lower Dale. I couldn't see down there from where I was standing, but I could hear the faint roar of the water and could picture the black cliff lifting sheer from the boiling river and on the other bank the gentle slope of turf where people from the towns came to sit and look in wonder.

Some of them were here now. A big, shiny car had drawn up and its occupants were disembarking. The driver, sleek, fat and impressive, strolled towards us and called out: 'We would like some tea.'

Mr Worley swung round on him. 'And you can 'ave some, maister, but when I'm ready. I have some very important business with this gentleman.' He turned his back on the man and began to ask me for final instructions about Queenie's foot.

The man was obviously taken aback and I couldn't blame him. It seemed to me that Mr Worley might have shown a little more tact – after all serving food and drink was his living – but as I came to know him better I realized that his pigs came first and everything else was an irritating intrusion.

Knowing Mr Worley better had its rewards. The time when I feel most like a glass of beer is not in the evening when the pubs are open but at around four-thirty on a hot afternoon after wrestling with young cattle in some stifling cow-shed. It was delightful to retire, sweating and weary, to the shaded sanctuary of Mr Worley's back kitchen and sip at the bitter ale, cool, frothing, straight from the cellar below.

The smooth working of the system was facilitated by the attitude of the local constable, PC Dalloway, a man whose benign disposition and elastic interpretation of the licensing laws had made him deeply respected in the district. Occasionally he joined us, took off his uniform jacket and, in shirt and braces, consumed a pint with a massive dignity which was peculiar to him.

But mostly Mr Worley and I were on our own and when he had brought the tall jug up from the cellar he would sit down and say, 'Well now, let's have a piggy talk!' His use of this particular phrase made me wonder if perhaps he had some humorous insight into his obsessive preoccupation with the porcine species. Maybe he had but for all that our conversations seemed to give him the deepest pleasure.

We talked about erysipelas and swine fever, brine poisoning and paratyphoid, the relative merits of dry and wet mash, while pictures of his peerless sows with their show rosettes looked down at us from the walls.

On one occasion, in the middle of a particularly profound discussion on the ventilation of farrowing houses Mr Worley stopped suddenly and, blinking rapidly behind his thick spectacles, burst out:

'You know, Mr Herriot, sitting here talking like this with you, I'm 'appy as the king of England!'

His devotion resulted in my being called out frequently for very trivial things and I swore freely under my breath when I heard his voice on the other end of the line at one o'clock one morning.

'Marigold pigged this afternoon, Mr Herriot, and I don't think she's got much milk. Little pigs look very hungry to me. Will you come?'

I groaned my way out of bed and downstairs and through the long garden to the yard. By the time I had got the car out into the lane I had begun to wake up and when I rolled up to the inn was able to greet Mr Worley fairly cheerfully.

But the poor man did not respond. In the light from the oil lamp his face was haggard with worry.

'I hope you can do something quick. I'm real upset about her – she's just laid there doing nothin' and it's such a lovely litter. Fourteen she's had.'

I could understand his concern as I looked into the pen. Marigold was stretched motionless on her side while the tiny piglets swarmed around her udder; they were rushing from teat to teat, squealing and falling over each other in their desperate quest for nourishment. And the little bodies had the narrow, empty look which meant they had nothing in their stomachs. I hated to see a litter die off from sheer starvation but it could happen so easily. There came a time when they stopped trying to suck and began to lie about the pen. After that it was hopeless.

Crouching behind the sow with my thermometer in her rectum I looked along the swelling flank, the hair a rich copper red in the light from the lamp. 'Did she eat anything tonight?'

'Aye, cleaned up just as usual.'

The thermometer reading was normal. I began to run my hands along the udder, pulling in turn at the teats. The ravenous piglets caught at my fingers with their sharp teeth as I pushed them to one side but my efforts failed to produce a drop of milk. The udder seemed full, even engorged, but I was unable to get even a bead down to the end of the teat.

'There's nowt there, is there?' Mr Worley whispered anxiously.

I straightened up and turned to him. 'This is simply agalactia. There's no mastitis and Marigold isn't really ill, but there's something interfering with the let-down mechanism of the milk. She's got plenty of milk and there's an injection which ought to bring it down.'

I tried to keep the triumphant look off my face as I spoke, because this was one of my favourite party tricks. There is a flavour of magic in the injection of pituitrin in these cases; it works within a minute and though no skill is required the effect is spectacular.

Marigold didn't complain as I plunged in the needle and administered 3 cc deep into the muscle of her thigh. She was too busy conversing with her owner – they were almost nose to nose, exchanging soft pig noises.

After I had put away my syringe and listened for a few moments to the cooing sounds from the front end I thought it might be time. Mr Worley looked up in surprise as I reached down again to the udder.

'What are you doing now?'

'Having a feel to see if the milk's come down yet.'

'Why damn, it can't be! You've only just given t'stuff and she's bone dry!'

Oh, this was going to be good. A roll of drums would be appropriate at this moment. With finger and thumb I took hold of one of the teats at the turgid back end of the udder. I suppose it is a streak of exhibitionism in me which always makes me send the jet of milk spraying against the opposite wall in these circumstances; this time I thought it would be more impressive if I directed my shot past the innkeeper's left ear, but I got my trajectory wrong and sprinkled his spectacles instead.

He took them off and wiped them slowly as if he couldn't believe what he had seen. Then he bent over and tried for himself.

'It's a miracle!' he cried as the milk spouted eagerly over his hand. 'I've never seen owt like it!'

It didn't take the little pigs long to catch on. Within a few seconds they had stopped their fighting and squealing and settled down in a long, silent row. Their utterly rapt expressions all told the same story – they were going to make up for lost time.

I went into the kitchen to wash my hands and was using the towel hanging behind the door when I noticed something odd; there was a subdued hum of conversation, the low rumble of many voices. It seemed unusual in a pub at 2 AM and I looked through the partly open door into the bar. The place was crowded. In the light of a single weak electric bulb I could see a row of men drinking at the counter while others sat behind foaming pint pots on the wooden settles against the walls.

Mr Worley grinned as I turned to him in surprise.

'Didn't expect to see this lot, did you? Well, I'll tell you, the real drinkers don't come in till after closing time. Aye, it's a rum 'un – every night I lock front door and these lads come in the back.'

I pushed my head round the door for another look. It was a kind of rogue's gallery of Darrowby. All the dubious characters in the town seemed to be gathered in that room; the names which regularly enlivened the columns of the weekly newspaper with their activities. Drunk and disorderly, non-payment of rates, wife-beating, assault and battery – I could almost see the headings as I went from face to face.

I had been spotted. Beery cries of welcome rang out and I was suddenly conscious that all eyes were fixed on me in the smoky atmosphere. Above the rest a voice said 'Are you going to have a drink?' What I wanted most was to get back to my bed, but it wouldn't look so good just to close the door and go. I went inside and over to the bar. I seemed to have plenty of friends there and within seconds was in the centre of a merry group with a pint glass in my hand.

My nearest neighbour was a well-known Darrowby worthy called Gobber Newhouse, an enormously fat man who had always seemed able to get through life without working at all. He occupied his time with drinking, brawling and gambling. At the moment he was in a mellow mood and his huge, sweating face, pushed close to mine, was twisted into a comradely leer.

'Nah then, Herriot, ow's dog trade?' he inquired courteously.

I had never heard my profession described in this way and was wondering how to answer when I noticed that the company were looking at me expectantly. Mr Worley's niece who served behind the bar was looking at me expectantly too.

'Six pints of best bitter – six shillings please,' she said, clarifying the situation.

I fumbled the money from my pocket. Obviously my first impression that somebody had invited me to have a drink with them had been mistaken. Looking round the faces, there was no way of telling who had called out, and as the beer disappeared, the group round the bar thinned out like magic; the members just drifted away as though by accident till I found myself alone. I was no longer an object of interest and nobody paid any attention as I drained my glass and left.

The glow from the pig pen showed through the darkness of the yard and as I crossed over, the soft rumble of pig and human voices told me that Mr Worley was still talking things over with his sow. He looked up as I came in and his face in the dim light was ecstatic.

'Mr Herriot,' he whispered. 'Isn't that a beautiful sight?'

He pointed to the little pigs who were lying motionless in a layered heap, sprawled over each other without plan or pattern, eyes tightly closed, stomachs bloated with Marigold's bountiful fluid.

'It is indeed,' I said, prodding the sleeping mass with my finger, but getting no response beyond the lazy opening of an eye. 'You'd have to go a long way to beat it.'

And I did share his pleasure; it was one of the satisfying little jobs. Climbing into the car I felt that the nocturnal visit had been worth while even though I had been effortlessly duped into buying a round with no hope of reciprocation. Not that I wanted to drink any more – my stomach wasn't used to receiving pints of ale at 2 AM and a few whimpers of surprise and indignation were already coming up – but I was just a bit ruffled by the off-hand, professional way those gentlemen in the tap room had handled me.

But, winding my way home through the empty, moonlit roads, I was unaware that the hand of retribution was hovering over that happy band. This was, in fact, a fateful night, because ten minutes after I had left, Mr Worley's pub was raided. Perhaps that is a rather dramatic word, but it happened that it was the constable's annual holiday and the relief man, a young policeman who did not share Mr Dalloway's liberal views, had come up on his bicycle and pinched everybody in the place.

The account of the court proceedings in the *Darrowby and Houlton Times* made good reading. Gobber Newhouse and company were all find £2 each and warned as to their future conduct. The magistrates, obviously a heartless lot, had remained unmoved by Gobber's passionate protestations that the beer in the glasses had all been purchased before closing time and that he and his friends had been lingering over it in light conversation for the subsequent four hours.

Mr Worley was fined £15 but I don't think he really minded; Marigold and her litter were doing well.

CHAPTER EIGHT

This was the last gate. I got out to open it since Tristan was driving, and looked back at the farm, a long way below us now, and at the marks our tyres had made on the steep grassy slopes. Strange places, some of these Dales farms; this one had no road to it – not even a track. From down there you just drove across the fields from gate to gate till you got to the main road above the valley. And this was the last one; ten minutes' driving and we'd be home.

Tristan was acting as my chauffeur, as my left hand had been infected after a bad calving and I had my arm in a sling. He didn't drive up through the gate but got out of the car, leaned his back against the gate post and lit a Woodbine.

Obviously he wasn't in any rush to leave. And with the sun warm on the back of his neck and the two bottles of Whitbread's nestling comfortably in his stomach I could divine that he felt pretty good. Come to think of it, it had been all right back there. He had taken some warts off a heifer's teats and the farmer had said he shaped well for a young 'un. ('Aye, you really framed at t'job, lad') and asked us in for a bottle of beer since it was so hot. Impressed by the ecstatic speed with which Tristan had consumed his, he had given him another.

Yes, it had been all right, and I could see Tristan thought so too. With a smile of utter content he took a long, deep gulp of moorland air and Woodbine smoke and closed his eyes.

He opened them quickly as a grinding noise came from the car. 'Christ! She's off, Jim!' he shouted.

The little Austin was moving gently backwards down the slope – it must have slipped out of gear and it had no brakes to speak of. We both leaped after it. Tristan was nearest and he just managed to touch the bonnet with one finger; the speed was too much for him. We gave it up and watched.

The hillside was steep and the little car rapidly gathered momentum, bouncing crazily over the uneven ground. I glanced at Tristan; his mind invariably worked quickly and clearly in a crisis and I had a good idea what he was thinking. It was only a fortnight since he had turned the Hillman over, taking a girl home from a dance. It had been a complete write-off and the insurance people had been rather nasty about it; and of course Siegfreid had gone nearly berserk and had finished by sacking him finally, once and for all – never wanted to see his face in the place again.

But he had been sacked so often; he knew he had only to keep out of his way for a bit and his brother would forget. And he had been lucky this time because Siegfried had talked his bank manager into letting him buy a beautiful new Rover and this had blotted everything else from his mind.

It was distinctly unfortunate that this should happen when he, as driver, was technically in charge of the Austin. The car appeared now to be doing about 70 mph hurtling terrifyingly down the long, green hill. One by one the doors burst open till all four flapped wildly and the car swooped downwards looking like a huge, ungainly bird.

From the open doors, bottles, instruments, bandages, cotton wool cascaded out on to the turf, leaving a long, broken trail. Now and again a packet of nux vomica and bicarb stomach powder would fly out and burst like a bomb, splashing vivid white against the green.

Tristan threw up his arms. 'Look! The bloody thing's going straight for that hut.' He drew harder on his Woodbine.

There was indeed only one obstruction on the bare hillside – a small building near the foot where the land levelled out and the Austin, as if drawn by a magnet, was thundering straight towards it.

I couldn't bear to watch. Just before the impact I turned away and focused my attention on the end of Tristan's cigarette which was glowing bright red when the crash came. When I looked back down the hill the building was no longer there. It had been completely flattened and everything I had ever heard about houses of cards surged into my mind. On top of the shattered timbers the little car lay peacefully on its side, its wheels still turning lazily.

As we galloped down the hill it was easy to guess Tristan's thoughts. He wouldn't be looking forward to telling Siegfried he had wrecked the Austin; in fact it was something the mind almost refused to contemplate. But as we neared the scene of devastation, passing on our way syringes, scalpels, bottles of vaccine, it was difficult to see any other outcome.

Arriving at the car, we made an anxious inspection. The body had been so bashed and dented before that it wasn't easy to identify any new marks. Certainly the rear end was pretty well caved in but it didn't show up very much. The only obvious damage was a smashed rear light. Our hopes rising, we set off for the farm for help.

The farmer greeted us amiably. 'Now then, you lads, hasta come back for more beer?'

'It wouldn't come amiss,' Tristan replied. 'We've had a bit of an accident.'

We went into the house and the hospitable man opened some more bottles. He didn't seem disturbed when he heard of the demolition of the hut. 'Nay, that's not mine. Belongs to t'golf club – it's t'club house.'

Tristan's eyebrows shot up. 'Oh no! Don't say we've flattened the headquarters of the Darrowby Golf Club!'

'Aye, lad, you must have. It's t'only wooden building in them fields. I rent that part of my land to the club and they've made a little nine hole course. Don't worry, hardly anybody plays on it – mainly t'bank manager and ah don't like that feller.'

Mr Prescott got a horse out of the stable and we went back to the car and pulled it upright again. Trembling a little, Tristan climbed in and pressed the starter. The sturdy little engine burst into a confident roar immediately and he drove carefully over the prostrate wooden walls on to the grass.

'Well thanks a lot, Mr Prescott,' he shouted. 'We seem to have got away with it.'

'Champion, lad, champion. You're as good as new.' Then the farmer winked and held up a finger. 'Now you say nowt about this job and I'll say nowt. Right?'

'Right! Come on, Jim, get in.' Tristan put his foot down and we chugged thankfully up the hill once more.

He seemed thoughtful on the way and didn't speak till we got on to the road. Then he turned to me.

'You know, Jim, it's all very well, but I've still got to confess to Siegfried about that rear light. And of course I'll get the lash again. Don't you think it's just a bit hard the way I get blamed for everything that happens to his cars? You've seen it over and over again – he gives me a lot of bloody old wrecks to drive and when they start to fall to bits it's always my fault. The bloody tyres are all down to the canvas but if I get a puncture there's hell to pay. It isn't fair.'

'Well Siegfried isn't the man to suffer in silence, you know.' I said. 'He's got to lash out and you're nearest.'

Tristan was silent for a moment then he took a deeper drag at his Woodbine, blew out his cheeks and assumed a judicial expression. 'Mind you, I'm not saying I was entirely blameless with regard to the Hillman –I was taking that sharp turn in Dringley at sixty with my arm round a little nurse – but all in all I've just had sheer bad luck. In fact, Jim, I'm a helpless victim of prejudice.'

Siegfried was out of sorts when we met in the surgery. He was starting a summer cold and was sniffly and listless, but he still managed to raise a burst of energy at the news.

'You bloody young maniac! It's the rear light now, is it? God help me, I think all I work for is to pay for the repair bills you run up. You'll ruin me before you're finished. Go on, get to hell out of it. I'm finished with you.'

Tristan retired with dignity and followed his usual policy of lying low. He didn't see his brother until the following morning. Siegfried's condition had deteriorated; the cold had settled in his throat, always his weak spot, and he was down with laryngitis. His neck was swathed in vinegar-soaked Thermogene and when Tristan and I came into the bedroom he was feebly turning over the pages of the *Darrowby and Houlton Times*.

He spoke in a tortured whisper. 'Have you seen this? It says here that the golf clubhouse was knocked down yesterday and there's no clue as to how it happened. Damn funny thing. On Prescott's land, isn't it?' His head jerked suddenly from the pillow and he glared at his brother. 'You were there yesterday!' he croaked, then he fell back, muttering. 'Oh no, no, I'm sorry, it's too ridiculous – and it's wrong of me to blame you for everything.'

Tristan stared. He had never heard this kind of talk from Siegfried before. I too felt a pang of anxiety; could my boss be delirious?

Siegfried swallowed painfully. 'I've just had an urgent call from Armitage of Sorton. He's got a cow down with milk fever and I want you to drive James out there straight away. Go on, now – get moving.'

'Afraid I can't,' Tristan shrugged. 'Jim's car is in Hammond's garage. They're fixing that light – it'll take them about an hour.'

'Oh God, yes, and they said they couldn't let us have a spare. Well, Armitage is in a bit of a panic – that cow could be dead in an hour. What the hell can we do?'

'There's the Rover,' Tristan said quietly.

Siegfried's form stiffened suddenly under the blankets and wild terror flickered in his eyes. For a few moments his head rolled about on the pillow and his long, bony fingers picked nervously at the quilt, then with an effort he heaved himself on to his side and stared into his brother's eyes. He spoke slowly and the agonized hissing of his voice lent menace to his words.

'Right, so you'll have to take the Rover. I never thought I'd see the day when I'd let a wrecker like you drive it, but just let me tell you this. If you put a scratch on that car I'll kill you. I'll kill you with my own two hands.'

The old pattern was asserting itself. Siegfried's eyes had begun to bulge, a dark flush was creeping over his cheeks while Tristan's face had lost all expression.

Using the last remnants of his strength, Siegfried hoisted himself even higher. 'Now do you really think you are capable of driving that car five miles to Sorton and back without smashing it up? All right then, get on with it, and just remember what I've said.'

Tristan withdrew in offended silence and as I followed him I took a last look at the figure in the bed. Siegfried had fallen back and was staring at the ceiling with feverish eyes. His lips moved feebly as though he were praying.

Outside the room, Tristan rubbed his hands delightedly. 'What a break, Jim! A chance in a lifetime! You know I never thought I'd get behind the wheel of that Rover in a hundred years.' He dropped his voice to a whisper. 'Just shows you – everything happens for the best.'

Five minutes later he was backing carefully out of the yard and into the lane and once on the Sorton road I saw he was beginning to enjoy himself. For two miles the way ahead stretched straight and clear except for a milk lorry approaching in the far distance; a perfect place to see what the Rover could do. He nestled down in the rich leather upholstery and pressed his foot hard on the accelerator.

We were doing an effortless eighty when I saw a car beginning to overtake the milk lorry; it was an ancient, square-topped, high-built vehicle like a biscuit tin on wheels and it had no business trying to overtake anything. I waited for it to pull back but it still came on. And the lorry, perhaps with a sporting driver, seemed to be spurting to make a race of it.

With increasing alarm I saw the two vehicles abreast and bearing down on us only a few hundred yards away and not a foot of space on either side of them. Of course the old car would pull in behind the lorry – it had to, there was no other way – but it was taking a long time about it. Tristan jammed on his brakes. If the lorry did the same, the other car would just be able to dodge between. But within seconds I realized nothing like that was going to happen and as they thundered towards us I resigned myself with dumb horror to a head-on collision.

Just before I closed my eyes I had a fleeting glimpse of a large, alarmed face behind the wheel of the old car, then something hit the left side of the Rover with a rending crash.

When I opened my eyes we were stationary. There was just Tristan and myself staring straight ahead at the road, empty and quiet, curving ahead of us into the peaceful green of the hills.

I sat motionless, listening to my thumping heart then I looked over my shoulder and saw the lorry disappearing at high speed round a distant bend; in passing I studied Tristan's face with interest – I had never seen a completely green face before.

After quite a long time feeling a draught from the left, I looked carefully round in that direction. There were no doors on that side – one was lying by the roadside a few yards back and the other hung from a single broken hinge; as I watched, this one too, clattered on to the tarmac with a note of flat finality. Slowly, as in a dream, I got out and surveyed the damage; the left side of the Rover was a desert of twisted metal where the old car, diving for the verge at the last split second, had ploughed its way.

Tristan had flopped down on the grass, his face blank. A nasty scratch on the paintwork might have sent him into a panic but this wholesale destruction seemed to have numbed his senses. But this state didn't last long; he began to blink, then his eyes narrowed and he felt for his Woodbines. His agile mind was back at work and it wasn't difficult to read his thoughts. What was he going to do now?

It seemed to me after a short appraisal of the situation that he had three possible courses of action. First, and most attractive, he could get out of Darrowby permanently – emigrate if necessary. Second, he could go straight to the railway station and board a train for Brawton where he could live quietly with his mother till this had blown over. Third, and it didn't bear thinking about, he could go back to Skeldale House and tell Siegfried he had smashed up his new Rover.

As I weighed up the possibilities I spotted the old car which had hit us; it was lying upside down in a ditch about fifty yards down the road. Hurrying towards it, I could hear a loud cackling coming from the interior and I remembered it was market day and many of the farmers would be bringing in crates of hens and maybe twenty or thirty dozen eggs to sell. We peered in through a window and Tristan gasped. A fat man, obviously unhurt, was lying in a great pool of smashed eggs. His face wore a wide, reassuring smile – in fact, his whole expression was ingratiating as far as it could be seen through the mask of egg which covered his features. The rest of the interior was filled with frantic hens which had escaped from their crates in the crash and were hunting for a way out.

The fat man, smiling up happily from his bed of eggs, was shouting something, but it was difficult to hear him above the wild cackling. I managed to pick up odd phrases: 'Very sorry indeed – entirely my fault – I'll make good the damage.' The words floated up cheerfully while the hens scampered across the man's beaming face and yolks coursed sluggishly down his clothes.

With an effort, Tristan managed to wrench open a door and was driven back immediately by a rush of hens. Some of them galloped off in various directions till they were lost to sight, while their less adventurous companions began to peck about philosophically by the roadside.

'Are you all right?' Tristan shouted.

'Yes, yes, young man. I'm not hurt. Please don't worry about me.' The fat man struggled vainly to rise from the squelching mass. 'Ee, I am sorry about this, but I'll see you right, you can be sure.'

He held up a dripping hand and we helped him out on to the road. Despite his saturated clothes and the pieces of shell sticking to his hair and moustache he hadn't lost his poise. In fact he radiated confidence, the same confidence, I thought, which made him think his old car could overtake that speeding lorry.

He laid a hand on Tristan's shoulder. 'There's a simple explanation, you know. The sun got in my eyes.'

It was twelve noon and the fat man had been driving due north, but there didn't seem much point in arguing.

We lifted the shattered doors from the road, put them inside the Rover, drove to Sorton, treated the milk fever cow and returned to Darrowby. Tristan gave me a single despairing look then squared his shoulders and marched straight to his brother's room. I followed close on his heels.

Siegfried was worse. His face was red with fever and his eyes burned deeply in their sockets. He didn't move when Tristan walked over to the foot of the bed.

'Well, how did you get on?' The whisper was barely audible.

'Oh fine, the cow was on her feet when we left. But there's just one thing – I had a bit of a bump with the car.'

Siegfried had been wheezing stertorously and staring at the ceiling but the breathing stopped as if it had been switched off. There was an eerie silence then from the completely motionless figure two strangled words escaped. 'What happened?'

'Wasn't my fault. Chap tried to overtake a lorry and didn't make it. Caught one side of the Rover.'

Again the silence and again the whisper.

'Much damage?'

'Front and rear wings pretty well mangled, I'm afraid – and both doors torn off the left side.'

As if operated by a powerful spring, Siegfried came bolt upright in the bed. It was startingly like a corpse coming to life and the effect was heightened by the coils of Thermogene which had burst loose and trailed in shroud-like garlands from the haggard head. The mouth opened wide in a completely soundless scream.

'You bloody fool! You're sacked!'

He crashed back on to the pillow as though the mechanism had gone into reverse and lay very still. We watched him for a few moments in some anxiety, but when we heard the breathing restart we tiptoed from the room.

On the landing Tristan blew out his cheeks and drew a Woodbine from its packet. 'A tricky little situation, Jim, but you know what I always say.' He struck a match and pulled the smoke down blissfully. 'Things usually turn out better than you expect.'

CHAPTER NINE

A lot of the Dales farms were anonymous and it was a help to find this one so plainly identified. 'Heston Grange' it said on the gate in bold black capitals.

I got out of the car and undid the latch. It was a good gate, too, and swung easily on its hinges instead of having to be dragged round with a shoulder under the top spar. The farmhouse lay below me, massive, grey-stoned, with a pair of bow windows which some prosperous Victorian had added to the original structure.

It stood on a flat, green neck of land in a loop of the river and the lushness of the grass and the quiet fertility of the surrounding fields contrasted sharply with the stark hills behind. Towering oaks and beeches sheltered the house and a thick pine wood covered the lower slopes of the fell.

I walked round the buildings shouting as I always did, because some people considered it a subtle insult to go to the house and ask if the farmer was in. Good farmers are indoors only at meal times. But my shouts drew no reply, so I went over and knocked at the door set deep among the weathered stones.

A voice answered 'Come in', and I opened the door into a huge, stone-flagged kitchen with hams and sides of bacon hanging from hooks in the ceiling. A dark girl in a check blouse and green linen slacks was kneading dough in a bowl. She looked up and smiled.

'Sorry I couldn't let you in. I've got my hands full.' She held up her arms, floury-white to the elbow.

'That's all right. My name is Herriot. I've come to see a calf. It's lame, I understand.'

'Yes, we think he's broken his leg. Probably got his foot in a hole when he was running about. If you don't mind waiting a minute, I'll come with you. My father and the men are in the fields. I'm Helen Alderson, by the way.'

She washed and dried her arms and pulled on a pair of short wellingtons. 'Take over this bread will you, Meg,' she said to an old woman who came through from an inner room 'I have to show Mr Herriot the calf.'

Outside, she turned to me and laughed. 'We've got a bit of a walk. I'm afraid. He's in one of the top buildings. Look, you can just see it up there.' She pointed to a squat, stone barn, high on the fell-side. I knew all about these top buildings, they were scattered all over the high country and I got a lot of healthy exercise going round them. They were used for storing hay and other things and as shelters for the animals on the hill pastures.

I looked at the girl for a few seconds. 'Oh, that's all right, I don't mind. I don't mind in the least.'

We went over the field to a narrow bridge spanning the river, and following her across, I was struck by a thought this new fashion of women wearing slacks might be a bit revolutionary but there was a lot to be said for it. The path led upward through the pine wood and here the sunshine was broken up into islands of brightness among the dark trunks, the sound of the river grew faint and we walked softly on a thick carpet of pine needles. It was cool in the wood and silent except when a bird call echoed through the trees.

Ten minutes of hard walking brought us out again into the hot sun on the open moor and the path curved steeper still round a series of rocky outcrops. I was beginning to puff, but the girl kept up a brisk pace, swinging along with easy strides. I was glad when we reached the level ground on the top and the barn came in sight again.

When I opened the half door I could hardly see my patient in the dark interior which was heavy with the fragrance of hay piled nearly to the roof. He looked very small and sorry for himself with his dangling foreleg which trailed uselessly along the strawed floor as he tried to walk.

'Will you hold his head while I examine him, please?' I said.

The girl caught the calf expertly, one hand under its chin, the other holding an ear. As I felt my way over the leg the little creature stood trembling, his face a picture of woe.

'Well, your diagnosis was correct. Clean fracture of the radius and ulna, but there's very little displacement so it should do well with a plaster on it.' I opened my bag, took out some plaster bandages then filled a bucket with water from a near-by spring. I soaked one of the bandages and applied it to the leg, following it with a second and a third till the limb was encased in a rapidly hardening white sheath from elbow to foot.

'We'll just wait a couple of minutes till it hardens, then we can let him go.' I kept tapping the plaster till I was satisfied it was set like stone. 'All right,' I said finally. 'He can go now.'

The girl released the head and the little animal trotted away. 'Look,' she cried. 'He's putting his weight on it already! And doesn't he look a lot happier!' I smiled. I felt I had really done something. The calf felt no pain now that the broken ends of the bone were immobilized; and the fear which always demoralizes a hurt animal had magically vanished.

'Yes,' I said. 'He certainly has perked up quickly.' My words were almost drowned by a tremendous bellow and the patch of blue above the half door was suddenly obscured by a large shaggy head. Two great liquid eyes stared down anxiously at the little calf and it answered with a high-pitched bawl. Soon a deafening duet was in progress.

'That's his mother,' the girl shouted above the din. 'Poor

old thing, she's been hanging about here all morning wondering what we've done with her calf. She hates being separated from him.'

I straightened up and drew the bolt on the door. 'Well she can come in now.'

The big cow almost knocked me down as she rushed past me. Then she started a careful, sniffing inspection of her calf, pushing him around with her muzzle and making muffled lowing noises deep in her throat.

The little creature submitted happily to all the fuss and when it was over and his mother was finally satisfied, he limped round to her udder and began to suck heartily.

'Soon got his appetite back,' I said and we both laughed.

I threw the empty tins into my bag and closed it. 'He'll have to keep the plaster on for a month, so if you'll give me a ring then I'll come back and take it off. Just keep an eye on him and make sure his leg doesn't get sore round the top of the bandage.'

As we left the barn the sunshine and the sweet warm air met us like a high wave. I turned and looked across the valley to the soaring green heights, smooth, enormous, hazy in the noon heat. Beneath my feet the grassy slopes fell away steeply to where the river glimmered among the trees.

'It's wonderful up here,' I said. 'Just look at that gorge over there. And that great hill – I suppose you could call it a mountain.' I pointed at a giant which heaved its heather-mottled shoulders high above the others.

'That's Heskit Fell – nearly two and a half thousand feet. And that's Eddleton just beyond, and Wedder Fell on the other side and Colver and Sennor.' The names with their wild, Nordic ring fell easily from her tongue; she spoke of them like old friends and I could sense the affection in her voice.

We sat down on the warm grass of the hillside, a soft breeze pulled at the heads of the moorland flowers, somewhere a curlew cried. Darrowby and Skeldale House and veterinary practice seemed a thousand miles away.

'You're lucky to live here,' I said. 'But I don't think you need me to tell you that.'

'No, I love this country. There's nowhere else quite like it.' She paused and looked slowly around her. 'I'm glad it appeals to you too – a lot of people find it too bare and wild. It almost seems to frighten them.'

I laughed. 'Yes, I know, but as far as I'm concerned I can't help feeling sorry for all the thousands of vets who don't work in the Yorkshire Dales.'

I began to talk about my work, then almost without knowing, I was going back over my student days, telling her of the good times, the friends I had made and our hopes and aspirations.

I surprised myself with my flow of talk – I wasn't much of a chatterbox usually – and I felt I must be boring my companion. But she sat quietly looking over the valley, her arms around her green-clad legs, nodding at times as though she understood. And she laughed in all the right places.

I wondered too, at the silly feeling that I would like to forget all about the rest of the day's duty and stay up here on this sunny hillside. It came to me that it had been a long time since I had sat down and talked to a girl of my own age. I had almost forgotten what it was like.

I didn't hurry back down the path and through the scented pine wood but it seemed no time at all before we were walking across the wooden bridge and over the field to the farm.

I turned with my hand on the car door. 'Well, I'll see you in a month.' It sounded like an awful long time.

The girl smiled. 'Thank you for what you've done.' As I started the engine she waved and went into the house.

'Helen Alderson?' Siegfried said later over lunch. 'Of course I know her. Lovely girl.'

Tristan, across the table, made no comment, but he laid down his knife and fork, raised his eyes reverently to the ceiling and gave a long, low whistle. Then he started to eat again.

Siegfried went on. 'Oh yes, I know her very well. And I admire her. Her mother died a few years ago and she runs the whole place. Cooks and looks after her father and a younger brother and sister.' He spooned some mashed potatoes on to his plate. 'Any men friends? Oh, half the young bloods in the district are chasing her but she doesn't seem to be going steady with any of them. Choosy sort, I think.'

CHAPTER TEN

It was when I was plodding up Mr Kay's field for the ninth time that it began to occur to me that this wasn't going to be my day. For some time now I had been an LVI, the important owner of a little certificate informing whosoever it may concern that James Herriot MRCVS was a Local Veterinary Inspector of the Ministry of Agriculture and Fisheries. It meant that I was involved in a lot of routine work like clinical examinations and tuberculin testing. It also highlighted something which I had been suspecting for some time – the Dales farmers' attitude to time was different from my own.

It had been all right when I was calling on them to see a sick animal; they were usually around waiting for me and the beast would be confined in some building when I arrived. It was very different, however, when I sent them a card saying I was coming to inspect their dairy cows or test their herd. It stated quite clearly on the card that the animals must be assembled indoors and that I would be there at a certain time and I planned my day accordingly; fifteen minutes or so for a clinical and anything up to several hours for a test depending on the size of the herd. If I was kept waiting for ten minutes at every clinical while they got the cows in from the field it meant simply that after six visits I was running an hour late.

So when I drove up to Mr Kay's farm for a tuberculin test and found his cows tied up in their stalls I breathed a sigh of relief. We were through them in no time at all and I thought I was having a wonderful start to the day when the farmer said he had only half a dozen young heifers to do to complete their job. It was when I left the buildings and saw the group of shaggy roans and reds grazing contentedly at the far end of a large field that I felt the old foreboding.

'I thought you'd have them inside, Mr Kay,' I said apprehensively.

Mr Kay tapped out his pipe on to his palm, mixed the sodden dottle with a few strands of villainous looking twist and crammed it back into the bowl. 'Nay, nay,' he said, puffing appreciatively, 'Ah didn't like to put them in on a grand 'ot day like this. We'll drive them up to that little house.' He pointed to a tumble down grey-stone barn at the summit of the long, steeply sloping pasture and blew out a cloud of choking smoke. 'Won't take many minutes.'

At his last sentence a cold hand clutched at me. I'd heard these dreadful words so many times before. But maybe it would be all right this time. We made our way to the bottom of the field and got behind the heifers.

'Cush, cush!' cried Mr Kay.

'Cush, cush!' I added encouragingly, slapping my hands against my thighs.

The heifers stopped pulling the grass and regarded us with mild interest, their jaws moving lazily, then in response to further cries they began to meander casually up the hill. We managed to coax them up to the door of the barn but there they stopped. The leader put her head inside for a moment then turned suddenly and made a dash down the hill. The others followed suit immediately and though we danced about and waved our arms they ran past us as if we weren't there. I looked thoughtfully at the young beasts thundering down the slope, their tails high, kicking up their heels like mustangs; they were enjoying this new game.

Down the hill once more and again the slow wheedling up to the door and again the sudden breakaway. This time one of them tried it on her own and as I galloped vainly to and fro trying to turn her the others charged with glee through the gap and down the slope again.

It was a long, steep hill and as I trudged up for the third time with the sun blazing on my back I began to regret being so conscientious about my clothes; in the instructions to the new LVIs the Ministry had been explicit that they expected us to be properly attired to carry out our duties. I had taken it to heart and rigged myself out in the required uniform but I realized now that a long oilskin coat and wellingtons was not an ideal outfit for the job in hand. The sweat was trickling into my eyes and my shirt was beginning to cling to me.

When, for the third time, I saw the retreating backs careering joyously down the hill, I thought it was time to do something about it.

'Just a minute,' I called to the farmer, 'I'm getting a bit warm.'

I took off the coat, rolled it up and placed it on the grass well away from the barn. And as I made a neat pile of my syringe, the box of tuberculin, my calipers, scissors, notebook and pencil, the thought kept intruding that I was being cheated in some way. After all, Ministry work was easy – any practitioner would tell you that. You didn't have to get up in the middle of the night, you had nice set hours and you never really had to exert yourself. In fact it was money for old rope – a pleasant relaxation from the real thing. I wiped my streaming brow and stood for a few seconds panting gently – this just wasn't fair.

We started again and at the fourth visit to the barn I thought we had won because all but one of the heifers strolled casually inside. But that last one just wouldn't have it. We cushed imploringly, waved and even got near enough to poke at its rump but it stood in the entrance regarding the interior with deep suspicion. Then the heads of its mates began to reappear in the doorway and I knew we had lost again; despite my frantic dancing and shouting they wandered out one by one before joining again in their happy downhill dash. This time I found myself galloping down after them in an agony of frustration.

We had another few tries during which the heifers introduced touches of variation by sometimes breaking away halfway up the hill or occasionally trotting round the back of the barn and peeping at us coyly from behind the old stones before frisking to the bottom again.

After the eighth descent I looked appealingly at Mr Kay who was relighting his pipe calmly and didn't appear to be troubled in any way. My time schedule was in tatters but I don't think he had noticed that we had been going on like this for about forty minutes.

'Look, we're getting nowhere,' I said. 'I've got a lot of other work waiting for me. Isn't there anything more we can do?'

The farmer stamped down the twist with his thumb, drew deeply and pleasurably a few times then looked at me with mild surprise. 'Well, let's see. We could bring dog out but – don't know as he'll be much good. He's nobbut a young 'un.'

He sauntered back to the farmhouse and opened a door. A shaggy cur catapulted out, barking in delight, and Mr Kay brought him over to the field. 'Get away by!' he cried gesturing towards the cattle who had resumed their grazing and the dog streaked behind them. I really began to hope as we went up the hill with the hairy little figure darting in, nipping at the heels, but at the barn the rot set in again. I could see the heifers beginning to sense the inexperience of the dog and one of them managed to kick him briskly under the chin as he came in. The little animal yelped and his tail went down. He stood uncertainly, looking at the beasts, advancing on him now, shaking their horns threateningly, then he seemed to come to a decision and slunk away. The young cattle went after him at increasing speed and in a moment I was looking at the extraordinary spectacle of the dog going flat out down the hill with the heifers drumming close behind him. At the foot he disappeared under a gate and we saw him no more.

Something seemed to give way in my head. 'Oh God,' I yelled, 'we're never going to get these damn things tested! I'll just have to leave them. I don't know what the Ministry is going to say, but I've had enough!'

The farmer looked at me ruminatively. He seemed to recognize that I was at breaking point. 'Aye, it's no good,' he said, tapping his pipe out on his heel. 'We'll have to get Sam.'

'Sam?'

'Aye, Sam Broadbent. Works for me neighbour. He'll get 'em in all right.'

'How's he going to do that?'

'Oh, he can imitate a fly.'

For a moment my mind reeled. 'Did you say imitate a fly?'

'That's right. A warble fly, tha knows. He's a bit slow is t'lad but by gaw he can imitate a fly. I'll go and get him – he's only two fields down the road.'

I watched the farmer's retreating back in disbelief then threw myself down on the ground. At any other time I would have enjoyed lying there on the slope with the sun on my face and the grass cool against my sweating back; the air was still and heavy with the fragrance of clover and when I opened my eyes the gentle curve of the valley floor was a vision of peace. But my mind was a turmoil. I had a full day's Ministry work waiting for me and I was an hour behind time already. I could picture the long succession of farmers waiting for me and cursing me heartily. The tension built in me till I could stand it no longer; I jumped to my feet and ran down to the gate at the foot. I could see along the road from there and was relieved to find Mr Kay was on his way back.

Just behind him a large, fat man was riding slowly on a very small bicycle, his heels on the pedals, his feet and knees sticking out at right angles. Tufts of greasy black hair stuck out at random from under a kind of skull cap which looked like an old bowler without the brim.

'Sam's come to give us a hand,' said Mr Kay with an air of quiet triumph.

'Good morning,' I said and the big man turned slowly and nodded. The eyes in the round, unshaven face were vacant and incurious and I decided that Sam did indeed look a bit slow. I found it difficult to imagine how he could possibly be of any help.

The heifers, standing near by, watched with languid interest as we came through the gate. They had obviously enjoyed every minute of the morning's entertainment and it seemed they were game for a little more fun if we so desired; but it was up to us, of course – they weren't worried either way.

Sam propped his bicycle against the wall and paced solemnly forward. He made a circle of his thumb and forefinger and placed it to his lips. His cheeks worked as though he was getting everything into place then he took a deep breath. And, from nowhere it seemed came a sudden swelling of angry sound, a vicious humming and buzzing which made me look round in alarm for the enraged insect zooming in for the kill.

The effect on the heifers was electric. Their superior air vanished and was replaced by rigid anxiety; then, as the noise increased in volume, they turned and charged up the hill. But it wasn't the carefree frolic of before – no tossing heads, waving tails and kicking heels; this time they kept shoulder to shoulder in a frightened block.

Mr Kay and I, trotting on either side, directed them yet again up to the building where they formed a group, looking nervously around them.

We had to wait for a short while for Sam to arrive. He was clearly a one-pace man and ascended the slope unhurriedly. At the top he paused to regain his breath, fixed the animals with a blank gaze and carefully adjusted his fingers against his mouth. A moment's tense silence then the humming broke out again, even more furious and insistent than before.

The heifers knew when they were beaten. With a chorus of startled bellows they turned and rushed into the building and I crashed the half door behind them; I stood leaning against it unable to believe my troubles were over. Sam joined me and looked into the dark interior. As if to finally establish his mastery he gave a sudden sharp blast, this time without his fingers, and his victims huddled still closer against the far wall.

A few minutes later, after Sam had left us, I was happily clipping and injecting the necks. I looked up at the farmer. 'You know, I can still hardly believe what I saw there. It was like magic. That chap has a wonderful gift.'

Mr Kay looked over the half door and I followed his gaze down the grassy slope to the road. Sam was riding away and the strange black headwear was just visible, bobbing along the top of the wall.

'Ay, he can imitate a fly all right. Poor awd lad, it's t'only thing he's good at.'

CHAPTER ELEVEN

Hurrying away from Mr Kay's to my second test I reflected that if I had to be more than an hour late for an appointment it was a lucky thing that my next call was at the Hugills. The four brothers and their families ran a herd which, with cows, followers and calves must have amounted to nearly two hundred and I had to test the lot of them; but I knew that my lateness wouldn't bring any querulous remarks on my head because the Hugills had developed the Dales tradition of courtesy to an extraordinary degree. The stranger within their gates was treated like royalty.

As I drove into the yard I could see everybody leaving their immediate tasks and advancing on me with beaming faces. The brothers were in the lead and they stopped opposite me as I got out of the car, and I thought as I always did that I had never seen such healthy-looking men. Their ages ranged from Walter, who was about sixty, down through Thomas and Fenwick to William, the youngest, who would be in his late forties, and I should say their average weight would be about fifteen stones. They weren't fat, either, just huge, solid men with bright red, shining faces and clear eyes.

William stepped forward from the group and I knew what was coming; this was always his job. He leaned forward, suddenly solemn, and looked into my face.

'How are you today, sorr?' he asked.

'Very well, thank you, Mr Hugill,' I replied.

'Good!' said William fervently, and the other brothers all repeated 'Good, good, good,' with deep satisfaction.

William took a deep breath. 'And how is Mr Farnon?'

'Oh, he's very fit, thanks.'

'Good!' Then the rapid fire of the responses from behind him: 'Good, good, good.'

William hadn't finished yet. He cleared his throat. 'And how is young Mr Farnon?'

'In really top form.'

'Good!' But this time William allowed himself a gentle smile and from behind him came a few dignified ho-ho's. Walter closed his eyes and his great shoulders shook silently. They all knew Tristan.

William stepped back into line, his appointed task done and we all went into the byre. I braced myself as I looked at the long row of backs, the tails swishing at the flies. There was some work ahead here.

'Sorry I'm so late,' I said, as I drew the tuberculin into the syringe. 'I was held up at the last place. It's difficult to forecast how long these tests will take.'

All four brothers replied eagerly. 'Aye, you're right, sorr. It's difficult. It IS difficult. You're right, you're right, it's difficult.' They went on till they had thrashed the last ounce out of the statement.

I finished filling the syringe, got out my scissors and began to push my way between the first two cows. It was a tight squeeze and I puffed slightly in the stifling atmosphere.

'It's a bit warm in here,' I said.

Again the volley of agreement. 'You're right, sorr. Aye, it's warm. It IS warm. You're right. It's warm. It's warm. Aye, you're right.' This was all delivered with immense conviction and vigorous nodding of heads as though I had made some incredible discovery; and as I looked at the grave, intent faces still pondering over my brilliant remark, I could feel my tensions beginning to dissolve. I was lucky to work here. Where else but in the high country of Yorkshire would I meet people like these?

I pushed along the cow and got hold of its ear, but Walter stopped me with a gentle cough.

'Nay, Mr Herriot, you won't have to look in the ears. I have all t'numbers wrote down.'

'Oh, that's fine. It'll save us a lot of time.' I had always found scratching the wax away to find ear tattoos an overrated pastime. And it was good to hear that the Hugills were attending to the clerical side; there was a section in the Ministry form which said: 'Are the herd records in good order?' I always wrote 'Yes,' keeping my fingers crossed as I thought of the scrawled figures on the backs of old bills, milk recording sheets, anything.

'Aye,' said Walter. 'I have 'em all set down proper in a book.'

'Great! Can you go and get it, then?'

'No need, sorr, I have it 'ere.' Walter was the boss, there was no doubt about it. They all seemed to live in perfect harmony but when the chips were down Walter took over automatically. He was the organizer, the acknowledged brains of the outfit. The battered trilby which he always wore in contrast with the others' caps gave him an extra air of authority.

Everybody watched respectfully as he slowly and deliberately extracted a spectacle case from an inside pocket. He opened it and took out an old pair of steel-rimmed spectacles, blowing away fragments of the hay and corn chaff with which the interior of the case was thickly powdered. There was a quiet dignity and importance in the way he unhurriedly threaded the side pieces over his ears and stood grimacing slightly to work everything into place. Then he put his hand into his waistcoat pocket.

When he took it out he was holding some object but it was difficult to identify, being almost obscured by his enormous thumb. Then I saw that it was a tiny, black-covered miniature diary about two inches square – the sort of novelty people give each other at Christmas.

'Is that the herd record?' I asked.

'Yes, this is it. It's all set down in here.' Walter daintily flicked over the pages with a horny forefinger and squinted through his spectacles. 'Now that fust cow – she's number eighty-fower.'

'Splendid!' I said. 'I'll just check this one and then we can go by the book.' I peered into the ear. 'That's funny, I make it twenty-six.'

The brothers had a look. 'You're right sorr, you're right. It IS twenty-six.'

Walter pursed his lips. 'Why, that's Bluebell's calf, isn't it?'

'Nay,' said Fenwick, 'she's out of awd Buttercup.'

'Can't be,' mumbled Thomas. 'Awd Buttercup was sold to Tim Jefferson afore this 'un was born. This is Brenda's calf.'

William shook his head. 'Ah'm sure we got her as a heifer at Bob Ashby's sale.'

'All right,' I said, holding up a hand. 'We'll put in twenty-six.' I had to cut in. It was in no way an argument, just a leisurely discussion but it looked as if it could go on for some time. I wrote the number in my notebook and injected the cow. 'Now how about this next one?'

'Well ah DO know that 'un,' said Walter confidently, stabbing at an entry in the diary. 'Can't make no mistake, she's number five.'

I looked in the ear. 'Says a hundred and thirty seven here.'

It started again. 'She was brought in, wasn't she?' 'Nay, nay, she's out of awd Dribbler.' 'Don't think so – Dribbler had nowt but bulls . . .'

I raised my hand again. 'You know, I really think it might be quicker to look in all the ears. Time's getting on.'

'Aye, you're right, sorr, it IS getting on.' Walter returned the herd record to his waistcoat pocket philosophically and we started the laborious business of clipping, measuring and injecting every animal, plus rubbing the inside of the ears with a cloth soaked in spirit to identify the numbers which had often faded to a few unrelated dots. Occasionally Walter referred to his tiny book. 'Ah, that's right, ninety-two. I thowt so. It's all set down here.'

Fighting with the loose animals in the boxes round the fold yard was like having a dirty Turkish bath while wearing oilskins. The brothers caught the big beasts effortlessly and even the strongest bullock grew quickly discouraged when it tried to struggle against those mighty arms. But I noticed one strange phenomenon: the men's fingers were so thick and huge that they often slipped out of the animals' noses through sheer immobility.

It took an awful long time but we finally got through. The last little calf had a space clipped in his shaggy neck and bawled heartily as he felt the needle, then I was out in the sweet air throwing my coat in the car boot. I looked at my watch – three o'clock. I was nearly two hours behind my schedule now and already I was hot and weary, with skinned toes on my right foot where a cow had trodden and a bruised left instep caused by the sudden descent of Fenwick's size thirteen hobnails during a particularly violent mêlée. As I closed the boot and limped round to the car door I began to wonder a little about this easy Ministry work.

Walter loomed over me and inclined his head graciously. 'Come in and sit down and have a drink o' tea.'

'It's very kind of you and I wish I could Mr Hugill. But I've got a long string of inspections waiting and I don't know when I'll get round them. I've fixed up far too many and I completely underestimated the time needed for your test. I really am an absolute fool.'

And the brothers intoned sincerely. 'Aye, you're right, sorr, you're right, you're right.'

Well, there was no more testing today, but ten inspections still to do and I should have been at the first one two hours ago. I roared off, feeling that little ball tightening in my stomach as it always did when I was fighting the clock. Gripping the wheel with one hand and exploring my lunch packet with the other, I pulled out a piece of Mrs Hall's ham and egg pie and began to gnaw at it as I went along.

But I had gone only a short way when reason asserted itself. This was no good. It was an excellent pie and I might as well enjoy it. I pulled off the unfenced road on to the grass, switched off the engine and opened the windows wide. The farm back there was like an island of activity in the quiet landscape and now that I was away from the noise and the stuffiness of the buildings the silence and emptiness enveloped me like a soothing blanket. I leaned my head against the back of the seat and looked out at the checkered greens of the little fields along the flanks of the hills; thrusting upwards between their walls till they gave way to the jutting rocks and the harsh brown of the heather which flooded the wild country above.

I felt better when I drove away and didn't particularly

mind when the farmer at the first inspection greeted me with a scowl.

'This isn't one o'clock, Maister!' he snapped. 'My cows have been in all afternoon and look at the bloody mess they've made. Ah'll never get the place clean again!'

I had to agree with him when I saw the muck piled up behind the cows; it was one of the snags about housing animals in grass time. And the farmer's expression grew blacker as most of them cocked their tails as though in welcome and added further layers to the heaps.

'I won't keep you much longer,' I said briskly, and began to work my way down the row. Before the tuberculin testing scheme came into being, these clinical examinations were the only means of detecting tuberculous cows and I moved from animal to animal palpating the udders for any unusual induration. The routine examinations were known jocularly in the profession as 'bag-snatching' or 'cow-punching' and it was a job that soon got tedious.

I found the only way to stop myself going nearly mad with boredom was to keep reminding myself what I was there for. So when I came to a gaunt red cow with a pendulous udder I straightened up and turned to the farmer.

'I'm going to take a milk sample from this one. She's a bit hard in that left hind quarter.'

The farmer sniffed. 'Please yourself. There's nowt wrong with her but I suppose it'll make a job for somebody.'

Squirting milk from the quarter into a two ounce bottle, I thought about Siegfried's veterinary friend who always took a pint sample from the healthiest udder he could find to go with his lunchtime sandwiches.

I labelled the bottle and put it into the car. We had a little electric centrifuge at Skeldale House and tonight I would spin this milk and examine the sediment on a slide after staining by Ziehl-Neelsen. Probably I would find nothing but at times there was the strange excitement of peering down the microscope at a clump of bright red, iridescent TB bacilli. When that happened the cow was immediately slaughtered and there was always the thought that I might have lifted the death sentence from some child – the meningitis, the spinal and lung infections which were so common in those days.

Returning to the byre I finished the inspection by examining the wall in front of each cow.

The farmer watched me dourly. 'What you on with now?'

'Well, if a cow has a cough you can often find some spit on the wall.' I had, in truth, found more tuberculous cows this way than any other – by scraping a little sputum on to a glass slide and then staining it as for the milk.

The modern young vet just about never sees a TB cow, thank heavens, but 'screws' were all too common thirty years ago. There were very few in the high Pennines but in the low country on the plain you found them; the cows that 'weren't doing right', the ones with the soft, careful cough and slightly accelerated breathing. Often they were good milkers and ate well, but they were killers and I was learning to spot them. And there were the others, the big, fat, sleek animals which could still be riddled with the disease. They were killers of a more insidious kind and nobody could pick them out. It took the tuberculin test to do that.

At the next four places I visited, the farmers had got tired of waiting for me and had turned their cows out. They had all to be brought in from the field and they came slowly and reluctantly; there was nothing like the rodeo I had had with Mr Kay's heifers but a lot more time was lost. The animals kept trying to turn back to the field while I sped around their flanks like a demented sheep dog; and as I panted to and fro each farmer told me the same thing – that cows only liked to come in at milking time.

Milking time did eventually come and I caught three of my herds while they were being milked, but it was after six when I came tired and hungry to my second last inspection. A hush hung over the place and after shouting my way round the buildings without finding anybody I walked over to the house.

'Is your husband in, Mrs Bell?' I asked.

'No, he's had to go into t'village to get the horse shod but he won't be long before he's back. He's left cows in for you,' the farmer's wife replied.

That was fine. I'd soon get through this lot. I almost ran into the byre and started the old routine, feeling sick to death of the sight and smell of cows and fed up with pawing at their udders. I was working along almost automatically when I came to a thin, rangy cow with a narrow red and white face; she could be a crossed Shorthorn Ayrshire. I had barely touched her udder when she lashed out with the speed of light and caught me just above the kneecap.

I hopped round the byre on one leg, groaning and swearing in my agony. It was some time before I was able to limp back to have another try and this time I scratched her back and cush-cushed her in a wheedling tone before sliding my hand gingerly between her legs. The same thing happened again only this time the sharp-edged cloven foot smacked slightly higher up my leg.

Crashing back against the wall, I huddled there, almost weeping with pain and rage. After a few minutes I reached a decision. To hell with her. If she didn't want to be examined she could take her luck. I had had enough for one day – I was in no mood for heroics.

Ignoring her, I proceeded down the byre till I had inspected the others. But I had to pass her on my way back and paused to have another look; and whether it was sheer stubbornness or whether I imagined she was laughing at me, I don't know, but I decided to have just one more go. Maybe she didn't like me coming from behind. Perhaps if I worked from the side she wouldn't mind so much.

Carefully I squeezed my way between her and her neighbour, gasping as the craggy pelvic bones dug into my ribs. Once in the space beyond, I thought, I would be free to do my job; and that was my big mistake. Because as soon as I had got there the cow went to work on me in earnest. Switching her back end round quickly to cut off my way of escape, she began to kick me systematically from head to foot. She kicked forward, reaching at times high on my chest as I strained back against the wall.

Since then I have been kicked by an endless variety of cows in all sorts of situations but never by such an expert as this one. There must be very few really venomous bovines and when one of them uses her feet it is usually an instinctive reaction to being hurt or frightened; and they kick blindly. But this cow measured me up before each blow and her judgement of distance was beautiful. And as she drove me further towards her head she was able to hook me in the back with her horns by way of variety. I am convinced she hated the human race.

My plight was desperate. I was completely trapped and it didn't help when the apparently docile cow next door began to get into the act by prodding me off with her horns as I pressed against her.

I don't know what made me look up, but there, in the thick wall of the byre was a hole about two feet square where some of the crumbling stone had fallen out. I pulled myself up with an agility that amazed me and as I crawled through head first a sweet fragrance came up to me. I was looking into a hay barn and, seeing a deep bed of finest clover just below I launched myself into space and did a very creditable roll in the air before landing safely on my back.

Lying there, bruised and breathless, with the front of my coat thickly patterned with claw marks I finally abandoned any lingering illusions I had had that Ministry work was a soft touch.

I was rising painfully to my feet when Mr Bell strolled in. 'Sorry ah had to go out,' he said, looking me over with interest, 'but I'd just about given you up. You're 'ellish late.'

I dusted myself down and picked a few strands of hay from my hair. 'Yes, sorry about that. But never mind, I managed to get the job done.'

'But . . . were you havin' a bit of a kip, then?'

'No, not exactly. I had some trouble with one of your cows.' There wasn't much point in standing on my dignity. I told him the story.

Even the friendliest farmer seems to derive pleasure from a vet's discomfiture and Mr Bell listened with an ever-widening grin of delight. By the time I had finished he was doubled up, beating his breeches knees with his hands.

'I can just imagine it. That Ayrshire cross! She's a right bitch. Picked her up cheap at market last spring and thought ah'd got a bargain, but ah soon found out. Took us a fortnight to get bugger tied up!'

'Well, I just wish I'd known,' I said, rather tight-lipped.

The farmer looked up at the hole in the wall. 'And you crawled through ...' he went into another convulsion which lasted some time, then he took off his cap and wiped his eyes with the lining.

'Oh dear, oh dear,' he murmured weakly. 'By gaw, I wish I'd been here.'

My last call was just outside Darrowby and I could hear the church clock striking a quarter past seven as I got stiffly out of the car. After my easy day in the service of the government I felt broken in mind and body; I had to suppress a scream when I saw yet another long line of cows' backsides awaiting me. The sun was low, and dark thunder clouds piling up in the west had thrown the countryside into an eerie darkness; and in the old-fashioned, slit-windowed byre the animals looked shapeless and ill-defined in the gloom.

Right, no messing about. I was going to make a quick job of this and get off home; home to some food and an armchair. I had no further ambitions. So left hand on the root of the tail, right hand between the hind legs, a quick feel around and on to the next one. Eyes half closed, my mind numb, I moved from cow to cow going through the motions like a robot with the far end of the byre seeming like the promised land.

And finally here it was, the very last one up against the wall. Left hand on tail, right hand between legs ... At first my tired brain didn't take in the fact that there was something different here, but there was ... something vastly different. A lot of space and instead of the udder a deeply cleft, pendulous something with no teats anywhere.

I came awake suddenly and looked along the animal's side. A huge woolly head was turned towards me and two wide-set eyes regarded me inquiringly. In the dull light I could just see the gleam of the copper ring in the nose.

The farmer who had watched me in silence, spoke up.

'You're wasting your time there, young man. There's nowt wrong wi' HIS bag.'

CHAPTER TWELVE

The card dangled above the old lady's bed. It read 'God is Near' but it wasn't like the usual religious text. It didn't have a frame or ornate printing. It was just a strip of cardboard about eight inches long with plain lettering which might have said 'No smoking' or 'Exit' and it was looped carelessly over an old gas bracket so that Miss Stubbs from where she lay could look up at it and read 'God is Near' in square black capitals.

There wasn't much more Miss Stubbs could see; perhaps a few feet of privet hedge through the frayed curtains but mainly it was just the cluttered little room which had been her world for so many years.

The room was on the ground floor and in the front of the cottage, and as I came up through the wilderness which had once been a garden I could see the dogs watching me from where they had jumped on to the old lady's bed. And when I knocked on the door the place almost erupted with their barking. It was always like this. I had been visiting regularly for over a year and the pattern never changed; the furious barking, then Mrs Broadwith who looked after Miss Stubbs would push all the animals but my patient into the back kitchen and open the door and I would go in and see Miss Stubbs in the corner in her bed with the card hanging over it.

She had been there for a long time and would never get up again. But she never mentioned her illness and pain to me; all her concern was for her three dogs and two cats.

Today it was old Prince and I was worried about him. It was his heart – just about the most spectacular valvular incompetence I had ever heard. He was waiting for me as I came in, pleased as ever to see me, his long, fringed tail waving gently.

The sight of that tail used to make me think there must be a lot of Irish Setter in Prince but I was inclined to change my mind as I worked my way forward over the bulging black and white body to the shaggy head and upstanding Alsatian ears. Miss Stubbs often used to call him 'Mr Heinz' and though he may not have had 57 varieties in him his hybrid vigour had stood him in good stead. With his heart he should have been dead long ago.

'I thought I'd best give you a ring, Mr Herriot,' Mrs Broadwith said. She was a comfortable, elderly widow with a square, ruddy face contrasting sharply with the pinched features on the pillow. 'He's been coughing right bad this week and this morning he was a bit staggery. Still eats well, though.'

'I bet he does.' I ran my hands over the rolls of fat on the ribs. 'It would take something really drastic to put old Prince off his grub.'

Miss Stubbs laughed from the bed and the old dog, his mouth wide, eyes dancing, seemed to be joining in the joke. I put my stethoscope over his heart and listened, knowing well what I was going to hear. They say the heart is supposed to go 'Lub-dup, lub-dup', but Prince's went 'swish-swoosh, swish-swoosh'. There seemed to be nearly as much blood leaking back as was being pumped into the circulatory system. And another thing, the 'swish-swoosh' was a good bit faster than last time; he was on oral digitalis but it wasn't quite doing its job.

Gloomily I moved the stethoscope over the rest of the chest. Like all old dogs with a chronic heart weakness he had an ever-present bronchitis and I listened without enthusiasm to the symphony of whistles, rales, squeaks and bubbles which signalled the workings of Prince's lungs. The old dog stood very erect and proud, his tail still waving slowly. He always took it as a tremendous compliment when I examined him and there was no doubt he was enjoying himself now. Fortunately his was not a very painful ailment.

Straightening up, I patted his head and he responded immediately by trying to put his paws on my chest. He didn't quite make it and even that slight exertion started his ribs heaving and his tongue lolling. I gave him an intramuscular injection of digitalin and another of morphine hydrochloride which he accepted with apparent pleasure as part of the game.

'I hope that will steady his heart and breathing, Miss Stubbs. You'll find he'll be a bit dopey for the rest of the day and that will help, too. Carry on with the tablets, and I'm going to leave you some more medicine for his bronchitis.' I handed over a bottle of my old standby mixture of ipecacuanha and ammonium acetate.

The next stage of the visit began now as Mrs Broadwith brought in a cup of tea and the rest of the animals were let out of the kitchen. There were Ben, a Sealyham, and Sally, a Cocker Spaniel, and they started a deafening barking contest with Prince. They were closely followed by the cats, Arthur and Susie, who stalked in gracefully and began to rub themselves against my trouser legs.

It was the usual scenario for the many cups of tea I had drunk with Miss Stubbs under the little card which dangled above her bed.

'How are you today?' I asked.

'Oh, much better,' she replied and immediately, as always, changed the subject.

Mostly she liked to talk about her pets and the ones she had known right back to her girlhood. She spoke a lot, too, about the days when her family were alive. She loved to describe the escapades of her three brothers and today she showed me a photograph which Mrs Broadwith had found at the bottom of a drawer.

I took it from her and three young men in the knee breeches and little round caps of the nineties smiled up at me from the yellowed old print; they all held long church warden pipes and the impish humour in their expressions came down undimmed over the years.

'My word, they look really bright lads, Miss Stubbs,' I said.

'Oh, they were young rips!' she exclaimed. She threw back her head and laughed and for a moment her face was radiant, transfigured by her memories.

The things I had heard in the village came back to me; about the prosperous father and his family who lived in the big house many years ago. Then the foreign investments which crashed and the sudden change in circumstances. 'When t'owd feller died he was about skint,' one old man had said. 'There's not much brass there now.'

Probably just enough brass to keep Miss Stubbs and her animals alive and to pay Mrs Broadwith. Not enough to keep the garden dug or the house painted or for any of the normal little luxuries.

And, sitting there, drinking my tea, with the dogs in a row by the bedside and the cats making themselves comfortable on the bed itself, I felt as I had often felt before – a bit afraid of the responsibility I had. The one thing which brought some light into the life of the brave old woman was the transparent devotion of this shaggy bunch whose eyes were never far from her face. And the snag was that they were all elderly.

There had, in fact, been four dogs originally, but one of them, a truly ancient golden Labrador, had died a few months previously. And now I had the rest of them to look after and none of them less than ten years old.

They were perky enough but all showing some of the signs of old age; Prince with his heart, Sally beginning to drink a lot of water which made me wonder if she was starting with a pyometra, Ben growing steadily thinner with his nephritis. I couldn't give him new kidneys and I hadn't much faith in the hexamine tablets I had prescribed. Another peculiar thing about Ben was that I was always having to clip his claws; they grew at an extraordinary rate.

The cats were better, though Susie was a big scraggy and I kept up a morbid kneading of her furry abdomen for signs of lymphosarcoma. Arthur was the best of the bunch; he never seemed to ail anything beyond a tendency for his teeth to tartar up.

This must have been in Miss Stubbs' mind because, when I had finished my tea, she asked me to look at him. I hauled him across the bedspread and opened his mouth.

'Yes, there's a bit of the old trouble there. Might as well fix it while I'm here.'

Arthur was a huge, grey, neutered Tom, a living denial of

all those theories that cats are cold-natured, selfish and the rest. His fine eyes, framed in the widest cat face I have ever seen, looked out on the world with an all-embracing benevolence and tolerance. His every movement was marked by immense dignity.

As I started to scrape his teeth his chest echoed with a booming purr like a distant outboard motor. There was no need for anybody to hold him; he sat there placidly and moved only once – when I was using forceps to crack off a tough piece of tartar from a back tooth and accidentally nicked his gum. He casually raised a massive paw as if to say 'Have a care, chum', but his claws were sheathed.

My next visit was less than a month later and was in response to an urgent summons from Mrs Broadwith at six o'clock in the evening. Ben had collapsed. I jumped straight into my car and in less than ten minutes was threading my way through the overgrown grass in the front garden with the animals watching from their window. The barking broke out as I knocked, but Ben's was absent. As I went into the little room I saw the old dog lying on his side, very still, by the bed.

DOA is what we write in the day book. Dead on arrival. Just three words but they cover all kinds of situations – the end of milk fever cows, bloated bullocks, calves in fits. And tonight they meant that I wouldn't be clipping old Ben's claws any more.

It wasn't often these nephritis cases went off so suddenly but his urine albumen had been building up dangerously lately.

'Well, it was quick, Miss Stubbs. I'm sure the old chap didn't suffer at all.' My words sounded lame and ineffectual.

The old lady was in full command of herself. No tears, only a fixity of expression as she looked down from the bed at her companion for so many years. My idea was to get him out of the place as quickly as possible and I pulled a blanket under him and lifted him up. As I was moving away, Miss Stubbs said, 'Wait a moment.' With an effort she turned on to her side and gazed at Ben. Still without changing expression, she reached and touched his head lightly. Then she lay back calmly as I hurried from the room.

In the back kitchen I had a whispered conference with Mrs Broadwith. 'I'll run down t'village and get Fred Manners to come and bury him,' she said. 'And if you've got time could you stay with the old lady while I'm gone. Talk to her, like, it'll do her good.'

I went back and sat down by the bed. Miss Stubbs looked out of the window for a few moments then turned to me. 'You know, Mr Herriot,' she said casually. 'It will be my turn next.'

'What do you mean?'

'Well, tonight Ben has gone and I'm going to be the next one. I just know it.'

'Oh, nonsense! You're feeling a bit low, that's all. We all do when something like this happens.' But I was disturbed. I had never heard her even hint at such a thing before.

'I'm not afraid,' she said. 'I know there's something better waiting for me. I've never had any doubts.' There was silence between us as she lay calmly looking up at the card on the gas bracket.

Then the head on the pillow turned to me again. 'I have only one fear.' Her expression changed with startling suddenness as if a mask had dropped. The brave face was almost unrecognizable. A kind of terror flickered in her eyes and she quickly grasped my hand.

'It's my dogs and cats, Mr Herriot. I'm afraid I might never see them when I'm gone and it worries me so. You see, I know I'll be reunited with my parents and my brothers but ... but ...'

'Well, why not with your animals?'

'That's just it.' She rocked her head on the pillow and for the first time I saw tears on her cheeks. 'They say animals have no souls.'

'Who says?'

'Oh, I've read it and I know a lot of religous people believe it.'

'Well I don't believe it.' I patted the hand which still grasped mine. 'If having a soul means being able to feel love and loyalty and gratitude, then animals are better off than a lot of humans. You've nothing to worry about there.'

'Oh, I hope you're right. Sometimes I lie at night thinking about it.'

'I know I'm right, Miss Stubbs, and don't you argue with me. They teach us vets all about animals' souls.'

The tension left her face and she laughed with a return of her old spirit. 'I'm sorry to bore you with this and I'm not going to talk about it again. But before you go, I want you to be absolutely honest with me. I don't want reassurance from you – just the truth. I know you are very young but please tell me – what are your beliefs? Will my animals go with me?'

She stared intently into my eyes. I shifted in my chair and swallowed once or twice.

'Miss Stubbs, I'm afraid I'm a bit foggy about all this,' I said. 'But I'm absolutely certain of one thing. Wherever you are going, they are going too.'

She still stared at me but her face was calm again. 'Thank you, Mr Herriot, I know you are being honest with me. That is what you really believe, isn't it?'

'I do believe it,' I said. 'With all my heart I believe it.'

It must have been about a month later and it was entirely by accident that I learned I had seen Miss Stubbs for the last time. When a lonely, penniless old woman dies people don't rush up to you in the street to tell you. I was on my rounds and a farmer happened to mention that the cottage in Corby village was up for sale.

'But what about Miss Stubbs?' I asked.

'Oh, went off sudden about three weeks ago. House is in a bad state, they say – nowt been done at it for years.'

'Mrs Broadwith isn't staying on, then?'

'Nay, I hear she's staying at t'other end of village.'

'Do you know what's happened to the dogs and cats?'

'What dogs and cats?'

I cut my visit short. And I didn't go straight home though it was nearly lunch time. Instead I urged my complaining little car at top speed to Corby and asked the first person I saw where Mrs Broadwith was living. It was a tiny house but attractive and Mrs Broadwith answered my knock herself.

'Oh, come in, Mr Herriot. It's right good of you to call.' I went inside and we sat facing each other across a scrubbed table top.

'Well, it was sad about the old lady,' she said.

'Yes, I've only just heard.'

'Any road, she had a peaceful end. Just slept away at finish.'

'I'm glad to hear that.'

Mrs Broadwith looked round the room. 'I was real lucky to get this place – it's just what I've always wanted.'

I could contain myself no longer. 'What's happened to the animals?' I blurted out.

'Oh, they're in t'garden,' she said calmly. 'I've got a grand big stretch at back.' She got up and opened the door and with a surge of relief I watched my old friends pour in.

Arthur was on my knee in a flash, arching himself ecstatically against my arm while his outboard motor roared softly above the barking of the dogs. Prince, wheezy as ever, tail fanning the air, laughed up at me delightedly between barks.

'They look great, Mrs Broadwith. How long are they going to be here?'

'They're here for good. I think just as much about them as t'old lady ever did and I couldn't be parted from them. They'll have a good home with me as long as they live.'

I looked at the typical Yorkshire country face, at the heavy cheeks with their grim lines belied by the kindly eyes. 'This is wonderful,' I said. 'But won't you find it just a bit . . . er . . . expensive to feed them?'

'Nay, you don't have to worry about that. I 'ave a bit put away.'

'Well fine, fine, and I'll be looking in now and then to see how they are. I'm through the village every few days.' I got up and started for the door.

Mrs Broadwith held up her hand. 'There's just one thing I'd like you to do before they start selling off the things at the cottage. Would you please pop in and collect what's left of your medicines. They're in t'front room.'

I took the key and drove along to the other end of the village. As I pushed open the rickety gate and began to walk through the tangled grass the front of the cottage looked strangely lifeless without the faces of the dogs at the window; and when the door creaked open and I went inside the silence was like a heavy pall.

Nothing had been moved. The bed with its rumpled blankets was still in the corner. I moved around, picking up half empty bottles, a jar of ointment, the cardboard box with old Ben's tablets – a lot of good they had done him.

When I had got everything I looked slowly round the little room. I wouldn't be coming here any more and at the door I paused and read for the last time the card which hung over the empty bed.

CHAPTER THIRTEEN

I was spending Tuesday evening as I spent all the Tuesday evenings – staring at the back of Helen Alderson's head at the Darrowby Music Society. It was a slow way of getting to know her better but I had been unable to think of a better idea.

Since the morning on the high moor when I had set the calf's leg, I had scanned the day book regularly in the hope of getting another visit to the farm. But the Aldersons seemed to have lamentably healthy stock. I had to be content with the thought that there was the visit at the month end to take off the plaster. The really crushing blow came when Helen's father rang up to say that, since the calf was going sound he had removed the plaster himself. He was pleased to say that the fracture had knitted perfectly and there was no sign of lameness.

I had come to admire the self-reliance and initiative of the

Dalesmen but I cursed it now at great length; and I joined the Music Society. I had seen Helen going into the schoolroom where the meeting were held and, with the courage of desperation, had followed her inside.

That was weeks ago and, I reflected miserably, I had made no progress at all. I couldn't remember how many tenors, sopranos and male voice choirs had come and gone and on one occasion the local brass band had packed themselves into the little room and almost burst my ear drums; but I was no further forward.

Tonight a string quartet was scraping away industriously, but I hardly heard them. My eyes, as usual, were focused on Helen, several rows in front of me, sitting between the two old ladies she always seemed to bring with her. That was part of the trouble; those two old girls were always there, cutting out any chance of private conversation, even at the half-time break for tea. And there was the general atmosphere of the place; the members were nearly all elderly, and over everything hung the powerful schoolroom scent of ink and exercise books and chalk and lead pencils. It was the sort of place where you just couldn't say without warning 'Are you doing anything on Saturday night?'

The scraping stopped and everybody clapped. The vicar got up from the front row and beamed on the company. 'And now, ladies and gentlemen, I think we might stop for fifteen minutes as I see our willing helpers have prepared tea. The price, as usual is threepence.' There was laughter and a general pushing back of chairs.

I went to the back of the hall with the others, put my threepence on the plate and collected a cup of tea and a biscuit. This was when I tried to get near Helen in the blind hope that something might happen. It wasn't always easy, because I was often buttonholed by the school headmaster and others who regarded a vet who liked music as an interesting curiosity, but tonight I managed to edge myself as if by accident into her group.

She looked at me over the top of her cup. 'Good evening, Mr Herriot, are you enjoying it?' Oh God, she always said that. And Mr Herriot! But what could I do? 'Call me Jim', would sound great. I replied, as always, 'Good evening, Miss Alderson. Yes, it's very nice, isn't it.' Things were going with a bang again.

I munched my biscuit while the old ladies talked about Mozart. It was going to be the same as all the other Tuesdays. It was about time I gave up the whole thing. I felt beaten.

The vicar approached our group, still beaming. 'I'm afraid I have to call on somebody for the washing-up rota. Perhaps our two young friends would take it on tonight.' His friendly gaze twinkled from Helen to me and back again.

The idea of washing up teacups had never held much attraction for me but suddenly it was like sighting the promised land. 'Yes, certainly, delighted – that is if it's all right with Miss Alderson.'

Helen smiled. 'Of course it's all right. We all have to take a turn, don't we?'

I wheeled the trolley of cups and saucers into the scullery. It was a cramped, narrow place with a sink and a few shelves and there was just about room for the two of us to get inside.

'Would you like to wash or dry?' Helen asked.

'I'll wash,' I replied and began to run the hot water into the sink. It shouldn't be too difficult now, I thought, to work the conversation round to where I wanted it. I'd never have a better chance than now, jammed into this little room with Helen.

But it was surprising how the time went by. Five whole minutes and we hadn't talked about anything but music. With mounting frustration I saw that we had nearly got through the pile of crockery and I had achieved nothing. The feeling changed to near panic when I lifted the last cup from the soapy water.

It had to be now. I held out the cup to Helen and she tried to take it from me; but I kept a grip on the handle while I waited for inspiration. She pulled gently but I clung to it tenaciously. It was developing into a tug of war. Then I heard a hoarse croak which I only just recognized as my own voice. 'Can I see you some time?'

For a moment she didn't answer and I tried to read her

face. Was she surprised, annoyed, even shocked? She flushed and replied, 'If you like.' I heard the croak again. 'Saturday evening?' She nodded, dried the cup and was gone.

I went back to my seat with my heart thudding. The strains of mangled Haydn from the quartet went unheeded. I had done it at last. But did she really want to come out? Had she been hustled into it against her will? My toes curled with embarrassment at the thought, but I consoled myself with the knowledge that for better or for worse it was a step forward. Yes, I had done it at last.

CHAPTER FOURTEEN

As I sat at breakfast I looked out at the autumn mist dissolving in the early sunshine. It was going to be another fine day but there was a chill in the old house this morning, a shiveriness as though a cold hand had reached out to remind us that summer had gone and the hard months lay just ahead.

'It says here,' Siegfried said, adjusting his copy of the *Darrowby and Houlton Times* with care against the coffee-pot, 'that farmers have no feeling for their animals.'

I buttered a piece of toast and looked across at him.

'Cruel, you mean?'

'Well, not exactly, but this chap maintains that to a farmer, livestock are purely commercial – there's no sentiment in his attitude towards them, no affection.'

'Well, it wouldn't do if they were all like poor Kit Bilton, would it? They'd all go mad.'

Kit was a lorry driver who, like so many of the working men of Darrowby, kept a pig at the bottom of his garden for family consumption. The snag was that when killing time came, Kit wept for three days. I happened to go into his house on one of these occasions and found his wife and daughter hard at it cutting up the meat for pies and brawn while Kit huddled miserably by the kitchen fire, his eyes swimming with tears. He was a huge man who could throw a twelve stone sack of meal on to his wagon with a jerk of his arms, but he seized my hand in his and sobbed at me 'I can't bear it, Mr Herriot. He was like a Christian was that pig, just like a Christian.'

'No, I agree,' Siegfreid leaned over and sawed off a slice of Mrs Hall's home-baked bread. 'But Kit isn't a real farmer. This article is about people who own large numbers of animals. The question is, is it possible for such men to become emotionally involved? Can the dairy farmer milking maybe fifty cows become really fond of any of them or are they just milk producing units?'

'It's an interesting point,' I said, 'And I think you've put your finger on it with the numbers. You know there are a lot of our farmers up in the high country who have only a few stock. They always have names for their cows – Daisy, Mabel, I even came across one called Kipperlugs the other day. I do think these small farmers have an affection for their animals but I don't see how the big men can possibly have.'

Siegfried rose from the table and stretched luxuriously. 'You're probably right. Anyway, I'm sending you to see a really big man this morning. John Skipton of Dennaby Close – he's got some tooth rasping to do. Couple of old horses losing condition. You'd better take all the instruments, it might be anything.'

I went through to the little room down the passage and surveyed the tooth instruments. I always felt at my most mediaeval when I was caught up in large animal dentistry and in the days of the draught horse it was a regular task. One of the commonest jobs was knocking the wolf teeth out of young horses. I have no idea how it got its name but you found the little wolf tooth just in front of the molars and if a young horse was doing badly it always got the blame.

It was no good the vets protesting that such a minute, vestigial object couldn't possibly have any effect on the horse's health and that the trouble was probably due to worms. The farmers were adamant; the tooth had to be removed.

We did this by having the horse backed into a corner, placing the forked end of a metal rod against the tooth and giving a sharp tap with an absurdly large wooden mallet. Since the tooth had no proper root the operation was not particularly painful, but the horse still didn't like it. We usually had a couple of fore-feet waving around our ears at each tap.

And the annoying part was that after we had done the job and pointed out to the farmer that we had only performed this bit of black magic to humour him, the horse would take an immediate turn for the better and thrive consistently from then on. Farmers are normally reticent about our successful efforts for fear we might put a bit more on the bill but in these cases they cast aside all caution. They would shout at us across the market place: 'Hey, remember that 'oss you knocked wolf teeth out of? Well he never looked back. It capped him.'

I looked again with distaste at the tooth instruments; the vicious forceps with two-feet-long arms, sharp-jawed shears, mouth gags, hammers and chisels, files and rasps; it was rather like a quiet corner in the Spanish Inquisition. We kept a long wooden box with a handle for carrying the things and I staggered out to the car with a fair selection.

Dennaby Close was not just a substantial farm, it was a monument to a man's endurance and skill. The fine old house, the extensive buildings, the great sweep of lush grass land along the lower slopes of the fell were all proof that old John Skipton had achieved the impossible; he had started as an uneducated farm labourer and he was now a wealthy landowner.

The miracle hadn't happened easily; old John had a lifetime of grinding toil behind him that would have killed most men, a lifetime with no room for a wife or family or creature comforts, but there was more to it than that; there was a brilliant acumen in agricultural matters that had made the old man a legend in the district. 'When all t'world goes one road, I go t'other' was one of his quoted sayings and it is true that the Skipton farms had made money in the hard times when others were going bankrupt. Dennaby was only one of

John's farms; he had two large arable places of about four hundred acres each lower down the Dale.

He had conquered, but to some people it seemed that he had himself been conquered in the process. He had battled against the odds for so many years and driven himself so fiercely that he couldn't stop. He could be enjoying all kinds of luxuries now but he just hadn't the time; they said that the poorest of his workers lived in better style than he did.

I paused as I got out of the car and stood gazing at the house as though I had never seen it before; and I marvelled again at the elegance which had withstood over three hundred years of the harsh climate. People came a long way to see Dennaby Close and take photographs of the graceful manor with its tall, leaded windows, the massive chimneys towering over the old moss-grown tiles; or to wander through the neglected garden and climb up the sweep of steps to the entrance with its wide stone arch over the great studded door.

There should have been a beautiful woman in one of those pointed hats peeping out from that mullioned casement or a cavalier in ruffles and hose pacing beneath the high wall with its pointed copings. But there was just old John stumping impatiently towards me, his tattered, buttonless coat secured only by a length of binder twine round his middle.

'Come in a minute, young man,' he cried. 'I've got a little bill to pay you.' He led the way round to the back of the house and I followed, pondering on the odd fact that it was always a 'little bill' in Yorkshire. We went in through a flagged kitchen to a room which was graceful and spacious but furnished only with a table, a few wooden chairs and a collapsed sofa.

The old man bustled over to the mantelpiece and fished out a bundle of papers from behind the clock. He leafed through them, threw an envelope on to the table then produced a cheque book and slapped it down in front of me. I did the usual – took out the bill, made out the amount on the cheque and pushed it over for him to sign. He wrote with a careful concentration, the small-featured, weathered face bent low, the peak of the old cloth cap almost touching the pen. His trousers had ridden up his legs as he sat down showing the skinny calves and bare ankles. There were no socks underneath the heavy boots.

When I had pocketed the cheque, John jumped to his feet. 'We'll have to walk down to t'river; 'osses are down there.' He left the house almost at a trot.

I eased my box of instruments from the car boot. It was a funny thing but whenever I had heavy equipment to lug about, my patients were always a long way away. This box seemed to be filled with lead and it wasn't going to get any lighter on the journey down through the walled pastures.

The old man seized a pitch fork, stabbed it into a bale of hay and hoisted it effortlessly over his shoulder. He set off again at the same brisk pace. We made our way down from one gateway to another, often walking diagonally across the fields. John didn't reduce speed and I stumbled after him, puffing a little and trying to put away the thought that he was at least fifty years older than me.

About half-way down we came across a group of men at the age-old task of 'walling' – repairing a gap in one of the dry stone walls which trace their patterns everywhere on the green slopes of the Dales. One of the men looked up. 'Nice mornin', Mr Skipton,' he sang out cheerfully.

'Bugger t'mornin'. Get on wi' some work,' grunted old John in reply and the man smiled contentedly as though he had received a compliment.

I was glad when we reached the flat land at the bottom. My arms seemed to have been stretched by several inches and I could feel a trickle of sweat on my brow. Old John appeared unaffected; he flicked the fork from his shoulder and the bale thudded on to the grass.

The two horses turned towards us at the sound. They were standing fetlock deep in the pebbly shallows just beyond a little beach which merged into the green carpet of turf; nose to tail, they had been rubbing their chins gently along each other's backs, unconscious of our approach. A high cliff overhanging the far bank made a perfect wind break while on either side of us clumps of oak and beech blazed in the autumn sunshine.

'They're in a nice spot, Mr Skipton,' I said.

'Aye, they can keep cool in the hot weather and they've got the barn when winter comes.' John pointed to a low, thick-walled building with a single door. 'They can come and go as they please.'

The sound of his voice brought the horses out of the river at a stiff trot and as they came near you could see they really were old. The mare was a chestnut and the gelding was a light bay but their coats were so flecked with grey that they almost looked like roans. This was most pronounced on their faces where the sprinkling of white hairs, the sunken eyes and the deep cavity above the eyes gave them a truly venerable appearance.

For all that, they capered around John with a fair attempt at skittishness, stamping their feet, throwing their heads about, pushing his cap over his eyes with their muzzles.

'Get by, leave off!' he shouted. 'Daft awd beggars.' But he tugged absently at the mare's forelock and ran his hand briefly along the neck of the gelding.

'When did they last do any work?' I asked.

'Oh, about twelve years ago, I reckon.'

I stared at John. 'Twelve years! And have they been down here all that time?'

'Aye, just lakin' about down here, retired like. They've earned it an' all.' For a few moments he stood silent, shoulders hunched, hands deep in the pockets of his coat, then he spoke quietly as if to himself. 'They were two slaves when I was a slave.' He turned and looked at me and for a revealing moment I read in the pale blue eyes something of the agony and struggle he had shared with the animals.

'But twelve years! How old are they, anyway?'

John's mouth twisted up at one corner. 'Well you're t'vet. You tell me.'

I stepped forward confidently, my mind buzzing with Galvayne's groove, shape of marks, degree of slope and the rest; I grasped the unprotesting upper lip of the mare and looked at her teeth.

'Good God!' I gasped, 'I've never seen anything like this.' The incisors were immensely long and projecting forward till they met at an angle of about forty-five degrees. There were no marks at all – they had long since gone.

I laughed and turned back to the old man. 'It's no good, I'd only be guessing. You'll have to tell me.'

'Well she's about thirty and gelding's a year or two younger. She's had fifteen grand foals and never ailed owt except a bit of teeth trouble. We've had them rasped a time or two and it's time they were done again, I reckon. They're both losing ground and dropping bits of half chewed hay from their mouths. Gelding's the worst – has a right job champin' his grub.'

I put my hand into the mare's mouth, grasped her tongue and pulled it out to one side. A quick exploration of the molars with my other hand revealed what I suspected; the outside edges of the upper teeth were overgrown and jagged and were irritating the cheeks while the inside edges of the lower molars were in a similar state and were slightly excoriating the tongue.

'I'll soon make her more comfortable, Mr Skipton. With those sharp edges rubbed off she'll be as good as new.' I got the rasp out of my vast box, held the tongue in one hand and worked the rough surface along the teeth, checking occasionally with my fingers till the points had been sufficiently reduced.

'That's about right,' I said after a few minutes. 'I don't want to make them too smooth or she won't be able to grind her food.'

John grunted. 'Good enough. Now have a look at t'other. There's summat far wrong with him.'

I had a feel at the gelding's teeth. 'Just the same as the mare. Soon put him right, too.'

But pushing at the rasp, I had an uncomfortable feeling that something was not quite right. The thing wouldn't go fully to the back of the mouth; something was stopping it. I stopped rasping and explored again, reaching with my fingers as far as I could. And I came upon something very strange, something which shouldn't have been there at all. It was like a great chunk of bone projecting down from the roof of the mouth.

It was time I had a proper look. I got out my pocket torch and shone it over the back of the tongue. It was easy to see the trouble now; the last upper molar was overlapping the lower one resulting in a gross overgrowth of the posterior border. The result was a sabre-like barb about three inches long stabbing down into the tender tissue of the gum.

That would have to come off – right now. My jauntiness vanished and I suppressed a shudder; it meant using the horrible shears – those great long-handled things with the screw operated by a cross bar. They gave me the willies because I am one of those people who can't bear to watch anybody blowing up a balloon and this was the same sort of thing only worse. You fastened the sharp blades of the shears on to the tooth and began to turn the bar slowly, slowly. Soon the tooth began to groan and creak under the tremendous leverage and you knew that any second it would break off and when it did it was like somebody letting off a rifle in your ear. That was when all hell usually broke loose but mercifully this was a quiet old horse and I wouldn't expect him to start dancing around on his hind legs. There was no pain for the horse because the overgrown part had no nerve supply – it was the noise that caused the trouble.

Returning to my crate I produced the dreadful instrument and with it a Haussman's gag which I inserted on the incisors and opened on its ratchet till the mouth gaped wide. Everything was easy to see then and, of course, there it was – a great prong at the other side of the mouth exactly like the first. Great, great, now I had two to chop off.

The old horse stood patiently, eyes almost closed, as though he had seen it all and nothing in the world was going to bother him. I went through the motions with my toes curling and when the sharp crack came, the white-bordered eyes opened wide, but only in mild surprise. He never even moved. When I did the other side he paid no attention at all; in fact, with the gag prising his jaws apart he looked exactly as though he was yawning with boredom.

As I bundled the tools away, John picked up the bony spicules from the grass and studied them with interest. 'Well, poor awd beggar. Good job I got you along, young man. Reckon he'll feel a lot better now.'

On the way back, old John, relieved of his bale, was able to go twice as fast and he stumped his way up the hill at a furious pace, using the fork as a staff. I panted along in the rear, changing the box from hand to hand every few minutes.

About halfway up, the thing slipped out of my grasp and it gave me a chance to stop for a breather. As the old man muttered impatiently I looked back and could just see the two horses; they had returned to the shallows and were playing together, chasing each other jerkily, their feet splashing in the water. The cliff made a dark backcloth to the picture – the shining river, the trees glowing bronze and gold and the sweet green of the grass.

Back in the farm yard, John paused awkwardly. He nodded once or twice, said 'Thank ye, young man,' then turned abruptly and walked away.

I was dumping the box thankfully into the boot when I saw the man who had spoken to us on the way down. He was sitting, cheerful as ever, in a sunny corner, back against a pile of sacks, pulling his dinner packet from an old army satchel.

'You've been down to see t'pensioners then? By gaw, awd John should know the way.'

'Regular visitor, is he?'

'Regular? Every day God sends you'll see t'awd feller ploddin' down there. Rain, snow or blow, never misses. And allus has summat with him – bag o' corn, straw for their bedding.'

'And he's done that for twelve years?'

The man unscrewed his thermos flask and poured himself a cup of black tea. 'Aye, them 'osses haven't done a stroke o' work all that time and he could've got good money for them from the horse flesh merchants. Rum 'un, isn't it?'

'You're right,' I said, 'it is a rum 'un.'

Just how rum it was occupied my thoughts on the way back to the surgery. I went back to my conversation with Siegfried that morning; we had just about decided that the man with a lot of animals couldn't be expected to feel affection for individuals among them. But those buildings back there were full of John Skipton's animals – he must have hundreds.

Yet what made him trail down that hillside every day in all weathers? Why had he filled the last years of those two old horses with peace and beauty? Why had he given them a final ease and comfort which he had withheld from himself?

It could only be love.

CHAPTER FIFTEEN

The longer I worked in Darrowby the more the charms of the Dales beguiled me. And there was one solid advantage of which I became more aware every day – the Dales farmers were all stocksmen. They really knew how to handle animals, and to a vet whose patients are constantly trying to thwart him or injure him it was a particular blessing.

So this morning I looked with satisfaction at the two men holding the cow. It wasn't a difficult job – just an intravenous injection of magnesium lactate – but still it was reassuring to have two such sturdy fellows to help me. Maurice Bennison, medium sized but as tough as one of his own hill beasts, had a horn in his right hand while the fingers of his left gripped the nose; I had the comfortable impression that the cow wouldn't jump very far when I pushed the needle in. His brother George whose job it was to raise the vein, held the choke rope limply in enormous hands like bunches of carrots. He grinned down at me amiably from his six feet four inches.

'Right, George,' I said. 'Tighten up that rope and lean against the cow to stop her coming round on me.' I pushed my way between the cow and her neighbour, past George's unyielding bulk and bent over the jugular vein. It was standing out very nicely. I poised the needle, feeling the big man's elbow on me as he peered over my shoulder, and thrust quickly into the vein.

'Lovely!' I cried as the dark blood fountained out and spattered thickly on the straw bedding beneath. 'Slacken your rope, George.' I fumbled in my pocket for the flutter valve. 'And for God's sake, get your weight off me!'

Because George had apparently decided to rest his full fourteen stones on me instead of the cow, and as I tried desperately to connect the tube to the needle. I felt my knees giving way. I shouted again, despairingly, but he was inert, his chin resting on my shoulder, his breathing stertorous in my ear.

There could only be one end to it. I fell flat on my face and lay there writhing under the motionless body. My cries went unheeded; George was unconscious.

Mr Bennison, attracted by the commotion, came in to the byre just in time to see me crawling out from beneath his eldest son. 'Get him out, quick!' I gasped, 'before the cows trample on him.' Wordlessly, Maurice and his father took an ankle apiece and hauled away in unison. George shot out from under the cows, his head beating a brisk tattoo on the cobbles, traversed the dung channel, then resumed his sleep on the byre floor.

Mr Bennison moved back to the cow and waited for me to continue with my injection but I found the presence of the sprawled body distracting. 'Look, couldn't we sit him up against the wall and put his head between his legs?' I suggested apologetically. The others glanced at each other then, as though deciding to humour me grabbed George's shoulders and trundled him over the floor with the expertise of men used to throwing around bags of fertilizer and potatoes. But even propped against the rough stones, his head slumped forward and his great long arms hanging loosely, the poor fellow still didn't look so good.

I couldn't help feeling a bit responsible. 'Don't you think we might give him a drink?'

But Mr Bennison had had enough. 'Nay, nay, he'll be right,' he muttered testily. 'Let's get on with t'job.' Evidently he felt he had pampered George too much already.

The incident started me thinking about this question of people's reactions to the sight of blood and other disturbing realities. Even though it was only my second year of practice I had already formulated certain rules about this and one was that it was always the biggest men who went down. (I had, by this time, worked out a few other, perhaps unscientific theories, e.g. big dogs were kept by people who lived in little houses and vice versa. Clients who said 'spare no expense' never paid their bills, ever. When I asked my way in the Dales and was told 'you can't miss it', I knew I'd soon be hopelessly lost.)

I had begun to wonder if perhaps country folk, despite their closer contact with fundamental things, were perhaps more susceptible than city people. Ever since Sid Blenkhorn had staggered into Skeldale House one evening. His face was ghastly white and he had obviously passed through a shattering experience. 'Have you got a drop o' whisky handy, Jim?' he quavered, and when I had guided him to a chair and Siegfried had put a glass in his hand he told us he had been at a first aid lecture given by Dr Allinson, a few doors down the street. 'He was talking about veins and arteries and things,' groaned Sid, passing a hand across his forehead. 'God, it was awful!' Apparently Fred Ellison the fishmonger had been carried out unconscious after only ten minutes and Sid himself had only just made it to the door. It had been a shambles.

I was interested because this sort of thing, I had found, was always just round the corner. I suppose we must have more trouble in this way than the doctors because in most cases when our medical colleagues have any cutting or carving to do they send their patients to hospital while the vets just have to get their jackets off and operate on the spot. It means that the owners and attendants of the animals are pulled in as helpers and are subjected to some unusual sights.

So, even in my short experience, I had become a fair authority on the various manifestations of 'coming over queer'. I suppose it was a bit early to start compiling statistics but I had never seen a woman or a little man pass out even though they might exhibit various shadings of the squeamish spectrum. The big chap was the best bet every time, especially the boisterous, super-confident type.

I have a vivid recollection of a summer evening when I had to carry out a rumenotomy on a cow. As a rule I was inclined to play for time when I suspected a foreign body – there were so many other conditions with similar symptoms that I was never in a hurry to make a hole in the animal's side. But this time diagnosis was easy; the sudden fall in milk yield, loss of cudding; grunting, and the rigid, sunken-eyed appearance of the cow. And to clinch it the farmer told me he had been repairing a hen house in the cow pasture – nailing up loose boards. I knew where one of the nails had gone.

The farm, right on the main street of the village, was a favourite meeting place for the local lads. As I laid out my instruments on a clean towel draped over a straw bale a row of grinning faces watched from above the half door of the box; not only watched but encouraged me with ribald shouts. When I was about ready to start it occurred to me that an extra pair of hands would be helpful and I turned to the door. 'How would one of you lads like to be my assistant?' There was even more shouting for a minute or two, then the door was opened and a huge young man with a shock of red hair ambled into the box; he was a magnificent sight with his vast shoulders and the column of sunburned neck rising from the open shirt. It needed only the bright blue eyes and the ruddy, high-cheekboned face to remind me that the Norsemen had been around the Dales a thousand years ago. This was a Viking.

I had him roll up his sleeves and scrub his hands in a bucket of warm water and antiseptic while I infiltrated the cow's flank with local anaesthetic. When I gave him artery forceps and scissors to hold he pranced around, making stabbing motions at the cow and roaring with laughter.

'Maybe you'd like to do the job yourself?' I asked. The Viking squared his great shoulders. 'Aye, I'll 'ave a go,' and the heads above the door cheered lustily.

As I finally poised my Bard Parker scalpel with its new razor-sharp blade over the cow, the air was thick with earthy witticisms. I had decided that this time I really would make the bold incision recommended in the surgery books; it was about time I advanced beyond the stage of pecking nervously at the skin. 'A veritable blow,' was how one learned author had described it. Well, that was how it was going to be.

I touched the blade down on the clipped area of the flank and with a quick motion of the wrist laid open a ten-inch wound. I stood back for a few seconds admiring the clean-cut edges of the skin with only a few capillaries spurting on to the glistening, twitching abdominal muscles. At the same time I noticed that the laughter and shouting from the heads had been switched off and was replaced by an eerie silence broken only by a heavy, thudding sound from behind me.

'Forceps please,' I said, extending my hand back. But nothing happened. I looked round; the top of the half door was bare – not a head in sight. There was only the Viking spreadeagled in the middle of the floor, arms and legs flung wide, chin pointing to the roof. The attitude was so theatrical that I thought he was still acting the fool, but a closer examination erased all doubts: the Viking was out cold. He must have gone straight over backwards like a stricken oak.

The farmer, a bent little man who couldn't have scaled much more than eight stones, had been steadying the cow's head. He looked at me with the faintest flicker of amusement in his eyes. 'Looks like you and me for it, then, guvnor.' He tied the halter to a ring on the wall, washed his hands methodically and took up his place at my side. Throughout the operation, he passed me my instruments, swabbed away the seeping blood and clipped the sutures, whistling tunelessly through his teeth in a bored manner; the only time he showed any real emotion was when I produced the offending nail from the depths of the reticulum. He raised his eyebrows slightly, said ' 'ello, 'ello,' then started whistling again.

We were too busy to do anything for the Viking. Halfway through, he sat up, shook himself a few times then got to his feet and strolled with elaborate nonchalance out of the box. The poor fellow seemed to be hoping that perhaps we had noticed nothing unusual.

I don't suppose we could have done much to bring him round anyway. There was only one time I discovered a means of immediate resuscitation and that was by accident.

It was when Henry Dickson asked me to show him how to castrate a ruptured pig without leaving a swelling. Henry was going in for pigs in a big way and had a burning ambition to equip himself with veterinary skills.

When he showed me the young pig with the gross scrotal swelling I demurred. 'I really think this is a vet's job, Henry. Castrate your normal pigs by all means but I don't think you could make a proper job of this sort of thing.'

'How's that, then?'

'Well, there's the local anaesthetic, danger of infection – and you really need a knowledge of anatomy to know what you're doing.'

All the frustrated surgeon in Henry showed in his eyes. 'Gaw, I'd like to know how to do it.'

'I'll tell you what,' I said. 'How about if I do this one as a demonstration and you can make up your own mind. I'll give him a general anaesthetic so you don't have to hold him.'

'Right, that's a good idea.' Henry thought for a moment. 'What'll you charge me to do 'im?'

'Seven and six.'

'Well I suppose you have to have your pound of flesh. Get on.'

I injected a few cc's of Nembutal into the little pig's peritoneum and after some staggering he rolled over in the straw and lay still. Henry had rigged up a table in the yard and we laid the sleeping animal on it. I was preparing to start when Henry pulled out a ten-shilling note.

'Better pay you now before I forget.'

'All right, but my hands are clean now – push it into my pocket and I'll give you the change when we finish.'

I rather fancy myself as a teacher and soon warmed to my task. I carefully incised the skin over the inguinal canal and pulled out the testicle, intact in its tunics. 'See there, Henry, the bowels have come down the canal and are lying in with the testicle.' I pointed to the loops of intestine, pale pink through the translucent membranes. 'Now if I do this, I can push them right back into the abdomen, and if I press here, out they pop again. You see how it works? There, they've gone; now they're out again. Once more I make them disappear and whoops, there they are back with us! Now in order to retain them permanently in the abdomen I take the spermatic cord and wind it in its coverings tightly down to the ...'

But my audience was no longer with me. Henry had sunk down on an upturned oil drum and lay slumped across the table, his head cradled on his arms. My disappointment was acute, and finishing off the job and inserting the sutures was a sad anticlimax with my student slumbering at the end of the table.

I put the pig back in his pen and gathered up my gear: then I remembered I hadn't given Henry his change, I don't know why I did it but instead of half-a-crown, I slapped down a shilling and sixpence on the wood a few inches from his face. The noise made him open his eyes and he gazed dully at the coins for a few seconds, then with almost frightening suddenness he snapped upright, ashenfaced but alert and glaring.

'Hey!' he shouted. ' want another shillin'!'

CHAPTER SIXTEEN

Vets are useless creatures, parasites on the agricultural community, expensive layabouts who really know nothing about animals or their diseases. You might as well get Jeff Mallock the knacker man as send for a vet.

At least that was the opinion, frequently expressed, of the Sidlow family. In fact, when you came right down to it, just about the only person for miles around who knew how to treat sick beasts was Mr Sidlow himself. If any of their cows or horses fell ill it was Mr Sidlow who stepped forward with his armoury of sovereign remedies. He enjoyed a God-like prestige with his wife and large family and it was an article of their faith that father was infallible in these matters; the only other being who had ever approached his skill was long-dead Grandpa Sidlow from whom father had learned so many of his cures.

Mind you, Mr Sidlow was a just and humane man. After maybe five or six days of dedicated nursing during which he would perhaps push half a pound of lard and raisins down the cow's throat three times a day, rub its udder vigorously with turpentine or maybe cut a bit off the end of the tail to let the bad out, he always in the end called the vet. Not that it would do any good, but he liked to give the animal every chance. When the vet arrived he invariably found a sunken-eyed, dying creature and the despairing treatment he gave was like a figurative administration of the last rites. The animal always died so the Sidlows were repeatedly confirmed in their opinion – vets were useless.

The farm was situated outside the normal area of the practice and we were the third firm Mr Sidlow had dealt with. He had been a client of Grier of Brawton but had found him wanting and moved to Wallace away over in Mansley. Wallace had disappointed him grievously so he had decided to try Darrowby. He had been with us for over a year but it was an uncomfortable relationship because Siegfried had offended him deeply on his very first visit. It was to a moribund horse, and Mr Sidlow, describing the treatment to date, announced that he had been pushing raw onions up the horse's rectum; he couldn't understand why it was so uneasy on its legs. Siegfried had pointed out that if he were to insert a raw onion in Mr Sidlow's rectum, he, Mr Sidlow, would undoubtedly be uneasy on his legs.

It was a bad start but there were really no other available vets left. He was stuck with us.

I had been uncannily lucky in that I had been at Darrowby for more than a year and had never had to visit this farm. Mr Sidlow rarely called us up during normal working hours as, after wrestling with his conscience for a few days, he always seemed to lose the battle around eleven o'clock at night (he made exceptions in the case of the occasional Sunday afternoon) and it had always landed on Siegfried's duty nights. It was Siegfried who had trailed out, swearing quietly, and returned, slightly pop-eyed in the small hours.

So when it did finally come round to my turn I didn't rush out with any great enthusiasm, even though the case was just a choking bullock and should present no difficulties. (This was when a beast got a piece of turnip or a potato stuck in its gullet, preventing regurgitation of gases and causing bloating which can be fatal. We usually either relieved the bloat by puncturing the stomach or we carefully pushed the obstruction down into the stomach by means of a long flexible leather instrument called a probang.) Anyway, they had realized they couldn't wait for days this time and by way of a change it was only four o'clock in the afternoon.

The farm was nearer Brawton than Darrowby and lay in the low country down on the Plain of York. I didn't like the look of the place; there was something depressing about the dilapidated brick buildings in the dreary setting of ploughing land with only the occasional mound of a potato clamp to relieve the flatness.

My first sight of Mr Sidlow reminded me that he and his family were members of a fanatically narrow religious sect. I had seen that gaunt, blue-jowled face with the tortured eyes staring at me from the pages of history books long ago. I had the feeling that Mr Sidlow would have burnt me at the stake without a qualm.

The bullock was in a gloomy box off the fold yard. Several of the family had filed in with us; two young men in their twenties and three teenage girls, all good-looking in a dark gipsy way, but all with the same taut, unsmiling look as their father. As I moved around, examining the animal, I noticed another peculiarity – they all looked at me, the bullock, each other, with quick sideways glances without any head movement. Nobody said anything.

I would have liked to break the silence but couldn't think of anything cheerful to say. This beast didn't have the look of an ordinary choke. I could feel the potato quite distinctly from the outside, halfway down the oesophagus but all around was an oedematous mass extending up and down the left side of the neck. Not only that, but there was a bloody foam dripping from the mouth. There was something funny here.

A thought struck me. 'Have you been trying to push the potato down with something?'

I could almost feel the battery of flitting glances, and the muscles of Mr Sidlow's clenched jaw stood out in a twitching ridge. He swallowed carefully. 'Aye, we've tried a bit.'

'What did you use?'

Again the rippling jaw muscles under the dark skin. 'Broom handle and a bit of hose pipe. Same as usual.'

That was enough; a sense of doom enveloped me. It would have been nice to be the first vet to make a good impression here but it wasn't to be. I turned to the farmer. 'I'm afraid you've ruptured the gullet. It's a very delicate tube, you know, and you only have to push a bit too hard and you're through. You can see the fluid collection round the rupture.'

A quivering silence answered me. I ploughed on. 'I've seen this happen before. It's a pretty black outlook.'

'All right,' Mr Sidlow ground out. 'What are you going to do about it?'

Well, we were at it now. What was I going to do about it? Maybe now, thirty years later, I might have tried to repair the gullet, packed the wound with antibiotic powder and given a course of penicillin injections. But there, in that cheerless place, looking at the patient animal gulping painfully, coughing up the gouts of blood. I knew I was whacked. A ruptured oesophagus was as near hopeless as anything could be. I searched my mind for a suitable speech.

'I'm sorry, Mr Sidlow, but I can't do anything about it.' The glances crackled around me and the farmer breathed in sharply through his nose. I didn't need to be told what they were all thinking – another no-good, useless vet. I took a deep breath and continued. 'Even if I shifted the potato the wound would get contaminated when the beast tried to eat. He'd have a gangrene in no time and that means a painful death. He's in pretty good condition – if I were you I'd have him slaughtered immediately.'

The only reply was a virtuoso display from the jaw muscles. I tried another tack. 'I'll give you a certificate. I'm sure the meat will pass for the butcher.'

No cries of joy greeted this remark. If anything, Mr Sidlow's expression became still more bleak.

'That beast isn't ready for killin' yet,' he whispered.

'No, but you'd be sending him in before long – another month, maybe. I'm sure you won't lose much. I tell you what,' with a ghastly attempt at heartiness, 'if I can come into the house I'll write you this chit now and we'll get the job over. There's really nothing else for it.'

I turned and headed across the fold yard for the farm kitchen. Mr Sidlow followed wordlessly with the family. I wrote the certificate quickly, waves of disapproval washing around me in the silent room. As I folded the paper I had the sudden conviction that Mr Sidlow wasn't going to pay the slightest attention to my advice. He was going to wait a day or two to see how things turned out. The picture of the big, uncomprehending animal trying vainly to swallow as his hunger and thirst increased was too strong for me. I walked over to the phone on the window sill.

'I'll just give Harry Norman a ring at the abattoir. I know he'll come straight up if I ask him.' I made the arrangements, hung up the receiver and started for the door, addressing Mr Sidlow's profile as I left. 'It's fixed, Harry will be along within half an hour. Much better to get it done immediately.'

Going across the yard, I had to fight the impulse to break into a gallop. As I got into the car I recalled Siegfried's advice: 'In sticky situations always get your car backed round before you examine the animal. Leave the engine running if necessary. The quick getaway is essential.' He was right, it took a long time reversing and manoeuvring under the battery of unseen eyes. I don't blush easily but my face was burning as I finally left the farm.

That was my first visit to the Sidlows and I prayed that it might be my last. But my luck had run out. From then on, every time they sent for us it just happened to be me on duty. I would rather not say anything about the cases I treated there except to record that something went wrong every time. The very name Sidlow became like a jinx. Try as I might I couldn't do a thing right on that farm so that within a short time I was firmly established with the family as the greatest menace to the animal population they had ever encountered. They didn't think much of vets as a whole and they'd met some real beauties in their time, but I was by far the worst. My position as the biggest nincompoop of them all was unassailable.

It got so bad that if I saw any Sidlows in the town I would dive down an alley to avoid them and one day in the market place I had the unnerving experience of seeing the entire family, somehow jammed into a large old car, passing within a few feet of me. Every face looked rigidly to the front but every eye, I knew, was trained balefully on me. Fortunately I was just outside the Drover's Arms, so I was able to reel inside and steady myself with a half-pint of Younger's Special Heavy.

However, the Sidlows were far from my mind on the Saturday morning when Siegfried asked me if I would go through and officiate at Brawton races.

'They've asked me to do it as Grier is on holiday,' he said. 'But I'd already promised to go through to Casborough to help Dick Henley with a rig operation. I can't let him down. There's nothing much to the race job: the regular course vet will be there and he'll keep you right.'

He hadn't been gone more than a few minutes when there was a call from the racecourse. One of the horses had fallen while being unloaded from its box and had injured its knee. Would I come right away.

Even now I am no expert on racehorses; they form a little branch of practice all by itself, with its own stresses, its own mystique. In my short spell in Darrowby I had had very little to do with them as Siegfried was fascinated by anything equine and usually gobbled up anything in that line which came along. So my practical experience was negligible.

I wasn't at all reassured when I saw my patient. The knee was a terrible mess. He had tripped at the bottom of the ramp and come down with his full weight on the stony ground. The lacerated skin hung down in bloody ribbons exposing the joint capsule over an area of about six inches and the extensor tendons gleamed through a tattered layer of fascia. The beautiful three-year-old held the limb up, trembling, with the toe just touching the ground; the ravaged knee made a violent contrast with the sleek, carefully groomed coat.

Examining the wound, gently feeling round the joint, I was immediately thankful for one thing – it was a quiet animal. Some light horses are so highly strung that the slightest touch sends them up in the air, but this one hardly moved as I tried to piece together the jigsaw of skin pieces. Another lucky break – there was nothing missing.

I turned to the stable head lad, small, square, hands deep in his coat pockets who was standing watching. 'I'll clean up the wound and stitch it but he'll need some expert care when you get him home. Can you tell me who will be treating him?'

'Yes sir, Mr Brayley-Reynolds. He'll have charge of 'im.'

I came bolt upright from my crouching position. The name was like a trumpet call echoing down from my student days. When you talked about horses you usually talked about Brayley-Reynolds sooner or later. I could imagine the great man inspecting my handiwork. 'And who did you say treated this? Herriot...? Herriot...?'

I got down to the job again with my heart beating faster. Mercifully the joint capsule and tendon sheaths were undamaged – no escape of synovia. Using a solution of Chinosol, I swabbed out every last cranny of the wound till the ground around me was white with cotton wool pledgets, then I puffed in some iodoform powder and tacked down the loose shreds of fascia. Now the thing was to make a really good job of the skin to avoid disfigurement if possible. I chose some fine silk and a very small suture needle and squatted down again.

I must have stayed there for nearly an hour, pulling the flaps of skin carefully into position and fastening them down with innumerable tiny sutures. There is a fascination in repairing a ragged wound and I always took pains over it even without an imaginary Brayley-Reynolds peering over my shoulder. When I finally straightened up I did so slowly, like an old man, easing the kinks from neck and back. With shaking knees I looked down at the head lad almost without recognition. He was smiling.

'You've made a proper job of that,' he said. 'It looks nearly as good as new. I want to thank you, sir – he's one of my favourites, not just because he's a good 'orse, but he's kind.' He patted the three-year-old's flank.

'Well, I hope he does all right.' I got out a packet of gauze and a bandage. 'I'm just going to cover the knee with this and then you can put on a stable bandage. I'll give him a shot against tetanus and that's it.'

I was packing my gear away in the car when the head lad hovered again at my side. 'Do you back 'orses?'

I laughed. 'No, hardly ever. Don't know much about it.'

'Well never mind.' The little man looked around him and lowered his voice. 'But I'll tell you something to back this afternoon. Kemal in the first race. He's one of ours and he's going to win. You'll get a nice price about him.'

'Well, thanks, it'll give me something to do. I'll have half-a-crown on him.'

The tough little face screwed up in disgust. 'No, no, put a fiver on him.' He walked rapidly away.

I don't know what madness took hold of me, but by the time I had got back to Darrowby I had decided to take his advice. There had been something compelling about that last hoarse whisper and the utter confidence in the black pebble eyes. The little chap was trying to do me a good turn. I had noticed him glancing at my old jacket and rumpled flannels, so different from the natty outfit of the typical horse vet; maybe he thought I needed the money.

I dropped in at the Midland Bank and drew out five pounds which at the time represented approximately half my available capital. I hurried round the remaining visits, had a quick lunch and got into my best suit. There was plenty of time to get to the course, meet the officials and get my fiver on Kemal before the first race at 2.30.

The phone rang just as I was about to leave the house. It was Mr Sidlow. He had a scouring cow which needed attention immediately. It was fitting, I thought dully, that in my moment of eager anticipation it should be my old jinx who should stretch out his cold hand and grasp me. And it was Saturday afternoon; that was fitting too. But I shook myself –

the farm was near Brawton and it shouldn't take long to deal with a scouring cow; I could still make it.

When I arrived, my immaculate appearance set up an immediate flurry of oblique glances among the assembled family while Mr Sidlow's rigid lips and square shoulders bore witness that he was prepared to endure another visit from me with courage.

A numbness filled me as we went into the byre. It continued as Mr Sidlow described how he had battled against this cow's recurring bouts of diarrhoea for several months; how he had started quietly with ground eggshells in gruel and worked up to his most powerful remedy, blue vitriol and dandelion tea, but all to no avail. I hardly heard him because it was fairly obvious at a glance that the cow had Jöhne's disease.

Nobody could be quite sure, of course, but the animal's advanced emaciation, especially in the hind end, and the stream of bubbly, foetid scour which she had ejected as I walked in were almost diagnostic. Instinctively I grasped her tail and thrust my thermometer into the rectum: I wasn't much interested in her temperature but it gave me a couple of minutes to think.

However, in this instance I got only about five seconds because, without warning, the thermometer disappeared from my fingers. Some sudden suction had drawn it inside the cow. I ran my fingers round just inside the rectum – nothing; I pushed my hand inside without success; with a feeling of rising panic I rolled up my sleeve and groped about in vain.

There was nothing else for it – I had to ask for a bucket of hot water, soap and a towel and strip off as though preparing for some large undertaking. Over my thirty-odd years in practice I can recall many occasions when I looked a complete fool, but there is a peculiarly piercing quality about the memory of myself, bare to the waist, the centre of a ring of hostile stares, guddling frantically inside that cow. At the time, all I could think of was that this was the Sidlow place; anything could happen here. In my mental turmoil I had discarded all my knowledge of pathology and anatomy and could visualize the little glass tube working its way rapidly along the intestinal tract until it finally pierced some vital organ. There was another hideous image of myself carrying out a major operation, a full-scale laparotomy on the cow to recover my thermometer.

It is difficult to describe the glorious relief which flooded through me when at last I felt the thing between my fingers; I pulled it out, filthy and dripping and stared down stupidly at the graduations on the tube.

Mr Sidlow cleared his throat. 'Well, wot does it say? Has she got a temperature?'

I whipped round and gave him a piercing look. Was it possible that this man could be making a joke? But the dark, tight-shut face was expressionless.

'No,' I mumbled in reply. 'No temperature.'

The rest of that visit has always been mercifully blurred in my mind. I know I got myself cleaned up and dressed and told Mr Sidlow that I thought his cow had Jöhne's disease which was incurable but I would take away a faeces sample to try to make sure. The details are cloudy but I do know that at no point was there the slightest gleam of light or hope.

I left the farm, bowed down by an ever greater sense of disgrace than usual and drove with my foot on the boards all the way to Brawton. I roared into the special car park at the racecourse, galloped through the owners' and trainers' entrance and seized the arm of the gatekeeper.

'Has the first race been run?' I gasped.

'Aye, just finished,' he replied cheerfully. 'Kemal won it – ten to one.'

I turned and walked slowly towards the paddock. Fifty pounds! A fortune snatched from my grasp by cruel fate. And hanging over the whole tragedy was the grim spectre of Mr Sidlow. I could forgive Mr Sidlow, I thought, for dragging me out at all sorts of ungodly hours; I could forgive him for presenting me with a long succession of hopeless cases which had lowered my self-esteem to rock bottom; I could forgive him for thinking I was the biggest idiot in Yorkshire and for proclaiming his opinion far and wide. But I'd never forgive him for losing me that fifty pounds.

CHAPTER SEVENTEEN

'The Reniston, eh?' I fidgeted uneasily. 'Bit grand, isn't it?'

Tristan lay rather than sat in his favourite chair and peered up through a cloud of cigarette smoke. 'Of course it's grand. It's the most luxurious hotel in the country outside of London, but for your purpose it's the only possible place. Look, tonight is your big chance isn't it? You want to impress this girl, don't you? Well, ring her up and tell her you're taking her to the Reniston. The food is wonderful and there's a dinner dance every Saturday night. And today is Saturday.' He sat up suddenly and his eyes widened. 'Can't you see it, Jim? The music oozing out of Benny Thornton's trombone and you, full of lobster thermidor, floating round the floor with Helen snuggling up to you. The only snag is that it will cost you a packet, but if you are prepared to spend about a fortnight's wages you can have a really good night.'

I hardly heard the last part, I was concentrating on the blinding vision of Helen snuggling up to me. It was an image which blotted out things like money and I stood with my mouth half open listening to the trombone. I could hear it quite clearly.

Tristan broke in. 'There's one thing – have you got a dinner-jacket? You'll need one.'

'Well, I'm not very well off for evening-dress. In fact, when I went to Mrs Pumphrey's party I hired a suit from Brawton, but I wouldn't have time for that now.' I paused and thought for a moment. 'I do have my first and only dinner-suit but I got it when I was about seventeen and I don't know whether I'd be able to get into it.'

Tristan waved this aside. He dragged the Woodbine smoke into the far depths of his lungs and released it reluctantly in little wisps and trickles as he spoke. 'Doesn't matter in the least, Jim. As long as you're wearing the proper gear they'll let you in, and with a big, good-looking chap like you the fit of the suit is unimportant.'

We went upstairs and extracted the garment from the bottom of my trunk. I had cut quite a dash in this suit at the college dances and though it had got very tight towards the end of the course it had still been a genuine evening-dress outfit and as such had commanded a certain amount of respect.

But now it had a pathetic, lost look. The fashion had changed and the trend was towards comfortable jackets and soft, unstarched shirts. This one was rigidly of the old school and included an absurd little waistcoat with lapels and a stiff, shiny-fronted shirt with a tall, winged collar.

My problems really started when I got the suit on. Hard work, Pennine air and Mrs Hall's good food had filled me out and the jacket failed to meet across my stomach by six inches. I seemed to have got taller, too, because there was a generous space between the bottom of the waistcoat and the top of the trousers. The trousers themselves were skin tight over the buttocks, yet seemed foolishly baggy lower down.

Tristan's confidence evaporated as I paraded before him and he decided to call on Mrs Hall for advice. She was an unemotional woman and endured the irregular life at Skeldale House without noticeable reaction, but when she came into the bedroom and looked at me her facial muscles went into a long, twitching spasm. She finally overcame the weakness, however, and became very businesslike.

'A little gusset at the back of your trousers will work wonders, Mr Herriot, and I think if I put a bit of silk cord across the front of your jacket it'll hold it nicely. Mind you, there'll be a bit of a space, like, but I shouldn't think that'll worry you. And I'll give the whole suit a good press – makes all the difference in the world.'

I had never gone in much for intensive grooming, but that night I really went to work on myself, scrubbing and anointing and trying a whole series of different partings in my hair before I was satisfied. Tristan seemed to have appointed himself master of the wardrobe and carried the suit tenderly upstairs, still warm from Mrs Hall's ironing board. Then, like a professional valet, he assisted in every step of the robing. The high collar gave most trouble and he drew strangled oaths from me as he trapped the flesh of my neck under the stud.

When I was finally arrayed he walked around me several times, pulling and patting the material and making delicate adjustments here and there.

Eventually he stopped his circling and surveyed me from the front. I had never seen him look so serious. 'Fine, Jim, fine – you look great. Distinguished, you know. It's not everybody who can wear a dinner-jacket – so many people look like conjurers, but not you. Hang on a minute and I'll get your overcoat.'

I had arranged to pick up Helen at seven o'clock and as I climbed from the car in the darkness outside her house a strange unease crept over me. This was different. When I had come here before it had been as a veterinary surgeon – the man who knew, who was wanted, who came to render assistance in time of need. It had never occurred to me how much this affected my outlook every time I walked on to a farm. This wasn't the same thing at all. I had come to take this man's daughter out. He might not like it, might positively resent it.

Standing outside the farmhouse door I took a deep breath. The night was very dark and still. No sound came from the great trees near by and only the distant roar of the Darrow disturbed the silence. The recent heavy rains had transformed the leisurely, wandering river into a rushing torrent which in places overflowed its banks and flooded the surrounding pastures.

I was shown into the large kitchen by Helen's young brother. The boy had a hand over his mouth in an attempt to hide a wide grin. He seemed to find the situation funny. His little sister sitting at a table doing her homework was pretending to concentrate on her writing but she, too, wore a fixed smirk as she looked down at her book.

Mr Alderson was reading the *Farmer and Stockbreeder*, his breeches unlaced, his stockinged feet stretched out towards a blazing pile of logs. He looked up over his spectacles.

'Come in, young man, and sit by the fire,' he said absently. I had the uncomfortable impression that it was a frequent and boring experience for him to have young men calling for his eldest daughter.

I sat down at the other side of the fire and Mr Alderson resumed his study of the *Farmer and Stockbreeder*. The ponderous tick-tock of a large wall clock boomed out into the silence. I stared into the red depths of the fire till my eyes began to ache, then I looked up at a big oil painting in a gilt frame hanging above the mantelpiece. It depicted shaggy cattle standing knee-deep in a lake of an extraordinary bright blue; behind them loomed a backcloth of fearsome, improbable mountains, their jagged summits wreathed in a sulphurous mist.

Averting my eyes from this, I examined, one by one, the sides of bacon and the hams hanging from the rows of hooks in the ceiling. Mr Alderson turned over a page. The clock ticked on. Over by the table, spluttering noises came from the children.

After about a year I heard footsteps on the stairs, then Helen came into the room. She was wearing a blue dress – the kind, without shoulder straps, that seems to stay up by magic. Her dark hair shone under the single pressure lamp which lit the kitchen, shadowing the soft curves of her neck and shoulders. Over one white arm she held a camel-hair coat.

I felt stunned. She was like a rare jewel in the rough setting of stone flags and whitewashed walls. She gave me her quiet, friendly smile and walked towards me. 'Hello, I hope I haven't kept you waiting too long.'

I muttered something in reply and helped her on with her coat. She went over and kissed her father who didn't look up but waved his hand vaguely. There was another outburst of giggling from the table. We went out.

In the car I felt unusually tense and for the first mile or two had to depend on some inane remarks about the weather to keep a conversation going. I was beginning to relax when I drove over a little hump-backed bridge into a dip in the road.

Then the car suddenly stopped. The engine coughed gently and then we were sitting silent and motionless in the darkness. And there was something else; my feet and ankles were freezing cold.

'My God!' I shouted. 'We've run into a bit of flooded road. The water's right into the car.' I looked round at Helen. 'I'm terribly sorry about this – your feet must be soaked.'

But Helen was laughing. She had her feet tucked up on the seat, her knees under her chin. 'Yes, I am a bit wet, but it's no good sitting about like this. Hadn't we better start pushing?'

Wading out into the black icy waters was a nightmare but there was no escape. Mercifully it was a little car and between us we managed to push it beyond the flooded patch. Then by torchlight I dried the plugs and got the engine going again.

Helen shivered as we squelched back into the car. 'I'm afraid I'll have to go back and change my shoes and stockings. And so will you. There's another road back through Fensley. You take the first turn on the left.'

Back at the farm, Mr Alderson was still reading the *Farmer and Stockbreeder* and kept his finger on the list of pig prices while he gave me a baleful glance over his spectacles. When he learned that I had come to borrow a pair of his shoes and socks he threw the paper down in exasperation and rose, groaning, from his chair. He shuffled out of the room and I could hear him muttering to himself as he mounted the stairs.

Helen followed him and I was left alone with the two young children. They studied my sodden trousers with undisguised delight. I had wrung most of the surplus water out of them but the final result was remarkable. Mrs Hall's knife-edge crease reached to just below the knee, but then there was chaos. The trousers flared out at that point in a crumpled, shapeless mass and as I stood by the fire to dry them a gentle steam rose about me. The children stared at me, wide-eyed and happy. This was a big night for them.

Mr Alderson reappeared at length and dropped some shoes and rough socks at my feet. I pulled on the socks quickly but shrank back when I saw the shoes. They were a pair of dancing slippers from the early days of the century and their cracked patent leather was topped by wide, black silk bows.

I opened my mouth to protest but Mr Alderson had dug himself deep into his chair and had found his place again among the pig prices. I had the feeling that if I asked for another pair of shoes Mr Alderson would attack me with the poker. I put the slippers on.

We had to take a roundabout road to avoid the floods but I kept my foot down and within half an hour we had left the steep sides of the Dale behind us and were heading out on to the rolling plain. I began to feel better. We were making good time and the little car, shuddering and creaking, was going well. I was just thinking that we wouldn't be all that late when the steering-wheel began to drag to one side.

I had a puncture most days and recognized the symptoms immediately. I had become an expert at changing wheels and with a word of apology to Helen was out of the car like a flash. With my rapid manipulation of the rusty jack and brace the wheel was off within three minutes. The surface of the crumpled tyre was quite smooth except for the lighter, frayed parts where the canvas showed through. Working like a demon, I screwed on the spare, cringing inwardly as I saw that this tyre was in exactly the same condition as the other. I steadfastly refused to think of what I would do if its frail fibres should give up the struggle.

By day, the Reniston dominated Brawton like a vast mediaeval fortress, bright flags fluttering arrogantly from its four turrets, but tonight it was like a dark cliff with a glowing cavern at street level where the Bentleys discharged their expensive cargoes. I didn't take my vehicle to the front entrance but tucked it away quietly at the back of the car park. A magnificent commissionaire opened the door for us and we trod noiselessly over the rich carpeting of the entrance hall.

We parted there to get rid of our coats, and in the men's cloakroom I scrubbed frantically at my oily hands. It didn't do much good; changing that wheel had given my finger nails a border of deep black which defied ordinary soap and water. And Helen was waiting for me.

I looked up in the mirror at the white-jacketed attendant hovering behind me with a towel. The man, clearly fascinated by my ensemble, was staring down at the wide-bowed pierrot shoes and the rumpled trouser bottoms. As he handed over the towel he smiled broadly as if in gratitude for this little bit of extra colour in his life.

I met Helen in the reception hall and we went over to the desk. 'What time does the dinner dance start?' I asked.

The girl at the desk looked surprised. 'I'm sorry, sir, there's no dance tonight. We only have them once a fortnight.'

I turned to Helen in dismay but she smiled encouragingly. 'It doesn't matter,' she said. 'I don't really care what we do.'

'We can have dinner, anyway,' I said. I tried to speak cheerfully but a little black cloud seemed to be forming just above my head. Was anything going to go right tonight? I could feel my morale slumping as I padded over the lush carpet and my first sight of the dining-room didn't help.

It looked as big as a football field with great marble pillars supporting a carved, painted ceiling. The Reniston had been built in the late Victorian period and all the opulence and ornate splendour of those days had been retained in this tremendous room. Most of the tables were occupied by the usual clientele, a mixture of the county aristocracy and industrialists from the West Riding. I had never seen so many beautiful women and masterful-looking men under one roof and I noticed with a twinge of alarm that, though the men were wearing everything from dark lounge suits to hairy tweeds, there wasn't another dinner jacket in sight.

A majestic figure in white tie and tails bore down on us. With his mane of white hair falling back from the lofty brow, the bulging waistline, the hooked nose and imperious expression he looked exactly like a Roman emperor. His eyes flickered expertly over me and he spoke tonelessly.

'You want a table, sir?'

'Yes please,' I mumbled, only just stopping myself saying 'Sir' to the man in return. 'A table for two.'

'Are you staying, sir?'

This question baffled me. How could I possibly have dinner here if I wasn't staying.

'Yes, I am staying.'

The emperor made a note on a pad. 'This way, sir.'

He began to make his way with great dignity among the tables while I followed abjectly in his wake with Helen. It was a long way to the table and I tried to ignore the heads which turned to have a second look at me as I passed. It was Mrs Hall's gusset that worried me most and I imagined it standing out like a beacon below the short jacket. It was literally burning my buttocks by the time we arrived.

The table was nicely situated and a swarm of waiters descended on us, pulling out our chairs and settling us into them, shaking out our napkins and spreading them on our laps. When they had dispersed the emperor took charge again. He poised a pencil over his pad.

'May I have your room number, sir?'

I swallowed hard and stared up at him over my dangerously billowing shirt front. 'Room number? Oh, I'm not living in the hotel.'

'Ah, NOT staying.' He fixed me for a moment with an icy look before crossing out something on the pad with unnecessary violence. He muttered something to one of the waiters and strode away.

It was about then that the feeling of doom entered into me. The black cloud over my head spread and descended, enveloping me in a dense cloud of misery. The whole evening had been a disaster and would probably get worse. I must have been mad to come to this sumptuous place dressed up like a knockabout comedian. I was as hot as hell inside this ghastly suit and the stud was biting viciously into my neck.

I took a menu card from a waiter and tried to hold it with my fingers curled inwards to hide my dirty nails. Everything was in French and in my numbed state the words were largely meaningless, but somehow I ordered the meal and, as we ate, I tried desperately to keep a conversation going. But long deserts of silence began to stretch between us; it seemed that only Helen and I were quiet among all the surrounding laughter and chatter.

Worst of all was the little voice which kept telling me that Helen had never really wanted to come out with me anyway. She had done it out of politeness and was getting through a boring evening as best she could.

The journey home was a fitting climax. We stared straight ahead as the headlights picked out the winding road back into the Dales. We made stumbling remarks then the strained silence took over again. By the time we drew up outside the farm my head had begun to ache.

We shook hands and Helen thanked me for a lovely evening. There was a tremor in her voice and in the moonlight her face was anxious and withdrawn. I said goodnight, got into the car and drove away.

CHAPTER EIGHTEEN

If only my car had had any brakes I would certainly have enjoyed looking down on Worton village from the high moor. The old stone houses straggling unevenly along the near bank of the river made a pleasant splash of grey on the green floor of the valley and the little gardens with their clipped lawns gave a touch of softness to the bare, rising sweep of the fellside on the other side of the Dale.

But the whole scene was clouded by the thought that I had to get down that road with its 1 in 4 gradient and those two villainous S bends. It was like a malevolent snake coiling almost headlong from where I sat. And, as I said, I had no brakes.

Of course the vehicle had originally been fitted with the means of bringing it to a halt, and during most of the year I had ridden in it a violent pressure on the pedal would have the desired effect even though it caused a certain amount of veering about on the road. But lately the response had been growing weaker and now it was nil.

During the gradual deterioration I had brought the matter

up with Siegfried now and then and he had expressed sympathy and concern.

'That won't do at all, James. I'll have a word with Hammond about it. Leave it with me.'

And then a few days later when I made a further appeal.

'Oh Lord, yes. I've been meaning to fix it up with Hammond. Don't worry, James, I'll see to it.'

Finally I had to tell him that when I put my foot on the pedal there was nothing at all and the only way I had of stopping the car was to crash it into bottom gear.

'Oh bad luck, James. Must be a nuisance for you. But never mind, I'll arrange everything.'

Some time later I asked Mr Hammond down at the garage if he had heard anything from Siegfried, but he hadn't. The motor man did, however, hop into the car and drive it slowly down the street. He came to a jerking, shuddering halt about fifty yards away and then got out. He made no attempt to back up but walked thoughtfully towards me. Normally an imperturbable man, he had gone rather pale and he looked at me wonderingly.

'And you mean to tell me, lad, that you do all your rounds in that car?'

'Well, yes, I do.'

'You ought to have a medal, then. I dursn't drive across market place in that bloody thing.'

There wasn't much I could do. The car was Siegfried's property and I'd have to await his pleasure. Of course I had had experience of this sort of thing before in the shape of the movable passenger seat he had in his own vehicle when I first came to Darrowby. He never seemed to notice when I went over backwards every time I sat in it and I don't suppose he would ever have done anything about it but for an incident one market day when he noticed an old lady with a large basket of vegetables walking into Darrowby and courteously offered her a lift.

'Poor old girl's feet went straight up in the air and she just disappeared into the back. Had a hell of a job getting her out – thought we'd have to get a block and tackle. Cabbages and cauliflowers rolling all over the place.'

I looked again down the steep track. The sensible thing, of course, would be to go back into Darrowby and take the low road into Worton. No danger that way. But it meant a round trip of nearly ten miles and I could actually see the smallholding I wanted to visit just a thousand feet below. The calf with joint ill was in that shed with the green door – in fact there was old Mr Robinson coming out of the house now and pottering across the yard with a bucket. I could almost reach out and touch him.

I thought, not for the first time, that if you had to drive a car with no brakes one of the last places in England you'd want to be was the Yorkshire Dales. Even on the flat it was bad enough but I got used to it after a week or two and often forgot all about it. As when one day I was busy with a cow and the farmer jumped into my car to move it so that one of his men could get past with a tractor. I never said a word as the unsuspecting man backed round quickly and confidently and hit the wall of the barn with a sickening crash. With typical Yorkshire understatement, all he said was: 'Your brakes aren't ower savage, mister.'

Anyway, I had to make up my mind. Was it to be back to Darrowby or straight over the top? It had become a common situation and every day I had the experience of sitting wrestling with myself on the edge of a hill with my heart thumping as it was now. There must have been scores of these unwitnessed dramas played out in the green silence of the fells. At last, I started the engine and did what I always did – took the quick way down.

But this hill really was a beauty, a notorious road even in this country, and as I nosed gingerly on to it, the whole world seemed to drop away from me. With the gear lever in bottom and my hand jammed against it I headed, dry-mouthed, down the strip of tarmac which now looked to be almost vertical.

It is surprising what speed you can attain in bottom gear if you have nothing else to hold you back and as the first bend rushed up at me the little engine started a rising scream of protest. When I hit the curve, I hauled the wheel round desperately to the right, the tyres spun for a second in the stones and loose soil of the verge, then we were off again.

This was a longer stretch and even steeper and it was like being on the big dipper with the same feeling of lack of control over one's fate. Hurtling into the bend, the idea of turning at this speed was preposterous but it was that or straight over the edge. Terror-stricken, I closed my eyes and dragged the wheel to the left. This time, one side of the car lifted and I was sure we were over, then it rocked back on to the other side and for a horrible second or two kept this up till it finally decided to stay upright and I was once more on my way.

Again a yawning gradient. But as the car sped downwards, engine howling, I was aware of a curious numbness. I seemed to have reached the ultimate limits of fear and hardly noticed as we shot round the third bend. One more to go and at last the road was levelling out; my speed dropped rapidly and at the last bend I couldn't have been doing more than twenty. I had made it.

It wasn't till I was right on to the final straight that I saw the sheep. Hundreds of them, filling the road. A river of woolly backs lapping from wall to wall. They were only yards from me and I was still going downhill. Without hesitation I turned and drove straight into the wall.

There didn't seem to be much damage. A few stones slithered down as the engine stalled and fell silent.

Slowly I sank back in my seat, relaxing my clenched jaws, releasing, finger by finger, the fierce grip on the wheel. The sheep continued to flow past and I took a sideways glance at the man who was shepherding them. He was a stranger to me and I prayed he didn't recognize me either because at that moment the role of unknown madman seemed to be the ideal one. Best not to say anything; appearing round a corner and driving deliberately into a wall is no basis for a rewarding conversation.

The sheep were still passing by and I could hear the man calling to his dogs. 'Get by, Jess. Come by, Nell.' But I kept up a steady stare at the layered stones in front of me, even though he passed within a few feet.

I suppose some people would have asked me what the hell I was playing at, but not a Dales shepherd. He went quietly by without invading my privacy, but when I looked in the mirror after a few moments I could see him in the middle of the road staring back at me, his sheep temporarily forgotten.

My brakeless period has always been easy to recall. There is a piercing clarity about the memory which has kept it fresh over the years. I suppose it lasted only a few weeks but it could have gone on indefinitely if Siegfried himself hadn't become involved.

It was when we were going to a case together. For some reason he decided to take my car and settled in the driver's seat. I huddled apprehensively next to him as he set off at his usual brisk pace.

Hinchcliffe's farm lies about a mile on the main road outside Darrowby. It is a massive place with a wide straight drive leading down to the house. We weren't going there, but as Siegfried spurted to full speed I could see Mr Hinchcliffe in his big Buick ahead of us proceeding in a leisurely way along the middle of the road. As Siegfried pulled out to overtake, the farmer suddenly stuck out his hand and began to turn right towards his farm – directly across our path. Siegfried's foot went hard down on the brake pedal and his eyebrows shot right up as nothing happened. We were going straight for the side of the Buick and there was no room to go round on the left.

Siegfried didn't panic. At the last moment he turned right with the Buick and the two cars roared side by side down the drive, Mr Hinchcliffe staring at me with bulging eyes from close range. The farmer stopped in the yard, but we continued round the back of the house because we had to.

Fortunately, it was one of those places where you could drive right round and we rattled through the stackyard and back to the front of the house behind Mr Hinchcliffe who had got out and was looking round the corner to see where we had gone. The farmer whipped round in astonishment and, open-mouthed watched us as we passed, but Siegfried, retaining his aplomb to the end, inclined his head and gave a little wave before we shot back up the drive.

Before we returned to the main road I had a look back at

Mr Hinchcliffe. He was still watching us and there was a certain rigidity in his pose which reminded me of the shepherd.

Once on the road, Siegfried steered carefully into a layby and stopped. For a few moments he stared straight ahead without speaking and I realized he was having a little difficulty in getting his patient look properly adjusted; but when he finally turned to me his face was transfigured, almost saintly.

I dug my nails into my palms as he smiled at me with kind eyes.

'Really, James,' he said, 'I can't understand why you keep things to yourself. Heaven knows how long your car has been in this condition, yet never a word from you.' He raised a forefinger and his patient look was replaced by one of sorrowing gravity. 'Don't you realize we might have been killed back there? You really ought to have told me.'

CHAPTER NINETEEN

There didn't seem much point in a millionaire filling up football pools coupons but it was one of the motive forces in old Harold Denham's life. It made a tremendous bond between us because, despite his devotion to the pools, Harold knew nothing about football, had never seen a match and was unable to name a single player in league football; and when he found that I could discourse knowledgeably not only about Everton and Preston North End but even about Arbroath and Cowdenbeath the respect with which he had always treated me deepened into a wide-eyed deference.

Of course we had first met over his animals. He had an assortment of dogs, cats, rabbits, budgies and goldfish which made me a frequent visitor to the dusty mansion whose Victorian turrets peeping above their sheltering woods could be seen for miles around Darrowby. When I first knew him, the circumstances of my visits were entirely normal – his fox terrier had cut its pad or the old grey tabby was having trouble with its sinusitis, but later on I began to wonder. He called me out so often on a Wednesday and the excuse was at times so trivial that I began seriously to suspect that there was nothing wrong with the animal but that Harold was in difficulties with his Nine Results or the Easy Six.

I could never be quite sure, but it was funny how he always received me with the same words. 'Ah, Mr Herriot, how are your pools?' He used to say the word in a long-drawn, loving way – pools. This inquiry had been unvarying ever since I had won sixteen shillings one week on the Three Draws. I can never forget the awe with which he fingered the little slip from Littlewoods, looking unbelievingly from it to the postal order. That was the only time I was a winner but it made no difference – I was still the oracle, unchallenged, supreme. Harold never won anything, ever.

The Denhams were a family of note in North Yorkshire. The immensely wealthy industrialists of the last century had become leaders in the world of agriculture. They were 'gentlemen farmers' who used their money to build up pedigree herds of dairy cows or pigs; they ploughed out the high, stony moorland and fertilized it and made it grow crops, they drained sour bogs and made them yield potatoes and turnips; they were the chairmen of committees, masters of fox hounds, leaders of the county society.

But Harold had opted out of all that at an early age. He had refuted the age old dictum that you can't be happy doing absolutely nothing; all day and every day he pottered around his house and his few untidy acres, uninterested in the world outside, not entirely aware of what was going on in his immediate vicinity, but utterly content. I don't think he ever gave a thought to other people's opinions which was just as well because they were often unkind; his brother, the eminent Basil Denham, referred to him invariably as 'that bloody fool' and with the country people it was often 'nobbut ninepence in t'shillin'.'

Personally I always found something appealing in him. He was kind, friendly, with a sense of fun and I enjoyed going to his house. He and his wife ate all their meals in the kitchen and in fact seemed to spend most of their time there, so I usually went round the back of the house.

On this particular day it was to see his Great Dane bitch which had just had pups and seemed unwell; since it wasn't Wednesday I felt that there really might be something amiss with her and hurried round. Harold gave me his usual greeting; he had the most attractive voice – round, fruity, mellow, like a bishop's, and for the hundredth time I thought how odd it was to hear those organ-like vocal cords intoning such incongruities as Mansfield Town or Bradford City.

'I wonder if you could advise me, Mr Herriot,' he said as we left the kitchen and entered a long, ill-lit passage. 'I'm searching for an Away winner and I wondered about Sunderland at Aston Villa?'

I stopped and fell into an attitude of deep thought while Harold regarded me anxiously. 'Well, I'm not sure, Mr Denham,' I replied. 'Sunderland are a good side but I happen to know that Raich Carter's auntie isn't too well at present and it could easily affect his game this Saturday.'

Harold looked crestfallen and he nodded his head gravely a few times; then he looked closely at me for a few seconds and broke into a shout of laughter. 'Ah, Mr Herriot, you're pulling my leg again.' He seized my arm, gave it a squeeze and shuffled off along the passage, chuckling deeply.

We traversed a labyrinth of gloomy, cobwebbed passages before he led the way into a little gun room. My patient was lying on a raised wooden dog bed and I recognized her as the enormous Dane I had seen leaping around at previous visits. I had never treated her, but my first sight of her had dealt a blow at one of my new-found theories – that you didn't find big dogs in big houses. Times without number I had critically observed Bull Mastiffs, Alsatians and Old English Sheep Dogs catapulting out of the tiny, back street dwellings of Darrowby, pulling their helpless owners on the end of a lead, while in the spacious rooms and wide acres of the stately homes I saw nothing but Border Terriers and Jack Russells. But Harold would have to be different.

He patted the bitch's head. 'She had the puppies yesterday

and she's got a nasty dark discharge. She's eating well, but I'd like you to look her over.'

Great Danes, like most of the big breeds, are usually placid animals and the bitch didn't move as I took her temperature. She lay on her side, listening contentedly to the squeals of her family as the little blind creatures climbed over each other to get at the engorged teats.

'Yes, she's got a slight fever and you're right about the discharge.' I gently palpated the long hollow of the flank. 'I don't think there's another pup there but I'd better have a feel inside her to make sure. Could you bring me some warm water, soap and towel please?'

As the door closed behind Harold I looked idly around the gun room. It wasn't much bigger than a cupboard and, since another of Harold's idiosyncrasies was that he never killed anything, was devoid of guns. The glass cases contained only musty bound volumes of *Blackwood's Magazine* and *Country Life*. I stood there for maybe ten minutes, wondering why the old chap was taking so long, then I turned to look at an old print on the wall; it was the usual hunting scene and I was peering through the grimy glass and wondering why they always drew those horses flying over the stream with such impossible long legs when I heard a sound behind me.

It was a faint growl, a deep rumble, soft but menacing. I turned and saw the bitch rising very slowly from her bed. She wasn't getting to her feet in the normal way of dogs, it was as though she were being lifted up by strings somewhere in the ceiling, the legs straightening almost imperceptibly, the body rigid, every hair bristling. All thc time she glared at me unblinkingly and for the first time in my life I realized the meaning of blazing eyes. I had only once seen anything like this before and it was on the cover of an old copy of *The Hound of the Baskervilles*. At the time I had thought the artist ridiculously fanciful but here were two eyes filled with the same yellow fire and fixed unwaveringly on mine.

She thought I was after her pups, of course. After all, her master had gone and there was only this stranger standing motionless and silent in the corner of the room, obviously up to no good. One thing was sure – she was going to come at me any second, and I blessed the luck that had made me stand right by the door. Carefully I inched my left hand towards the handle as the bitch still rose with terrifying slowness, still rumbling deep in her chest. I had almost reached the handle when I made the mistake of making a quick grab for it. Just as I touched the metal the bitch came out of the bed like a rocket and sank her teeth into my wrist.

I thumped her over the head with my right fist and she let go and seized me high up on the inside of the left thigh. This really made me yell out and I don't know just what my immediate future would have been if I hadn't bumped up against the only chair in the room; it was old and flimsy but it saved me. As the bitch, apparently tiring of gnawing my leg, made a sudden leap at my face I snatched the chair up and fended her off.

The rest of my spell in the gun room was a sort of parody of a lion-taming act and would have been richly funny to an impartial observer. In fact, in later years I have often wished I could have a cine film of the episode; but at the time, with that great animal stalking me round those few cramped yards of space, the blood trickling down my leg and only a rickety chair to protect me I didn't feel a bit like laughing. There was a dreadful dedication in the way she followed me and those maddened eyes never left my face for an instant.

The pups, furious at the unceremonious removal of their delightful source of warmth and nourishment, were crawling blindly across the bed and bawling, all nine of them, at the top of their voices. The din acted as a spur to the bitch and the louder it became the more she pressed home her attack. Every few seconds she would launch herself at me and I would prance about, stabbing at her with my chair in best circus fashion. Once she bore me back against the wall, chair and all; on her hind legs she was about as tall as me and I had a disturbing close-up of the snarling gaping jaws.

My biggest worry was that my chair was beginning to show signs of wear; the bitch had already crunched two of the spars effortlessly away and I tried not to think of what would happen if the whole thing finally disintegrated. But I was working my way back to the door and when I felt the handle at my back I knew I had to do something about it. I gave a final, intimidating shout, threw the remains of the chair at the bitch and dived out into the corridor. As I slammed the door behind me and leaned against it I could feel the panels quivering as the big animal threw herself against the wood.

I was sitting on the floor with my back against the passage wall, pants round my ankles, examining my wounds when I saw Harold pass across the far end, pottering vaguely along with a basin of steaming water held in front of him and a towel over his shoulder. I could understand now why he had been so long – he had been wandering around like that all the time; being Harold it was just possible he had been lost in his own house. Or maybe he was just worrying about his Four Aways.

Back at Skeldale House I had to endure some unkind remarks about my straddling gait, but later, in my bedroom, the smile left Siegfried's face as he examined my leg.

'Right up there, by God.' He gave a low, awed whistle. 'You know, James, we've often made jokes about what a savage dog might do to us one day. Well, I tell you boy, it damn nearly happened to you.'

CHAPTER TWENTY

This was my second winter in Darrowby so I didn't feel the same sense of shock when it started to be really rough in November. When they were getting a drizzle of rain down there on the plain the high country was covered in a few hours by a white blanket which filled in the roads, smoothed out familiar landmarks, transformed our world into something strange and new. This was what they meant on the radio when they talked about 'snow on high ground'.

When the snow started in earnest it had a strangling effect

on the whole district. Traffic crawled laboriously between the mounds thrown up by the snow ploughs. Herne Fell hung over Darrowby like a great gleaming whale and in the town the people dug deep paths to their garden gates and cleared the drifts from their front doors. They did it without fuss, with the calm of long use and in the knowledge that they would probably have to do it again tomorrow.

Every new fall struck a fresh blow at the vets. We managed to get to most of our cases but we lost a lot of sweat in the process. Sometimes we were lucky and were able to bump along in the wake of a council plough but more often we drove as far as we could and walked the rest of the way.

On the morning when Mr Clayton of Pike House rang up we had had a night of continuous snow.

'Young beast with a touch o' cold,' he said. 'Will you come?'

To get to his place you had to cross over Pike Edge and then drop down into a little valley. It was a lovely drive in the summer, but I wondered.

'What's the road like?' I asked.

'Road? road?' Mr Clayton's reaction was typically airy. Farmers in the less accessible places always brushed aside such queries. 'Road's right enough. Just tek a bit o' care and you'll get here without any trouble.'

Siegfried wasn't so sure. 'You'll certainly have to walk over the top and it's doubtful whether the ploughs will have cleared the lower road. It's up to you.'

'Oh, I'll have a go. There's not much doing this morning and I feel like a bit of exercise.'

In the yard I found that old Boardman had done a tremendous job in his quiet way; he had dug open the big double doors and cleared a way for the cars to get out. I put what I thought I would need into a small rucksack – some expectorant mixture, a tub of electuary, a syringe and a few ampoules of pneumonia serum. Then I threw the most important item of my winter equipment, a broad-bladed shovel, into the back and left.

The bigger roads had already been cleared by the council ploughs which had been clanking past Skeldale House since before dawn, but the surface was rough and I had a slow, bumpy ride. It was more than ten miles to the Clayton farm and it was one of those iron days when the frost piled thickly on the windscreen blotting out everything within minutes. But this morning I was triumphant. I had just bought a wonderful new invention – a couple of strands of wire mounted on a strip of Bakelite and fastened to the windscreen with rubber suckers. It worked from the car batteries and cleared a small space of vision.

No more did I have to climb out wearily and scrub and scratch at the frozen glass every half mile or so. I sat peering delightedly through a flawlessly clear semicircle about eight inches wide at the countryside unwinding before me like a film show; the grey stone villages, silent and withdrawn under their smothering white cloak; the low, burdened branches of the roadside trees.

I was enjoying it so much that I hardly noticed the ache in my toes. Freezing feet were the rule in those days before car heaters, especially when you could see the road flashing past through the holes in the floor boards. On long journeys I really began to suffer towards the end. It was like that today when I got out of the car at the foot of the Pike Edge road; my fingers too, throbbed painfully as I stamped around and swung my arms.

The ploughs hadn't even attempted to clear the little side road which wound its way upwards and into the valley beyond. Its solid, creamy, wall-to-wall filling said 'No, you can't come up here', with that detached finality I had come to know so well. But as always, even in my disappointment, I looked with wonder at the shapes the wind had sculpted in the night; flowing folds of the most perfect smoothness tapering to the finest of points, deep hollows with knife-edge rims, soaring cliffs with overhanging margins almost transparent in their delicacy.

Hitching the rucksack on my shoulder I felt a kind of subdued elation. With a leather golf jacket buttoned up to my neck and an extra pair of thick socks under my wellingtons I felt ready for anything. No doubt I considered there was something just a bit dashing and gallant in the picture of the dedicated young vet with his magic potions on his back battling against the odds to succour a helpless animal.

I stood for a moment gazing at the fell, curving clean and cold into the sullen sky. An expectant hush lay on the fields, the frozen river and the still trees as I started off.

I kept up a good pace. First over a bridge with the river white and silent beneath then up and up, picking my way over the drifts till the road twisted, almost invisible, under some low cliffs. Despite the cold, the sweat was beginning to prick on my back when I got to the top.

I looked around me. I had been up here several times in June and July and I could remember the sunshine, the smell of the warm grass, and the scent of flowers and pines that came up the hill from the valley below. But it was hard to relate the smiling landscape of last summer with this desolation.

The flat moorland on the fell top was a white immensity rolling away to the horizon with the sky pressing down like a dark blanket. I could see the farm down there in its hollow and it, too, looked different; small, remote, like a charcoal drawing against the hills bulking smooth and white beyond. A pine wood made a dark smudge on the slopes but the scene had been wiped clean of most of its familiar features.

I could see the road only in places – the walls were covered over most of their length, but the farm was visible all the way. I had gone about half a mile towards it when a sudden gust of wind blew up the surface snow into a cloud of fine particles. Just for a few seconds I found myself completely alone. The farm, the surrounding moor, everything disappeared and I had an eerie sense of isolation till the veil cleared.

It was hard going in the deep snow and in the drifts I sank over the tops of my wellingtons. I kept at it, head down, to within a few hundred yards of the stone buildings. I was just thinking that it had all been pretty easy, really, when I looked up and saw a waving curtain of a million black dots bearing down on me. I quickened my steps and just before the blizzard hit me I marked the position of the farm. But after ten minutes' stumbling and slithering I realized I had missed the place. I was heading for a shape that didn't exist; it was etched only in my mind.

I stood for a few moments feeling again the chilling sense of isolation. I was convinced I had gone too far to the left and after a few gasping breaths, struck off to the right. It wasn't long before I knew I had gone in the wrong direction again. I began to fall into deep holes, up to the arm-pits in the snow reminding me that the ground was not really flat on these high moors but pitted by countless peat haggs.

As I struggled on I told myself that the whole thing was ridiculous. I couldn't be far from the warm fireside at Pike House – this wasn't the North Pole. But my mind went back to the great empty stretch of moor beyond the farm and I had to stifle a feeling of panic.

The numbing cold seemed to erase all sense of time. Soon I had no idea of how long I had been falling into the holes and crawling out. I did know that each time it was getting harder work dragging myself out. And it was becoming more and more tempting to sit down and rest, even sleep; there was something hypnotic in the way the big, soft flakes brushed noiselessly across my skin and mounted thickly on my closed eyes.

I was trying to shut out the conviction that if I fell down many more times I wouldn't get up when a dark shape hovered suddenly ahead. Then my outflung arms touched something hard and rough. Unbelievingly I felt my way over the square stone blocks till I came to a corner. Beyond that was a square of light – it was the kitchen window of the farm.

Thumping on the door, I leaned against the smooth timbers, mouth gaping, chest heaving agonizingly. My immense relief must have bordered on hysteria because it seemed to me that when the door was opened the right thing would be to fall headlong into the room. My mind played with the picture of the family crowding round the prostrate figure, plying him with brandy.

When the door did open, however, something kept me on my feet. Mr Clayton stood there for a few seconds, apparently unmoved by the sight of the distraught snowman in front of him.

'Oh, it's you, Mr Herriot. You couldn't have come better – I've just finished me dinner. Hang on a minute till I get me 'at. Beast's just across yard.'

He reached behind the door, stuck a battered trilby on his head, put his hands in his pockets and sauntered over the cobbles, whistling. He knocked up the latch of the calf house and with a profound sense of release I stepped inside; away from the relentless cold, the sucking swirling snow into an animal warmth and the scent of hay.

As I rid myself of my rucksack, four long-haired little bullocks regarded me calmly from over a hurdle, their jaws moving rhythmically. They appeared as unconcerned at my appearance as their owner. They showed a mild interest, nothing more. Behind the shaggy heads I could see a fifth small beast with a sack tied round it and a purulent discharge coming from its nose.

It reminded me of the reason for my visit. As my numb fingers fumbled in a pocket for my thermometer a great gust of wind buffeted the door, setting the latch clicking softly and sending a faint powdering of snow into the dark interior.

Mr Clayton turned and rubbed the pane of the single small window with his sleeve. Picking his teeth with his thumb-nail he peered out at the howling blizzard.

'Aye,' he said, and belched pleasurably. 'It's a plain sort o' day.'

CHAPTER TWENTY-ONE

As I waited for Siegfried to give me my morning list I pulled my scarf higher till it almost covered my eyes, turned up the collar of my overcoat and buttoned it tightly under my chin. Then I drew on a pair of holed woollen gloves.

A biting north wind was driving the snow savagely past the window almost parallel with the ground, obliterating the street and everything else with big, swirling flakes.

Siegfried bent over the day book. 'Now let's see what we've got. Barnett, Gill, Sunter, Dent, Cartwright . . .' He began to scribble on a pad. 'Oh, and I'd better see Scruton's calf – you've been attending it, I know, but I'm going right past the door. Can you tell me about it?'

'Yes, it's been breathing a bit fast and running a temperature around 103 – I don't think there's any pneumonia there. In fact I rather suspect it may be developing diphtheria – it has a bit of a swelling on the jaw and the throat glands are up.'

All the time I was speaking, Siegfried continued to write on the pad and only stopped once to whisper to Miss Harbottle. Then he looked up brightly. 'Pneumonia, eh? How have you been treating it?'

'No, I said I didn't think it was pneumonia. I've been injecting Prontosil and I left some liniment to rub into the throat region.'

But Siegfried was writing hard again. He said nothing till he had made out two lists. He tore one from the pad and gave it to me. 'Right, you've been applying liniment to the chest. Suppose it might do a bit of good. Which liniment exactly?'

'Lin. methyl. sal., but they're rubbing it on the calf's throat, not the chest.' But Siegfried had turned away to tell Miss Harbottle the order of his visits and I found myself talking to the back of his head.

Finally he straightened up and came away from the desk. 'Well, that's fine. You have your list – let's get on.' But half way across the floor he hesitated in his stride and turned back. 'Why the devil are you rubbing that liniment on the calf's throat?'

'Well, I thought it might relieve the inflammation a bit.'

'But James, why should there be any inflammation there? Don't you think the liniment would do more good on the chest wall?' Siegfried was wearing his patient look again.

'No, I don't. Not in a case of calf diphtheria.'

Siegfried put his head on one side and a smile of saintly sweetness crept over his face. He laid his hand on my shoulder. 'My dear old James, perhaps it would be a good idea if you started right at the beginning. Take all the time you want – there's no hurry. Speak slowly and calmly and then you won't become confused. You told me you were treating a calf with pneumonia – now take it from there.'

I thrust my hands deep into my coat pockets and began to churn among the thermometers and scissors and little bottles which always dwelt there. 'Look, I told you right at the start that I didn't think there was any pneumonia but that I suspected early diphtheria. There was also a bit of fever – 103.'

Siegfried was looking past me at the window. 'God, just look at that snow. We're going to have some fun getting round today.' He dragged his eyes back to my face. 'Don't you think that with a temperature of 103 you should be injecting some Prontosil?' He raised his arms sideways and let them fall. 'Just a suggestion, James – I wouldn't interfere for the world but I honestly think that the situation calls for a little Prontosil.'

'But hell, I am using it!' I shouted. 'I told you that way back but you weren't listening. I've been doing my damnedest to get this across to you but what chance have I got...'

'Come come, dear boy, come come. No need to upset yourself.' Siegfried's face was transfigured by an internal radiance. Sweetness and charity, forgiveness, tolerance and affection flowed from him in an enveloping wave. I battled with an impulse to kick him swiftly on the shin.

'James, James.' The voice was caressing. 'I've not the slightest doubt you tried in your own way to tell me about this case, but we haven't all got the gift of communication. You're the most excellent fellow but must apply yourself to this. It is simply a matter of marshalling your facts and presenting them in an orderly manner. Then you wouldn't get confused and mixed up as you've done this morning; it's only a question of practice, I'm sure.' He gave an encouraging wave of the hand and was gone.

I strode quickly through to the stock room and, seeing a big, empty cardboard box on the floor, dealt it a vicious kick. I put so much venom into it that my foot went clear through the cardboard and I was trying to free myself when Tristan came in. He had been stoking the fire and had witnessed the conversation.

He watched silently as I plunged about the room swearing and trying to shake the box loose. 'What's up, Jim? Has my big brother been getting under your skin?'

I got rid of the box at last and sank down on one of the lower shelves. 'I don't know. Why should he be getting under my skin now? I've known him quite a long time and he's always been the same. He's never been any different but it hasn't bothered me before – not like this, anyway. Any other time I'd laugh that sort of thing off. What the hell's wrong with me?'

Tristan put down his coal bucket and looked at me thoughtfully. 'There's nothing much wrong with you, Jim, but I can tell you one thing – you've been just a bit edgy since you went out with the Alderson woman.'

'Oh God,' I groaned and closed my eyes. 'Don't remind me. Anyway, I've not seen her or heard from her since, so that's the end of that and I can't blame her.'

Tristan pulled out his Woodbines and squatted down by the coal bucket. 'Yes, that's all very well, but look at you. You're suffering and there's no need for it. All right, you had a disastrous night and she's given you the old heave ho. Well, so what? Do you know how many times I've been spurned?'

'Spurned? I never even got started.'

'Very well then, but you're still going around like a bullock with bellyache. Forget it, lad, and get out into the big world. The rich tapestry of life is waiting for you out there. I've been watching you – working all hours and when you're not working you're reading up your cases in the text books – and I tell you this dedicated vet thing is all right up to a point. But you've got to live a little. Think of all the lovely little lasses in Darrowby – you can hardly move for them. And every one just waiting for a big handsome chap like you to gallop up on his white horse. Don't disappoint them.' He leaned over and slapped my knee. 'Tell you what. Why don't you let me fix something up? A nice little foursome – just what you need.'

'Ach I don't know. I'm not keen, really.'

'Nonsense!' Tristan said. 'I don't know why I haven't thought of it before. This monkish existence is bad for you. Leave all the details to me.'

I decided to have an early night and was awakened around eleven o'clock by a heavy weight crashing down on the bed. The room was dark but I seemed to be enveloped in beer-scented smoke. I coughed and sat up. 'Is that you, Triss?'

'It is indeed,' said the shadowy figure on the end of the bed. 'And I bring you glad tidings. You remember Brenda?'

'That little nurse I've seen you around with?'

'The very same. Well, she's got a pal, Connie, who's even more beautiful. The four of us are going dancing at the Poulton Institute on Tuesday night.' The voice was thick with beery triumph.

'You mean me, too?'

'By God I do, and you're going to have the best time you've ever had. I'll see to that.' He blew a last choking blast of smoke into my face and left, chuckling.

CHAPTER TWENTY-TWO

'We're having a 'ot dinner and entertainers.'

My reaction to the words surprised me. They stirred up a mixture of emotions, all of them pleasant; fulfilment, happy acceptance, almost triumph.

I know by now that there is not the slightest chance of anybody asking me to be President of the Royal College of Veterinary Surgeons, but if they had, I wonder if I'd have been more pleased than when I heard about the 'ot dinner.

The reason, I suppose, was that the words reflected the attitude of a typical Dales farmer towards myself. And this was important because, though after just over a year I was becoming accepted as a vet, I was always conscious of the gulf which was bound to exist between these hill folk and a city product like me. Much as I admired them I was aware always that we were different; it was inevitable, I knew, but it still rankled so that a sincere expression of friendship from one of them struck a deep answering chord in me.

Especially when it came from somebody like Dick Rudd. I had first met Dick last winter on the doorstep of Skeldale House at six o'clock on the kind of black morning when country vets wonder about their choice of profession. Shivering as the ever-present passage draught struck at my pyjamaed legs, I switched on the light and opened the door. I saw a small figure muffled in an old army greatcoat and balaclava leaning on a bicycle. Beyond him the light spilled onto a few feet of streaming pavement where the rain beat down in savage swathes.

'Sorry to ring your bell at this hour, guvnor,' he said. 'My name's Rudd, Birch Tree Farm, Coulston. I've got a heifer calvin' and she's not getting on with t'job. Will you come?'

I looked closer at the thin face, at the water trickling down the cheeks and dripping from the end of the nose. 'Right, I'll get dressed and come straight along. But why don't you leave your bike here and come with me in the car? Coulston's about four miles isn't it and you must be soaked through.'

'Nay, nay, it'll be right.' The face broke into the most cheerful of grins and under the sopping balaclava a pair of lively blue eyes glinted at me. 'I'd only have to come back and get it another time. I'll get off now and you won't be there long afore me.'

He mounted the bike quickly and pedalled away. People who think farming is a pleasant, easy life should have been there to see the hunched figure disappear into the blackness and the driving rain. No car, no telephone, a night up with the heifer, eight miles biking in the rain and a back-breaking day ahead of him. Whenever I thought of the existence of the small farmer it made my own occasional bursts of activity seem small stuff indeed.

I produced a nice live heifer calf for Dick that first morning and later, gratefully drinking a cup of hot tea in the farmhouse kitchen, I was surprised at the throng of young Rudds milling around me; there were seven of them and they were unexpectedly grown up. Their ages ranged from twenty odd down to about ten and I hadn't thought of Dick as middle-aged; in the dim light of the doorway at Skeldale House and later in the byre lit only by a smoke-blackened oil lamp his lively movements and perky manner had seemed those of a man in his thirties. But as I looked at him now I could see that the short, wiry hair was streaked with grey and a maze of fine wrinkles spread from around his eyes onto his cheeks.

In their early married life the Rudds, anxious like all farmers for male children, had observed with increasing chagrin the arrival of five successive daughters. 'We nearly packed up then,' Dick confided to me once; but they didn't and their perseverance was rewarded at last by the appearance of two fine boys. A farmer farms for his sons and Dick had something to work for now.

As I came to know them better I used to observe the family with wonder. The five girls were all tall, big-limbed, handsome, and already the two chunky young boys gave promise of massive growth. I kept looking from them to their frail little parents – 'not a pickin' on either of us', as Mrs Rudd used to say – and wonder how the miracle had happened.

It puzzled me, too, how Mrs Rudd, armed only with the milk cheque from Dick's few shaggy cows, had managed to feed them all, never mind bring them to this state of physical perfection. I gained my first clue one day when I had been seeing some calves and I was asked to have a 'bit o' dinner' with them. Butcher's meat was a scarce commodity on the hill farms and I was familiar with the usual expedients for filling up the eager stomachs before the main course – the doughy slab of Yorkshire pudding or the heap of suet dumplings. But Mrs Rudd had her own method – a big bowl of rice pudding with lots of milk was her *hors d'oeuvres*. It was a new one on me and I could see the family slowing down as they ploughed their way through. I was ravenous when I sat down but after the rice I viewed the rest of the meal with total detachment.

Dick believed in veterinary advice for everything so I was a frequent visitor at Birch Tree Farm. After every visit there was an unvarying ritual; I was asked into the house for a cup of tea and the whole family downed tools and sat down to watch me drink it. On weekdays the eldest girl was out at work and the boys were at school but on Sundays the ceremony reached its full splendour with myself sipping the tea and all nine Rudds sitting around in what I can only call an admiring circle. My every remark was greeted with nods and smiles all round. There is no doubt it was good for my ego to have an entire family literally hanging on my words, but at the same time it made me feel curiously humble.

I suppose it was because of Dick's character. Not that he was unique in any way – there were thousands of small farmers just like him – but he seemed to embody the best qualities of the Dalesman; the indestructibility, the tough philosophy, the unthinking generosity and hospitality. And there were the things that were Dick's own; the integrity which could be read always in his steady eyes and the humour which was never very far away. Dick was no wit but he was always trying to say ordinary things in a funny way. If I asked him to get hold of a cow's nose for me he would say solemnly 'Ah'll endeavour to do so', or I remember when I was trying to lift a square of plywood which was penning a calf in a corner he said 'Just a minute till ah raise portcullis'. When he broke into a smile a kind of radiance flooded his pinched features.

When I held my audiences in the kitchen with all the family reflecting Dick's outlook in their eager laughter I marvelled at their utter contentment with their lot. None of them had known ease or softness but it didn't matter; and they looked on me as a friend and I was proud.

Whenever I left the farm I found something on the seat of my car – a couple of home-made scones, three eggs. I don't know how Mrs Rudd spared them but she never failed.

Dick had a burning ambition – to upgrade his stock until he had a dairy herd which would live up to his ideals. Without money behind him he knew it would be a painfully slow business but he was determined. It probably wouldn't be in his own lifetime but some time, perhaps when his sons were grown up, people would come and look with admiration at the cows of Birch Tree.

I was there to see the very beginning of it. When Dick stopped me on the road one morning and asked me to come up to his place with him I knew by his air of suppressed excitement that something big had happened. He led me into the byre and stood silent. He didn't need to say anything because I was staring unbelievingly at a bovine aristocrat.

Dick's cows had been scratched together over the years and they were a motley lot. Many of them were old animals discarded by more prosperous farmers because of their pendulous udders or because they were 'three titted 'uns'. Others had been reared by Dick from calves and tended to be rough-haired and scruffy. But half way down the byre, contrasting almost violently with her neighbours was what seemed to me a perfect Dairy Shorthorn cow.

In these days when the Friesian has surged over England in a black and white flood and inundated even the Dales which were the very home of the Shorthorn, such cows as I looked at that day at Dick Rudd's are no longer to be seen, but she represented all the glory and pride of her breed. The wide pelvis tapering to fine shoulders and a delicate head, the level udder thrusting back between the hind legs, and the glorious colour – dark roan. That was what they used to call a 'good colour' and whenever I delivered a dark roan calf the farmer would say 'It's a good-coloured 'un', and it would be more valuable accordingly. The geneticists are perfectly right, of course: the dark roaned cows gave no more milk than the reds or the whites, but we loved them and they were beautiful.

'Where did she come from Dick?' I said, still staring.

Dick's voice was elaborately casual. 'Oh, ah went over to Weldon's of Cranby and picked her out. D'you like her?'

'She's a picture – a show cow. I've never seen one better.' Weldons were the biggest pedigree breeders in the northern Dales and I didn't ask whether Dick had cajoled his bank manager or had been saving up for years just for this.

'Aye, she's a seven galloner when she gets goin' and top butter fat, too. Reckon she'll be as good as two of my other cows and a calf out of her'll be worth a bit.' He stepped forward and ran his hand along the perfectly level, smoothly-fleshed back. 'She's got a great fancy pedigree name but missus 'as called her Strawberry.'

I knew as I stood there in the primitive, cobbled byre with its wooden partitions and rough stone walls that I was looking not just at a cow but at the foundation of the new herd, at Dick Rudd's hopes for the future.

It was about a month later that he phoned me. 'I want you to come and look at Strawberry for me,' he said. 'She's been doing grand, tipplin' the milk out, but there's summat amiss with her this morning.'

The cow didn't really look ill and, in fact, she was eating when I examined her, but I noticed that she gulped slightly when she swallowed. Her temperature was normal and her lungs clear but when I stood up by her head I could just hear a faint snoring sound.

'It's her throat, Dick,' I said. 'It may be just a bit of inflammation but there's a chance that she's starting a little abscess in there.' I spoke lightly but I wasn't happy. Post-pharyngeal abscesses were, in my limited experience, nasty things. They were situated in an inaccessible place, right away behind the back of the throat and if they got very large could interfere seriously with the breathing. I had been lucky with the few I had seen; they had either been small and regressed or had ruptured spontaneously.

I gave an injection of Prontosil and turned to Dick. 'I want you to foment this area behind the angle of the jaw with hot water and rub this salve well in afterwards. You may manage to burst it that way. Do this at least three times a day.'

I kept looking in at her over the next ten days and the picture was one of steady development of the abscess. The cow was still not acutely ill but she was eating a lot less, she was thinner and was going off her milk. Most of the time I felt rather helpless as I knew that only the rupture of the abscess would bring relief and the various injections I was giving her were largely irrelevant. But the infernal thing was taking a long time to burst.

It happened that just then Siegfried went off to an equine conference which was to last a week; for a few days I was at full stretch and hardly had time to think about Dick's cow until he biked in to see me one morning. He was cheerful as usual but he had a strained look.

'Will you come and see Strawberry? She's gone right down t'nick over the last three days. I don't like look of her.'

I dashed straight out and was in the byre at Birch Tree before Dick was half way home. The sight of Strawberry stopped me in mid-stride and I stared, dry-mouthed at what had once been a show cow. The flesh had melted from her incredibly and she was little more than a hide-covered skeleton. Her rasping breathing could be heard all over the byre and she exhaled with a curious out-puffing of the cheeks which I had never seen before. Her terrified eyes were fixed rigidly on the wall in front of her. Occasionally she gave a painful little cough which brought saliva drooling from her mouth.

I must have stood there a long time because I became aware of Dick at my shoulder.

'She's the worst screw in the place now,' he said grimly.

I winced inwardly. 'Hell, Dick, I'm sorry. I'd no idea she'd got to this state. I can't believe it.'

'Aye well it all happened sudden like. I've never seen a cow alter so fast.'

'The abscess must be right at its peak,' I said. 'She hasn't much space to breathe through now.' As I spoke the cow's limbs began to tremble and for a moment I thought she would fall. I ran out to the car and got a tin of Kaolin poultice. 'Come on, let's get this on to her throat. It just might do the trick.'

When we had finished I looked at Dick. 'I think tonight will do it. It's just got to burst.'

'And if it doesn't she'll snuff it tomorrow,' he grunted. I must have looked very woebegone because suddenly his undefeated grin flashed out. 'Never mind, lad, you've done everything anybody could do.'

But as I walked away I wasn't so sure. Mrs Rudd met me at the car. It was her baking day and she pushed a little loaf into my hand. It made me feel worse.

CHAPTER TWENTY-THREE

That night I sat alone in the big room at Skeldale House and brooded. Siegfried was still away, I had nobody to turn to and I wished to God I knew what I was going to do with that cow of Dick's in the morning. By the time I went to bed I had decided that if nothing further had happened I would have to go in behind the angle of the jaw with a knife.

I knew just where the abscess was but it was a long way in and en route there were such horrific things as the carotid artery and the jugular vein. I tried hard to keep them out of my mind but they haunted my dreams; huge, throbbing, pulsating things with their precious contents threatening to burst at any moment through their fragile walls. I was awake by six o'clock and after an hour of staring miserably at the ceiling I could stand it no longer. I got up and, without washing or shaving, drove out to the farm.

As I crept fearfully into the byre I saw with a sick dismay that Strawberry's stall was empty. So that was that. She was dead. After all, she had looked like it yesterday. I was turning away when Dick called to me from the doorway.

'I've got her in a box on t'other side of the yard. Thought she'd be a bit more comfortable in there.'

I almost ran across the cobbles and as we approached the door the sound of the dreadful breathing came out to us. Strawberry was off her legs now – it had cost her the last of her strength to walk to the box and she lay on her chest, her head extended straight in front of her, nostrils dilated, eyes staring, cheeks puffing in her desperate fight for breath.

But she was alive and the surge of relief I felt seemed to prick me into action, blow away my hesitations.

'Dick,' I said, 'I've just got to operate on your cow. This thing is never going to burst in time, so it's now or never. But there's one thing I want you to know – the only way I can think of doing it is to go in from behind the jaw. I've never done this before, I've never seen it before and I've never heard of anybody doing it. If I nick any of those big blood vessels in there it'll kill her within a minute.'

'She can't last much longer like this,' Dick grunted. 'There's nowt to lose – get on with it.'

In most operations in large bovines we have to pull the animal down with ropes and then use general anaesthesia, but there was no need for this with Strawberry. She was too far gone. I just pushed gently at her shoulder and she rolled onto her side and lay still.

I quickly infiltrated the area from beneath the ear to the angle of the jaw with local anaesthetic then laid out my instruments.

'Stretch her head straight out and slightly back, Dick,' I said. Kneeling in the straw I incised the skin, cut carefully through the long thin layer of the brachiocephalic muscle and held the fibres apart with retractors. Somewhere down there was my objective and I tried to picture the anatomy of the region clearly in my mind. Just there the maxillary veins ran together to form the great jugular and, deeper and more dangerous, was the branching, ramifying carotid. If I pushed my knife straight in there, behind the mandibular salivary gland, it'd just about hit the spot. But as I held the razor-sharp blade over the small space I had cleared, my hand began to tremble. I tried to steady it but I was like a man with malaria. The fact had to be faced that I was too scared to cut any further. I put the scalpel down, lifted a pair of long artery forceps and pushed them steadily down through the hole in the muscle. It seemed that I had gone an incredibly long way when, almost unbelievingly, I saw a thin trickle of pus along the gleaming metal. I was into the abscess.

Gingerly, I opened the forceps as wide as possible to enlarge the drainage hole and as I did the trickle became a creamy torrent which gushed over my hand, down the cow's neck and onto the straw. I stayed quite still till it had stopped, then withdrew the forceps.

Dick looked at me from the other side of the head. 'Now what, boss?' he said softly.

'Well, I've emptied the thing, Dick,' I said, 'and by all the laws she should soon be a lot better. Come on, let's roll her onto her chest again.'

When we had got the cow settled comfortably with a bale of straw supporting her shoulder, I looked almost entreatingly at her. Surely she would show some sign of improvement. She must feel some relief from that massive evacuation. But Strawberry looked just the same. The breathing, if anything, was worse.

I dropped the soiled instruments into a bucket of hot water and antiseptic and began to wash them. 'I know what it is. The walls of the abscess have become indurated – thickened and hardened, you know – because it's been there a long time. We'll have to wait for them to collapse.'

Next day as I hurried across the yard I felt buoyantly confident. Dick was just coming out of the loose box and I shouted across to him, 'Well, how is she this morning?'

He hesitated and my spirits plummeted to zero. I knew what this meant; he was trying to find something good to say.

'Well, I reckon she's about t'same.'

'But dammit,' I shouted, 'she should be much better! Let's have a look at her.'

The cow wasn't just the same, she was worse. And on top of all the other symptoms she had a horribly sunken eye – the sign, usually, of approaching death in the bovine.

We both stood looking at the grim wreck of the once beautiful cow, then Dick broke the silence, speaking gently. 'Well, what do you think? Is it Mallock for her?'

The sound of the knacker man's name added the final note of despair. And indeed, Strawberry looked just like any of the other broken down animals that man came to collect.

I shuffled my feet miserably. 'I don't know what to say, Dick. There's nothing more I can do.' I took another look at the gasping staring head, the mass of bubbling foam around the lips and nostrils. 'You don't want her to suffer any more and neither do I. But don't get Mallock yet – she's distressed but not actually in pain, and I want to give her another day. If she's just the same tomorrow, send her in.' The very words sounded futile – every instinct told me the thing was hopeless. I turned to go, bowed down by a sense of failure heavier than I had ever known. As I went out into the yard, Dick called after me.

'Don't worry, lad, these things happen. Thank ye for all you've done.'

The words were like a whip across my back. If he had cursed me thoroughly I'd have felt a lot better. What had he to thank me for with his cow dying back there, the only good cow he'd ever owned? This disaster would just about floor Dick Rudd and he was telling me not to worry.

When I opened the car door I saw a cabbage on the seat. Mrs Rudd, too, was still at it. I leaned my elbow on the roof of the car and the words flowed from me. It was as if the sight of the cabbage had tapped the deep well of my frustration and I directed a soliloquy at the unheeding vegetable in which I ranged far over my many inadequacies. I pointed out the injustice of a situation where kindly people like the Rudds, in dire need of skilled veterinary assistance, had called on Mr Herriot who had responded by falling flat on his face. I drew attention to the fact that the Rudds, instead of hounding me off the place as I deserved, had thanked me sincerely and started to give me cabbages.

I went on for quite a long time and when I had finally finished I felt a little better. But not much, because, as I drove home I could not detect a glimmer of hope. If the walls of that abscess had been going to collapse they would have done so by now. I should have sent her in – she would be dead in the morning anyway.

I was so convinced of this that I didn't hurry to Birch Tree next day. I took it in with the round and it was almost midday when I drove through the gates. I knew what I would find – the usual grim signs of a vet's failure; the box door open and the drag marks where Mallock had winched the carcass across the yard on to his lorry. But everything was as usual and as I walked over to the silent box I steeled myself. The knacker man hadn't arrived yet but there was nothing surer than that my patient was lying dead in there. She couldn't possibly have hung on till now. My fingers fumbled at the catch as though something in me didn't want to look inside, but with a final wrench I threw the door wide.

Strawberry was standing there, eating hay from the rack; and not just eating it but jerking it through the bars almost playfully as cows do when they are really enjoying their food. It looked as though she couldn't get it down fast enough, pulling down great fragrant tufts and dragging them into her mouth with her rasp-like tongue. As I stared at her an organ began to play somewhere in the back of my mind; not just a little organ but a mighty instrument with gleaming pipes climbing high into the shadows of the cathedral roof. I went into the box, closed the door behind me and sat down in the straw in a corner. I had waited a long time for this. I was going to enjoy it.

The cow was almost a walking skeleton with her beautiful dark roan skin stretched tightly over the jutting bones. The once proud udder was a shrivelled purse dangling uselessly above her hocks. As she stood, she trembled from sheer weakness, but there was a light in her eye, a calm intensity in the way she ate which made me certain she would soon fight her way back to her old glory.

There was just the two of us in the box and occasionally Strawberry would turn her head towards me and regard me steadily, her jaws moving rhythmically. It seemed like a friendly look to me – in fact I wouldn't have been surprised if she had winked at me.

I don't know just how long I sat in there but I savoured every minute. It took some time for it to sink in that what I was watching was really happening; the swallowing was effortless, there was no salivation, no noise from her breathing. When I finally went out and closed the door behind me the cathedral organ was really blasting with all stops out, the exultant peals echoing back from the vaulted roof.

The cow made an amazing recovery. I saw her three weeks later and her bones were magically clothed with flesh, her skin shone and, most important, the magnificent udder bulged turgid beneath her, a neat little teat proudly erect at each corner.

I was pretty pleased with myself but of course a cold assessment of the case would show only one thing – that I had done hardly anything right from start to finish. At the very beginning I should have been down that cow's throat with a knife, but at that time I just didn't know how. In later years I have opened many a score of these abscesses by going in through a mouth gag with a scalpel tied to my fingers. It was a fairly heroic undertaking as the cow or bullock didn't enjoy it and was inclined to throw itself down with me inside it almost to the shoulder. It was simply asking for a broken arm.

When I talk about this to the present-day young vets they are inclined to look at me blankly because most of these abscesses undoubtedly had a tuberculous origin and since attestation they are rarely seen. But I can imagine it might bring a wry smile to the faces of my contemporaries as their memories are stirred.

The post-pharyngeal operation had the attraction that recovery was spectacular and rapid and I have had my own share of these little triumphs. But none of them gave me as much satisfaction as the one I did the wrong way.

It was a few weeks after the Strawberry episode and I was back in my old position in the Rudds' kitchen with the family around me. This time I was in no position to drop my usual pearls of wisdom because I was trying to cope with a piece of Mrs Rudd's apple tart. Mrs Rudd, I knew, could make delicious apple tarts but this was a special kind she produced for ' 'lowance' time – for taking out to Dick and the family when they were working in the fields. I had chewed at the two-inch pastry till my mouth had dried out. Somewhere inside there was no doubt a sliver of apple but as yet I had been unable to find it. I didn't dare try to speak in case I blew out a shower of crumbs and in the silence which followed I wondered if anybody would help me out. It was Mrs Rudd who spoke up.

'Mr Herriot,' she said in her quiet matter-of-fact way, 'Dick has something to say to you.'

Dick cleared his throat and sat up straighter in his chair. I turned towards him expectantly, my cheeks still distended by the obdurate mass. He looked unusually serious and I felt a twinge of apprehension.

'What I want to say is this,' he said. 'It'll soon be our silver wedding anniversary and we're going to 'ave a bit of a do. We want you to be our guest.'

I almost choked. 'Dick, Mrs Rudd, that's very kind of you. I'd love that – I'd be honoured to come.'

Dick inclined his head gravely. He still looked portentous as though there was something big to follow. 'Good, I think you'll enjoy it, because it's goin' to be a right do. We've got a room booked at t'King's Head at Carsley.'

'Gosh, sounds great!'

'Aye, t'missus and me have worked it all out.' He squared his thin shoulders and lifted his chin proudly.

'We're having an 'ot dinner and entertainers.'

CHAPTER TWENTY-FOUR

As time passed and I painfully clothed the bare bones of my theoretical knowledge with practical experience I began to realize there was another side to veterinary practice they didn't mention in the books. It had to do with money. Money has always formed a barrier between the farmer and the vet. I think this is because there is a deeply embedded, maybe subconscious conviction in many farmers' minds that they know more about their stock than any outsider and it is an admission of defeat to pay somebody else to doctor them.

The wall was bad enough in those early days when they had to pay the medical practitioners for treating their own ailments and when there was no free agricultural advisory service. But it is worse now when there is the Health Service and NAAS and the veterinary surgeon stands pitilessly exposed as the only man who has to be paid.

Most farmers, of course, swallow the pill and get out their cheque books, but there is a proportion – maybe about ten per cent – who do their best to opt out of the whole business.

We had our own ten per cent in Darrowby and it was a

small but constant irritation. As an assistant I was not financially involved and it didn't seem to bother Siegfried unduly except when the quarterly bills were sent out. Then it really got through to him.

Miss Harbottle used to type out the accounts and present them to him in a neat pile and that was when it started. He would go through them one by one and it was a harrowing experience to watch his blood pressure gradually rising.

I found him crouched over his desk one night. It was about eleven o'clock and he had had a hard day. His resistance was right down. He was scrutinizing each bill before placing it face down on a pile to his left. On his right there was a smaller pile and whenever he placed one there it was to the accompaniment of a peevish muttering or occasionally a violent outburst.

'Would you believe it?' he grunted as I came in. 'Henry Bransom – more than two years since we saw a penny of his money, yet he lives like a sultan. Never misses a market for miles around, gets as tight as an owl several nights a week and I saw him putting ten pounds on a horse at the races last month.'

He banged the piece of paper down and went on with his job, breathing deeply. Then he froze over another account. 'And look at this one! Old Summers of Low Ness. I bet he's got thousands of pounds hidden under his bed but by God he won't part with any of it to me.'

He was silent for a few moments as he transferred several sheets to the main pile then he swung round on me with a loud cry, waving a paper in my face.

'Oh no! Oh Christ, James, this is too much! Bert Mason here owes me twenty-seven and sixpence. I must have spent more than that sending him bills year in year out and do you know I saw him driving past the surgery yesterday in a brand new car. The bloody scoundrel!'

He hurled the bill down and started his scrutiny again. I noticed he was using only one hand while the other churned among his hair. I hoped fervently that he might hit upon a seam of good payers because I didn't think his nervous system could take much more. And it seemed that my hopes were answered because several minutes went by with only the quiet lifting and laying of the paper sheets. Then Siegfried stiffened suddenly in his chair and sat quite motionless as he stared down at his desk. He lifted an account and held it for several seconds at eye level. I steeled myself. This must be a beauty.

But to my surprise Siegfried began to giggle softly then he threw back his head and gave a great bellow of laughter. He laughed until he seemed to have no strength to laugh any more, then he turned to me.

'It's the Major, James,' he said weakly. 'The dear old gallant Major. You know, you can't help admiring the man. He owed my predecessor a fair bit when I bought the practice and he still owes it. And I've never had a sou for all the work I've done for him. The thing is he's the same with everybody and yet he gets away with it. He's a genuine artist – these other fellows are just fumbling amateurs by comparison.'

He got up, reached up into the glass-fronted cupboard above the mantelpiece and pulled out the whisky bottle and two glasses. He carelessly tipped a prodigal measure into each glass and handed one to me, then he sank back into his chair, still grinning. The Major had magically restored his good humour.

Sipping my drink, I reflected that there was no doubt Major Bullivant's character had a rich, compelling quality. He presented an elegant, patrician front to the world; beautiful Shakespearean actor voice, impeccable manners and an abundance of sheer presence. Whenever he unbent sufficiently to throw me a friendly word I felt honoured even though I knew I was doing his work for nothing.

He had a small, cosy farm, a tweed-clad wife and several daughters who had ponies and were active helpers for the local hunt. Everything in his entire ménage was right and fitting. But he never paid anybody.

He had been in the district about three years and on his arrival the local tradesmen, dazzled by his façade, had fallen over each other to win his custom. After all, he appeared to be just their type because they preferred inherited wealth in Darrowby. In contrast to what I had always found in Scotland, the self-made man was regarded with deep suspicion and there was nothing so damning among the townsfolk as the darkly muttered comment: 'He had nowt when he first came 'ere.'

Of course, when the scales had fallen from their eyes they fought back, but ineffectually. The local garage impounded the Major's ancient Rolls Royce and hung on to it fiercely for a while but he managed to charm it back. His one failure was that his telephone was always being cut off; it seemed that the Postmaster General was one of the few who were immune to his blandishments.

But time runs out for even the most dedicated expert. I was driving one day through Hollerton, a neighbouring market town about ten miles away, and I noticed the Bullivant girls moving purposefully among the shops armed with large baskets. The Major, it seemed, was having to cast his net a little wider and I wondered at the time if perhaps he was ready to move on. He did, in fact, disappear from the district a few weeks later leaving a lot of people licking their wounds. I don't know if he ever paid anybody before he left but Siegfried didn't get anything.

Even after his departure Siegfried wasn't at all bitter, preferring to regard the Major as a unique phenomenon, a master of his chosen craft. 'After all, James,' he said to me once, 'putting ethical considerations to one side, you must admit that anybody who can run up a bill of fifty pounds for shaves and haircuts at the Darrowby barber's shop must command a certain amount of respect.'

Siegfried's attitude to his debtors was remarkably ambivalent. At times he would fly into a fury at the mention of their names, at others he would regard them with a kind of wry benevolence. He often said that if ever he threw a cocktail party for the clients he'd have to invite the non-payers first because they were all such charming fellows.

Nevertheless he waged an inexorable war against them by means of a series of letters graduated according to severity which he called his PNS system (Polite, Nasty, Solicitor's) and in which he had great faith. It was a sad fact, however, that the system seldom worked with the real hard cases who were accustomed to receiving threatening letters with their morning mail. These people yawned over the polite and nasty ones and were unimpressed by the solicitor's because they knew from experience that Siegfried always shrank from following through to the limit of the law.

When the PNS system failed Siegfried was inclined to come up with some unorthodox ideas to collect his hard-earned fees. Like the scheme he devised for Dennis Pratt. Dennis was a tubby, bouncy little man and his high opinion of himself showed in the way he always carried his entire five feet three inches proudly erect. He always seemed to be straining upwards, his chest thrust forward, his fat little bottom stuck out behind him at an extraordinary angle.

Dennis owed the practice a substantial amount and about eighteen months ago had been subjected to the full rigour of the PNS system. This had induced him to part with five pounds 'on account' but since then nothing more had been forthcoming. Siegfried was in a quandary because he didn't like getting tough with such a cheerful, hospitable man.

Dennis was always either laughing or about to laugh. I remember when we had to anaesthetize a cow on his farm to remove a growth from between its cleats. Siegfried and I went to the case together and on the way we were talking about something which had amused us. As we got out of the car we were both laughing helplessly and just then the farmhouse door opened and Dennis emerged.

We were at the far end of the yard and we must have been all of thirty yards away. He couldn't possibly have heard anything of our conversation but when he saw us laughing he threw back his head immediately and joined in at the top of his voice. He shook so much on his way across the yard that I thought he would fall over. When he arrived he was wiping the tears from his eyes.

After a job he always asked us in to sample Mrs Pratt's baking. In fact on cold days he used to keep a thermos of hot coffee ready for our arrival and he had an endearing habit of sloshing rum freely into each cup before pouring in the coffee.

'You can't put a man like that in court,' Siegfried said. 'But we've got to find some way of parting him from his brass.' He looked ruminatively at the ceiling for a few moments then thumped a fist into his palm.

'I think I've got it, James! You know it's quite possible it just never occurs to Dennis to pay a bill. So I'm going to pitch him into an environment where it will really be brought home to him. The accounts have just gone out and I'll arrange to meet him in here at two o'clock next market day. I'll say I want to discuss his mastitis problem. He'll be right in the middle of all the other farmers paying their bills and I'll deliberately leave him with them for half an hour or so. I'm sure it will give him the notion.'

I couldn't help feeling dubious. I had known Siegfried long enough to realize that some of his ideas were brilliant and others barmy; and he had so many ideas and they came in such a constant torrent that I often had difficulty in deciding which was which. Clearly in this case he was working on the same lines as a doctor who turns on a water tap full force to induce a pent up patient to urinate into a bottle.

The scheme may have merit – it was possible that the flutter of cheque books, the chink of coins, the rustle of notes might tap the long-buried well of debt in Dennis and bring it gushing from him in a mighty flood; but I doubted it.

My doubts must have shown on my face because Siegfried laughed and thumped me on the shoulder. 'Don't look so worried – we can only try. And it'll work. Just you wait.'

After lunch on market day I was looking out of the window when I saw Dennis heading our way. The street was busy with the market bustle but he was easy to pick out. Chin in air, beaming around him happily, every springing step taking him high on tiptoe he was a distinctive figure. I let him in at the front door and he strutted past me along the passage, the back of his natty sports jacket lying in a neat fold over his protruding buttocks.

Siegfried seated him strategically by Miss Harbottle's elbow, giving him an unimpeded view of the desk. Then he excused himself, saying he had a dog to attend to in the operating room. I stayed behind to answer the clients' queries and to watch developments. I hadn't long to wait; the farmers began to come in, a steady stream of them, clutching their cheque books. Some of them stood patiently by the desk, others sat in the chairs along the walls waiting their turn.

It was a typical bill-paying day with the usual quota of moans. The most common expression was that Mr Farnon had been 'ower heavy wi' t'pen' and many of them wanted a 'bit knockin' off'. Miss Harbottle used her discretion in these matters and if the animal had died or the bill did seem unduly large she would make some reduction.

There was one man who didn't get away with it. He had truculently demanded a 'bit of luck' on an account and Miss Harbottle fixed him with a cold eye.

'Mr Brewiss,' she said. 'This account has been owing for over a year. You should really be paying us interest. I can only allow discount when a bill is paid promptly. It's too bad of you to let it run on for this length of time.'

Dennis, sitting bolt upright, his hands resting on his knees, obviously agreed with every word. He pursed his lips in disapproval as he looked at the farmer and turned towards me with a positively scandalized expression.

Among the complaints was an occasional bouquet. A stooping old man who had received one of the polite letters was full of apologies. 'I'm sorry I've missed paying for a few months. The vets allus come out straight away when I send for them so I reckon it's not fair for me to keep them waiting for their money.'

I could see that Dennis concurred entirely with this sentiment. He nodded vigorously and smiled benevolently at the old man.

Another farmer, a hard-looking character, was walking out without his receipt when Miss Harbottle called him back. 'You'd better take this with you or we might ask you to pay again,' she said with a heavy attempt at roguishness.

The man paused with his hand on the door knob. 'I'll tell you summat, missis, you're bloody lucky to get it once – you'd never get it twice.'

Dennis was right in the thick of it all. Watching closely as the farmers slapped their cheque books on the desk for Miss Harbottle to write (they never wrote their own cheques) then signed them slowly and painstakingly. He looked with open fascination at the neat bundles of notes being tucked away in the desk drawer and I kept making little provocative remarks like 'It's nice to see the money coming in. We can't carry on without that, can we?'

The queue began to thin out and sometimes we were left alone in the room. On these occasions we conversed about many things – the weather, Dennis's stock, the political situation. Finally, Siegfried came in and I left to do a round.

When I got back, Siegfried was at his evening meal. I was eager to hear how his scheme had worked out but he was strangely reticent. At length I could wait no longer.

'Well, how did it go?' I asked.

Siegfried speared a piece of steak with his fork and applied some mustard. 'How did what go?'

'Well – Dennis. How did you make out with him?'

'Oh, fine. We went into his mastitis problem very thoroughly. I'm going out there on Tuesday morning to infuse every infected quarter in the herd with acriflavine solution. It's a new treatment – they say it's very good.'

'But you know what I mean. Did he show any sign of paying his bill?'

Siegfried chewed impassively for a few moments and swallowed. 'No, never a sign.' He put down his knife and fork and a haggard look spread over his face. 'It didn't work, did it?'

'Oh well, never mind. As you said, we could only try.' I hesitated. 'There's something else, Siegfried. I'm afraid you're going to be annoyed with me. I know you've told me never to dish out stuff to people who don't pay, but he talked me into letting him have a couple of bottles of fever drink. I don't know what came over me.'

'He did, did he?' Siegfried stared into space for a second then gave a wintry smile. 'Well, you can forget about that. He got six tins of stomach powder out of me.'

CHAPTER TWENTY-FIVE

There was one client who would not have been invited to the debtors' cocktail party. He was Mr Horace Dumbleby, the butcher of Aldgrove. As an inveterate non-payer he fulfilled the main qualification for the function but he was singularly lacking in charm.

His butcher shop in the main street of picturesque Aldgrove village was busy and prosperous but most of his trade was done in the neighbouring smaller villages and among the scattered farmhouses of the district. Usually the butcher's wife and married daughter looked after the shop while Mr Dumbleby himself did the rounds. I often saw his blue van standing with the back doors open and a farmer's wife waiting while he cut the meat, his big, shapeless body hunched over the slab. Sometimes he would look up and I would catch a momentary glimpse of a huge, bloodhound face and melancholy eyes.

Mr Dumbleby was a farmer himself in a small way. He sold milk from six cows which he kept in a tidy little byre behind his shop and he fattened a few bullocks and pork pigs which later appeared as sausages, pies, roasting cuts and chops in his front window. In fact Mr Dumbleby seemed to be very nicely fixed and it was said he owned property all over the place. But Siegfried had only infrequent glimpses of his money.

All the slow payers had one thing in common – they would not tolerate slowness from the vets. When they were in trouble they demanded immediate action. 'Will you come at once?', 'How long will you be?', 'You won't keep me waiting, will you?', 'I want you to come out here straight away'. It used to alarm me to see the veins swelling on Siegfried's forehead, the knuckles whitening as he gripped the phone.

After one such session with Mr Dumbleby at ten o'clock on a Sunday night he had flown into a rage and unleashed the full fury of the PNS system on him. It had no loosening effect on the butcher's purse strings but it did wound his feelings deeply. He obviously considered himself a wronged man. From that time on, whenever I saw him with his van out in the country he would turn slowly and direct a blank stare at me till I was out of sight. And strangely, I seemed to see him more and more often – the thing became unnerving.

And there was something worse. Tristan and I used to frequent the little Aldgrove pub where the bar was cosy and the beer measured up to Tristan's stringent standards. I had never taken much notice of Mr Dumbleby before although he always occupied the same corner, but now, every time I looked up, the great sad eyes were trained on me in disapproval. I tried to forget about him and listen to Tristan relating his stories from the backs of envelopes but all the time I could feel that gaze upon me. My laughter would trail away and I would have to look round. Then the excellent bitter would be as vinegar in my mouth.

In an attempt to escape, I took to visiting the snug instead of the bar and Tristan, showing true nobility of soul, came with me into an environment which was alien to him; where there was a carpet on the floor, people sitting around at little shiny tables drinking gin and hardly a pint in sight. But even this sacrifice was in vain because Mr Dumbleby changed his position in the bar so that he could look into the snug through the communicating hatch. The odd hours I was able to spend there took on a macabre quality. I was like a man trying desperately to forget. But quaff the beer as I might, laugh, talk, even sing, half of me was waiting in a state of acute apprehension for the moment when I knew I would have to look round. And when I did, the great sombre face looked even more forbidding framed by the wooden surround of the hatch. The hanging jowls, the terraced chins, the huge, brooding eyes – all were dreadfully magnified by their isolation in that little hole in the wall.

It was no good, I had to stop going to the place. This was very sad because Tristan used to wax lyrical about a certain unique, delicate nuttiness which he could discern in the draught bitter. But it had lost its joy for me; I just couldn't take any more of Mr Dumbleby.

In fact I did my best to forget all about the gentleman, but he was brought back forcibly into my mind when I heard his voice on the phone at 3 AM one morning. It was nearly always the same thing when the bedside phone exploded in your ear in the small hours – a calving.

Mr Dumbleby's call was no exception but he was more peremptory than might have been expected. There was no question about apologizing about ringing at such an hour as most farmers would do. I said I would come immediately but that wasn't good enough – he wanted to know exactly in minutes how long I would be. In a sleepy attempt at sarcasm I started to recite a programme of so many minutes to get up and dressed, so many to go downstairs and get the car out etc, but I fear it was lost on him.

When I drove into the sleeping village a light was showing in the window of the butcher's shop. Mr Dumbleby almost trotted out into the street and paced up and down, muttering, as I fished out my ropes and instruments from the boot. Very impatient, I thought, for a man who hadn't paid his vet bill for over a year.

We had to go through the shop to get to the byre in the rear. My patient was a big, fat white cow which didn't seem particularly perturbed by her situation. Now and then she strained, pushing a pair of feet a few inches from her vulva. I took a keen look at those feet – it is the vet's first indication of how tough the job is going to be. Two huge hooves sticking out of a tiny heifer have always been able to wipe the smile off my face. These feet were big enough but not out of the way, and in truth the mother looked sufficiently roomy. I wondered what was stopping the natural sequence.

'I've had me hand in,' said Mr Dumbleby. 'There's a head there but I can't shift owt. I've been pulling them legs for half an hour.'

As I stripped to the waist (it was still considered vaguely cissy to wear a calving overall) I reflected that things could be a lot worse. So many of the buildings where I had to take my shirt off were primitive and draughty but this was a modern cow house and the six cows provided a very adequate central heating. And there was electricity in place of the usual smoke-blackened oil lamp.

When I had soaped and disinfected my arms I made my first exploration and it wasn't difficult to find the cause of the trouble.

There was a head and two legs all right, but they belonged to different calves.

'We've got twins here,' I said. 'These are hind legs you've been pulling – a posterior presentation.'

'Arse fust, you mean?'

'If you like. And the calf that's coming the right way has both his legs back along his sides. I'll have to push him back out of the way and get the other one first.'

This was going to be a pretty tight squeeze. Normally I like a twin calving because the calves are usually so small, but these seemed to be quite big. I put my hand against the little muzzle in the passage, poked a finger into the mouth and was rewarded by a jerk and flip of the tongue; he was alive, anyway.

I began to push him steadily back into the uterus, wondering at the same time what the little creature was making of it all. He had almost entered the world – his nostrils had been a couple of inches from the outside air – and now he was being returned to the starting post.

The cow didn't think much of the idea either because she started a series of straining heaves with the object of frustrating me. She did a pretty fair job, too, since a cow is a lot stronger than a man, but I kept my arm rigid against the calf and though each heave forced me back I maintained a steady pressure till I had pushed him to the brim of the pelvis.

I turned to Mr Dumbleby and gasped: 'I've got this head out of the way. Get hold of those feet and pull the other calf out.'

The butcher stepped forward ponderously and each of his big, meaty hands engulfed a foot. Then he closed his eyes and with many facial contortions and noises of painful effort he began to go through the motions of tugging. The calf didn't move an inch and my spirits drooped. Mr Dumbleby was a grunter. (This expression had its origin in an occasion when Siegfried and a farmer had a foot apiece at a calving and the farmer was making pitiful sounds without exerting himself in the slightest. Siegfried had turned to him and said: 'Look, let's come to an arrangement – you do the pulling and I'll do the grunting.')

It was clear I was going to get no help from the big butcher and decided to have one go by myself. I might be lucky. I let go the muzzle and made a quick grab for those hind feet, but the cow was too quick for me. I had just got a slippery grasp when she made a single expulsive effort and pushed calf number two into the passage again. I was back where I started.

Once more I put my hand against the wet little muzzle and began the painful process of repulsion. And as I fought against the big cow's straining I was reminded that it was 4 AM when none of us feels very strong. By the time I had worked the head back to the pelvic inlet I was feeling the beginning of that deadly creeping weakness and it seemed as though somebody had removed most of the bones from my arm.

This time I took a few seconds to get my breath back before I made my dive for the feet, but it was no good. The cow beat me easily with a beautifully timed contraction. Again that intruding head was jammed tight in the passage.

I had had enough. And it occurred to me that the little creature inside must also be getting a little tired of this back and forth business. I shivered my way through the cold, empty shop out into the silent street and collected the local anaesthetic from the car. Eight cc's into the epidural space and the cow, its uterus completely numbed, lost all interest in the proceedings. In fact she pulled a little hay from her rack and began to chew absently.

From then on it was like working inside a mail bag; whatever I pushed stayed put instead of surging back at me. The only snag was that once I had got everything straight there were no uterine contractions to help me. It was a case of pulling. Leaning back on a hind leg and with Mr Dumbleby panting in agony on the other, the posterior presentation was soon delivered. He had inhaled a fair amount of placental fluid but I held him upside down till he had coughed it up. When I laid him on the byre floor he shook his head vigorously and tried to sit up.

Then I had to go in after my old friend the second calf. He was lying well inside now, apparently sulking. When I finally brought him snuffling and kicking into the light I couldn't have blamed him if he had said 'Make up your mind, will you!'

Towelling my chest I looked with the sharp stab of pleasure I always felt at the two wet little animals wriggling on the floor as Mr Dumbleby rubbed them down with a handful of straw.

'Big 'uns for twins,' the butcher muttered.

Even this modest expression of approval surprised me and it seemed I might as well push things along a bit.

'Yes, they're two grand calves. Twins are often dead when they're mixed up like that – good job we got them out alive.' I paused a moment. 'You know, those two must be worth a fair bit.'

Mr Dumbleby didn't answer and I couldn't tell whether the shaft had gone home.

I got dressed, gathered up my gear and followed him out of the byre and into the silent shop past the rows of beef cuts hanging from hooks, the trays of offal, the mounds of freshly-made sausages. Near the outside door the butcher halted and stood, irresolute, for a moment. He seemed to be thinking hard. Then he turned to me.

'Would you like a few sausages?'

I almost reeled in my astonishment. 'Yes, thank you very much, I would.' It was scarcely credible but I must have touched the man's heart.

He went over, cut about a pound of links, wrapped them quickly in grease-proof paper and handed the parcel to me.

I looked down at the sausages, feeling the cold weight on my hand. I still couldn't believe it. Then an unworthy thought welled in my mind. It wasn't fair, I know – the poor fellow couldn't have known the luxury of many generous impulses – but some inner demon drove me to put him to the test. I put a hand in my trouser pocket, jingled my loose change and looked him in the eye.

'Well, how much will that be?' I asked.

Mr Dumbleby's big frame froze suddenly into immobility and he stood for a few seconds perfectly motionless. His face, as he stared at me, was almost without expression, but a single twitch of the cheek and a slowly rising anguish in the eyes betrayed the internal battle which was raging. When he did speak it was in a husky whisper as though the words had been forced from him by a power beyond his control.

'That,' he said, 'will be two and sixpence.'

CHAPTER TWENTY-SIX

It was a new experience for me to be standing outside the hospital waiting for the nurses to come off duty, but it was old stuff to Tristan who was to be found there several nights a week. His experience showed in various ways, but mainly in the shrewd position he took up in a dark corner of the doorway of the gas company office just beyond the splash of light thrown by the street lamp. From there he could look straight across the road into the square entrance of the hospital and the long white corridor leading to the nurses' quarters. And there was the other advantage that if Siegfried should happen to pass that way, Tristan would be invisible and safe.

At half past seven he nudged me. Two girls had come out of the hospital and down the steps and were standing expectantly in the street. Tristan looked warily in both directions before taking my arm. 'Come on, Jim, here they are. That's Connie on the left – the coppery blonde – lovely little thing.'

We went over and Tristan introduced me with characteristic charm. I had to admit that if the evening had indeed been arranged for therapeutic purposes I was beginning to feel better already. There was something healing in the way the two pretty girls looked up at me with parted lips and shining eyes as though I was the answer to every prayer they had ever offered.

They were remarkably alike except for the hair. Brenda was very dark but Connie was fair with a deep, fiery glow where the light from the doorway touched her head. Both of them projected a powerful image of bursting health – fresh cheeks, white teeth, lively eyes and something else which I found particularly easy to take; a simple desire to please.

Tristan opened the back door of the car with a flourish. 'Be careful with him in there Connie, he looks quiet but he's a devil with women. Known far and wide as a great lover.'

The girls giggled and studied me with even greater interest. Tristan leaped into the driver's seat and we set off at breakneck speed.

As the dark countryside hastened past the windows I leaned back in the corner and listened to Tristan who was in full cry; maybe in a kindly attempt to cheer me or maybe because he just felt that way, but his flow of chatter was unceasing. The girls made an ideal audience because they laughed in delight at everything he said. I could feel Connie shaking against me. She was sitting very close with a long stretch of empty seat on the other side of her. The little car swayed round a sharp corner and threw her against me and she stayed there quite naturally with her head on my shoulder. I felt her hair against my cheek. She didn't use much perfume but smelt cleanly of soap and antiseptic. My mind went back to Helen – I didn't think much about her these days. It was just a question of practice; to scotch every thought of her as soon as it came up. I was getting pretty good at it now. Anyway, it was over – all over before it had begun.

I put my arm round Connie and she lifted her face to me. Ah well, I thought as I kissed her. Tristan's voice rose in song from the front seat. Brenda giggled, the old car sped over the rough road with a thousand rattles.

We came at last to Poulton, a village on the road to nowhere. Its single street straggled untidily up the hillside to the dead end where there was a circular green with an ancient stone cross and a steep mound on which was perched the institute hall.

This was where the dance was to be held, but Tristan had other plans first. 'There's a lovely little pub here. We'll just have a toothful to get us in the mood.' We got out of the car and Tristan ushered us into a low stone building.

There was nothing of the olde worlde about the place; just a large, square, whitewashed room with a black cooking range enclosing a bright fire and a long high-backed wooden settle facing it. Over the fireplace stretched a single immense beam, gnarled and pitted with the years and blackened with smoke.

We hurried over to the settle, feeling the comfort of it as a screen against the cold outside. We had the place to ourselves.

The landlord came in. He was dressed informally – no jacket, striped, collarless shirt, trousers and braces which were reinforced by a broad, leather belt around his middle. His cheerful round face lit up at the sight of Tristan. 'Now then, Mr Farnon, are you very well?'

'Never better, Mr Peacock, and how are you?'

'Nicely, sir, very nicely. Can't complain. And I recognize the other gentleman. Been in my place before, haven't you?'

I remembered then. A day's testing in the Poulton district and I had come in here for a meal, freezing and half starved after hours of wrestling with young beasts on the high moor. The landlord had received me unemotionally and had set to immediately with his frying-pan on the old black range while I sat looking at his shirt back and the braces and the shining leather belt. The meal had taken up the whole of the round oak table by the fire – a thick steak of home cured ham overlapping the plate with two fresh eggs nestling on its bosom, a newly baked loaf with the knife sticking in it, a dish of farm butter, some jam, a vast pot of tea and a whole Wensleydale cheese, circular, snow white, about eighteen inches high.

I could remember eating unbelievingly for a long time and finishing with slice after slice of the moist, delicately flavoured cheese. The entire meal had cost me half a crown.

'Yes, Mr Peacock, I have been here before and if I'm ever

starving on a desert island I'll think of that wonderful meal you gave me.'

The landlord shrugged. 'Well it was nowt much, sir. Just t'usual stuff.' But he looked pleased.

'That's fine, then,' Tristan said impatiently. 'But we haven't come to eat, we've come for a drink and Mr Peacock keeps some of the finest draught Magnet in Yorkshire. I'd welcome your opinion on it, Jim. Perhaps you would be kind enough to bring us up two pints and two halves, Mr Peacock.'

I noticed there was no question of asking the girls what they would like to have, but they seemed quite happy with the arrangement. The landlord reappeared from the cellar, puffing slightly. He was carrying a tall, white enamelled jug from which he poured a thin brown stream, varying the height expertly till he had produced a white, frothy head on each glass.

Tristan raised his pint and looked at it with quiet reverence. He sniffed it carefully and then took a sip which he retained in his mouth for a few seconds while his jaw moved rapidly up and down. After swallowing he smacked his lips a few times with the utmost solemnity then closed his eyes and took a deep gulp. He kept his eyes closed for a long time and when he opened them they were rapturous, as though he had seen a beautiful vision.

'It's an experience coming here,' he whispered. 'Keeping beer in the wood is a skilful business, but you, Mr Peacock, are an artist.'

The landlord inclined his head modestly and Tristan, raising his glass in salute, drained it with an easy upward motion of the elbow.

Little oohs of admiration came from the girls but I saw that they, in their turn, had little difficulty in emptying their glasses. With an effort I got my own pint down and the enamel jug was immediately in action again.

I was always at a disadvantage in the company of a virtuoso like Tristan, but as the time passed and the landlord kept revisiting the cellar with his jug it seemed to become easier. In fact, a long time later, as I drew confidently on my eighth pint, I wondered why I had ever had difficulty with large amounts of fluid. It was easy and it soothed and comforted. Tristan was right – I had been needing this.

It puzzled me that I hadn't realized until now that Connie was one of the most beautiful creatures I had ever seen. Back there in the street outside the hospital she had seemed attractive, but obviously the light had been bad and I had failed to notice the perfection of her skin, the mysterious greenish depths of her eyes and the wonderful hair catching lights of gold and deep red-bronze from the flickering fire. And the laughing mouth, shining, even teeth and little pink tongue – she hardly ever stopped laughing except to drink her beer. Everything I said was witty, brilliantly funny in fact, and she looked at me all the time, peeping over the top of her glass in open admiration. It was profoundly reassuring.

As the beer flowed, time slowed down and finally lurched to a halt and there was neither past nor future, only Connie's face and the warm, untroubled present.

I was surprised when Tristan pulled at my arm, I had forgotten he was there and when I focused on him it was the same as with Connie – there was just the face swimming disembodied in an empty room. Only this face was very red and puffy and glassy-eyed.

'Would you care for the mad conductor?' the face said.

I was deeply touched. Here was another sign of my friend's concern for me. Of all Tristan's repertoire his imitation of a mad conductor was the most exacting. It involved tremendous expenditure of energy and since Tristan was unused to any form of physical activity, it really took it out of him. Yet here he was, ready and willing to sacrifice himself. A wave of treacly sentiment flooded through me and I wondered for a second if it might not be the proper thing to burst into tears; but instead I contented myself with wringing Tristan's hand.

'There's nothing I would like more, my dear old chap,' I said thickly. 'I greatly appreciate the kind thought. And may I take this opportunity of telling you that I consider that in all Yorkshire there is no finer gentleman breathing than T. Farnon.'

The big red face grew very solemn. 'You honour me with those words, old friend.'

'Not a bit of it,' I slurred. 'My stumbling sentences cannot hope to express my extremely high opinion of you.'

'You are too kind,' hiccuped Tristan.

'Nothing of the sort. It's a privlish, a rare privlish to know you.'

'Thank you, thank you,' Tristan nodded gravely at me from a distance of about six inches. We were staring into each other's eyes with intense absorption and the conversation might have gone on for a long time if Brenda hadn't broken in.

'Hey, when you two have finished rubbing noses I'd rather like another drink.'

Tristan gave her a cold look. 'You'll have to wait just a few minutes. There's something I have to do.' He rose, shook himself and walked with dignity to the centre of the floor. When he turned to face his audience he looked exalted. I felt this would be an outstanding performance.

Tristan raised his arms and gazed imperiously over his imaginary orchestra, taking in the packed rows of strings, the woodwind, brass and tympani in one sweeping glance. Then with a violent downswing he led them into the overture. Rossini, this time, I thought or maybe Wagner as I watched him throwing his head about, bringing in the violins with a waving clenched fist or exhorting the trumpets with a glare and a trembling, outstretched hand.

It was somewhere near the middle of the piece that the rot always set in and I watched enthralled as the face began to twitch and the lips to snarl. The arm waving became more and more convulsive then the whole body jerked with uncontrollable spasms. It was clear that the end was near – Tristan's eyes were rolling, his hair hung over his face and he had lost control of the music which crashed and billowed about him. Suddenly he grew rigid, his arms fell to his sides and he crashed to the floor.

I was joining in the applause and laughter when I noticed that Tristan was very still. I bent over him and found that he had struck his head against the heavy oak leg of the settle and was almost unconscious. The nurses were quickly into action. Brenda expertly propped up his head while Connie ran for a basin of hot water and a cloth. When he opened his eyes they were bathing a tender lump above his ear. Mr Peacock hovered anxiously in the background. 'Ista all right? Can ah do anything?'

Tristan sat up and sipped weakly at his beer. He was very pale. 'I'll be all right in a minute and there is something you can do. You can bring us one for the road and then we must be getting on to this dance.'

The landlord hurried away and returned with the enamel jug brimming. The final pint revived Tristan miraculously and he was soon on his feet. Then we shook hands affectionately with Mr Peacock and took our leave. After the brightness of the inn the darkness pressed on us like a blanket and we groped our way up the steep street till we could see the institute standing on its grassy mound. Faint rays of light escaped through the chinks in the curtained windows and we could hear music and a rhythmic thudding.

A cheerful young farmer took our money at the door and when we went into the hall we were swallowed up in a tight mass of dancers. The place was packed solidly with young men in stiff-looking dark suits and girls in bright dresses all sweating happily as they swayed and wheeled to the music.

On the low platform at one end, four musicians were playing their hearts out – piano, accordion, violin and drums. At the other end, several comfortable, middle-aged women stood behind a long table on trestles, presiding over the thick sandwiches of ham and brawn, home made pies, jugs of milk and trifles generously laid with cream.

All round the walls more lads were standing, eyeing the unattached girls. I recognized a young client. 'What do you call this dance?' I yelled above the din.

'The Eva Three Step,' came back the reply.

This was new to me but I launched out confidently with Connie. There was a lot of twirling and stamping and when the men brought their heavy boots down on the boards the hall shook and the noise was deafening. I loved it – I was right on the peak and I whirled Connie effortlessly among the throng. I was dimly aware of bumping people with my shoulders but, try as I might, I couldn't feel my feet touching the floor. The floating sensation was delicious. I decided that I had never been so happy in my life.

After half a dozen dances I felt ravenous and floated with Connie towards the food table. We each ate an enormous wedge of ham and egg pie which was so exquisite that we had the same again. Then we had some trifle and plunged again into the crush. It was about halfway through a St Bernard's Waltz that I began to feel my feet on the boards again – quite heavy and dragging somewhat. Connie felt heavy too. She seemed to be slumped in my arms.

She looked up. Her face was very white. 'Jus' feeling a bit queer – 'scuse me.' She broke away and began to tack erratically towards the ladies' room. A few minutes later she came out and her face was no longer white. It was green. She staggered over to me. 'Could do with some fresh air. Take me outside.'

I took her out into the darkness and it was as if I had stepped aboard a ship; the ground pitched and heaved under my feet and I had to straddle my legs to stay upright. Holding Connie's arm, I retreated hastily to the wall of the institute and leaned my back against it. This didn't help a great deal because the wall, too, was heaving about. Waves of nausea swept over me. I thought of the ham and egg pie and groaned loudly.

Open mouthed, gulping in the sharp air, I looked up at the clean, austere sweep of the night sky and at the ragged clouds driving across the cold face of the moon. 'Oh God,' I moaned at the unheeding stars, 'Why did I drink all that bloody beer?'

But I had to look after Connie. I put my arm round her. 'Come on, we'd better start walking.' We began to reel blindly round the building, pausing after every two or three circuits while I got my breath back and shook my head violently to try to clear my brain.

But our course was erratic and I forgot that the institute was perched on a little steep-sided hill. There was an instant when we were treading on nothing, then we were sprawling down a muddy bank. We finished in a tangled heap on the hard road at the bottom.

I lay there peacefully till I heard a pitiful whimpering near by. Connie! Probably a compound fracture at least; but when I helped her up I found she was unhurt and so, surprisingly, was I. After our large intake of alcohol we must have been as relaxed as rag dolls when we fell.

We went back into the institute and stood just inside the door. Connie was unrecognizable; her beautiful hair hung across her face in straggling wisps, her eyes were vacant and tears coursed slowly through the muddy smears on her cheeks. My suit was splattered with clay and I could feel more of it drying on one side of my face. We stood close, leaning miserably on each other in the doorway. The dancers were a shapeless blur. My stomach heaved and tossed.

Then I heard somebody say 'Good evening'. It was a woman's voice and very close. There were two figures looking at us with interest. They seemed to have just come through the door.

I concentrated fiercely on them and they swam into focus for a few seconds. It was Helen and a man. His pink, scrubbed-looking face, the shining fair hair plastered sideways across the top of his head was in keeping with the spotless British warm overcoat. He was staring at me distastefully. They went out of focus again and there was only Helen's voice. 'We thought we would just look in for a few moments to see how the dance was going. Are you enjoying it?'

Then, unexpectedly, I could see her clearly. She was smiling her kind smile but her eyes were strained as she looked from me to Connie and back again. I couldn't speak but stood gazing at her dully, seeing only her calm beauty in the crush and noise. It seemed, for a moment, that it would be the most natural thing in the world to throw my arms around her but I discarded the idea and, instead, just nodded stupidly.

'Well then, we must be off,' she said and smiled again. 'Good night.'

The fair haired man gave me a cold nod and they went out.

CHAPTER TWENTY-SEVEN

It looked as though I was going to make it back to the road all right. And I was thankful for it because seven o'clock in the morning with the wintry dawn only just beginning to lighten the eastern rim of the moor was no time to be digging my car out of the snow.

This narrow, unfenced road skirted a high tableland and gave on to a few lonely farms at the end of even narrower tracks. It hadn't actually been snowing on my way out to this early call – a uterine haemorrhage in a cow – but the wind had been rising steadily and whipping the top surface from the white blanket which had covered the fell-tops for weeks. My headlights had picked out the creeping drifts; pretty, pointed fingers feeling their way inch by inch across the strip of tarmac.

This was how all blocked roads began, and at the farm as I injected pituitrin and packed the bleeding cervix with a clean sheet I could hear the wind buffeting the byre door and wondered if I would win the race home.

On the way back the drifts had stopped being pretty and lay across the road like white bolsters; but my little car had managed to cleave through them, veering crazily at times, wheels spinning, and now I could see the main road a few hundred yards ahead, reassuringly black in the pale light.

But just over there on the left, a field away, was Cote House. I was treating a bullock there – he had eaten some frozen turnips – and a visit was fixed for today. I didn't fancy trailing back up here if I could avoid it and there was a light in the kitchen window. The family were up, anyway. I turned and drove down into the yard.

The farmhouse door lay within a small porch and the wind had driven the snow inside forming a smooth, two-foot heap against the timbers. As I leaned across to knock, the surface of the heap trembled a little, then began to heave. There was something in there, something quite big. It was eerie standing in the half light watching the snow parting to reveal a furry body. Some creature of the wild must have strayed in, searching for warmth – but it was bigger than a fox or anything else I could think of.

Just then the door opened and the light from the kitchen streamed out. Peter Trenholm beckoned me inside and his wife smiled at me from the bright interior. They were a cheerful young couple.

'What's that?' I gasped, pointing at the animal which was shaking the snow vigorously from its coat.

'That?' Peter grinned, 'That's awd Tip.'

'Tip? Your dog? But what's he doing under a pile of snow?'

'Just blew in on him, I reckon. That's where he sleeps, you know, just outside back door.'

I stared at the farmer. 'You mean he sleeps there, out in the open, every night?'

'Aye, allus. Summer and winter. But don't look at me like that Mr Herriot – it's his own choice. The other dogs have a warm bed in the cow house but Tip won't entertain it. He's fifteen now and he's been sleeping out there since he were a pup. I remember when me father was alive he tried all ways to get t'awd feller to sleep inside but it was no good.'

I looked at the old dog in amazement. I could see him more clearly now; he wasn't the typical sheep dog type, he was bigger boned, longer in the hair, and he projected a bursting vitality that didn't go with his fifteen years. It was difficult to believe that any animal living in these bleak uplands should choose to sleep outside – and thrive on it. I had to look closely to see any sign of his great age. There was the slightest stiffness in his gait as he moved around, perhaps a fleshless look about his head and face and of course the tell-tale lens opacity in the depths of his eyes. But the general impression was of an unquenchable jauntiness.

He shook the last of the snow from his coat, pranced jerkily up to the farmer and gave a couple of reedy barks. Peter Trenholm laughed. 'You see he's ready to be off – he's a beggar for work is Tip.' He led the way towards the buildings and I followed, stumbling over the frozen ruts, like iron under the snow, and bending my head against the knife-like wind. It was a relief to open the byre door and escape into the sweet bovine warmth.

There was a fair mixture of animals in the long building. The dairy cows took up most of the length, then there were a few young heifers, some bullocks and finally, in an empty stall deeply bedded with straw, the other farm dogs. The cats were there too, so it had to be warm. No animal is a better judge of comfort than a cat and they were just visible as furry balls in the straw. They had the best place, up against the wooden partition where the warmth came through from the big animals.

Tip strode confidently among his colleagues – a young dog and a bitch with three half-grown pups. You could see he was boss.

One of the bullocks was my patient and he was looking a bit better. When I had seen him yesterday his rumen (the big first stomach) had been completely static and atonic following an over eager consumption of frozen turnips. He had been slightly bloated and groaning with discomfort. But today as I leaned with my ear against his left side I could hear the beginnings of the surge and rumble of the normal rumen instead of the deathly silence of yesterday. My gastric lavage had undoubtedly tickled things up and I felt that another of the same would just about put him right. Almost lovingly I got together the ingredients of one of my favourite treatments, long since washed away in the flood of progress; the ounce of formalin, the half pound of common salt, the can of black treacle from the barrel which you used to find in most cow houses, all mixed up in a bucket with two gallons of hot water.

I jammed the wooden gag into the bullock's mouth and buckled it behind the horns, then as Peter held the handles I passed the stomach tube down into the rumen and pumped in the mixture. When I had finished the bullock opened his eyes wide in surprise and began to paddle his hind legs. Listening again at his side, I could hear the reassuring bubbling of the stomach contents. I smiled to myself in satisfaction. It worked. It always worked.

Wiping down the tube I could hear the hiss-hiss as Peter's brother got on with the morning's milking, and as I prepared to leave he came down the byre with a full bucket on the way to the cooler. As he passed the dogs' stall he tipped a few pints of the warm milk into their dishes and Tip strolled forward casually for his breakfast. While he was drinking, the young dog tried to push his way in but a soundless snap from Tip's jaws missed his nose by a fraction and he retired to another dish. I noticed, however, that the old dog made no protest as the bitch and pups joined him. The cats, black and white, tortoise-shell, tabby grey, appeared, stretching, from the straw and advanced in a watchful ring. Their turn would come.

Mrs Trenholm called me in for a cup of tea and when I came out it was fully daylight. But the sky was a burdened grey and the sparse trees near the house strained their bare branches against the wind which drove in long, icy gusts over the white empty miles of moor. It was what the Yorkshiremen called a 'thin wind' or sometimes a 'lazy wind' – the kind that couldn't be bothered to blow round you but went straight through instead. It made me feel that the best place on earth was by the side of that bright fire in the farmhouse kitchen.

Most people would have felt like that, but not old Tip. He was capering around as Peter loaded a flat cart with some hay bales for the young cattle in the outside barns; and as Peter shook the reins and the cob set off over the fields, he leapt on to the back of the cart.

As I threw my tackle into the boot I looked back at the old dog, legs braced against the uneven motion, tail waving, barking defiance at the cold world. I carried away the memory of Tip who scorned the softer things and slept in what he considered the place of honour – at his master's door.

A little incident like this has always been able to brighten my day and fortunately I have the kind of job where things of this kind happened. And sometimes it isn't even a happening – just a single luminous phrase.

As when I was examining a cow one morning while its neighbour was being milked. The milker was an old man and he was having trouble. He was sitting well into the cow, his cloth-capped head buried in her flank, the bucket gripped tightly between his knees, but the stool kept rocking about as the cow fidgeted and weaved. Twice she kicked the bucket over and she had an additional little trick of anointing her tail with particularly liquid faeces then lashing the old man across the face with it.

Finally he could stand it no longer. Leaping to his feet he dealt a puny blow at the cow's scraggy back and emitted an exasperated shout.

'Stand still, thou shittin' awd bovril!'

Or the day when I had to visit Luke Benson at his smallholding in Hillom village. Luke was a powerful man of about sixty and had the unusual characteristic of speaking always through his clenched teeth. He literally articulated every word by moving only his lips, showing the rows of square, horse-like incisors clamped tightly together. It leant a peculiar intensity to his simplest utterance; and as he spoke, his eyes glared.

Most of his conversation consisted of scathing remarks about the other inhabitants of Hillom. In fact he seemed to harbour a cordial dislike of the human race in general. Yet strangely enough I found him a very reasonable man to deal with; he accepted my diagnoses of his animals' ailments without question and appeared to be trying to be friendly by addressing me repeatedly as 'Jems', which was the nearest he could get to my name with his teeth together.

His fiercest hatred was reserved for his neighbour and fellow smallholder, a little lame man called Gill to whom Luke referred invariably and unkindly as 'Yon 'oppin youth'. A bitter feud had raged between them for many years and I had seen Luke smile on only two occasions – once when Mr Gill's sow lost its litter and again when he had a stack burnt down.

When Mr Gill's wife ran away with a man who came round the farms selling brushes it caused a sensation. Nothing like that had ever happened in Hillom before and a wave of delighted horror swept through the village. This, I thought, would be the high point of Luke Benson's life and when I had to visit a heifer of his I expected to find him jubilant. But Luke was gloomy.

As I examined and treated his animal he remained silent and it wasn't until I went into the kitchen to wash my hands that he spoke. He glanced round warily at his wife, a gaunt, grim-faced woman who was applying blacklead to the grate.

'You'll have heard about yon 'oppin youth's missus runnin' off?' he said.

'Yes,' I replied. 'I did hear about it.' I waited for Luke to gloat but he seemed strangely ill at ease. He fidgeted until I had finished drying my hands then he glared at me and bared his strong teeth.

'Ah'll tell you something, Jems,' he ground out. 'Ah wish somebody would tek MA bugger!'

And there was that letter from the Bramleys – that really made me feel good. You don't find people like the Bramleys now; radio, television and the motorcar have carried the outside world into the most isolated places so that the simple people you used to meet on the lonely farms are rapidly becoming like people anywhere else. There are still a few left, of course – old folk who cling to the ways of their fathers and when I come across any of them I like to make some excuse to sit down and talk with them and listen to the old Yorkshire words and expressions which have almost disappeared.

But even in the thirties when there were many places still untouched by the flood of progress the Bramleys were in some ways unique. There were four of them; three brothers, all middle-aged bachelors, and an older sister, also unmarried, and their farm lay in a wide, shallow depression in the hills. You could just see the ancient tiles of Scar House through the top branches of the sheltering trees if you stood outside the pub in Drewburn village and in the summer it was possible to drive down over the fields to the farm. I had done it a few times, the bottles in the boot jingling and crashing as the car bounced over the rig and furrow. The other approach to the place was right on the other side through Mr Broom's stack-yard and then along a track with ruts so deep that only a tractor could negotiate it.

There was, in fact, no road to the farm, but that didn't bother the Bramleys because the outside world held no great attraction for them. Miss Bramley made occasional trips to Darrowby on market days for provisions and Herbert, the middle brother, had come into town in the spring of 1929 to have a tooth out, but apart from that they stayed contentedly at home.

A call to Scar House always came as rather a jolt because it meant that at least two hours had been removed from the working day. In all but the driest weather it was safer to leave the car at Mr Broom's and make the journey on foot. One February night at about eight o'clock I was splashing my way along the track, feeling the mud sucking at my wellingtons; it was to see a horse with colic and my pockets were stuffed with the things I might need – arecoline, phials of morphia, a bottle of Paraphyroxia. My eyes were half closed against the steady drizzle but about half a mile ahead I could see the lights of the house winking among the trees.

After twenty minutes of slithering in and out of the unseen puddles and opening a series of broken, string-tied gates, I reached the farm yard and crossed over to the back door. I was about to knock when I stopped with my hand poised. I found I was looking through the kitchen window and in the interior, dimly lit by an oil lamp, the Bramleys were sitting in a row.

They weren't grouped round the fire but were jammed tightly on a long, high-backed wooden settle which stood against the far wall. The strange thing was the almost exact similarity of their attitudes; all four had their arms folded, chins resting on their chests, feet stretched out in front of them. The men had removed their heavy boots and were stocking-footed, but Miss Bramley wore an old pair of carpet slippers.

I stared, fascinated by the curious immobility of the group. They were not asleep, not talking or reading or listening to the radio – in fact they didn't have one – they were just sitting.

I had never seen people just sitting before and I stood there for some minutes to see if they would make a move or do anything at all, but nothing happened. It occurred to me that this was probably a typical evening; they worked hard all day, had their meal, then they just sat till bedtime.

A month or two later I discovered another unsuspected side of the Bramleys when they started having trouble with their cats. I knew they were fond of cats by the number and variety which swarmed over the place and perched confidently on my car bonnet on cold days with their unerring instinct for a warm place. But I was unprepared for the family's utter desolation when the cats started to die. Miss Bramley was on the doorstep at Skeldale House nearly every day carrying an egg basket with another pitiful patient – a cat or sometimes a few tiny kittens – huddling miserably inside.

Even today with the full range of modern antibiotics, the treatment of feline enteritis is unrewarding and I had little success with my salicylates and non-specific injections. I did my best. I even took some of the cats in and kept them at the surgery so that I could attend them several times a day, but the mortality rate was high.

The Bramleys were stricken as they saw their cats diminishing. I was surprised at their grief because most farmers look on cats as pest killers and nothing more. But when Miss Bramley came in one morning with a fresh consignment of invalids she was in a sorry state. She stared at me across the surgery table and her rough fingers clasped and unclasped on the handle of the egg basket.

'Is it going to go through 'em all?' she quavered.

'Well, it's very infectious and it looks as though most of your young cats will get it anyway.'

For a moment Miss Bramley seemed to be struggling with herself, then her chin began to jerk and her whole face twitched uncontrollably. She didn't actually break down but her eyes brimmed and a couple of tears wandered among the network of wrinkles on her cheeks. I looked at her helplessly as she stood there, wisps of grey hair straggling untidily from under the incongruous black beret which she wore pulled tightly over her ears.

'It's Topsy's kittens I'm worried about,' she gasped out at length. 'There's five of 'em and they're the best we've got.'

I rubbed my chin. I had heard a lot about Topsy, one of a strain of incomparable ratters and mousers. Her last family were only about ten weeks old and it would be a crushing blow to the Bramleys if anything happened to them. But what the devil could I do? There was, as yet, no protective vaccine against the disease – or wait a minute, was there? I remembered that I'd heard a rumour that Burroughs Wellcome were working on one.

I pulled out a chair. 'Just sit down a few minutes, Miss Bramley. I'm going to make a phone call.' I was soon through to the Wellcome Laboratory and half expected a sarcastic reply. But they were kind and cooperative. They had had encouraging results with the new vaccine and would be glad to let me have five doses if I would inform them of the result.

I hurried back to Miss Bramley. 'I've ordered something for your kittens. I can't guarantee anything but there's nothing else to do. Have them down here on Tuesday morning.'

The vaccine arrived promptly and as I injected the tiny creatures Miss Bramley extolled the virtues of the Topsy line. 'Look at the size of them ears! Did you ever see bigger 'uns on kittens?'

I had to admit that I hadn't. The ears were enormous, sail-like and they made the ravishingly pretty little faces look even smaller.

Miss Bramley nodded and smiled with satisfaction. 'Aye, you can allus tell. It's the sure sign of a good mouser.'

The injection was repeated a week later. The kittens were still looking well.

'Well that's it,' I said. 'We'll just have to wait now. But remember I want to know the outcome of this, so please don't forget to let me know.'

I didn't hear from the Bramleys for several months and had almost forgotten about the little experiment when I came upon a grubby envelope which had apparently been pushed under the surgery door. It was the promised report and was, in its way, a model of conciseness. It communicated all the information I required without frills or verbiage.

It was in a careful, spidery scrawl and said simply: 'Dere Sir, Them kittens is now big cats. Yrs trly, R. Bramley.'

CHAPTER TWENTY-EIGHT

As I stopped my car by the group of gipsies I felt I was looking at something which should have been captured by a camera. The grass verge was wide on this loop of the road and there were five of them squatting round the fire; it seemed like the mother and father and three little girls. They sat very still, regarding me blankly through the drifting smoke while a few big snowflakes floated across the scene and settled lazily on the tangled hair of the children. Some unreal quality in the wild tableau kept me motionless in my seat, staring through the glass, forgetful of the reason for my being here. Then I wound down the window and spoke to the man.

'Are you Mr Myatt? I believe you have a sick pony.' The man nodded. 'Aye, that's right. He's over here.' It was a strange accent with no trace of Yorkshire in it. He got up from the fire, a thin, dark-skinned unshaven little figure, and came over to the car holding out something in his hand. It was a ten shilling note and I recognized it as a gesture of good faith.

The gipsies who occasionally wandered into Darrowby were always regarded with a certain amount of suspicion. They came, unlike the Myatts, mainly in the summer to camp down by the river and sell their horses and we had been caught out once or twice before. A lot of them seemed to be called Smith and it wasn't uncommon to go back on the second day and find that patient and owner had gone. In fact Siegfried had shouted to me as I left the house this morning: 'Get the brass if you can.' But he needn't have worried – Mr Myatt was on the up and up.

I got out of the car and followed him over the grass, past the shabby, ornate caravan and the lurcher dog tied to the wheel to where a few horses and ponies were tethered. My patient was easy to find; a handsome piebald of about thirteen hands with good, clean legs and a look of class about him. But he was in a sorry state. While the other animals moved around on their tethers, watching us with interest, the piebald stood as though carved from stone.

Even from a distance I could tell what was wrong with him. Only acute laminitis could produce that crouching posture and as I moved nearer I could see that all four feet were probably affected because the pony had his hind feet right under his body in a desperate attempt to take his full weight on his heels.

I pushed my thermometer into the rectum. 'Has he been getting any extra food, Mr Myatt?'

'Aye, he getten into a bag of oats last night.' The little man showed me the big, half empty sack in the back of the caravan. It was difficult to understand him but he managed to convey that the pony had broken loose and gorged himself on the oats. And he had given him a dose of castor oil – he called it 'casta ile'.

The thermometer read 104 and the pulse was rapid and bounding. I passed my hand over the smooth, trembling hooves, feeling the abnormal heat, then I looked at the taut face, the dilated nostrils and terrified eyes. Anybody who has had an infection under a finger-nail can have an inkling of the agony a horse goes through when the sensitive laminae of the foot are inflamed and throbbing against the unyielding wall of the hoof.

'Can you get him to move?' I asked.

The man caught hold of the head collar and pulled, but the pony refused to budge.

I took the other side of the collar. 'Come on, it's always better if they can get moving.'

We pulled together and Mrs Myatt slapped the pony's rump. He took a couple of stumbling steps but it was as though the ground was red hot and he groaned as his feet came down. Within seconds he was crouching again with his weight on his heels.

'It seems he just won't have it.' I turned and went back to the car. I'd have to do what I could to give him relief and the first thing was to get rid of as much as possible of that belly-full of oats. I fished out the bottle of arecoline and gave an injection into the muscle of the neck, then I showed the little man how to tie cloths round the hooves so that he could keep soaking them with cold water.

Afterwards I stood back and looked again at the pony. He was salivating freely from the arecoline and he had cocked his tail and evacuated his bowel; but his pain was undiminished and it would stay like that until the tremendous inflammation subsided – if it ever did. I had seen cases like this where serum had started to ooze from the coronet; that usually meant shedding of the hooves – even death.

As I turned over the gloomy thoughts the three little girls went up to the pony. The biggest put her arms round his neck and laid her cheek against his shoulder while the others stroked the shivering flanks. There were no tears, no change in the blank expressions, but it was easy to see that that pony really meant something to them.

Before leaving I handed over a bottle of tincture of aconite mixture. 'Get a dose of this down him every four hours, Mr Myatt, and be sure to keep putting cold water on the feet. I'll come and see him in the morning.'

I closed the car door and looked through the window again at the slow-rising smoke, the drifting snowflakes and the three children with their ragged dresses and uncombed hair still stroking the pony.

'Well you got the brass, James,' Siegfried said at lunch, carelessly stuffing the ten shilling note into a bulging pocket. 'What was the trouble?'

'Worst case of laminitis I've ever seen. Couldn't move the pony at all and he's going through hell. I've done the usual things but I'm pretty sure they aren't going to be enough.'

'Not a very bright prognosis, then?'

'Really black. Even if he gets over the acute stage he'll have deformed feet, I'd like to bet. Grooved hooves, dropped soles, the lot. And he's a grand little animal, lovely piebald. I wish to God there was something else I could do.'

Siegfried sawed two thick slices off the cold mutton and dropped them on my plate. He looked thoughtfully at me for a moment. 'You've been a little distrait since you came back. These are rotten jobs, I know, but it's no good worrying.'

'Ach, I'm not worrying, exactly, but I can't get it off my mind. Maybe it's those people – the Myatts. They were something new to me. Right out of the world. And three raggedy little girls absolutely crazy about that pony. They aren't going to like it at all.'

As Siegfried chewed his mutton I could see the old glint coming into his eyes; it showed when the talk had anything to do with horses. I knew he wouldn't push in but he was waiting for me to make the first move. I made it.

'I wish you'd come along and have a look with me. Maybe there's something you could suggest. Do you think there could be?'

Siegfried put down his knife and fork and stared in front of him for a few seconds, then he turned to me. 'You know, James, there just might be. Quite obviously this is a right pig of a case and the ordinary remedies aren't going to do any good. We have to pull something out of the bag and I've got an idea. There's just one thing.' He gave me a crooked smile. 'You may not like it.'

'Don't bother about me,' I said. 'You're the horseman. If you can help this pony I don't care what you do.'

'Right, eat up then and we'll go into action together.' We finished our meal and he led me through to the instrument room. I was surprised when he opened the cupboard where old Mr Grant's instruments were kept. It was a kind of museum.

When Siegfried had bought the practice from the old vet who had worked on into his eighties these instruments had come with it and they lay there in rows, unused but undisturbed. It would have been logical to throw them out, but maybe Siegfried felt the same way about them as I did. The polished wooden boxes of shining, odd-shaped scalpels, the enema pumps and douches with their perished rubber and brass fittings, the seaton needles, the ancient firing irons – they were a silent testament to sixty years of struggle. I often used to open that cupboard door and try to picture the old man wrestling with the same problems as I had, travelling the same narrow roads as I did. He had done it absolutely on his own and for sixty years. I was only starting but I knew a little about the triumphs and disasters, the wondering and worrying, the hopes and disappointments – and the hard labour. Anyway, Mr Grant was dead and gone, taking with him all the skills and knowledge I was doggedly trying to accumulate.

Siegfried reached to the back of the cupboard and pulled out a long flat box. He blew the dust from the leather covering and gingerly unfastened the clasp. Inside, a fleam, glittering on its bed of frayed velvet, lay by the side of a round, polished blood stick.

I looked at my employer in astonishment. 'You're going to bleed him, then?'

'Yes, my boy, I'm going to take you back to the Middle Ages.' He looked at my startled face and put a hand on my arm. 'But don't start beating me over the head with all the scientific arguments against blood-letting. I've no strong views either way.'

'But have you ever done it? I've never seen you use this outfit.'

'I've done it. And I've seen some funny things after it, too.' Siegfried turned away as if he wanted no more discussion. He cleaned the fleam thoroughly and dropped it into the sterilizer. His face was expressionless as he stood listening to the hiss of the boiling water.

The gipsies were again hunched over the fire when we got there and Mr Myatt, sensing that reinforcements had arrived, scrambled to his feet and shuffled forward, holding out another ten shilling note.

Siegfried waved it away. 'Let's see how we get on, Mr Myatt,' he grunted. He strode across the grass to where the pony still trembled in his agonized crouch. There was no improvement; in fact the eyes stared more wildly and I could hear little groans as the piebald carefully eased himself from foot to foot.

Siegfried spoke softly without looking at me, 'Poor beggar. You weren't exaggerating, James. Bring that box from the car, will you?'

When I came back he was tying a choke rope round the base of the pony's neck. 'Pull it up tight,' he said. As the jugular rose up tense and turgid in its furrow he quickly clipped and disinfected a small area and inserted a plaque of local anaesthetic. Finally he opened the old leather-covered box and extracted the fleam, wrapped in sterile lint.

Everything seemed to start happening then. Siegfried placed the little blade of the fleam against the bulging vein and without hesitation gave it a confident smack with the stick. Immediately an alarming cascade of blood spouted from the hole and began to form a dark lake on the grass. Mr Myatt gasped and the little girls set up a sudden chatter. I could understand how they felt. In fact I was wondering how long the pony could stand this tremendous outflow without dropping down.

It didn't seem to be coming out fast enough for Siegfried, however, because he produced another stick from his pocket, thrust it into the pony's mouth and began to work the jaws. And as the animal champed, the blood gushed more fiercely.

When at least a gallon had come away Siegfried seemed satisfied. 'Slacken the rope, James,' he cried, then rapidly closed the wound on the neck with a pin suture. Next he trotted over the grass and looked over a gate in the roadside wall. 'Thought so,' he shouted. 'There's a little beck in that field. We've got to get him over to it. Come on, lend a hand everybody!'

He was clearly enjoying himself and his presence was having its usual effect. The Myatts were spurred suddenly into action and began to run around aimlessly, bumping into each other. I was gripped by a sudden tension and preparedness and even the pony seemed to be taking an interest in his surroundings for the first time.

All five of the gipsies pulled at the halter, Siegfried and I looped our arms behind the pony's thighs, everybody gave encouraging shouts and at last he began to move forward. It was a painful process but he kept going – through the gate and across the field to where the shallow stream wandered among its rushes. There were no banks to speak of and it was easy to push him out into the middle. As he stood there with the icy water rippling round his inflamed hooves I fancied I could read in his eyes a faint dawning of an idea that things were looking up at last.

'Now he must stand in there for an hour,' Siegfried said. 'And then you'll have to make him walk round the field. Then another hour in the beck. As he gets better you can give him more and more exercise but he must come back to the beck. There's a lot of work for somebody here, so who's going to do it?'

The three little girls came shyly round him and looked up, wide-eyed, into his face. Siegfried laughed. 'You three want the job, do you? Right, I'll tell you just what to do.'

He pulled out the bag of peppermint drops which was ever-present among his widely-varied pocket luggage and I settled myself for a long wait. I had seen him in action with the children on the farms and when that bag of sweets came out, everything stopped. It was the one time Siegfried was never in a hurry.

The little girls each solemnly took a sweet, then Siegfried squatted on his heels and began to address them like a professor with his class. They soon began to thaw and put a word in for themselves. The smallest launched into a barely intelligible account of the remarkable things the pony had done when he was a foal and Siegfried listened intently, nodding his head gravely now and then. There was all the time in the world.

His words obviously went home because, over the next few days whenever I passed the gipsy camp I could see the three wild little figures either grouped around the pony in the beck or dragging him round the field on a long halter shank. I didn't need to butt in – I could see he was improving all the time.

It was about a week later that I saw the Myatts on their way out of Darrowby, the red caravan rocking across the market place with Mr Myatt up front wearing a black velvet cap, his wife by his side. Tethered to various parts of the caravan the family of horses clopped along and right at the rear was the piebald, a bit stiff perhaps, but going very well. He'd be all right.

The little girls were looking out of the back door and as they spotted me I waved. They looked back at me unsmilingly until they had almost turned the corner into Hallgate then one of them shyly lifted her hand. The others followed suit and my last sight was of them waving eagerly back.

I strolled into the Drovers and took a thoughtful half pint into a corner. Siegfried had done the trick there all right but I was wondering what to make of it because in veterinary practice it is difficult to draw definite conclusions even after spectacular results. Was it my imagination or did that pony seem to feel relief almost immediately after the blood-letting? Would we ever have got him moving without it? Was it really the right thing in these cases to bash a hole in the jugular and release about a bucketful of the precious fluid? I still don't have the answers because I never dared try it for myself.

CHAPTER TWENTY-NINE

'Could Mr Herriot see my dog, please?'

Familiar enough words coming from the waiting-room but it was the voice that brought me to a slithering halt just beyond the door.

It couldn't be, no of course it couldn't, but it sounded just like Helen. I tiptoed back and applied my eye without hesitation to the crack in the door. Tristan was standing there looking down at somebody just beyond my range of vision.

All I could see was a hand resting on the head of a patient sheep dog, the hem of a tweed skirt and two silk stockinged legs.

They were nice legs – not skinny – and could easily belong to a big girl like Helen. My cogitations were cut short as a head bent over to speak to the dog and I had a close up in profile of the small straight nose and the dark hair falling across the milky smoothness of the cheek.

I was still peering, bemused, when Tristan shot out of the room and collided with me. Stifling an oath, he grabbed my arm and hauled me along the passage into the dispensary. He shut the door and spoke in a hoarse whisper.

'It's her! The Alderson woman! And she wants to see you! Not Siegfried, not me, but you, Mr Herriot himself!'

He looked at me wide-eyed for a few moments then, as I stood hesitating he opened the door and tried to propel me into the passage.

'What the hell are you waiting for?' he hissed.

'Well, it's a bit embarrassing, isn't it? After that dance, I mean. Last time she saw me I was a lovely sight – so pie-eyed I couldn't even speak.'

Tristan struck his forehead with his hand. 'God help us! You worry about details, don't you? She's asked to see you – what more do you want? Go on, get in there!'

I was shuffling off irresolutely when he raised a hand. 'Just a minute. Stay right there.' He trotted off and returned in a few seconds holding out a white lab coat.

'Just back from the laundry,' he said as he began to work my arms into the starched sleeves. 'You'll look marvellous in this Jim – the immaculate young surgeon.'

I stood unresisting as he buttoned me into the garment but struck away his hand when he started to straighten my tie. As I left him he gave me a final encouraging wave before heading for the back stairs.

I didn't give myself any more time to think but marched straight into the waiting-room. Helen looked up and smiled. And it was just the same smile. Nothing behind it. Just the same friendly, steady-eyed smile as when I first met her.

We faced each other in silence for some moments then

when I didn't say anything she looked down at the dog.

'It's Dan in trouble this time,' she said. 'He's our sheep dog but we're so fond of him that he's more like one of the family.'

The dog wagged his tail furiously at the sound of his name but yelped as he came towards me. I bent down and patted his head. 'I see he's holding up a hind leg.'

'Yes, he jumped over a wall this morning and he's been like that ever since. I think it's something quite bad – he can't put any weight on the leg.'

'Right, bring him through to the other room and I'll have a look at him. But take him on in front of me, will you, and I'll be able to watch how he walks.'

I held the door open and she went through ahead of me with the dog.

Watching how Helen walked distracted me over the first few yards, but it was a long passage and by the time we had reached the second bend I had managed to drag my attention back to my patient.

And glory be, it was a dislocated hip. It had to be with that shortening of the limb and the way he carried it underneath his body with the paw just brushing the ground.

My feelings were mixed. This was a major injury but on the other hand the chances were I could put it right quickly and look good in the process. Because I had found, in my brief experience, that one of the most spectacular procedures in practice was the reduction of a dislocated hip. Maybe I had been lucky, but with the few I had seen I had been able to convert an alarmingly lame animal into a completely sound one as though by magic.

In the operating room I hoisted Dan on to the table. He stood without moving as I examined the hip. There was no doubt about it at all – the head of the femur was displaced upwards and backwards, plainly palpable under my thumb.

The dog looked round only once – when I made a gentle attempt to flex the limb – but turned away immediately and stared resolutely ahead. His mouth hung open a little as he panted nervously but like a lot of the placid animals which arrived on our surgery table he seemed to have resigned himself to his fate. I had the strong impression that I could have started to cut his head off and he wouldn't have made much fuss.

'Nice, good-natured dog,' I said. 'And a bonny one, too.'

Helen patted the handsome head with the broad blaze of white down the face; the tail waved slowly from side to side.

'Yes,' she said. 'He's just as much a family pet as a working dog. I do hope he hasn't hurt himself too badly.'

'Well, he has a dislocated hip. It's a nasty thing but with a bit of luck I ought to be able to put it back.'

'What happens if it won't go back?'

'He'd have to form a false joint up there. He'd be very lame for several weeks and probably always have a slightly short leg.'

'Oh dear, I wouldn't like that,' Helen said. 'Do you think he'll be all right?'

I looked at the docile animal still gazing steadfastly to his front. 'I think he's got a good chance, mainly because you haven't hung about for days before bringing him in. The sooner these things are tackled the better.'

'Oh good. When will you be able to start on him?'

'Right now.' I went over to the door. 'I'll just give Tristan a shout. This is a two man job.'

'Couldn't I help?' Helen said. 'I'd very much like to if you wouldn't mind.'

I looked at her doubtfully. 'Well I don't know. You mightn't like playing tug of war with Dan in the middle. He'll be anaesthetized of course but there's usually a lot of pulling.'

Helen laughed. 'Oh, I'm quite strong. And not a bit squeamish. I'm used to animals, you know, and I like working with them.'

'Right,' I said. 'Slip on this spare coat and we'll begin.'

The dog didn't flinch as I pushed the needle into his vein and as the Nembutal flowed in, his head began to slump against Helen's arm and his supporting paw to slide along the smooth top of the table. Soon he was stretched unconscious on his side.

I held the needle in the vein as I looked down at the sleeping animal. 'I might have to give him a bit more. They have to be pretty deep to overcome the muscular resistance.'

Another cc and Dan was as limp as any rag doll. I took hold of the affected leg and spoke across the table. 'I want you to link your hands underneath his thigh and try to hold him there when I pull. OK? Here we go, then.'

It takes a surprising amount of force to pull the head of a displaced femur over the rim of the acetabulum. I kept up a steady traction with my right hand, pressing on the head of the femur at the same time with my left. Helen did her part efficiently, leaning back against the pull, her lips pushed forward in a little pout of concentration.

I suppose there must be a foolproof way of doing this job – a method which works the very first time – I have never been able to find it. Success has always come to me only after a fairly long period of trial and error and it was the same today. I tried all sorts of angles, rotations and twists on the flaccid limb, trying not to think of how it would look if this just happened to be the one I couldn't put back. I was wondering what Helen, still hanging on determinedly to her end, must be thinking of this wrestling match when I heard the muffled click. It was a sweet and welcome sound.

I flexed the hip joint once or twice. No resistance at all now. The femoral head was once more riding smoothly in its socket.

'Well that's it,' I said. 'Hope it stays put – we'll have to keep our fingers crossed. The odd one does pop out again but I've got a feeling this is going to be all right.'

Helen ran her hand over the silky ears and neck of the sleeping dog. 'Poor old Dan. He wouldn't have jumped over that wall this morning if he'd known what was in store for him. How long will it be before he comes round?'

'Oh, he'll be out for the rest of the day. When he starts to wake up tonight I want you to be around to steady him in case he falls and puts the thing out again. Perhaps you'd give me a ring. I'd like to know how things are.'

I gathered Dan up in my arms and was carrying him along the passage, staggering under his weight, when I met Mrs Hall. She was carrying a tray with two cups.

'I was just having a drink of tea, Mr Herriot,' she said. 'I thought you and the young lady might fancy a cup.'

I looked at her narrowly. This was unusual. Was it possible she had joined Tristan in playing Cupid? But the broad, dark-skinned face was as unemotional as ever. It told me nothing.

'Well, thanks very much, Mrs Hall. I'll just put this dog outside first.' I went out and settled Dan on the back seat of Helen's car; with only his eyes and nose sticking out from under a blanket he looked at peace with the world.

Helen was already sitting with a cup in her lap and I thought of the other time I had drunk tea in this room with a girl. On the day I had arrived in Darrowby. She had been one of Siegfried's followers and surely the toughest of them all.

This was a lot different. During the struggle in the operating room I had been able to observe Helen at close range and I had discovered that her mouth turned up markedly at the corners as though she was just going to smile or had just been smiling; also that the deep warm blue of the eyes under the smoothly arching brows made a dizzying partnership with the rich black-brown of her hair.

And this time the conversation didn't lag. Maybe it was because I was on my own ground – perhaps I never felt fully at ease unless there was a sick animal involved somewhere, but at any rate I found myself prattling effortlessly just as I had done up on that hill when we had first met.

Mrs Hall's teapot was empty and the last of the biscuits gone before I finally saw Helen off and started on my round.

The same feeling of easy confidence was on me that night when I heard her voice on the phone.

'Dan is up and walking about,' she said. 'He's still a bit wobbly but he's perfectly sound on that leg.'

'Oh great, he's got the first stage over. I think everything's going to be fine.'

There was a pause at the other end of the line, then: 'Thank you so much for what you've done. We were terribly worried about him, especially my young brother and sister. We're very grateful.'

'Not at all, I'm delighted too. He's a grand dog.' I hesitated for a moment – it had to be now. 'Oh, you remember we were talking about Scotland today. Well, I was passing the Plaza this afternoon and I see they're showing a film about the Hebrides. I thought maybe . . . I wondered if perhaps, er . . . you might like to come and see it with me.'

Another pause and my heart did a quick thud-thud.

'All right,' Helen said. 'Yes, I'd like that. When? Friday night? Well, thank you – goodbye till then.'

I replaced the receiver with a trembling hand. Why did I make such heavy weather of these things? But it didn't matter – I was back in business.

CHAPTER THIRTY

Rheumatism is a terrible thing in a dog. It is painful enough in humans but an acute attack can reduce an otherwise healthy dog to terrified, screaming immobility.

Very muscular animals suffered most and I went carefully as my fingers explored the bulging triceps and gluteals of the little Staffordshire bull terrier. Normally a tough little fellow, afraid of nothing, friendly, leaping high in an attempt to lick people's faces; but today, rigid, trembling, staring anxiously in front of him. Even to turn his head a little brought a shrill howl of agony.

Mercifully it was something you could put right and quickly too. I pulled the Novalgin into the syringe and injected it rapidly. The little dog, oblivious to everything but the knife-like stabbing of the rheumatism did not stir at the prick of the needle. I counted out some salicylate tablets into a box, wrote the directions on the lid and handed the box to the owner.

'Give him one of those as soon as the injection has eased

him, Mr Tavener. Then repeat in about four hours. I'm pretty sure he'll be greatly improved by then.'

Mrs Tavener snatched the box away as her husband began to read the directions. 'Let me see it,' she snapped. 'No doubt I'll be the one who has the job to do.'

It had been like that all the time, ever since I had entered the beautiful house with the terraced gardens leading down to the river. She had been at him ceaselessly while he was holding the dog for me. When the animal had yelped she had cried: 'Really, Henry, don't grip the poor thing like that, you're hurting him!' She had kept him scuttling about for this and that and when he was out of the room she said: 'You know, this is all my husband's fault. He will let the dog swim in the river. I knew this would happen.'

Halfway through, daughter Julia had come in and it was clear from the start that she was firmly on Mama's side. She helped out with plenty of 'How could you, Daddy!' and 'For God's sake, Daddy!' and generally managed to fill in the gaps when her mother wasn't in full cry.

The Taveners were in their fifties. He was a big, floridly handsome man who had made millions in the Tyneside shipyards before pulling out of the smoke to this lovely place. I had taken an instant liking to him; I had expected a tough tycoon and had found a warm, friendly, curiously vulnerable man, obviously worried sick about his dog.

I had reservations about Mrs Tavener despite her still considerable beauty. Her smile had a switched-on quality and there was a little too much steel in the blue of her eyes. She had seemed less concerned about the dog than with the necessity of taking it out on her husband.

Julia, a scaled-down model of her mother, drifted about the room with the aimless, bored look of the spoiled child; glancing blankly at the dog or me, staring without interest through the window at the smooth lawns, the tennis court, the dark band of river under the trees.

I gave the terrier a final reassuring pat on the head and got up from my knees. As I put away the syringe, Tavener took my arm. 'Well, that's fine, Mr Herriot. We're very grateful to you for relieving our minds. I must say I thought the old boy's time had come when he started yelling. And now you'll have a drink before you go.'

The man's hand trembled on my arm as he spoke. It had been noticeable too, when he had been holding the dog's head and I had wondered; maybe Parkinson's disease, or nerves, or just drink. Certainly he was pouring a generous measure of whisky into his glass, but as he tipped up the bottle his hand was seized by an even more violent tremor and he slopped the spirit on to the polished sideboard.

'Oh God! Oh God!' Mrs Tavener burst out. There was a bitter note of oh no, not again, in her cry and Julia struck her forehead with her hand and raised her eyes to heaven. Tavener shot a single hunted look at the women then grinned as he handed me my glass.

'Come and sit down, Mr Herriot,' he said. 'I'm sure you have time to relax for a few minutes.'

We moved over to the fireside and Tavener talked pleasantly about dogs and the countryside and the pictures which hung on the walls of the big room. Those pictures were noted in the district; many of them were originals by famous painters and they had become the main interest in Tavener's life. His other passion was clocks and as I looked round the room at the rare and beautiful timepieces standing among elegant period furniture it was easy to believe the rumours I had heard about the wealth within these walls.

The women did not drink with us; they had disappeared when the whisky was brought out, but as I drained my glass the door was pushed open and they stood there, looking remarkably alike in expensive tweed coats and fur-trimmed hats. Mrs Tavener pulling on a pair of motoring gloves, looked with distaste at her husband. 'We're going into Brawton,' she said. 'Don't know when we'll be back.'

Behind her, Julia stared coldly at her father; her lip curled slightly.

Tavener did not reply. He sat motionless as I listened to the roar of the car engine and the spatter of whipped-up gravel beyond the window; then he looked out, blank-faced, empty-eyed at the drifting cloud of exhaust smoke in the drive.

There was something in his expression which chilled me. I

put down my glass and got to my feet. 'Afraid I must be moving on, Mr Tavener. Thanks for the drink.'

He seemed suddenly to be aware of my presence; the friendly smile returned. 'Not at all. Thank you for looking after the old boy. He seems better already.'

In the driving mirror, the figure at the top of the steps looked small and alone till the high shrubbery hid him from my view.

The next call was to a sick pig, high on Marstang Fell. The road took me at first along the fertile valley floor, winding under the riverside trees past substantial farmhouses and rich pastures; but as the car left the road and headed up a steep track the country began to change. The transition was almost violent as the trees and bushes thinned out and gave way to the bare, rocky hillside and the miles of limestone walls.

And though the valley had been rich with the fresh green of the new leaves, up here the buds were unopened and the naked branches stretched against the sky still had the look of winter.

Tim Alton's farm lay at the top of the track and as I pulled up at the gate I wondered as I always did how the man could scrape a living from those few harsh acres with the grass flattened and yellowed by the wind which always blew. At any rate, many generations had accomplished the miracle and had lived and struggled and died in that house with its outbuildings crouching in the lee of a group of stunted, wind-bent trees, its massive stones crumbling under three centuries of fierce weathering.

Why should anybody want to build a farm in such a place? I turned as I opened the gate and looked back at the track threading between the walls down and down to where the white stones of the river glittered in the spring sunshine. Maybe the builder had stood here and looked across the green vastness and breathed in the cold, sweet air and thought it was enough.

I saw Tim Alton coming across the yard. There had been no need to lay down concrete or cobbles here; they had just swept away the thin soil and there, between house and buildings was a sloping stretch of fissured rock. It was more than a durable surface – it was everlasting.

'It's your pig this time, then, Tim,' I said and the farmer nodded seriously.

'Aye, right as owt yesterday and laid flat like a dead 'un this morning. Never looked up when I filled his trough and by gaw when a pig won't tackle his grub there's summat far wrong.' Tim dug his hands inside the broad leather belt which encircled his oversized trousers and which always seemed to be about to nip his narrow frame in two and led the way gloomily into the sty. Despite the bitter poverty of his existence he was a man who took misfortune cheerfully. I had never seen him look like this and I thought I knew the reason; there is something personal about the family pig.

Smallholders like Tim Alton made their meagre living from a few cows; they sold their milk to the big dairies or made butter. And they killed a pig or two each year and cured it themselves for home consumption. On the poorer places it seemed to me that they ate little else; whatever meal I happened to stumble in on, the cooking smell was always the same – roasting fat bacon.

It appeared to be a matter of pride to make the pig as fat as possible; in fact, on these little wind-blown farms where the people and the cows and the dogs were lean and spare, the pig was about the only fat thing to be seen.

I had seen the Alton pig before. I had been stitching a cow's torn teat about a fortnight ago and Tim had patted me on the shoulder and whispered: 'Now come along wi' me, Mr Herriot and I'll show tha summat.' We had looked into the sty at a twenty-five-stone monster effortlessly emptying a huge trough of wet meal. I could remember the pride in the farmer's eyes and the way he listened to the smacking and slobbering as if to great music.

It was different today. The pig looked, if possible, even more enormous as it lay on its side, eyes closed, filling the entire floor of the sty like a beached whale. Tim splashed a stick among the untouched meal in the trough and made encouraging noises but the animal never stirred. The farmer looked at me with haggard eyes.

'He's bad, Mr Herriot. It's serious whatever it is.'

I had been taking the temperature and when I read the thermometer I whistled. 'A hundred and seven. That's some fever.'

The colour drained from Tim's face. 'Oh 'ell! A hundred and seven! It's hopeless, then. It's ower with him.'

I had been feeling along the animal's side and I smiled reassuringly. 'No, don't worry, Tim. I think he's going to be all right. He's got erysipelas. Here, put your fingers along his back. You can feel a lot of flat swellings on his skin – those are the diamonds. He'll have a beautiful rash within a few hours but at the moment you can't see it, you can only feel it.'

'And you can make him better?'

'I'm nearly sure I can. I'll give him a whacking dose of serum and I'd like to bet you he'll have his nose in that trough in a couple of days. Most of them get over it all right.'

'Well that's a bit o' good news, any road,' said Tim, a smile flooding over his face. 'You had me worried there with your hundred and seven, dang you!'

I laughed. 'Sorry, Tim, didn't mean to frighten you. I'm often happier to see a high temperature than a low one. But it's a funny time for erysipelas. We usually see it in late summer.'

'All right, I'll let ye off this time. Come in and wash your hands.'

In the kitchen I ducked my head but couldn't avoid bumping the massive side of bacon hanging from the beamed ceiling. The heavy mass rocked gently on its hooks; it was about eight inches thick in parts – all pure white fat. Only by close inspection was it possible to discern a thin strip of lean meat.

Mrs Alton produced a cup of tea and as I sipped I looked across at Tim who had fallen back into a chair and lay with his hands hanging down; for a moment he closed his eyes and his face became a mask of weariness. I thought for the hundredth time about the endless labour which made up the lives of these little farmers. Alton was only forty but his body was already bent and ravaged by the constant demands he made on it; you could read his story on the corded forearm, the rough, work-swollen fingers. He told me once that the last time he missed a milking was twelve years ago and that was for his father's funeral.

I was taking my leave when I saw Jennie. She was the Altons' eldest child and was pumping vigorously at the tyre of her bicycle which was leaning against the wall just outside the kitchen door.

'Going somewhere?' I asked and the girl straightened up quickly, pushing back a few strands of dark hair from her forehead. She was about eighteen with delicate features and large, expressive eyes; in her wild, pinched prettiness there was something of the wheeling curlews, the wind and the sun, the wide emptiness of the moors.

'I'm going down to t'village.' She stole a glance into the kitchen. 'I'm going to get a bottle of Guinness for dad.'

'The village! It's a long way to go for a bottle of Guinness. It must be two miles and then you've got to push back up this hill. Are you going all that way just for one bottle?'

'Ay, just one,' she whispered, counting out a sixpence and some coppers into her palm with calm absorption. 'Dad's been up all night waiting for a heifer to calve – he's tired out. I won't be long and he can have his Guinness with his dinner. That's what he likes.' She looked up at me conspiratorially. 'It'll be a surprise for him.'

As she spoke, her father, still sprawled in the chair, turned his head and looked at her; he smiled and for a moment I saw a serenity in the steady eyes, a nobility in the seamed face.

Jennie looked at him for a few seconds, a happy secret look from under her lowered brows; then she turned quickly, mounted her bicycle and began to pedal down the track at surprising speed.

I followed her more slowly, the car, in second gear, bumping and swaying over the stones. I stared straight ahead, lost in thought. I couldn't stop my mind roaming between the two houses I had visited; between the gracious mansion by the river and the crumbling farmhouse I had just left; from Henry Tavener with his beautiful clothes, his well-kept hands, his rows of books and pictures and clocks to Tim Alton with his worn, chest-high trousers nipped in by that great belt, his daily, monthly, yearly grind to stay alive on that unrelenting hilltop.

But I kept coming back to the daughters; to the contempt in Julia Tavener's eyes when she looked at her father and the shining tenderness in Jennie Alton's.

It wasn't so easy to work out as it seemed; in fact it became increasingly difficult to decide who was getting the most out of their different lives. But as I guided the car over the last few yards of the track and pulled on to the smooth tarmac of the road it came to me with unexpected clarity. Taking it all in all, if I had the choice to make, I'd settle for the Guinness.

CHAPTER THIRTY-ONE

Tristan was unpacking the UCM's. These bottles contained a rich red fluid which constituted our last line of defence in the battle with animal disease. Its full name, Universal Cattle Medicine, was proclaimed on the label in big black type and underneath it pointed out that it was highly efficacious for coughs, chills, scours, garget, milk fever, pneumonia, felon and bloat. It finished off on a confident note with the assurance: 'Never Fails to Give Relief' and we had read the label so often that we half believed it.

It was a pity it didn't do any good because there was something compelling about its ruby depths when you held it up to the light and about the solid camphor-ammonia jolt when you sniffed at it and which made the farmers blink and shake their heads and say 'By gaw, that's powerful stuff,' with deep respect. But our specific remedies were so few and the possibilities of error so plentiful that it was comforting in cases of doubt to be able to hand over a bottle of the old standby. Whenever an entry of Siegfried's or mine appeared in the day book stating 'Visit attend cow, advice, 1 UCM' it was a pretty fair bet we didn't know what was wrong with the animal.

The bottles were tall and shapely and they came in elegant white cartons, so much more impressive than the unobtrusive containers of the antibiotics and steroids which we use today. Tristan was lifting them out of the tea chest and stacking them on the shelves in deep rows. When he saw me he ceased his labours, sat on the chest and pulled out a packet of Woodbines. He lit one, pulled the smoke a long way down then fixed me with a non-committal stare.

'You're taking her to the pictures then?'

Feeling vaguely uneasy under his eye, I tipped a pocketful of assorted empties into the waste basket. 'Yes, that's right. In about an hour.'

'Mm.' He narrowed his eyes against the slowly escaping smoke. 'Mm, I see.'

'Well what are you looking like that for?' I said defensively. 'Anything wrong with going to the pictures?'

'No-no. No-no-no. Nothing at all, Jim. Nothing, nothing. A very wholesome pursuit.'

'But you don't think I should be taking Helen there.'

'I never said that. No, I'm sure you'll have a nice time. It's just that ...' He scratched his head. 'I thought you might have gone in for something a bit more ... well ... enterprising.'

I gave a bitter laugh. 'Look, I tried enterprise at the Reniston. Oh, I'm not blaming you, Triss, you meant well, but as you know it was a complete shambles. I just don't want anything to go wrong tonight. I'm playing safe.'

'Well, I won't argue with you there,' Tristan said. 'You couldn't get much safer than the Darrowby Plaza.'

And later, shivering in the tub in the vast, draughty bathroom, I couldn't keep out the thought that Tristan was right. Taking Helen to the local cinema was a form of cowardice, a shrinking away from reality into what I hoped would be a safe, dark intimacy. But as I towelled myself, hopping about to keep warm, and looked out through the fringe of wistaria at the darkening garden there was comfort in the thought that it was another beginning, even though a small one.

And as I closed the door of Skeldale House and looked along the street to where the first lights of the shops beckoned in the dusk I felt a lifting of the heart. It was as though a breath from the near-by hills had touched me. A fleeting fragrance which said winter had gone. It was still cold – it was always cold in Darrowby until well into May – but the promise was there, of sunshine and warm grass and softer days.

You had to look closely or you could easily miss the Plaza, tucked in as it was between Pickersgills the ironmongers and Howarths the chemists. There had never been much attempt at grandeur in its architecture and the entrance was hardly wider than the average shop front. But what puzzled me as I approached was that the place was in darkness. I was in good time but the show was due to start in ten minutes or so and there was no sign of life.

I hadn't dared tell Tristan that my precautions had extended as far as arranging to meet Helen here. With a car like mine there was always an element of doubt about arriving anywhere in time or indeed at all and I had thought it prudent to eliminate all transport hazards.

'Meet you outside the cinema.' My God, it wasn't very bright was it? It took me back to my childhood, to the very first time I had taken a girl out. I was just fourteen and on my way to meet her I tendered my only half-crown to a bloody-minded Glasgow tram conductor and asked for a penny fare He vented his spleen on me by ransacking his bag and giving me my change entirely in halfpennies. So when the cinema queue reached the pay box I had to stand there with my little partner and everybody else watching while I paid for our shilling tickets with great handfuls of copper. The shame of it left a scar – it was another four years before I took out a girl again.

But the black thoughts were dispelled when I saw Helen picking her way across the market-place cobbles. She smiled and waved cheerfully as if being taken to the Darrowby Plaza was the biggest treat a girl could wish for, and when she came right up to me there was a soft flush on her cheeks and her eyes were bright.

Everything was suddenly absolutely right. I felt a surging conviction that this was going to be a good night – nothing was going to spoil it. After we had said hello she told me that Dan was running about like a puppy with no trace of a limp and the news was another wave on the high tide of my euphoria.

The only thing that troubled me was the blank, uninhabited appearance of the cinema entrance.

'Strange there's nobody here,' I said. 'It's nearly starting time. I suppose the place is open?'

'Must be,' Helen said. 'It's open every night but Sunday. Anyway, I'm sure these people are waiting too.'

I looked around. There was no queue as such but little groups were standing here and there; a few couples, mostly middle-aged, a bunch of small boys rolling and fighting on the pavement. Nobody seemed worried.

And indeed there was no cause. Exactly two minutes before the picture was due to start a figure in a mackintosh coat pedalled furiously round the corner of the street, head down, legs pistoning, the bicycle lying over at a perilous angle with the ground. He came to a screeching halt outside the entrance, inserted a key in the lock and threw wide the doors. Reaching inside, he flicked a switch and a single neon strip flickered fitfully above our heads and went out. It did this a few times and seemed bent on mischief till he stood on tiptoe and beat it into submission with a masterful blow of his fist. Then he whipped off the mackintosh revealing faultless evening-dress. The manager had arrived.

While this was going on a very fat lady appeared from nowhere and wedged herself into the pay box. The show was ready to roll.

We all began to shuffle inside. The little boys put down their ninepences and punched each other as they passed through a curtain into the stalls, while the rest of us proceeded decorously upstairs to the one-and-sixpenny seats in the balcony. The manager, his white shirt front and silk lapels gleaming, smiled and bowed with great courtesy as we passed.

We paused at a row of pegs at the top of the stairs while

some people hung up their coats. I was surprised to see Maggie Robinson the blacksmith's daughter there, taking the tickets, and she appeared to be intrigued by the sight of us. She simpered and giggled darted glances at Helen and did everything but dig me in the ribs. Finally she parted the curtains and we went inside.

It struck me immediately that the management were determined that their patrons wouldn't feel cold because if it hadn't been for the all-pervading smell of old sofas we might have been plunging into a tropical jungle. Maggie steered us through the stifling heat to our places and as I sat down I noticed that there was no arm between the two seats.

'Them's the courting seats,' she blurted out and fled with her hand to her mouth.

The lights were still on and I looked round the tiny balcony. There were only about a dozen people dotted here and there sitting in patient silence under the plain distempered walls. By the side of the screen the hands of a clock stood resolutely at twenty-past four.

But it was all right sitting there with Helen. I felt fine except for a tendency to gasp like a goldfish in the airless atmosphere. I was settling down cosily when a little man seated in front of us with his wife turned slowly round. The mouth in the haggard face was pursed grimly and he fixed his eyes on mine in a long, challenging stare. We faced each other for several silent moments before he finally spoke.

'She's dead,' he said.

A thrill of horror shot through me. 'Dead?'

'Aye, she is. She's dead.' He dragged the word out slowly with a kind of mournful satisfaction while his eyes still stared into mine.

I swallowed a couple of times. 'Well, I'm sorry to hear that. Truly sorry.'

He nodded grimly and continued to regard me with a peculiar intensity as though he expected me to say more. Then with apparent reluctance he turned away and settled in his seat.

I looked helplessly at the rigid back, at the square, narrow shoulders muffled in a heavy overcoat. Who in God's name was this? And what was he talking about? I knew the face from somewhere – must be a client. And what was dead? Cow? Ewe? Sow? My mind began to race over the cases I had seen during the past week but that face didn't seem to fit in anywhere.

Helen was looking at me questioningly and I managed a wan smile. But the spell was shattered. I started to say something to her when the little man began to turn again with menacing deliberation.

He fixed me once more with a hostile glare. 'Ah don't think there was ever owt wrong with her stomach,' he declared.

'You don't, eh?'

'No, young man, ah don't.' He dragged his eyes unwillingly from my face and turned towards the screen again.

The effect of this second attack was heightened because the lights went off suddenly and an incredible explosion of noise blasted my ear drums. It was the Gaumont News. The sound machine, like the heating system, had apparently been designed for something like the Albert Hall and for a moment I cowered back under the assault. As a voice bellowed details of fortnight-old events I closed my eyes and tried again to place the man in front of me.

I often had trouble identifying people outside their usual environment and had once discussed the problem with Siegfried.

He had been airy. 'There's an easy way, James. Just ask them how they spell their names. You'll have no trouble at all.'

I had tried this on one occasion and the farmer had looked at me strangely, replied 'S-M-I-T-H' and hurried away. So there seemed nothing to do now but sit sweating with my eyes on the disapproving back and search through my memory. When the news finished with a raucous burst of music I had got back about three weeks without result.

There was a blessed respite of a few seconds before the uproar broke out again. This was the main feature – the film about Scotland was on later – and was described outside as a tender love story. I can't remember the title but there was a lot of embracing which would have been all right except that every kiss was accompanied by a chorus of long-drawn sucking noises from the little boys downstairs. The less romantic blew raspberries.

And all the time it got hotter. I opened my jacket wide and unbuttoned my shirt collar but I was beginning to feel decidedly light-headed. The little man in front, still huddled in his heavy coat, seemed unperturbed. Twice the projector broke down and we stared for several minutes at a blank screen while a storm of whistling and stamping came up from the stalls.

Maggie Robinson, standing in the dim light by the curtain, still appeared to be fascinated by the sight of Helen and me. Whenever I looked up I found her eyes fixed upon us with a knowing leer. About halfway through the film, however, her concentration was disturbed by a commotion on the other side of the curtain and she was suddenly brushed aside as a large form burst through.

With a feeling of disbelief I recognized Gobber Newhouse. I had had previous experience of his disregard of the licensing laws and it was clear he had been at it again. He spent most afternoons in the back rooms of the local pubs and here he was, come to relax after a rough session.

He reeled up the aisle, turned, to my dismay, into our row, rested briefly on Helen's lap, trod on my toe and finally spread his enormous carcass over the seat on my left. Fortunately it was another courting seat with no central arm to get in his way but for all that he had great difficulty in finding a comfortable position. He heaved and squirmed about and the wheezing and snuffling and grunting in the darkness might have come from a pen of bacon pigs. But at last he found a spot and with a final cavernous belch composed himself for slumber.

The tender love story never did have much of a chance but Gobber sounded its death knell. With his snores reverberating in my ear and a dense pall of stale beer drifting over me I was unable to appreciate any of the delicate nuances.

It was a relief when the last close-up came to an end and the lights went up. I was a bit worried about Helen. I had noticed as the evening wore on that her lips had a tendency to twitch occasionally and now and then she drew her brows down in a deep frown. I wondered if she was upset. But Maggie appeared providentially with a tray round her neck and stood over us, still leering while I purchased two chocolate ices.

I had taken only one bite when I noticed a stirring under the overcoat in front of me. The little man was returning to the attack. The eyes staring from the grim mask were as chilling as ever.

'Ah knew,' he said. 'Right from start, that you were on the wrong track.'

'Is that so?'

'Aye, I've been among beasts for fifty years and they never go on like that when it's the stomach.'

'Don't they? You're probably right.'

The little man twisted higher in his seat and for a moment I thought he was going to climb over at me. He raised a forefinger. 'For one thing a beast wi' a bad stomach is allus hard in its muck.'

'I see.'

'And if you think back, this un's muck was soft, real soft.'

'Yes, yes, quite,' I said hastily, glancing across at Helen. This was great – just what I needed to complete the romantic atmosphere.

He sniffed and turned away and once again, as if the whole thing had been stage-managed, we were plunged into blackness and the noise blasted out again. I was lying back quivering when it came through to me that something was wrong. What was this strident Western music? Then the title flashed on the screen. Arizona Guns.

I turned to Helen in alarm. 'What's going on? This is supposed to be the Scottish film, isn't it? The one we came to see?'

'It's supposed to be.' Helen paused and looked at me with a half-smile. 'But I'm afraid it isn't going to be. The thing is they often change the supporting film without warning. Nobody seems to mind.'

I slumped wearily in my seat. Well I'd done it again. No dance at the Reniston, wrong picture tonight. I was a genius in my own way.

'I'm sorry,' I said. 'I hope you don't mind too much.'

She shook her head. 'Not a bit. Anyway, let's give this one a chance. It may be all right.'

But as the ancient horse opera crackled out its cliché-ridden message I gave up hope. This was going to be another of those evenings. I watched apathetically as the posse galloped for the fourth time past the same piece of rock and I was totally unprepared for the deafening fusilade of shots which rang out. It made me jump and it even roused Gobber from his sleep.

''Ellow! 'ellow! 'ellow!' he bawled jerking upright and thrashing around him with his arms. A backhander on the side of the head drove me violently against Helen's shoulder and I was beginning to apologize when I saw that her twitching and frowning had come on again. But this time it spread and her whole face seemed to break up. She began to laugh, silently and helplessly.

I had never seen a girl laugh like this. It was as though it was something she had wanted to do for a long time. She abandoned herself utterly to it, lying back with her head on the back of the seat, legs stretched out in front of her, arms dangling by her side. She took her time and waited until she had got it all out of her system before she turned to me.

She put her hand on my arm. 'Look,' she said faintly. 'Next time, why don't we just go for a walk?'

I settled down. Gobber was asleep again and his snores, louder than ever, competed with the bangs and howls from the screen. I still hadn't the slightest idea who that little man in front could be and I had the feeling he wasn't finished with me yet. The clock still stood at twenty-past four. Maggie was still staring at us and a steady trickle of sweat ran down my back.

The environment wasn't all I could have desired, but never mind. There was going to be a next time.

CHAPTER THIRTY-TWO

Siegfried had a habit of pulling at the lobe of his ear and staring blankly ahead when preoccupied. He was doing it now, his other hand, outstretched, crumbling a crust of bread on his plate.

I didn't usually pry into my boss's meditations and anyway, I wanted to be off on the morning round, but there was something portentous in his face which made me speak.

'What's the matter? Something on your mind?'

Siegfried turned his head slowly and his eyes glared sightlessly for a few moments until recognition dawned. He stopped his lobe-pulling, got to his feet, walked over to the window and looked out at the empty street.

'There is, James, there is indeed. In fact, I was just about to ask your advice. It's about this letter I got this morning.' He ransacked his pockets impatiently, pulling out handkerchiefs, thermometers, crumpled bank-notes, lists of calls, till he found a long blue envelope. 'Here, read it.'

I opened the envelope and quickly scanned the single sheet. I looked up, puzzled. 'Sorry, I don't get it. All it says here is that H. W. St J. Ransom, Maj Gen, would like the pleasure of your company at Brawton races on Saturday. No problem there, is there? You like racing.'

'Ah, but it's not so simple as that,' Siegfried said, starting again on the lobe. 'This is in the nature of a trial. General Ransom is one of the big boys in the North West Racing Circuit and he's bringing one of his pals along on Saturday to vet me. They're going to examine me for soundness.'

I must have looked alarmed because he grinned. 'Look, I'd better start at the beginning. And I'll cut it short. The officials of the North West Circuit are looking for a veterinary surgeon to supervise all meetings. You know the local man attends if there's a racecourse in his town and he is on call in case of injury to the horses, but this would be different. This supervisory vet would deal with cases of suspected doping and the like – in fact he'd have to be a bit of a specialist. Well I've had a whisper that they think I might be the man for the job and that's what Saturday's about. I know old Ransom but I haven't met his colleague. The idea is to have a day at the races with me and size me up.'

'If you got the job would it mean giving up general practice?' I asked. And a chill wind seemed to creep around me at the idea.

'No, no, but it would mean spending something like three days a week on racecourses and I'm wondering if that wouldn't be just a bit much.'

'Well, I don't know.' I finished my coffee and pushed back my chair. 'I'm not really the one to advise you on this. I haven't had a lot of experience with racehorses and I'm not interested in racing. You'll have to make up your own mind. But you've often talked of specializing in horse work and you love the atmosphere of a racecourse.'

'You're right there, James, I do. And there's no doubt the extra money would come in very useful. It's what every practice needs – a contract of some sort, a regular income from somewhere to make you less dependent on the farmers paying their bills.' He turned away from the window. 'Anyway, I'll go to Brawton races with them on Saturday and we'll see how it turns out. And you must come too.'

'Me! Why?'

'Well it says in the letter "and partner".'

'That means some woman. They'll have their wives with them, no doubt.'

'Doesn't matter what it means, James, you're coming with me. A day out and a bit of free food and booze will do you good. Tristan can hold the fort for a few hours.'

It was nearly noon on Saturday when I answered the door bell. As I walked along the passage it was easy to identify the people beyond the glass door.

General Ransom was short and square with a moustache of surprising blackness thrusting aggressively from his upper lip. Colonel Tremayne was tall, hawk-nosed and stooping but he shared with his companion the almost tangible aura of authority which comes from a lifetime of command. Two tweedy women stood behind them on the lower step.

I opened the door, feeling my shoulders squaring and my heels coming together under the battery of fierce, unsmiling glares.

'Mr Farnon!' barked the general. 'Expectin' us, I think.'

I retreated a pace and opened the door. 'Oh yes, certainly, please come in.'

The two women swept in first, Mrs Ransom as squat and chunky and even tougher-looking than her husband, then Mrs Tremayne, much younger and attractive in a hard-boiled fashion. All of them completely ignored me except the colonel who brought up the rear and fixed me for a moment with a fishy eye.

I had been instructed to dispense sherry, and once inside the sitting-room I began to pour from a decanter. I was half-way up the second glass when Siegfried walked in. I spilt some of the sherry. My boss had really spruced up for the occasion. His lean frame was draped in cavalry twill of flawless cut; the long, strong-boned face was freshly shaven, the small sandy moustache neatly clipped. He swept off a brand-new bowler as he came in and I put down my decanter and gazed at him with proprietary pride. Maybe there had been a few dukes or the odd earl in Siegfried's family tree but be that as it may, the two army men seemed in an instant to have become low bred and a trifle scruffy.

There was something almost ingratiating in the way the general went up to Seigfried. 'Farnon, me dear feller, how are you? Good to see you again. Let me introduce you to me wife, Mrs Tremayne, Colonel Tremayne.'

The colonel astonishingly dug up a twisted smile, but my main interest was in the reaction of the ladies. Mrs Ransom, looking up at Siegfried as he bent over her, just went to pieces. It was unbelievable that this formidable fortress should crumble at the first shot, but there it was; the tough lines melted from her face and she was left with a big sloppy smile looking like anybody's dear old mum.

Mrs Tremayne's response was different but no less dramatic. As the steady grey eyes swept her she seemed to wither and it was as if a spasm of exquisite pain twisted her cheeks. She controlled herself with an effort but looked after Siegfried with wistful hunger as he turned back to the men.

I began to slosh the sherry violently into the glasses. Damn it, there it was again. The same old thing. And yet he didn't do anything. Just looked at them. Hell, it wasn't fair.

Sherry over, we moved outside and installed ourselves in Siegfried's Rover on which an immaculate coach-building job had been done since the disaster of last summer. It was an impressive turnout. The car, after a morning's forced labour by Tristan with hose and leather, shone like a mirror. Siegfried, in the driver's seat, extended an elegant arm to his brother as we drove away. I couldn't help feeling that the only superfluous object was myself, squatting uncomfortably on a little let-down seat, facing the two army men who sat to attention in the back seat, their bowlers pointing rigidly to the front. Between them Mrs Tremayne stared wonderingly at the back of Siegfried's head.

We lunched on the course, Siegfried comfortably at home with the smoked salmon, the cold chicken and the champagne. There was no doubt he had scored a tremendous success during the meal, discussing racing knowledgeably with the men and dispensing charm equally to their wives. The tough Mrs Ransom positively simpered as he marked her card for her. It was quite certain that if the new appointment hung upon his behaviour today, a vote at this time would have seen him home and dry.

After lunch we went down to the paddock and had a look at the horses parading for the first race. I could see Siegfried expanding as he took in the scene; the jostling crowds, the shouting bookies, the beautiful animals pacing round, the jockeys, tiny, colourful, durable, chatting to the trainers out in the middle. He had got through enough champagne at lunch to sharpen his appreciation and he was the very picture of a man who just knew he was going to have a successful day.

Merryweather, the course vet, joined us to watch the first

race. Siegfried knew him slightly and they were chatting after the race when the 'vet wanted' sign went up. A man hurried up to Merryweather. 'That horse that slipped at the last bend is still down and doesn't look like getting up.'

The vet started for his car which was parked in readiness near the rails. He turned towards us 'You two want to come?' Siegfried looked inquiringly at his party and received gracious nods of assent. We hurried after our colleague.

Within seconds we were racing down the course towards the last bend. Merryweather, hanging on to the wheel as we sped over the grass, grunted half to himself: 'Hell, I hope this thing hasn't got a fracture – if there's one thing I mortally hate it's shooting horses.'

It didn't look good when we got to the spot. The sleek animal lay flat on its side showing no movement apart from the laboured rise and fall of its ribs. The jockey, blood streaming from a cut brow, knelt by its head. 'What do you think, sir? Has he broken a leg?'

'Let's have a look.' Merryweather began to palpate the extended limbs, running strong fingers over one bone then another, carefully flexing the joints of fetlock, knee, shoulder, hock. 'Nothing wrong there. Certainly no fracture.' Then he pointed suddenly at the head. 'Look at his eyes.'

We looked; they were glazed and there was a slight but unmistakable nystagmus.

'Concussion?' Siegfried said.

'That's it, he's just had a bang on the head.' Merryweather got off his knees, looking happier. 'Come on, we'll push him onto his chest. I think he ought to be able to get up with a bit of help.'

There were plenty of helpers from the crowd and the horse was rolled easily till he rested on his sternum, forelegs extended forward. After a couple of minutes in this position he struggled to his feet and stood swaying slightly. A stable lad walked him away.

Merryweather laughed. 'Well, that wasn't so bad. Good horse that. I think he'll be all right after a rest.'

Siegfried had started to reply when we heard a 'Psst, psst!' from beyond the rails. We looked up and saw a stout, red-faced figure gesturing at us eagerly. 'Hey! Hey!' it was saying. 'Come over here a minute.'

We went over. There was something about the face which Siegfried seemed to find intriguing. He looked closer at the grinning, pudgy features, the locks of oily black hair falling over the brow and cried out in delight.

'God help us! Stewie Brannon! Here, James, come and meet another colleague – we came through college together.'

Siegfried had told me a lot about Stewie Brannon. So much, in fact, that I seemed to be shaking hands with an old, well-remembered friend. Sometimes, when the mood was on us, Siegfried and I would sit up nearly till dawn over a bottle in the big room at Skeldale House chewing over old times and recalling the colourful characters we had known. I remembered he had told me he had overtaken Stewie about halfway through the course and had qualified while Stewie was still battling in his third year. Siegfried had described him as totally unambitious, averse to study, disinclined to wash or shave; in fact, his idea of the young man least likely to succeed. But there had been something touching about him; the ingenuousness of a child, a huge, all-embracing affection for his fellow humans, an impregnable cheerfulness.

Siegfried called over to Merryweather. 'Will you give my apologies to my friends when you go back? There's a chap here I have to see – I'll only be a few minutes.'

Merryweather waved, got into his car and drove back up the course as we ducked under the rails.

Siegfried seized the bulky figure by the arm. 'Come on, Stewie, where can we get a drink?'

CHAPTER THIRTY-THREE

We went into a long, low bar under the stand and I experienced a slight shock of surprise. This was the four and sixpenny end and the amenities were rather different from the paddock. The eating and drinking was done mainly in the vertical position and the cuisine seemed to consist largely of pies and sausage rolls.

Siegfried fought his way to the bar and collected three whiskies. We sat down at one of the few available tables – an unstable, metal-topped structure. At the next table a sharp faced character studied the *Pink 'Un* while he took great swigs at a pint and tore savagely at a pork pie.

'Now, my lad,' Siegfried said. 'What have you been doing for the past six years?'

'Well, let's see,' said Stewie, absently downing his whisky at a gulp. 'I got into finals shortly after you left and I didn't do so bad at all, really. Pipped them both first go, then I had a bit of bother with surgery a couple of times, but I was launched on the unsuspecting animal population four years ago. I've been around quite a lot since then. North, South, even six months in Ireland. I've been trying to find a place with a living wage. This three or four quid a week lark isn't much cop when you have a family to keep.'

'Family? You're married then?'

'Not half. You remember little Meg Hamilton – I used to bring her to the college dances. We got married when I got into final year. We've got five kids now and another on the way.'

Siegfried choked on his whisky. 'Five kids! For God's sake, Stewie!'

'Ah, it's wonderful really, Siegfried. You probably wonder how we manage to exist. Well I couldn't tell you. I don't know myself. But we've kept one jump ahead of ruin and we've been happy, too. I think we're going to be OK now. I stuck up my plate in Hensfield a few months ago and I'm doing all right. Been able to clear the housekeeping and that's all that matters.'

'Hensfield, eh?' Siegfried said. I pictured the grim West Riding town. A wilderness of decaying brick bristling with factory chimneys. It was the other Yorkshire. 'Mainly small animal, I suppose?'

'Oh yes. I earn my daily bread almost entirely by separating the local tom cats from their knackers. Thanks to me, the feline females of Hensfield can walk the streets unmolested.'

Siegfried laughed and caught the only waitress in the place lightly by the arm as she hurried by. She whipped round with a frown and an angry word but took another look and smiled. 'Yes, sir?'

Siegfried looked into her face seriously for a few moments, still holding her arm. Then he spoke quietly. 'I wonder if you'd be kind enough to bring us three large whiskies and keep repeating the order whenever you see our glasses are empty. Would you be able to do that?'

'Certainly, sir, of course.' The waitress was over forty but she was blushing like a young girl.

Stewie's chins quivered with silent laughter. 'You old bugger, Farnon. It does me good to see you haven't changed.'

'Really? Well that's rather nice, isn't it?'

'And the funny thing is I don't think you really try.'

'Try? Try what?'

'Ah, nothing. Forget it – here's our whisky.'

As the drinks kept coming they talked and talked. I didn't butt in – I sat listening, wrapped in a pleasant euphoria and pushing every other glassful unobtrusively round to Stewie who put it out of sight with a careless jerk of the wrist.

As Siegfried sketched out his own progress, I was struck by the big man's total absence of envy. He was delighted to hear about the rising practice, the pleasant house, the assistant. Siegfried had described him as plump in the old days but he was fat now, despite his hard times. And I had heard about that overcoat; it was the 'navy nap' which had been his only protection through the years at college. It couldn't have looked so good then, but it was a sad thing now, the seams strained to bursting by the bulging flesh.

'Look, Stewie.' Siegfried fumbled uncomfortably with his glass. 'I'm sure you're going to do well at Hensfield but if by some mischance things got a bit rough, I hope you wouldn't hesitate to turn to me. I'm not so far off in Darrowby, you know. In fact.' He paused and swallowed. 'Are you all right now? If a few quid would help, I've got 'em here.'

Stewie tossed back what must have been the tenth double whisky and gazed at his old friend with gentle benevolence. 'You're a kind old bugger, Siegfried, but no thanks. As I said we're clearing the housekeeping and we'll be OK. But I appreciate it – you always were kind. A strange old bugger, but kind.'

'Strange?' Siegfried was interested.

'No, not strange. Wrong word. Different. That's it, you were as different as hell.'

'Different?' queried Siegfried, swallowing his whisky as if it had stopped tasting of anything a long time ago. 'I'm sure you're wrong there, Stewie.'

'Don't worry your head about it,' Stewie said, and reached across the table to thump his friend on the shoulder. But his judgement was way out and instead he swept Siegfried's bowler from his head. It rolled to the feet of the man at the next table.

During the conversation I had been aware of this gentleman rushing out and trailing slowly back to resume his study of the *Pink 'Un* and renew his attack on the food and drink. The man looked down at the hat. His face was a picture of misery and frustration born of too much beer, semi-masticated pork pies and unwise investment. Convulsively he lashed out with a foot at the bowler and looked better immediately.

The hat, deeply dented, soared back to Siegfried who caught it and replaced it on his head with unruffled aplomb. He didn't seem in the least annoyed; apparently considered the man's reaction perfectly normal.

We all stood up and I was mildly surprised by a slight swaying and blurring of my surroundings. When things came to rest I had another surprise; the big bar was nearly empty. The beer machines were hidden by white cloths. The barmaids were collecting the empty glasses.

'Stewie,' Siegfried said. 'The meeting's over. Do you realize we've been nattering here for over two hours?'

'And very nice too. Far better than giving the hard-earned coppers to the bookies.' As Stewie rose to his feet he clutched at the table and stood blinking for a few seconds.

'There's one thing, though,' Siegfried said. 'My friends. I came here with a party and they must be wondering where I've got to. Tell you what, come and meet them. They'll understand when they realize we haven't seen each other for years.'

We worked our way round to the paddock. No sign of the general and company. We finally found them in the car park grouped unsmilingly around the Rover. Most of the other cars had gone. Siegfried strode up confidently, his dented bowler cocked at a jaunty angle.

'I'm sorry to have left you but a rather wonderful thing happened back there. I would like to present Mr Stewart Brannon, a professional colleague and a very dear friend.'

Four blank stares turned on Stewie. His big, meaty face was redder than ever and he smiled sweetly through a faint dew of perspiration. I noticed that he had made a lopsided job of buttoning the navy nap overcoat; there was a spare button hole at the top and a lack of alignment at the bottom. It made the straining, tortured garment look even more grotesque.

The general nodded curtly, the colonel appeared to be grinding his teeth, the ladies froze visibly and looked away.

'Yes, yes, quite,' grunted the general. 'But we've been waitin' here some time and we want to be gettin' home.' He stuck out his jaw and his moustache bristled.

Siegfried waved a hand. 'Certainly, certainly, by all means. We'll leave right away.' He turned to Stewie. 'Well, goodbye for now, my lad. We'll get together again soon. I'll ring you.'

He began to feel through his pockets for his ignition key. He started quite slowly but gradually stepped up his pace. After he had explored the pockets about five times he stopped, closed his eyes and appeared to give himself over to intense thought. Then, as though he had decided to do the thing systematically, he commenced to lay out the contents of his pockets one by one, using the car bonnet as a table, and as the pile grew so did my conviction that doom was very near.

It wasn't just the key that worried me. Siegfried had consumed a lot more whisky than I had and with its usual delayed action it had begun to creep up on him. He was swaying slightly, his dented bowler had slid forward over one eyebrow and he kept dropping things as he pulled them from his pocket and examined them owlishly.

A man with a long brush and a handcart was walking slowly across the car park when Siegfried grabbed his arm. 'Look, I want you to do something for me. Here's five bob.'

'Right, mister.' The man pocketed the money. 'What d'you want me to do?'

'Find my car key.'

The man began to peer round Siegfried's feet. 'I'll do me best. Dropped it round 'ere, did you?'

'No, no. I've no idea where I dropped it.' Siegfried waved vaguely. 'It's somewhere on the course.'

The man looked blank for a moment then he gazed out over the acres of littered ground, the carpet of discarded race cards, torn up tickets. He turned back to Siegfried and giggled suddenly then he walked away, still giggling.

I stole a glance at our companions. They had watched the search in stony silence and none of them seemed to be amused. The general was the first to explode.

'Great heavens, Farnon, have you got the blasted key or haven't you? If the damn thing's lost, then we'd better make other arrangements. Can't keep the ladies standing around here.'

A gentle cough sounded in the background. Stewie was still there. He shambled forward and whispered in his friend's ear and after a moment Siegfried wrung his hand fervently.

'By God, Stewie, that's kind of you! You've saved the situation.' He turned back to the party. 'There's nothing to worry about – Mr Brannon has kindly offered to provide us with transport. He's gone to get his car from the other park.' He pointed triumphantly at the shiny back of the bulging navy overcoat navigating unsteadily through the gate.

Siegfried did his best to keep a conversation going but it was hard slogging. Nobody replied to any of his light sallies and he stopped abruptly when he saw a look of rage and disbelief spread over the general's face. Stewie had come back.

The car was a tiny Austin Seven dwarfed even further by the massive form in the driver's seat. I judged from the rusted maroon paintwork and cracked windows that it must be one of the very earliest models, a 'tourer' whose hood had long since disintegrated and been replaced by a home-made canvas cover fastened to the twisted struts by innumerable loops of string.

Stewie struggled out, dragged open the passenger door and inclined his head with modest pride. He motioned towards a pile of sacks which lay on the bare boards where the passenger seat should have been; there were no seats in the back either, only a couple of rough wooden boxes bearing coloured labels with the legend 'Finest American Apples'. From the boxes peeped a jumble of medicine bottles, stethoscopes, powders, syringe cases.

'I thought,' said Stewie. 'If we put the sacks on top of the boxes . . .'

The general didn't let him finish. 'Dammit, is this supposed to be a joke?' His face was brick red and the veins on his neck were swelling dangerously. 'Are you tryin' to insult me friend and these ladies? You want horsewhippin' for this afternoon's work, Farnon. That's what you want – horsewhippin'!'

He was halted by a sudden roar from the Rover's engine. The colonel, a man of resource as befitted his rank, had shorted the ignition. Fortunately the doors were not locked.

The ladies took their places in the back with the colonel and I slunk miserably on to my little seat. The general had regained control of himself. 'Get in! I'll drive!' he barked at Siegfried as though addressing an erring lance corporal.

But Siegfried held up a restraining hand. 'Just one moment,' he slurred. 'The windscreen is very dirty. I'll give it a rub for you.'

The ladies watched him silently as he weaved round to the back of the car and began to rummage in the boot. The love light had died from their eyes. I don't know why he took the trouble; possibly it was because, through the whisky mists, he felt he must re-establish himself as a competent and helpful member of the party.

But the effort fell flat; the effect was entirely spoiled. He was polishing the glass with a dead hen.

It was a couple of weeks later, again at the breakfast table that Siegfried, reading the morning paper with his third cup of coffee, called out to me.

'Ah, I see Herbert Jarvis MRCVS, one time Captain, RAVC, has been appointed to the North West Circuit as supervisory veterinary surgeon. I know Jarvis. Nice chap. Just the man for the job.'

I looked across at my boss for some sign of disappointment or regret. I saw none.

Siegfried put down his cup, wiped his lips on his napkin and sighed contentedly. 'You know, James, everything happens for the best. Old Stewie was sent by providence or heaven or anything you like. I was never meant to get that job and I'd have been miserable as hell if I had got it. Come on, lad, let's get off into those hills.'

Let Sleeping Vets Lie

To my Wife
with love

CHAPTER ONE

As the faint rumbling growl rolled up from the rib cage into the ear pieces of my stethoscope the realization burst upon me with uncomfortable clarity that this was probably the biggest dog I had ever seen. In my limited past experience some Irish Wolfhounds had undoubtedly been taller and a certain number of Bull Mastiffs had possibly been broader, but for sheer gross poundage this one had it. His name was Clancy.

It was a good name for an Irishman's dog and Joe Mulligan was very Irish despite his many years in Yorkshire. Joe had brought him into the afternoon surgery and as the huge hairy form ambled along, almost filling the passage, I was reminded of the times I had seen him out in the fields around Darrowby enduring the frisking attentions of smaller animals with massive benignity. He looked like a nice friendly dog.

But now there was this ominous sound echoing round the great thorax like a distant drum roll in a subterranean cavern, and as the chest piece of the stethoscope bumped along the ribs the sound swelled in volume and the lips fluttered over the enormous teeth as though a gentle breeze had stirred them. It was then that I became aware not only that Clancy was very big indeed but that my position, kneeling on the floor with my right ear a few inches from his mouth, was infinitely vulnerable.

I got to my feet and as I dropped the stethoscope into my pocket the dog gave me a cold look – a sideways glance without moving his head; and there was a chilling menace in his very immobility. I didn't mind my patients snapping at me but this one, I felt sure, wouldn't snap. If he started something it would be on a spectacular scale.

I stepped back a pace. 'Now what did you say his symptoms were, Mr Mulligan?'

'Phwaat's that?' Joe cupped his ear with his hand. I took a deep breath. 'What's the trouble with him?' I shouted.

The old man looked at me with total incomprehension from beneath the straightly adjusted cloth cap. He fingered the muffler knotted immediately over his larynx and the pipe which grew from the dead centre of his mouth puffed blue wisps of puzzlement.

Then, remembering something of Clancy's past history, I moved close to Mr Mulligan and bawled with all my power into his face. 'Is he vomiting?'

The response was immediate. Joe smiled in great relief and removed his pipe. 'Oh aye, he's womitin' sorr. He's womitin' bad.' Clearly he was on familiar ground.

Over the years Clancy's treatment had all been at long range. My young boss, Siegfried Farnon, had told me on the first day I had arrived in Darrowby two years ago that there was nothing wrong with the dog, which he had described as a cross between an Airedale and a donkey, but his penchant for eating every bit of rubbish in his path had the inevitable result. A large bottle of bismuth, mag carb mixture had been dispensed at regular intervals. He had also told me that Clancy, when bored, used occasionally to throw Joe to the ground and worry him like a rat just for a bit of light relief. But his master still adored him.

Prickings of conscience told me I should carry out a full examination. Take his temperature, for instance. All I had to do was to grab hold of that tail, lift it and push a thermometer into his rectum. The dog turned his head and met my eye with a blank stare; again I heard the low booming drum roll and the upper lip lifted a fraction to show a quick gleam of white.

'Yes, yes, right, Mr Mulligan,' I said briskly. 'I'll get you a bottle of the usual.'

In the dispensary, under the rows of bottles with their Latin names and glass stoppers I shook up the mixture in a ten ounce bottle, corked it, stuck on a label and wrote the directions. Joe seemed well satisfied as he pocketed the familiar white medicine but as he turned to go my conscience smote me again. The dog did look perfectly fit but maybe he ought to be seen again.

'Bring him back again on Thursday afternoon at two o'clock,' I yelled into the old man's ear. 'And please come on time if you can. You were a bit late today.'

I watched Mr Mulligan going down the street, preceded by his pipe from which regular puffs rose upwards as though from a departing railway engine. Behind him ambled Clancy, a picture of massive calm. With his all-over covering of tight brown curls he did indeed look like a gigantic Airedale.

Thursday afternoon, I ruminated. That was my half day and at two o'clock I'd probably be watching the afternoon cinema show in Brawton.

The following Friday morning Siegfried was sitting behind his desk, working out the morning rounds. He scribbled a list of visits on a pad, tore out the sheet and handed it to me.

'Here you are, James, I think that'll just about keep you out of mischief till lunch time.' Then something in the previous day's entries caught his eye and he turned to his younger brother who was at his morning task of stoking the fire.

'Tristan, I see Joe Mulligan was in yesterday afternoon with his dog and you saw it. What did you make of it?'

Tristan put down his bucket. 'Oh, I gave him some of the bismuth mixture.'

'Yes, but what did your examination of the patient disclose?'

'Well now, let's see.' Tristan rubbed his chin. 'He looked pretty lively, really.'

'Is that all?'

'Yes . . . yes . . . I think so.'

Siegfried turned back to me. 'And how about you, James? You saw the dog the day before. What were your findings?'

'Well it was a bit difficult,' I said. 'That dog's as big as an elephant and there's something creepy about him. He seemed to me to be just waiting his chance and there was only old Joe to hold him. I'm afraid I wasn't able to make a close examination but I must say I thought the same as Tristan – he did look pretty lively.'

Siegfried put down his pen wearily. On the previous night, fate had dealt him one of the shattering blows which it occasionally reserves for vets – a call at each end of his sleeping time. He had been dragged from his bed at 1 AM and again at 6 AM and the fires of his personality were temporarily damped.

He passed a hand across his eyes. 'Well God help us. You, James, a veterinary surgeon of two years' experience and you, Tristan, a final year student can't come up with anything better between you than the phrase "pretty lively". It's a bloody poor thing! Hardly a worthy description of clinical findings is it? When an animal comes in here I expect you to record pulse, temperature and respiratory rate. To auscultate the chest and thoroughly palpate the abdomen. To open his mouth and examine teeth, gums and pharynx. To check the condition of the skin. To catheterize him and examine the urine if necessary.'

'Right,' I said.

'OK,' said Tristan.

My employer rose from his seat. 'Have you fixed another appointment?'

'I have, yes.' Tristan drew his packet of Woodbines from his pocket. 'For Monday. And since Mr Mulligan's always late for the surgery I said we'd visit the dog at his home in the evening.'

'I see.' Siegfried made a note on the pad, then he looked up suddenly. 'That's when you and James are going to the young farmers' meeting, isn't it?'

The young man drew on his cigarette. 'That's right. Good for the practice for us to mix with the young clients.'

'Very well,' Siegfried said as he walked to the door. 'I'll see the dog myself.'

On the following Tuesday I was fairly confident that Siegfried would have something to say about Mulligan's dog, if only to point out the benefits of a thorough clinical examination. But he was silent on the subject.

It happened that I came upon old Joe in the market place sauntering over the cobbles with Clancy inevitably trotting at his heels.

I went up to him and shouted in his ear. 'How's your dog?'

Mr Mulligan removed his pipe and smiled with slow benevolence. 'Oh foine, sorr, foine. Still vomitin' a bit, but not bad.'

'Mr Farnon fixed him up, then?'

'Aye, gave him some more of the white medicine. It's wonderful stuff, sorr, wonderful stuff.'

'Good, good,' I said. 'He didn't find anything else when he examined him?'

Joe took another suck at his pipe. 'No he didn't now, he didn't. He's a clever man, Mr Farnon – I've niver seen a man work as fast, no I haven't.'

'What do you mean?'

'Well now he saw all he wanted in tree seconds, so he did.'

I was mystified. 'Three seconds?'

'Yis,' said Mr Mulligan firmly. 'Not a moment more.'

'Amazing. What happened?'

Joe tapped out his pipe on his heel and without haste took out a knife and began to carve a refill from an evil looking coil of black twist. 'Well now I'll tell ye. Mr Farnon is a man who moves awful sudden, and that night he banged on our front door and jumped into the room.' (I knew those cottages. There was no hall or lobby – you walked straight from the street into the living-room.) 'And as he came in he was pullin' his thermometer out of its case. Well now Clancy was lyin' by the fire and he rose up in a flash and he gave a bit of a wuff, so he did.'

'A bit of a wuff, eh?' I could imagine the hairy monster leaping up and baying into Siegfried's face. I could see the gaping jaws, the gleaming teeth.

'Aye, just a bit of a wuff. Well, Mr Farnon just put the

thermometer straight back in its case turned round and went out the door.'

'Didn't he say anything?' I asked.

'No, divil a word. Just turned about like a soldier and marched out the door, so he did.'

It sounded authentic. Siegfried was a man of instant decisions. I put my hand out to pat Clancy but something in his eyes made me change my mind.

'Well, I'm glad he's better,' I shouted.

The old man ignited his pipe with an ancient brass lighter, puffed a cloud of choking blue smoke into my face and tapped a little metal lid on to the bowl. 'Aye, Mr Farnon sent round a big bottle of the white stuff and it's done 'im good. Mind yous,' he gave a beatific smile, 'Clancy's allus been one for the womitin', so he has.'

Nothing more was said about the big dog for over a week, but Siegfried's professional conscience must have been niggling at him because he came into the dispensary one afternoon when Tristan and I were busy at the tasks which have passed into history – making up fever drinks, stomach powders, boric acid pessaries. He was elaborately casual.

'Oh by the way, I dropped a note to Joe Mulligan. I'm not entirely convinced that we have adequately explored the causes of his dog's symptoms. This womiting . . . er, vomiting is almost certainly due to depraved appetite but I just want to make sure. So I have asked him to bring him round tomorrow afternoon between two and two thirty when we'll all be here.'

No cries of joy greeted his statement, so he continued. 'I suppose you could say that this dog is to some degree a difficult animal and I think we should plan accordingly.' He turned to me. 'James, when he arrives you get hold of his back end, will you?'

'Right,' I replied without enthusiasm.

He faced his brother. 'And you, Tristan, can deal with the head. OK?'

'Fine, fine,' the young man muttered, his face expressionless.

His brother continued. 'I suggest you get a good grip with your arms round his neck and I'll be ready to give him a shot of sedative.'

'Splendid, splendid,' said Tristan.

'Ah well, that's capital.' My employer rubbed his hands together. 'Once I get the dope into him the rest will be easy. I do like to satisfy my mind about these things.'

It was a typical Dales practice at Darrowby; mainly large animal and we didn't have packed waiting rooms at surgery times. But on the following afternoon we had nobody in at all, and it added to the tension of waiting. The three of us mooched about the office, making aimless conversation, glancing with studied carelessness into the front street, whistling little tunes to ourselves. By two twenty-five we had all fallen silent. Over the next five minutes we consulted our watches about every thirty seconds, then at exactly two thirty Siegfried spoke up.

'This is no damn good. I told Joe he had to be here before half past but he's taken not a bit of notice. He's always late and there doesn't seem to be any way to get him here on time.' He took a last look out of the window at the empty street. 'Right we're not waiting any longer. You and I, James, have got that colt to cut and you, Tristan, have to see that beast of Wilson's. So let's be off.'

Up till then, Laurel and Hardy were the only people I had ever seen getting jammed together in doorways but there was a moment when the three of us gave a passable imitation of the famous comics as we all fought our way into the passage at the same time. Within seconds we were in the street and Tristan was roaring off in a cloud of exhaust smoke. My employer and I proceeded almost as rapidly in the opposite direction.

At the end of Trengate we turned into the market place and I looked around in vain for signs of Mr Mulligan. It wasn't until we had reached the outskirts of the town that we saw him. He had just left his house and was pacing along under a moving pall of blue smoke with Clancy as always bringing up the rear.

'There he is!' Siegfried exclaimed. 'Would you believe it? At the rate he's going he'll get to the surgery around three o'clock. Well we won't be there and it's his own fault.' He looked at the great curly-coated animal tripping along, a picture of health and energy. 'Well, I suppose we'd have been wasting our time examining that dog in any case. There's nothing really wrong with him.'

For a moment he paused, lost in thought, then he turned to me.

'He does look pretty lively, doesn't he?'

CHAPTER TWO

This was my second spring in the Dales but it was like the one before – and all the springs after. The kind of spring, that is, that a country vet knows; the din of the lambing pens, the bass rumble of the ewes and the high, insistent bawling of the lambs. This, for me, has always heralded the end of winter and the beginning of something new. This and the piercing Yorkshire wind and the hard, bright sunshine flooding the bare hillsides.

At the top of the grassy slope the pens, built of straw bales, formed a long row of square cubicles each holding a ewe with her lambs and I could see Rob Benson coming round the far end carrying two feeding buckets. Rob was hard at it; at this time of the year he didn't go to bed for about six weeks; he would maybe take off his boots and doze by the kitchen fire at night but he was his own shepherd and never very far from the scene of action.

'Ah've got a couple of cases for you today, Jim.' His face, cracked and purpled by the weather, broke into a grin, 'It's not really you ah need, it's that little lady's hand of yours and right sharpish, too.'

He led the way to a bigger enclosure, holding several

sheep. There was a scurry as we went in but he caught expertly at the fleece of a darting ewe. 'This is the first one. You can see we haven't a deal o' time.'

I lifted the woolly tail and gasped. The lamb's head was protruding from the vagina, the lips of the vulva clamped tightly behind the ears, and it had swollen enormously to more than twice its size. The eyes were mere puffed slits in the great oedematous ball and the tongue, blue and engorged, lolled from the mouth.

'Well I've seen a few big heads, Rob, but I think this takes the prize.'

'Aye, the little beggar came with his legs back. Just beat me to it. Ah was only away for an hour but he was up like a football. By hell it doesn't take long. I know he wants his legs bringin' round but what can I do with bloody great mitts like mine.' He held out his huge hands, rough and swollen with the years of work.

While he spoke I was stripping off my jacket and as I rolled my shirt sleeves high the wind struck like a knife at my shrinking flesh. I soaped my fingers quickly and began to feel for a space round the lamb's neck. For a moment the little eyes opened and regarded me disconsolately.

'He's alive, anyway,' I said. 'But he must feel terrible and he can't do a thing about it.'

Easing my way round, I found a space down by the throat where I thought I might get through. This was where my 'lady's hand' came in useful and I blessed it every spring; I could work inside the ewes with the minimum of discomfort to them and this was all-important because sheep, despite their outdoor hardiness, just won't stand rough treatment.

With the utmost care I inched my way along the curly wool of the neck to the shoulder. Another push forward and I was able to hook a finger round the leg and draw it forward until I could feel the flexure of the knee; a little more twiddling and I had hold of the tiny cloven foot and drew it gently out into the light of day.

Well that was half the job done. I got up from the sack where I was kneeling and went over to the bucket of warm water. For the other leg I'd use my left hand and I began to soap it thoroughly while one of the ewes, marshalling her lambs around her, glared at me indignantly and gave a warning stamp of her foot.

Turning, I kneeled again and began the same procedure and, as I once more groped forward, a tiny lamb dodged under my arm and began to suck at my patient's udder. He was clearly enjoying it, too, if the little tail, twirling inches from my face, meant anything.

'Where did this bloke come from?' I asked, still feeling round.

The farmer smiled. 'Oh that's Herbert. Poor little youth's mother won't have 'im at any price. Took a spite at him at birth though she thinks world of her other lamb.'

'Do you feed him, then?'

'Nay, I was going to put him with the pet lambs but I saw he was fendin' for himself. He pops from one ewe to t'other and gets a quick drink whenever he gets chance. I've never seen owt like it.'

'Only a week old and an independent spirit, eh?'

'That's about the size of it, Jim. I notice 'is belly's full every mornin' so I reckon his ma must let him have a do during the night. She can't see him in the dark – it must be the look of him she can't stand.'

I watched the little creature for a moment. To me he seemed as full of knock-kneed charm as any of the others. Sheep were funny things.

I soon had the other leg out and once that obstruction was removed the lamb followed easily. He was a grotesque sight lying on the strawed grass, his enormous head dwarfing his body, but his ribs were heaving reassuringly and I knew the head would shrink back to normal as quickly as it had expanded. I had another search round inside the ewe but the uterus was empty.

'There's no more, Rob,' I said.

The farmer grunted. 'Aye, I thowt so, just a big single 'un. They're the ones that cause the trouble.'

Drying my arms, I watched Herbert. He had left my patient when she moved round to lick her lamb and he was moving speculatively among the other ewes. Some of them warned him off with a shake of the head but eventually he managed to sneak up on a big, wide-bodied sheep and pushed his head underneath her. Immediately she swung round and with a fierce upward butt of her hard skull she sent the little animal flying high in the air in a whirl of flailing legs. He landed with a thud on his back and as I hurried towards him he leaped to his feet and trotted away.

'Awd bitch!' shouted the farmer and as I turned to him in some concern he shrugged. 'I know, poor little sod, it's rough, but I've got a feelin' he wants it this way rather than being in the pen with the pet lambs. Look at 'im now.'

Herbert, quite unabashed, was approaching another ewe and as she bent over her feeding trough he nipped underneath her and his tail went into action again. There was no doubt about it – that lamb had guts.

'Rob,' I said as he caught my second patient, 'why do you call him Herbert?'

'Well that's my youngest lad's name and that lamb's just like 'im the way he puts his head down and gets stuck in, fearless like.'

I put my hand into the second ewe. Here was a glorious mix up of three lambs; little heads, legs, a tail, all fighting their way towards the outside world and effectively stopping each other from moving an inch.

'She's been hanging about all morning and painin',' Rob said. 'I knew summat was wrong.'

Moving a hand carefully around the uterus I began the fascinating business of sorting out the tangle which is just about my favourite job in practice. I had to bring a head and two legs up together in order to deliver a lamb; but they had to belong to the same lamb or I was in trouble. It was a matter of tracing each leg back to see if it was hind or fore, to find if it joined the shoulder or disappeared into the depths.

After a few minutes I had a lamb assembled inside with his proper appendages but as I drew the legs into view the neck telescoped and the head slipped back; there was barely room for it to come through the pelvic bones along with the shoulders and I had to coax it through with a finger in the eye socket. This was groaningly painful as the bones squeezed my hand but only for a few seconds because the ewe gave a final strain and the little nose was visible. After that it was easy and I had him on the grass within seconds. The little creature gave a convulsive shake of his head and the farmer wiped him down quickly with straw before pushing him to his mother's head.

The ewe bent over him and began to lick his face and neck with little quick darts of her tongue; and she gave the deep chuckle of satisfaction that you hear from a sheep only at this time. The chuckling continued as I produced another pair of lambs from inside her, one of them hind end first, and, towelling my arms again, I watched her nosing round her triplets delightedly.

Soon they began to answer her with wavering high-pitched cries and as I drew my coat thankfully over my cold-reddened arms, lamb number one began to struggle to his knees; he couldn't quite make it to his feet and kept toppling on to his face but he knew where he was going, all right; he was headed for that udder with a singleness of purpose which would soon be satisfied.

Despite the wind cutting over the straw bales into my face I found myself grinning down at the scene; this was always the best part, the wonder that was always fresh, the miracle you couldn't explain.

I heard from Rob Benson again a few days later. It was a Sunday afternoon and his voice was strained, almost panic-stricken.

'Jim, I've had a dog in among me in-lamb ewes. There was some folk up here with a car about dinner time and my neighbour said they had an Alsatian and it was chasing the sheep all over the field. There's a hell of a mess – I tell you I'm frightened to look.'

'I'm on my way.' I dropped the receiver and hurried out to the car. I had a sinking dread of what would be waiting for me; the helpless animals lying with their throats torn, the terrifying lacerations of limbs and abdomen. I had seen it all before. The ones which didn't have to be slaughtered would need stitching and on the way I made a mental check of the stock of suture silk in the boot.

The in-lamb ewes were in a field by the roadside and my heart gave a quick thump as I looked over the wall; arms resting on the rough loose stones I gazed with sick dismay across the pasture. This was worse than I had feared. The long slope of turf was dotted with prostrate sheep – there must have been about fifty of them, motionless woolly mounds scattered at intervals on the green.

Rob was standing just inside the gate. He hardly looked at me. Just gestured with his head.

'Tell me what you think. I daren't go in there.'

I left him and began to walk among the stricken creatures, rolling them over, lifting their legs, parting the fleece of their necks to examine them. Some were completely unconscious, others comatose; none of them could stand up. But as I worked my way up the field I felt a growing bewilderment. Finally I called back to the farmer.

'Rob, come over here. There's something very strange.'

'Look,' I said as the farmer approached hesitantly. 'There's not a drop of blood nor a wound anywhere and yet all the sheep are flat out. I can't understand it.'

Rob went over and gently raised a lolling head. 'Aye, you're right. What the hell's done it, then?'

At that moment I couldn't answer him, but a little bell was tinkling far away in the back of my mind. There was something familiar about that ewe the farmer had just handled. She was one of the few able to support herself on her chest and she was lying there, blank-eyed, oblivious of everything; but ... that drunken nodding of the head, that watery nasal discharge ... I had seen it before. I knelt down and as I put my face close to hers I heard a faint bubbling – almost a rattling – in her breathing. I knew then.

'It's calcium deficiency,' I cried and began to gallop down the slope towards the car.

Rob trotted alongside me. 'But what the 'ell? They get that after lambin', don't they?'

'Yes, usually,' I puffed. 'But sudden exertion and stress can bring it on.'

'Well ah never knew that,' panted Rob. 'How does it happen?'

I saved my breath. I wasn't going to start an exposition on the effects of sudden derangement of the parathyroid. I was more concerned with wondering if I had enough calcium in the boot for fifty ewes. It was reassuring to see the long row of round tin caps peeping from their cardboard box; I must have filled up recently.

I injected the first ewe in the vein just to check my diagnosis – calcium works as quickly as that in sheep – and felt a quiet elation as the unconscious animal began to blink and tremble, then tried to struggle on to its chest.

'We'll inject the others under the skin,' I said. 'It'll save time.'

I began to work my way up the field. Rob pulled forward the fore leg of each sheep so that I could insert the needle under the convenient patch of unwoolled skin just behind the elbow; and by the time I was halfway up the slope the ones at the bottom were walking about and getting their heads into the food troughs and hay racks.

It was one of the most satisfying experiences of my working life. Not clever, but a magical transfiguration; from despair to hope, from death to life within minutes.

I was throwing the empty bottles into the boot when Rob spoke. He was looking wonderingly up at the last of the ewes getting to its feet at the far end of the field.

'Well, Jim, I'll tell you. I've never seen owt like that afore. But there's one thing bothers me.' He turned to me and his weathered features screwed up in puzzlement. 'Ah can understand how gettin' chased by a dog could affect some of them ewes, but why should the whole bloody lot go down?'

'Rob,' I said. 'I don't know.'

And, thirty years later, I still wonder. I still don't know why the whole bloody lot went down.

I thought Rob had enough to worry about at the time, so I

didn't point out to him that other complications could be expected after the Alsatian episode. I wasn't surprised when I had a call to the Benson farm within days.

I met him again on the hillside with the same wind whipping over the straw bale pens. The lambs had been arriving in a torrent and the noise was louder than ever. He led me to my patient.

'There's one with a bellyful of dead lambs, I reckon,' he said, pointing to a ewe with her head drooping, ribs heaving. She stood quite motionless and made no attempt to move away when I went up to her; this one was really sick and as the stink of decomposition came up to me I knew the farmer's diagnosis was right.

'Well I suppose it had to happen to one at least after that chasing round,' I said. 'Let's see what we can do, anyway.'

This kind of lambing is without charm but it has to be done to save the ewe. The lambs were putrid and distended with gas and I used a sharp scalpel to skin the legs to the shoulders so that I could remove them and deliver the little bodies with the least discomfort to the mother. When I had finished, the ewe's head was almost touching the ground, she was panting rapidly and grating her teeth. I had nothing to offer her – no wriggling new creature for her to lick and revive her interest in life. What she needed was an injection of penicillin, but this was 1939 and the antibiotics were still a little way round the corner.

'Well I wouldn't give much for her,' Rob grunted. 'Is there owt more you can do?'

'Oh, I'll put some pessaries in her and give her an injection, but what she needs most is a lamb to look after. You know as well as I do that ewes in this condition usually give up if they've nothing to occupy them. You haven't a spare lamb to put on her, have you?'

'Not right now, I haven't. And it's now she needs it. Tomorrow'll be too late.'

Just at that moment a familiar figure wandered into view. It was Herbert, the unwanted lamb, easily recognizable as he prowled from sheep to sheep in search of nourishment.

'Hey, do you think she'd take that little chap?' I asked the farmer.

He looked doubtful. 'Well I don't know – he's a bit old. Nearly a fortnight and they like 'em newly born.'

'But it's worth a try isn't it? Why not try the old trick on her?'

Rob grinned. 'OK, we'll do that. There's nowt to lose. Anyway the little youth isn't much bigger than a new-born 'un. He hasn't grown as fast as his mates.' He took out his penknife and quickly skinned one of the dead lambs, then he tied the skin over Herbert's back and round his jutting ribs.

'Poor little bugger, there's nowt on 'im,' he muttered. 'If this doesn't work he's going in with the pet lambs.'

When he had finished he set Herbert on the grass and the lamb, resolute little character that he was, bored straight in under the sick ewe and began to suck. It seemed he wasn't having much success because he gave the udder a few peremptory thumps with his hard little head; then his tail began to wiggle.

'She's lettin' him have a drop, any road,' Rob laughed.

Herbert was a type you couldn't ignore and the big sheep, sick as she was, just had to turn her head for a look at him. She sniffed along the tied-on skin in a non-committal way, then after a few seconds she gave a few quick licks and the merest beginning of the familiar deep chuckle.

I began to gather up my gear. 'I hope he makes it,' I said. 'Those two need each other.' As I left the pen Herbert, in his new jacket, was still working away.

For the next week I hardly seemed to have my coat on. The flood of sheep work was at its peak and I spent hours of every day with my arms in and out of buckets of hot water in all corners of the district – in the pens, in dark nooks in farm buildings or very often in the open fields, because the farmers of those days didn't find anything disturbing in the sight of a vet kneeling in his shirt sleeves for an hour in the rain.

I had one more visit to Rob Benson's place. To a ewe with

a prolapsed uterus after lambing – a job whose chief delight was comparing it with the sweat of replacing a uterus in a cow.

It was so beautifully easy. Rob rolled the animal on to her side then held her more or less upside down by tying a length of rope to her hind legs and passing it round her neck. In that position she couldn't strain and I disinfected the organ and pushed it back with the minimum of effort, gently inserting an arm at the finish to work it properly into place.

Afterwards the ewe trotted away unperturbed with her family to join the rapidly growing flock whose din was all around us.

'Look!' Rob cried. 'There's that awd ewe with Herbert. Over there on t'right – in the middle of that bunch.' They all looked the same to me but to Rob, like all shepherds, they were as different as people and he picked out these two effortlessly.

They were near the top of the field and as I wanted to have a close look at them we manoeuvred them into a corner. The ewe, fiercely possessive, stamped her foot at us as we approached, and Herbert, who had discarded his woolly jacket, held close to the flank of his new mother. He was, I noticed, faintly obese in appearance.

'You couldn't call him a runt now, Rob,' I said.

The farmer laughed. 'Nay, t'awd lass has a bag like a cow and Herbert's gettin' the lot. By gaw, he's in clover is that little youth and I reckon he saved the ewe's life – she'd have pegged out all right, but she never looked back once he came along.'

I looked away, over the noisy pens, over the hundreds of sheep moving across the fields. I turned to the farmer. 'I'm afraid you've seen a lot of me lately, Rob. I hope this is the last visit.'

'Aye well it could be. We're getting well through now ... but it's a hell of a time, lambin' isn't it?'

'It is that. Well I must be off – I'll leave you to it.' I turned and made my way down the hillside, my arms raw and chafing in my sleeves, my cheeks whipped by the eternal wind gusting over the grass. At the gate I stopped and gazed back at the wide landscape, ribbed and streaked by the last of the winter's snow, and at the dark grey banks of cloud riding across on the wind followed by lakes of brightest blue; and in seconds the fields and walls and woods burst into vivid life and I had to close my eyes against the sun's glare. As I stood there the distant uproar came faintly down to me, the tumultuous harmony from deepest bass to highest treble; demanding, anxious, angry, loving.

The sound of the sheep, the sound of spring.

CHAPTER THREE

'Them masticks,' said Mr Pickersgill judicially, 'is a proper bugger.'

I nodded my head in agreement that his mastitis problem was indeed giving cause for concern; and reflected at the same time that while most farmers would have been content with the local word 'felon' it was typical that Mr Pickersgill should make a determined if somewhat inaccurate attempt at the scientific term.

Sometimes he got very wide of the mark as one time long after this when Artificial Insemination or AI was gaining a foothold in the Dales he made my day by telling me he had a cow in calf to the ICI.

However he usually did better than this – most of his efforts were near misses or bore obvious evidence of their derivation – but I could never really fathom where he got the masticks. I did know that once he fastened on to an expression it never changed; mastitis had always been 'them masticks' with him and it always would be. And I knew, too, that nothing would ever stop him doggedly trying to be right.

Because Mr Pickersgill had what he considered to be a scholastic background. He was a man of about sixty and when in his teens he had attended a two week course of instruction for agricultural workers at Leeds University. This brief glimpse of the academic life had left an indelible impression on his mind, and it was as if the intimation of something deep and true behind the facts of his everyday work had kindled a flame in him which had illumined his subsequent life.

No capped and gowned don ever looked back to his years among the spires of Oxford with more nostalgia than did Mr Pickersgill to his fortnight at Leeds and his conversation was usually laced with references to a godlike Professor Malleson who had apparently been in charge of the course.

'Ah don't know what to make of it,' he continued. 'In ma college days I was allus told that you got a big swollen bag and dirty milk with them masticks but this must be another kind. Just little bits of flakes in the milk off and on – neither nowt nor something, but I'm right fed up with it, I'll tell you.'

I took a sip from the cup of tea which Mrs Pickersgill had placed in front of me on the kitchen table. 'Yes, it's very worrying the way it keeps going on and on. I'm sure there's a definite factor behind it all – I wish I could put my finger on it.'

But in fact I had a good idea what was behind it. I had happened in at the little byre late one afternoon when Mr Pickersgill and his daughter Olive were milking their ten cows. I had watched the two at work as they crouched under the row of roan and red backs and one thing was immediately obvious; while Olive drew the milk by almost imperceptible movements of her fingers and with a motionless wrist, her father hauled away at the teats as though he was trying to ring in the new year.

This insight coupled with the fact that it was always the cows Mr Pickersgill milked that gave trouble was enough to convince me that the chronic mastitis was of traumatic origin.

But how to tell the farmer that he wasn't doing his job right and that the only solution was to learn a more gentle technique or let Olive take over all the milking?

It wouldn't be easy because Mr Pickersgill was an impressive man. I don't suppose he had a spare penny in the world but even as he sat there in the kitchen in his tattered, collarless flannel shirt and braces he looked, as always, like an industrial tycoon. You could imagine that massive head with its fleshy cheeks, noble brow and serene eyes looking out from the financial pages of *The Times*. Put him in a bowler and striped trousers and you'd have the perfect chairman of the board.

I was very chary of affronting such natural dignity and anyway, Mr Pickersgill was fundamentally a fine stocksman. His few cows, like all the animals of that fast-dying breed of small farmer, were fat and sleek and clean. You had to look after your beasts when they were your only source of income and somehow Mr Pickersgill had brought up a family by milk production eked out by selling a few pigs and the eggs from his wife's fifty hens.

I could never quite work out how they did it but they lived, and they lived graciously. All the family but Olive had married and left home but there was still a rich decorum and harmony in that house. The present scene was typical. The farmer expounding gravely, Mrs Pickersgill bustling about in the background, listening to him with quiet pride. Olive too, was happy. Though in her late thirties, she had no fears of spinsterhood because she had been assiduously courted for fifteen years by Charlie Hudson from the Darrowby fish shop and though Charlie was not a tempestuous suitor there was nothing flighty about him and he was confidently expected to pop the question over the next ten years or so.

Mr Pickersgill offered me another buttered scone and when I declined he cleared his throat a few times as though trying to find words. 'Mr Herriot,' he said at last, 'I don't like to tell anybody his job, but we've tried all your remedies for them masticks and we've still got trouble. Now when I studied under Professor Malleson I noted down a lot of good cures and I'd like to try this 'un. Have a look at it.'

He put his hand in his hip pocket and produced a yellowed slip of paper almost falling apart at the folds. 'It's an udder salve. Maybe if we gave the bags a good rub with it it'd do t'trick.'

I read the prescription in the fine copperplate writing. Camphor, eucalyptus, zinc oxide – a long list of the old familiar names. I couldn't help feeling a kind of affection for them but it was tempered by a growing disillusion. I was about to say that I didn't think rubbing anything on the udder would make the slightest difference when the farmer groaned loudly.

The action of reaching into his hip pocket had brought on a twinge of his lumbago and he sat very upright, grimacing with pain.

'This bloody old back of mine! By gaw, it does give me some stick, and doctor can't do nowt about it. I've had enough pills to make me rattle but ah get no relief.'

I'm not brilliant but I do get the odd blinding flash and I had one now.

'Mr Pickersgill,' I said solemnly, 'You've suffered from that lumbago ever since I've known you and I've just thought of something. I believe I know how to cure it.'

The farmer's eyes widened and he stared at me with a childlike trust in which there was no trace of scepticism. This could be expected, because just as people place more reliance on the words of knacker men and meal travellers than their vets' when their animals are concerned it was natural that they would believe the vet rather than their doctor with their own ailments.

'You know how to put me right?' he said faintly.

'I think so, and it has nothing to do with medicine. You'll have to stop milking.'

'Stop milking! What the 'ell . . . ?'

'Of course. Don't you see, it's sitting crouched on that little stool night and morning every day of the week that's doing it. You're a big chap and you've got to bend to get down there – I'm sure it's bad for you.'

Mr Pickersgill gazed into space as though he had seen a vision. 'You really think . . .'

'Yes, I do. You ought to give it a try, anyway. Olive can do the milking. She's always saying she ought to do it all.'

'That's right, Dad,' Olive chimed in. 'I like milking, you know I do, and it's time you gave it up – you've done it ever since you were a lad.'

'Dang it, young man, I believe you're right! I'll pack it in, now – I've made my decision!' Mr Pickersgill threw up his fine head, looked imperiously around him and crashed his fist on the table as though he had just concluded a merger between two oil companies.

I stood up. 'Fine, fine. I'll take this prescription with me and make up the udder salve. It'll be ready for you tonight and I should start using it immediately.'

It was about a month later that I saw Mr Pickersgill. He was on a bicycle, pedalling majestically across the market place and he dismounted when he saw me.

'Now then, Mr Herriot,' he said, puffing slightly. 'I'm glad I've met you. I've been meaning to come and tell you that we don't have no flakes in the milk now. Ever since we started with t'salve they began to disappear and milk's as clear as it can be now.'

'Oh, great. And how's your lumbago?'

'Well I'll tell you, you've really capped it and I'm grateful. Ah've never milked since that day and I hardly get a twinge now.' He paused and smiled indulgently. 'You gave me some good advice for me back, but we had to go back to awd Professor Malleson to cure them masticks, didn't we?'

My next encounter with Mr Pickersgill was on the telephone.

'I'm speaking from the cossack,' he said in a subdued shout.

'From the what?'

'The cossack, the telephone cossack in t'village.'

'Yes, indeed,' I said, 'and what can I do for you?'

'I want you to come out as soon as possible, to treat a calf for semolina.'

'I beg your pardon?'

'I 'ave a calf with semolina.'

'Semolina?'

'Aye, that's right. A feller was on about it on t'wireless the other morning.'

'Oh! Ah yes, I see.' I too had heard a bit of the farming talk on Salmonella infection in calves. 'What makes you think you've got this trouble?'

'Well it's just like that feller said. Me calf's bleeding from the rectrum.'

'From the ... ? Yes, yes, of course. Well I'd better have a look at him – I won't be long.'

The calf was pretty ill when I saw him and he did have rectal bleeding, but it wasn't like Salmonella.

'There's no diarrhoea, you see, Mr Pickersgill,' I said. 'In fact, he seems to be constipated. This is almost pure blood coming away from him. And he hasn't got a very high temperature.'

The farmer seemed a little disappointed. 'Dang, I thowt it was just same as that feller was talking about. He said you could send samples off to the labrador.'

'Eh? To the what?'

'The investigation labrador – you know.'

'Oh yes, quite, but I don't think the lab would be of any help in this case.'

'Aye well, what's wrong with him, then? Is something the matter with his rectrum?'

'No, no,' I said. 'But there seems to be some obstruction high up his bowel which is causing this haemorrhage.' I looked at the little animal standing motionless with his back up. He was totally preoccupied with some internal discomfort and now and then he strained and grunted softly.

And of course I should have known straight away – it was so obvious. But I suppose we all have blind spells when we can't see what is pushed in front of our eyes, and for a few days I played around with that calf in a haze of ignorance, giving it this and that medicine which I'd rather not talk about.

But I was lucky. He recovered in spite of my treatment. It wasn't until Mr Pickersgill showed me the little roll of necrotic tissue which the calf had passed that the thing dawned on me.

I turned, shame-faced, to the farmer. 'This is a bit of dead bowel all telescoped together – an intussusception. It's usually a fatal condition but fortunately in this case the obstruction has sloughed away and your calf should be all right now.'

'What was it you called it?'

'An intussusception.'

Mr Pickersgill's lips moved tentatively and for a moment I thought he was going to have a shot at it. But he apparently decided against it. 'Oh,' he said. 'That's what it was, was it?'

'Yes, and it's difficult to say just what caused it.'

The farmer sniffed. 'I'll bet I know what was behind it. I always said this one 'ud be a weakly calf. When he was born he bled a lot from his biblical cord.'

Mr Pickersgill hadn't finished with me yet. It was only a week later that I heard him on the phone again.

'Get out here, quick. There's one of me pigs going bezique.'

'Bezique?' With an effort I put away from me a mental picture of two porkers facing each other over a green baize table. 'I'm afraid I don't quite . . .'

'Aye, ah gave him a dose of worm medicine and he started jumpin' about and rollin' on his back. I tell you he's going proper bezique.'

'Ah! Yes, yes I see, right. I'll be with you in a few minutes.'

The pig had quietened down a bit when I arrived but was still in considerable pain, getting up, lying down, trotting in spurts round the pen. I gave him half a grain of morphine hydrochloride as a sedative and within a few minutes he began to relax and finally curled up in the straw.

'Looks as though he's going to be all right,' I said. 'But what's this worm medicine you gave him?'

Mr Pickersgill produced the bottle sheepishly.

'Bloke was coming round sellin' them. Said it would shift any worms you cared to name.'

'It nearly shifted your pig, didn't it?' I sniffed at the mixture. 'And no wonder. It smells almost like pure turpentine.'

'Turpentine! Well by gaw is that all it is? And bloke said it was summat new. Charged me an absorbent price for it too.'

I gave him back the bottle. 'Well never mind, I don't think there's any harm done, but I think the dustbin's the best place for that.'

As I was getting into my car I looked up at the farmer. 'You must be about sick of the sight of me. First the mastitis, then the calf and now your pig. You've had a bad run.'

Mr Pickersgill squared his shoulders and gazed at me with massive composure. Again I was conscious of the sheer presence of the man.

'Young feller,' he said. 'That don't bother me. Where there's stock there's trouble and ah know from experience that trouble allus comes in cyclones.'

CHAPTER FOUR

I knew I shouldn't do it, but the old Drovers' Road beckoned to me irresistibly. I ought to be hurrying back to the surgery after my morning call but the broad green path wound beguilingly over the moor top between its crumbling walls and almost before I knew, I was out of the car and treading the wiry grass.

The wall skirted the hill's edge and as I looked across and away to where Darrowby huddled far below between its folding green fells the wind thundered in my ears; but when I squatted in the shelter of the grey stones the wind was only a whisper and the spring sunshine hot on my face. The best kind of sunshine – not heavy or cloying but clear and bright and clean as you find it down behind a wall in Yorkshire with the wind singing over the top.

I slid lower till I was stretched on the turf, gazing with half-closed eyes into the bright sky, luxuriating in the sensation of being detached from the world and its problems.

This form of self-indulgence had become part of my life and still is; a reluctance to come down from the high country; a penchant for stepping out of the stream of life and loitering on the brink for a few minutes as an uninvolved spectator.

And it was easy to escape, lying up there quite alone with no sound but the wind sighing and gusting over the empty miles and, far up in the wide blue, the endless brave trilling of the larks.

Not that there was anything unpleasant about going back down the hill to Darrowby. I had worked there for two years now and Skeldale House had become home and the two bright minds in it my friends. It didn't bother me that both the brothers were cleverer than I was. Siegfried – unpredictable, explosive, generous; I had been lucky to have him as a boss. As a city bred youth trying to tell expert stock farmers how to treat their animals I had needed all his skill and guidance behind me. And Tristan; a rum lad as they said, but very sound. His humour and zest for life had lightened my days.

And all the time I was adding practical experience to my theory. The mass of facts I had learned at college were all coming to life, and there was the growing realization, deep and warm, that this was for me. There was nothing else I'd rather do.

It must have been fifteen minutes later when I finally rose, stretched pleasurably, took a last deep gulp of the crisp air and pottered slowly back to the car for the six mile journey back down the hill to Darrowby.

When I drew up by the railings with Siegfried's brass plate hanging lopsidedly by the fine Georgian doorway I looked up at the tall old house with the ivy swarming untidily over the weathered brick. The white paint on windows and doors was flaking and that ivy needed trimming but the whole place had style, a serene, unchangeable grace.

But I had other things on my mind at the moment. I went inside, stepping quietly over the coloured tiles which covered the floor of the long passage till I reached the long offshoot at the back of the house. And I felt, as I always did, subdued excitement as I breathed the smell of our trade which always hung there; ether, carbolic and pulv aromat. The latter was the spicy powder which we mixed with the cattle medicines to make them more palatable and it had a distinctive bouquet which even now can take me back thirty years with a single sniff.

And today the thrill was stronger than usual because my visit was of a surreptitious nature. I almost tiptoed along the last stretch of passage, dodged quickly round the corner and into the dispensary. Gingerly I opened the cupboard door at one end and pulled out a little drawer. I was pretty sure Siegfried had a spare hoof knife hidden away within and I had to suppress a cackle of triumph when I saw it lying there; almost brand new with a nicely turned gleaming blade and a polished wooden handle.

My hand was outstretched to remove it when a cry of anger exploded in my right ear.

'Caught in the act! Bloody red-handed, by God!' Siegfried, who had apparently shot up through the floorboards was breathing fire into my face.

The shock was so tremendous that the instrument dropped from my trembling fingers and I cowered back against a row of bottles of formalin bloat mixture.

'Oh hello, Siegfried,' I said with a ghastly attempt at nonchalance. 'Just on my way to that horse of Thompson's. You know – the one with the pus in the foot. I seem to have mislaid my knife so I thought I'd borrow this one.'

'Thought you'd nick it, you mean! My spare hoof knife! By heaven, is nothing sacred, James?'

I smiled sheepishly. 'Oh you're wrong. I'd have given it back to you straight away.'

'A likely story!' Siegfried said with a bitter smile. 'I'd never have seen it again and you know damn well I wouldn't. Anyway, where's your own knife? You've left it on some farm, haven't you?'

'Well as a matter of fact I laid it down at Willie Denholm's place after I'd finished trimming his cow's overgrown foot and I must have forgotten to pick it up.' I gave a light laugh.

'But God help us, James, you're always forgetting to pick things up. And you're always making up the deficiency by purloining my equipment.' He stuck his chin out. 'Have you any idea how much all this is costing me?'

'Oh but I'm sure Mr Denholm will drop the knife in at the surgery the first time he's in town.'

Siegfried nodded gravely. 'He may, I'll admit that, he may. But on the other hand he might think it is the ideal tool for cutting up his plug tobacco. Remember when you left your calving overall at old Fred Dobson's place? The next time I saw it was six months later and Fred was wearing it. He said it was the best thing he'd ever found for stooking corn in wet weather.'

'Yes, I remember. I'm sorry about it all.' I fell silent, breathing in the pungency of the pulv aromat. Somebody had let a bagful burst on the floor and the smell was stronger than ever.

My employer kept his fiery gaze fixed on me for a few moments more then he shrugged his shoulders. 'Ah well, there's none of us perfect, James. And I'm sorry I shouted at you. But you know I'm deeply attached to that knife and this business of leaving things around is getting under my skin.' He took down a Winchester of his favourite colic draught and polished it with his handkerchief before replacing it carefully on its shelf. 'I tell you what, let's go and sit down for a few minutes and talk about this problem.'

We went back along the passage and as I followed him into the big sitting-room Tristan got up from his favourite chair and yawned deeply. His face looked as boyish and innocent as ever but the lines of exhaustion round his eyes and mouth told an eloquent story. Last night he had travelled with the darts team from the Lord Nelson and had taken part in a gruelling match against the Dog and Gun at

Drayton. The contest had been followed by a pie and peas supper and the consumption of something like twelve pints of bitter a man. Tristan had crawled into bed at 3 AM and was clearly in a delicate condition.

'Ah, Tristan,' Siegfried said. 'I'm glad you're here because what I have to say concerns you just as much as James. It's about leaving instruments on farms and you're as guilty as he is.' (It must be remembered that before the Veterinary Surgeons' act of 1948 it was quite legal for students to treat cases and they regularly did so. Tristan in fact had done much sterling work when called on and was very popular with the farmers.)

'Now I mean this very seriously,' my employer said, leaning his elbow on the mantelpiece and looking from one of us to the other. 'You two are bringing me to the brink of ruin by losing expensive equipment. Some of it is returned but a lot of it is never seen again. What's the use of sending you to visits when you come back without your artery forceps or scissors or something else? The profit's gone, you see?'

We nodded silently.

'After all, there's nothing difficult about bringing your instruments away, is there? You may wonder why I never leave anything behind – well I can tell you it's just a matter of concentration. When I lay a thing down I always impress on my mind that I've got to lift it up again. That's all there is to it.'

The lecture over, he became very brisk. 'Right, let's get on. There's nothing much doing, James, so I'd like you to come with me to Kendall's of Brookside. He's got a few jobs including a cow with a tumour to remove. I don't know the details but we may have to cast her. You can go on to Thompson's later.' He turned to his brother. 'And you'd better come too, Tristan. I don't know if we'll need you but an extra man might come in handy.'

We made quite a procession as we trooped into the farm yard and Mr Kendall met us with his customary ebullience.

'Hello, 'ello, we've got plenty of man power today, I see. We'll be able to tackle owt with this regiment.'

Mr Kendall had the reputation in the district of being a 'bit clever' and the phrase has a different meaning in Yorkshire from elsewhere. It meant he was something of a know-all; and the fact that he considered himself a wag and leg-puller of the first degree didn't endear him to his fellow farmers either.

I always felt he was a good-hearted man, but his conviction that he knew everything and had seen it all before made him a difficult man to impress.

'Well what d'you want to see first, Mr Farnon?' he asked. He was a thick-set little man with a round, smooth-skinned face and mischievous eyes.

'I believe you have a cow with a bad eye,' Siegfried said. 'Better begin with that.'

'Right squire,' the farmer cried, then he put his hand in his pocket. 'But before we start, here's something for you.' He pulled forth a stethoscope. 'You left it last time you were 'ere.'

There was a silence, then Siegfried grunted a word of thanks and grabbed it hastily from his hand.

Mr Kendall continued. 'And the time afore that you left your bloodless castrators. We did a swop over, didn't we? I gave you back the nippers and you left me the earphones.' He burst into a peal of laughter.

'Yes, yes, quite,' Siegfried snapped, glancing uneasily round at us, 'but we must be getting on. Where is ... ?'

'You know lads,' chuckled the farmer, turning to us. 'Ah don't think I've ever known 'im come here without leaving summat.'

'Really?' said Tristan interestedly.

'Aye, if I'd wanted to keep 'em all I'd have had a drawerful by now.'

'Is that so?' I said.

'Aye it is, young man. And it's the same with all me neighbours. One feller said to me t'other day, "He's a kind man is Mr Farnon – never calls without leavin' a souvenir." ' He threw back his head and laughed again.

We were enjoying the conversation but my employer was

stalking up the byre. 'Where's this damn cow, Mr Kendall? We haven't got all day.'

The patient wasn't hard to find; a nice light roan cow which looked round at us carefully, one eye almost closed. From between the lashes a trickle of tears made a dark stain down the hair of the face, and there was an eloquent story of pain in the cautious movements of the quivering lids.

'There's something in there,' murmured Siegfried.

'Aye, ah know!' Mr Kendall always knew. 'She's got a flippin' great lump of chaff stuck on her eyeball but I can't get to it. Look here.' He grabbed the cow's nose with one hand and tried to prise the eyelids apart with the fingers of the other, but the third eyelid came across and the whole orbit rolled effortlessly out of sight leaving only a blank expanse of white sclera.

'There!' he cried. 'Nowt to see. You can't make her keep her eye still.'

'I can, though.' Siegfried turned to his brother. 'Tristan, get the chloroform muzzle from the car. Look sharp!'

The young man was back in seconds and Siegfried quickly drew the canvas bag over the cow's face and buckled it behind the ears. From a bottle of spirit he produced a small pair of forceps of an unusual type with tiny jaws operated by a spring. He poised them just over the closed eye.

'James,' he said. 'Give her about an ounce.'

I dribbled the chloroform on to the sponge in the front of the muzzle. Nothing happened for a few moments while the animal took a few breaths then her eyes opened wide in surprise as the strange numbing vapour rolled into her lungs.

The whole area of the affected eye was displayed, with a broad golden piece of chaff splayed out across the dark cornea. I only had a glimpse of it before Siegfried's little forceps had seized it and whisked it away.

'Squeeze in some of that ointment, Tristan,' said my employer. 'And get the muzzle off, James, before she starts to rock.'

With the bag away from her face and the tormenting little

object gone from her eye the cow looked around her, vastly relieved. The whole thing had taken only a minute or two and was as slick a little exhibition as you'd wish to see, but Mr Kendall didn't seem to think a great deal of it.

'Aye right,' he grunted. 'Let's get on with t'next job.'

As we went down the byre I looked out and saw a horse being led across the yard. Siegfried pointed to it.

'Is that the gelding I operated on for fistulous withers?' he asked.

'That's the one.' The farmer's voice was airy.

We went out and Siegfried ran his hand over the horse's shoulders. The broad fibrous scar over the withers was all that was left of the discharging, stinking sinus of a few weeks back. Healing was perfect. These cases were desperately difficult to treat and I remembered my boss cutting and chiselling at the mass of necrotic tissue, curetting deeply till only healthy flesh and bone remained. His efforts had been rewarded; it was a brilliant success.

Siegfried gave the gelding a final pat on the neck. 'That's done rather well.'

Mr Kendall shrugged and turned back towards the byre. 'Aye, not so bad, I suppose.' But he really wasn't impressed.

The cow with the tumour was standing just inside the door. The growth was in the perineal region, a smooth round object like an apple projecting from the animal's rear end, clearly visible an inch to the right of the tail.

Mr Kendall was in full cry again. 'Now we'll see what you're made of. How are you chaps going to get that thing off, eh? It's a big 'un – you'll need a carving knife or a hack saw for t'job. And are you goin' to put her to sleep or tie her up or what?' He grinned and his bright little eyes darted at each of us in turn.

Siegfried reached out and grasped the tumour, feeling round the base with his fingers. 'Hmm ... yes ... hmm ... bring me some soap and water and a towel, will you please?'

'I have it just outside t'door.' The farmer scuttled into the yard and back again with the bucket.

'Thank you very much,' Siegfried said. He washed his hands and gave them a leisurely towelling. 'Now I believe you have another case to see. A scouring calf, wasn't it?'

The farmer's eyes widened. 'Yes, I 'ave. But how about getting this big lump off the cow first?'

Siegfried folded the towel and hung it over the half door. 'Oh, I've removed the tumour,' he said quietly.

'What's that?' Mr Kendall stared at the cow's backside. We all stared at it. And there was no doubt about it – the growth was gone. And there was another funny thing – there wasn't even a scar or mark remaining. I was standing quite close to the animal and I could see exactly to a fraction of an inch where that big ugly projection had been; and there was nothing, not a drop of blood, nothing.

'Aye,' Mr Kendall said irresolutely. 'You've er . . . you've removed . . . you've removed it, aye, that's right.' The smile had vanished from his face and his entire personality seemed suddenly deflated. Being a man who knew everything and was surprised by nothing he was unable to say, 'When the devil did you do it? And how? And what on earth have you done with it?' He had to maintain face at all costs, but he was rattled. He darted little glances around the byre, along the channel. The cow was standing in a clean-swept stall with no straw and there was nothing lying on the floor there or anywhere. Casually, as though by accident, he pushed a milking stool to one side with his foot – still nothing.

'Well now, perhaps we can see the calf.' Siegfried began to move away.

Mr Kendall nodded. 'Yes . . . yes . . . the calf. He's in t'corner there. I'll just lift bucket first.'

It was a blatant excuse. He went over to the bucket and as he passed behind the cow he whipped out his spectacles, jammed them on his nose and directed a piercing glare at the cow's bottom. He only took an instant because he didn't want to show undue concern, but when he turned back towards us his face registered utter despair and he put his spectacles away with a weary gesture of defeat.

As he approached I turned and brushed against my employer.

'Where the hell is it?' I hissed.

'Up my sleeve,' murmured Siegfried without moving his lips or changing expression.

'What . . . ?' I began, but Siegfried was climbing over a gate into the makeshift pen where the calf was cornered.

He was in expansive mood as he examined the little creature and injected it. He kept up a steady flow of light conversation and Mr Kendall, showing great character, managed to get his smile back on and answer back. But his preoccupied manner, the tortured eyes and the repeated incredulous glances back along the byre floor in the direction of the cow betrayed the fact that he was under immense strain.

Siegfried didn't hurry over the calf and when he had finished he lingered a while in the yard, chatting about the weather, the way the grass was springing, the price of fat bullocks.

Mr Kendall hung on grimly but by the time Siegfried finally waved farewell the farmer's eyes were popping and his face was an anguished mask. He bolted back into the byre and as the car backed round I could see him bent double with his glasses on again, peering into the corners.

'Poor fellow,' I said. 'He's still looking for that thing. And for God's sake where is it, anyway?'

'I told you, didn't I?' Siegfried removed one arm from the wheel and shook it. A round fleshy ball rolled down into his hand.

I stared at it in amazement. 'But . . . I never saw you take it off . . . what happened?'

'I'll tell you.' My employer smiled indulgently. 'I was fingering it over to see how deeply it was attached when I felt it begin to move. The back of it was merely encapsulated by the skin and when I gave another squeeze it just popped out and shot up my sleeve. And after it had gone the lips of the skin sprang back together again so that you couldn't see where it had been. Extraordinary thing.'

Tristan reached over from the back seat. 'Give it to me,' he said. 'I'll take it back to college with me and get it sectioned. We'll find out what kind of tumour it is.'

His brother smiled. 'Yes, I expect they'll give it some fancy name, but I'll always remember it as the only thing that shook Mr Kendall.'

'That was an interesting session in there,' I said. 'And I must say I admired the way you dealt with that eye, Siegfried. Very smooth indeed.'

'You're very kind, James,' my boss murmured. 'That was just one of my little tricks – and of course the forceps helped a lot.'

I nodded. 'Yes, wonderful little things. I've never seen anything like them. Where did you get them?'

'I picked them up on an instrument stall at the last Veterinary Congress. They cost me a packet but they've been worth it. Here, let me show them to you.' He put his hand in his breast pocket, then his side pockets, and as he continued to rummage all over his person a look of sick dismay spread slowly across his face.

Finally he abandoned the search, cleared his throat and fixed his eyes on the road ahead.

'I'll er . . . I'll show you them some other time, James,' he said huskily.

I didn't say anything but I knew and Siegfried knew and Tristan knew.

He'd left them on the farm.

CHAPTER FIVE

'Well, it's a good sign.' Tristan reluctantly expelled a lungful of Woodbine smoke and looked at me with wide, encouraging eyes.

'You think so?' I said doubtfully.

Tristan nodded. 'Sure of it. Helen just rang you up, did she?'

'Yes, out of the blue. I haven't seen her since I took her to the pictures that night and it's been hectic ever since with the lambing – and suddenly there she was asking me to tea on Sunday.'

'I like the sound of it,' Tristan said. 'But of course you don't want to get the idea you're home and dry or anything like that. You know there are others in the field?'

'Hell, yes, I suppose I'm one of a crowd.'

'Not exactly, but Helen Alderson is really something. Not just a looker but . . . mm-mm, very nice. There's a touch of class about that girl.'

'Oh I know, I know. There's bound to be a mob of blokes after her. Like young Richard Edmundson – I hear he's very well placed.'

'That's right,' Tristan said. 'Old friends of the family, big farmers, rolling in brass. I understand old man Alderson fancies Richard strongly as a son-in-law.'

I dug my hands into my pockets. 'Can't blame him. A ragged-arsed young vet isn't much competition.'

'Well, don't be gloomy, old lad, you've made a bit of progress, haven't you?'

'In a way,' I said with a wry smile. 'I've taken her out twice – to a dinner dance which wasn't on and to a cinema showing the wrong film. A dead loss the first time and not much better the second. I just don't seem to have any luck there – something goes wrong every time. Maybe this invitation is just a polite gesture – returning hospitality or something like that.'

'Nonsense!' Tristan laughed and patted me on the shoulder. 'This is the beginning of better things. You'll see – nothing will go wrong this time.'

And on Sunday afternoon as I got out of the car to open the gate to Heston Grange it did seem as if all was right with the world. The rough track snaked down from the gate through the fields to Helen's home slumbering in the sunshine by the curving river, and the grey-stoned old building was like a restful haven against the stark backcloth of the fells beyond.

I leaned on the gate for a moment, breathing in the sweet

air. There had been a change during the last week; the harsh winds had dropped, everything had softened and greened and the warming land gave off its scents. On the lower slopes of the fell, in the shade of the pine woods, a pale mist of bluebells drifted among the dead bronze of the bracken and their fragrance came up to me on the breeze.

I drove down the track among the cows relishing the tender young grass after their long winter in the byres and as I knocked on the farmhouse door I felt a surge of optimism and well-being. Helen's younger sister answered and it wasn't until I walked into the big flagged kitchen that I experienced a qualm. Maybe it was because it was so like that first disastrous time I had called for Helen; Mr Alderson was there by the fireside, deep in the *Farmer and Stockbreeder* as before, while above his head the cows in the vast oil painting still paddled in the lake of startling blue under the shattered peaks. On the whitewashed wall the clock still tick-tocked inexorably.

Helen's father looked up over his spectacles just as he had done before. 'Good afternoon, young man, come and sit down.' And as I dropped into the chair opposite to him he looked at me uncertainly for a few seconds. 'It's a better day,' he murmured, then his eyes were drawn back irresistibly to the pages on his knee. As he bent his head and started to read again I gained the strong impression that he hadn't the slightest idea who I was.

It came back to me forcibly that there was a big difference in coming to a farm as a vet and visiting socially. I was often in farm kitchens on my rounds, washing my hands in the sink after kicking my boots off in the porch, chatting effortlessly to the farmer's wife about the sick beast. But here I was in my good suit sitting stiffly across from a silent little man whose daughter I had come to court. It wasn't the same at all.

I was relieved when Helen came in carrying a cake which she placed on the big table. This wasn't easy as the table was already loaded; ham and egg pies rubbing shoulders with snowy scones, a pickled tongue, cheek by jowl with a bowl of mixed salad, luscious-looking custard tarts jockeying for position with sausage rolls, tomato sandwiches, fairy cakes. In a clearing near the centre a vast trifle reared its cream-topped head. It was a real Yorkshire tea.

Helen came over to me. 'Hello, Jim, it's nice to see you – you're quite a stranger.' She smiled her slow, friendly smile.

'Hello, Helen. Yes, you know what lambing time's like. I hope things will ease up a bit now.'

'Well I hope so too. Hard work's all right up to a point but you need a break some time. Anyway, come and have some tea. Are you hungry?'

'I am now,' I said, gazing at the packed foodstuffs. Helen laughed. 'Well come on, sit in. Dad, leave your precious *Farmer and Stockbreeder* and come over here. We were going to sit you in the dining-room, Jim, but Dad won't have his tea anywhere but in here, so that's all about it.'

I took my place along with Helen, young Tommy and Mary, her brother and sister, and Auntie Lucy, Mr Alderson's widowed sister who had recently come to live with the family. Mr Alderson groaned his way over the flags, collapsed on to a high-backed wooden chair and began to saw phlegmatically at the tongue.

As I accepted my laden plate I can't say I felt entirely at ease. In the course of my work I had eaten many meals in the homes of the hospitable Dalesmen and I had discovered that light chatter was not welcomed at table. The accepted thing, particularly among the more old-fashioned types, was to put the food away in silence and get back on the job, but maybe this was different. Sunday tea might be a more social occasion; I looked round the table, waiting for somebody to lead the way.

Helen spoke up. 'Jim's had a busy time among the sheep since we saw him last.'

'Oh yes?' Auntie Lucy put her head on one side and smiled. She was a little bird-like woman, very like her brother and the way she looked at me made me feel she was on my side.

The young people regarded me fixedly with twitching mouths. The only other time I had met them they had found me an object of some amusement and things didn't seem to have changed. Mr Alderson sprinkled some salt on a radish, conveyed it to his mouth and crunched it impassively.

'Did you have much twin lamb disease this time, Jim?' Helen asked, trying again.

'Quite a bit,' I replied brightly. 'Haven't had much luck with treatment, though. I tried dosing the ewes with glucose this year and I think it did a bit of good.'

Mr Alderson swallowed the last of his radish. 'I think nowt to glucose,' he grunted. 'I've had a go with it and I think nowt to it.'

'Really?' I said. 'Well now that's interesting. Yes ... yes ... quite.'

I buried myself in my salad for a spell before offering a further contribution.

'There's been a lot of sudden deaths in the lambs,' I said. 'Seems to be more Pulpy Kidney about.'

'Fancy that,' said Auntie Lucy, smiling encouragingly.

'Yes,' I went on, getting into my stride. 'It's a good job we've got a vaccine against it now.'

'Wonderful things, those vaccines,' Helen chipped in. 'You'll soon be able to prevent a lot of the sheep diseases that way.' The conversation was warming up.

Mr Alderson finished his tongue and pushed his plate away. 'I think nowt to the vaccines. And those sudden deaths you're on about – they're caused by wool ball on t'stomach. Nowt to do wi' the kidneys.'

'Ah yes, wool ball eh? I see, wool ball.' I subsided and decided to concentrate on the food.

And it was worth concentrating on. As I worked my way through I was aware of a growing sense of wonder that Helen had probably baked the entire spread. It was when my teeth were sinking into a poem of a curd tart that I really began to appreciate the miracle that somebody of Helen's radiant attractiveness should be capable of this.

I looked across at her. She was a big girl, nothing like her little wisp of a father. She must have taken after her mother. Mrs Alderson had been dead for many years and I wondered if she had had that same wide, generous mouth that smiled so easily, those same warm blue eyes under the soft mass of black-brown hair.

A spluttering from Tommy and Mary showed that they had been appreciatively observing me gawping at their sister.

'That's enough, you two,' Auntie Lucy reproved. 'Anyway you can go now, we're going to clear the table.'

Helen and she began to move the dishes to the scullery beyond the door while Mr Alderson and I returned to our chairs by the fireside.

The little man ushered me to mine with a vague wave of the hand. 'Here . . . take a seat, er . . . young man.'

A clattering issued from the kitchen as the washing-up began. We were alone.

Mr Alderson's hand strayed automatically towards his *Farmer and Stockbreeder*, but he withdrew it after a single hunted glance in my direction and began to drum his fingers on the arm of the chair, whistling softly under his breath.

I groped desperately for an opening gambit but came up with nothing. The ticking of the clock boomed out into the silence. I was beginning to break out into a sweat when the little man cleared his throat.

'Pigs were a good trade on Monday,' he vouchsafed.

'They were, eh? Well, that's fine – jolly good.'

Mr Alderson nodded, fixed his gaze somewhere above my left shoulder and started drumming his fingers again. Once more the heavy silence blanketed us and the clock continued to hammer out its message.

After several years Mr Alderson stirred in his seat and gave a little cough. I looked at him eagerly.

'Store cattle were down, though,' he said.

'Ah, too bad, what a pity,' I babbled. 'But that's how it goes, I suppose, eh?'

Helen's father shrugged and we settled down again. This time I knew it was hopeless. My mind was a void and my companion had the defeated look of a man who has shot his conversational bolt. I lay back and studied the hams and sides of bacon hanging from their hooks in the ceiling, then I worked my way along the row of plates on the big oak dresser to a gaudy calendar from a cattle cake firm which dangled from a nail on the wall. I took a chance then and stole a glance at Mr Alderson out of the corner of my eye and my toes curled as I saw he had chosen that precise moment to have a sideways peep at me. We both looked away hurriedly.

By shifting round in my seat and craning my neck I was able to get a view of the other side of the kitchen where there was an old-fashioned roll top desk surmounted by a wartime picture of Mr Alderson looking very stern in the uniform of the Yorkshire Yeomanry, and I was proceeding along the wall from there when Helen opened the door and came quickly into the room.

'Dad,' she said, a little breathlessly. 'Stan's here. He says one of the cows is down with staggers.'

Her father jumped up in obvious relief. I think he was delighted he had a sick cow and I, too, felt like a released prisoner as I hurried out with him.

Stan, one of the cowmen, was waiting in the yard.

'She's at t'top of t'field, boss,' he said. 'I just spotted 'er when I went to get them in for milkin'.'

Mr Alderson looked at me questioningly and I nodded at him as I opened the car door.

'I've got the stuff with me,' I said. 'We'd better drive straight up.'

The three of us piled in and I set course to where I could see the stretched-out form of a cow near the wall in the top corner. My bottles and instruments rattled and clattered as we bumped over the rig and furrow.

This was something every vet gets used to in early summer; the urgent call to milk cows which have collapsed suddenly a week or two after being turned out to grass. The farmers called it grass staggers and, as its scientific name of hypomagesaemia implied, it was associated with lowered magnesium level in the blood. An alarming and highly fatal condition but fortunately curable by injection of magnesium in most cases.

Despite the seriousness of the occasion I couldn't repress a twinge of satisfaction. It had got me out of the house and it gave me a chance to prove myself by doing something useful. Helen's father and I hadn't established anything like a rapport as yet, but maybe when I gave his unconscious cow my magic injection and it leaped to its feet and walked away he might look at me in a different light. And it often happened that way; some of the cures were really dramatic.

'She's still alive, any road,' Stan said as we roared over the grass. 'I saw her legs move then.'

He was right, but as I pulled up and jumped from the car I felt a tingle of apprehension. Those legs were moving too much.

This was the kind that often died; the convulsive type. The animal, prone on her side, was pedalling frantically at the air with all four feet, her head stretched backwards, eyes staring, foam bubbling from her mouth. As I hurriedly unscrewed the cap from the bottle of magnesium lactate she stopped and went into a long, shuddering spasm, legs stiffly extended, eyes screwed tightly shut; then she relaxed and lay inert for a frightening few seconds before recommencing the wild thrashing with her legs.

My mouth had gone dry. This was a bad one. The strain on the heart during these spasms was enormous and each one could be her last.

I crouched by her side, my needle poised over the milk vein. My usual practice was to inject straight into the bloodstream to achieve the quickest possible effect, but in this case I hesitated. Any interference with the heart's action could kill this cow; best to play safe – I reached over and pushed the needle under the skin of the neck.

As the fluid ran in, bulging the subcutaneous tissues and starting a widening swelling under the roan-coloured hide, the cow went into another spasm. For an agonizing few seconds she lay there, the quivering limbs reaching desperately out at nothing, the eyes disappearing deep down under tight-twisted lids. Helplessly I watched her, my heart thudding, and this time as she came out of the rigor and started to move again it wasn't with the purposeful pedalling of before; it was an aimless laboured pawing and as even this grew weaker her eyes slowly opened and gazed outwards with a vacant stare.

I bent and touched the cornea with my finger, there was no response.

The farmer and cowman looked at me in silence as the animal gave a final jerk then lay still.

'I'm afraid she's dead, Mr Alderson,' I said.

The farmer nodded and his eyes moved slowly over the still form, over the graceful limbs, the fine dark roan flanks, the big, turgid udder that would give no more milk.

'I'm sorry,' I said. 'I'm afraid her heart must have given out before the magnesium had a chance to work.'

'It's a bloody shame,' grunted Stan. 'She was a right good cow, that 'un.'

Mr Alderson turned quietly back to the car. 'Aye well, these things happen,' he muttered.

We drove down the field to the house.

Inside, the work was over and the family was collected in the parlour. I sat with them for a while but my overriding emotion was an urgent desire to be elsewhere. Helen's father had been silent before but now he sat hunched miserably in an armchair taking no part in the conversation. I wondered whether he thought I had actually killed his cow. It certainly hadn't looked very good, the vet walking up to the sick animal, the quick injection and hey presto, dead. No, I had been blameless but it hadn't looked good.

On an impulse I jumped to my feet.

'Thank you very much for the lovely tea,' I said, 'but I really must be off. I'm on duty this evening.'

Helen came with me to the door. 'Well it's been nice seeing you again, Jim.' She paused and looked at me doubtfully. 'I wish you'd stop worrying about that cow. It's a pity but you couldn't help it. There was nothing you could do.'

'Thanks, Helen, I know. But it's a nasty smack for your father isn't it?'

She shrugged and smiled her kind smile. Helen was always kind.

Driving back through the pastures up to the farm gate I could see the motionless body of my patient with her companions sniffing around her curiously in the gentle evening sunshine. Any time now the knacker man would be along to winch the carcase on to his wagon. It was the grim epilogue to every vet's failure.

I closed the gate behind me and looked back at Heston Grange. I had thought everything would be all right this time but it hadn't worked out that way.

The jinx was still on.

CHAPTER SIX

'Monday morning disease' they used to call it. The almost unbelievably gross thickening of the hind limb in cart horses which had stood in the stable over the weekend. It seemed that the sudden suspension of their normal work and exercise produced the massive lymphangitis and swelling which gave many a farmer a nasty jolt right at the beginning of the week.

But it was Wednesday evening now and Mr Crump's big Shire gelding was greatly improved.

'That leg's less than half the size it was,' I said, running my hand over the inside of the hock, feeling the remains of the oedema pitting under my fingers. 'I can see you've put in some hard work here.'

'Aye, ah did as you said.' Mr Crump's reply was typically laconic, but I knew he must have spent hours fomenting and massaging the limb and forcibly exercising the horse as I had told him when I gave the arecoline injection on Monday.

I began to fill the syringe for a repeat injection. 'He's having no corn, is he?'

'Nay, nowt but bran.'

'That's fine. I think he'll be back to normal in a day or two if you keep up the treatment.'

The farmer grunted and no sign of approval showed in the big, purple-red face with its perpetually surprised expression. But I knew he was pleased all right; he was fond of the horse and had been unable to hide his concern at the animal's pain and distress on my first visit.

I went into the house to wash my hands and Mr Crump led the way into the kitchen, his big frame lumbering clumsily ahead of me. He proffered soap and towel in his slow-moving way and stood back in silence as I leaned over the long shallow sink of brown earthenware.

As I dried my hands he cleared his throat and spoke hesitantly. 'Would you like a drink of ma wine?'

Before I could answer, Mrs Crump came bustling through from an inner room. She was pulling on her hat and behind her her teenage son and daughter followed, dressed ready to go out.

'Oh Albert, stop it!' she snapped, looking up at her husband. 'Mr Herriot doesn't want your wine. I wish you wouldn't pester people so with it!'

The boy grinned. 'Dad and his wine, he's always looking for a victim.' His sister joined in the general laughter and I had an uncomfortable feeling that Mr Crump was the odd man out in his own home.

'We're going down t'village institute to see a school play, Mr Herriot,' the wife said briskly. 'We're late now so we must be off.' She hurried away with her children, leaving the big man looking after her sheepishly.

There was a silence while I finished drying my hands, then I turned to the farmer. 'Well, how about that drink, Mr Crump?'

He hesitated for a moment and the surprised look deepened. 'Would you . . . you'd really like to try some?'

'I'd love to. I haven't had my evening meal yet – I could just do with an aperitif.'

'Right, I'll be back in a minute.' He disappeared into the large pantry at the end of the kitchen and came back with a bottle of amber liquid and glasses.

'This is ma rhubarb,' he said, tipping out two good measures.

I took a sip and then a good swallow, and gasped as the liquid blazed a fiery trail down to my stomach.

'It's strong stuff,' I said a little breathlessly, 'but the taste is very pleasant. Very pleasant indeed.'

Mr Crump watched approvingly as I took another drink. 'Aye, it's just right. Nearly two years old.'

I drained the glass and this time the wine didn't burn so much on its way down but seemed to wash around the walls of my empty stomach and send glowing tendrils creeping along my limbs.

'Delicious,' I said. 'Absolutely delicious.'

The farmer expanded visibly. He refilled the glasses and watched with rapt attention as I drank. When we had finished the second glass he jumped to his feet.

'Now for a change I want you to try summat different.' He almost trotted to the pantry and produced another bottle, this time of colourless fluid. 'Elderflower,' he said, panting slightly.

When I tasted it I was amazed at the delicate flavour, the bubbles sparkling and dancing on my tongue.

'Gosh, this is terrific! It's just like champagne. You know, you really have a gift – I never thought home-made wines could taste like this.'

Mr Crump stared at me for a moment then one corner of his mouth began to twitch and incredibly a shy smile spread slowly over his face. 'You're about fust I've heard say that. You'd think I was trying to poison folks when I offer them ma wine – they always shy off but they can sup plenty of beer and whisky.'

'Well they don't know what they're missing, Mr Crump.' I watched while the farmer replenished my glass. 'I wouldn't have believed you could make stuff as good as this at home.' I sipped appreciatively at the elderflower. It still tasted like champagne.

I hadn't got more than halfway down the glass before Mr Crump was clattering and clinking inside the pantry again. He emerged with a bottle with contents of a deep blood red. 'Try that,' he gasped.

I was beginning to feel like a professional taster and rolled the first mouthful around my mouth with eyes half closed. 'Mm, mm, yes. Just like an excellent port, but there's something else here – a fruitiness in the background – something familiar about it – it's . . . it's . . .'

'Blackberry!' shouted Mr Crump triumphantly. 'One of t'best I've done. Made it two back-ends since – it were a right good year for it.'

Leaning back in the chair I took another drink of the rich, dark wine; it was round-flavoured, warming, and behind it there was always the elusive hint of the brambles. I could almost see the heavy-hanging clusters of berries glistening black and succulent in the autumn sunshine. The mellowness of the image matched my mood which was becoming more expansive by the minute and I looked round with leisurely appreciation at the rough comfort of the farmhouse kitchen; at the hams and sides of bacon hanging from their hooks in the ceiling, and at my host sitting across the table, watching me eagerly. He was, I noticed for the first time, still wearing his cap.

'You know,' I said, holding the glass high and studying its ruby depths against the light. 'I can't make up my mind which of your wines I like best. They're all excellent and yet so different.'

Mr Crump, too, had relaxed. He threw back his head and laughed delightedly before hurriedly refilling both of our tumblers. 'But you haven't started yet. Ah've got dozens of bottles in there – all different. You must try a few more.' He shambled again over to the pantry and this time when he reappeared he was weighed down by an armful of bottles of differing shapes and colours.

What a charming man he was, I thought. How wrong I had been in my previous assessment of him; it had been so easy to put him down as lumpish and unemotional but as I looked at him now his face was alight with friendship, hospitality, understanding. He had cast off his inhibitions and as he sat down surrounded by the latest batch he began to talk rapidly and fluently about wines and wine making.

Wide-eyed and impassioned he ranged at length over the niceties of fermentation and sedimentation, of flavour and bouquet. He dealt learnedly with the relative merits of Chambertin and Nuits St George, Montrachet and Chablis.

Enthusiasts are appealing but a fanatic is irresistible and I sat spellbound while Mr Crump pushed endless samples of his craft in front of me, mixing and adjusting expertly.

'How did you find that 'un?'

'Very nice . . .'

'But sweet, maybe?'

'Well, perhaps . . .'

'Right, try some of this with it.' The meticulous addition of a few drops of nameless liquid from the packed rows of bottles. 'How's that?'

'Marvellous!'

'Now this 'un. Perhaps a bit sharpish, eh?'

'Possibly . . . yes . . .'

Again the tender trickling of a few mysterious droplets into my drink and again the anxious enquiry.

'Is that better?'

'Just right.'

The big man drank with me, glass by glass. We tried parsnip and dandelion, cowslip and parsley, clover, gooseberry, beetroot and crab apple. Incredibly, we had some stuff made from turnips which was so exquisite that I insisted on a refill.

Everything gradually slowed down as we sat there. Time slowed down till it was finally meaningless. Mr Crump and I slowed down and our speech and actions became more and more deliberate. The farmer's visits to the pantry developed into laboured, unsteady affairs; sometimes he took a roundabout route to reach the door and on one occasion there was a tremendous crash from within and I feared he had fallen among his bottles. But I couldn't be bothered to get up to see and in due course he reappeared, apparently unharmed.

It was around nine o'clock that I heard the soft knocking on the outer door. I ignored it as I didn't want to interrupt Mr Crump who was in the middle of a deep exposition.

'Thish,' he was saying, leaning close to me and tapping a bulbous flagon with his forefinger. 'Thish is, in my 'pinion, comp'rable to a fine Moselle. Made it lash year and would 'preciate it if you'd tell me what you think.' He bent low over the glass, blinking, heavy-eyed as he poured.

'Now then, wha' d'you say? Ish it or ishn't it?'

I took a gulp and paused for a moment. It all tasted the same now and I had never drunk Moselle anyway, but I nodded and hiccuped solemnly in reply.

The farmer rested a friendly hand on my shoulder and was about to make a further speech when he, too, heard the knocking. He made his way across the floor with some difficulty and opened the door. A young lad was standing there and I heard a few muttered words.

'We 'ave a cow on calving and we phoned surgery and they said vitnery might still be here.'

Mr Crump turned to face me. 'It's the Bamfords of Holly Bush. They wan' you to go there – jush a mile along t'road.'

'Right,' I heaved myself to my feet then gripped the table tightly as the familiar objects of the room began to whirl rapidly around me. When they came to rest Mr Crump appeared to be standing at the head of a fairly steep slope. The kitchen floor had seemed perfectly level when I had come in but now it was all I could do to fight my way up the gradient.

When I reached the door Mr Crump was staring owlishly into the darkness.

' 'Sraining,' he said. ' 'Sraining like 'ell.'

I peered out at the steady beat of the dark water on the cobbles of the yard, but my car was just a few yards away and I was about to set out when the farmer caught my arm.

'Jus' minute, can't go out like that.' He held up a finger then went over and groped about in a drawer. At length he produced a tweed cap which he offered me with great dignity.

I never wore anything on my head whatever the weather but I was deeply touched and wrung my companion's hand in silence. It was understandable that a man like Mr Crump who wore his cap at all times, indoors and out, would recoil in horror from the idea of anybody venturing uncovered into the rain.

The tweed cap which I now put on was the biggest I had

ever seen; a great round flat pancake of a thing which even at that moment I felt would keep not only my head but my shoulders and entire body dry in the heaviest downpour.

I took my leave of Mr Crump with reluctance and as I settled in the seat of the car trying to remember where first gear was situated I could see his bulky form silhouetted against the light from the kitchen; he was waving his hand with gentle benevolence and it struck me as I at length drove away what a deep and wonderful friendship had been forged that night.

Driving at walking pace along the dark narrow road, my nose almost touching the windscreen, I was conscious of some unusual sensations. My mouth and lips felt abnormally sticky as though I had been drinking liquid glue instead of wine, my breath seemed to be whistling in my nostrils like a strong wind blowing under a door, and I was having difficulty focusing my eyes. Fortunately I met only one car and as it approached and flashed past in the other direction I was muzzily surprised by the fact that it had two complete sets of headlights which kept merging into each other and drawing apart again.

In the yard at Holly Bush I got out of the car, nodded to the shadowy group of figures standing there, fumbled my bottle of antiseptic and calving ropes from the boot and marched determinedly into the byre. One of the men held an oil lamp over a cow lying on a deep bed of straw in one of the standings; from the vulva a calf's foot protruded a few inches and as the cow strained a little muzzle showed momentarily then disappeared as she relaxed.

Far away inside me a stone cold sober veterinary surgeon murmured: 'Only a leg back and a big roomy cow. Shouldn't be much trouble.' I turned and looked at the Bamfords for the first time. I hadn't met them before but it was easy to classify them; simple, kindly, anxious-to-please people – two middle-aged men, probably brothers, and two young men who would be the sons of one or the other. They were all staring at me in the dim light, their eyes expectant, their mouths slightly open as though ready to smile or laugh if given half a chance.

I squared my shoulders, took a deep breath and said in a loud voice: 'Would you please bring me a bucket of hot water, some soap and a towel.' Or at least that's what I meant to say, because what actually issued from my lips was a torrent of something that sounded like Swahili. The Bamfords, poised, ready to spring into action to do my bidding, looked at me blankly. I cleared my throat, swallowed, took a few seconds' rest and tried again. I cleared my throat, swallowed, another volley of gibberish echoing uselessly round the cow house.

Clearly I had a problem. It was essential to communicate in some way, particularly since these people didn't know me and were waiting for some action. I suppose I must have appeared a strange and enigmatic figure standing there, straight and solemn, surmounted and dominated by a vast cap. But through the mists a flash of insight showed me where I was going wrong. It was over-confidence. It wasn't a bit of good trying to speak loudly like that. I tried again in the faintest of whispers.

'Could I have a bucket of hot water, some soap and a towel, please.' It came out beautifully though the oldest Mr Bamford didn't quite get it first time. He came close, cupped an ear with his hand and watched my lips intently. Then he nodded eagerly in comprehension, held up a forefinger at me, tiptoed across the floor like a tight-rope walker to one of the sons and whispered in his ear. The young man turned and crept out noiselessly, closing the door behind him with the utmost care; he was back in less than a minute, padding over the cobbles daintily in his heavy boots and placing the bucket gingerly in front of me.

I managed to remove my jacket, tie and shirt quite efficiently and they were taken from me in silence and hung upon nails by the Bamfords who were moving around as though in church. I thought I was doing fine till I started to wash my arms. The soap kept shooting from my arms, slithering into the dung channel, disappearing into the dark corners of the byre with the Bamfords in hot pursuit. It was worse still when I tried to work up to the top of my arms. The soap flew over my shoulders like a live thing, at times cannoning off the walls, at others gliding down my back. The farmers never knew where the next shot was going and they took on the appearance of a really sharp fielding side crouching around me with arms outstretched waiting for a catch.

However I did finally work up a lather and was ready to start, but the cow refused firmly to get to her feet, so I had to stretch out behind her, face down on the unyielding cobbles. It wasn't till I got down there that I felt the great cap dropping over my ears; I must have put it on again after removing my shirt though it was difficult to see what purpose it might serve.

Inserting a hand gently into the vagina I pushed along the calf's neck, hoping to come upon a flexed knee or even a foot, but I was disappointed; the leg really was right back, stretching from the shoulder away flat against the calf's side. Still, I would be all right – it just meant a longer reach.

And there was one reassuring feature; the calf was alive. As I lay, my face was almost touching the rear end of the cow and I had a close up of the nose which kept appearing every few seconds; it was good to see the little nostrils twitching as they sought the outside air. All I had to do was get that leg round.

But the snag was that as I reached forward the cow kept straining, squeezing my arm cruelly against her bony pelvis making me groan and roll about in agony for a few seconds till the pressure went off. Quite often in these crises my cap fell on to the floor and each time gentle hands replaced it immediately on my head.

At last the foot was in my hand – there would be no need for ropes this time – and I began to pull it round. It took me longer than I thought and it seemed to me that the calf was beginning to lose patience with me because when its head was forced out by the cow's contractions we were eye to eye and I fancied the little creature was giving me a disgusted 'For heaven's sake get on with it' look.

When the leg did come round it was with a rush and in an instant everything was laid as it should have been.

'Get hold of the feet,' I whispered to the Bamfords and

after a hushed consultation they took up their places. In no time at all a fine heifer calf was wriggling on the cobbles shaking its head and snorting the placental fluid from its nostrils.

In response to my softly hissed instructions the farmers rubbed the little creature down with straw wisps and pulled it round for its mother to lick.

It was a happy ending to the most peaceful calving I have ever attended. Never a voice raised, everybody moving around on tiptoe. I got dressed in a cathedral silence, went out to the car, breathed a final goodnight and left with the Bamfords waving mutely.

To say I had a hangover next morning would be failing even to hint at the utter disintegration of my bodily economy and personality. Only somebody who had consumed two or three quarts of assorted home-made wines at a sitting could have an inkling of the quaking nausea, the raging inferno within, the jangling nerves, the black despairing outlook.

Tristan had seen me in the bathroom running the cold tap on my tongue and had intuitively administered a raw egg, aspirins and brandy which, as I came downstairs, lay in a cold, unmoving blob in my outraged stomach.

'What are you walking like that for, James?' asked Siegfried in what sounded like a bull's bellow as I came in on him at breakfast. 'You look as though you'd pee'd yourself.'

'Oh it's nothing much.' It was no good telling him I was treading warily across the carpet because I was convinced that if I let my heels down too suddenly it would jar my eyeballs from their sockets. 'I had a few glasses of Mr Crump's wine last night and it seems to have upset me.'

'A few glasses! You ought to be more careful – that stuff's dynamite. Could knock anybody over.' He crashed his cup into its saucer then began to clatter about with knife and fork as if trying to give a one man rendering of the Anvil Chorus. 'I hope you weren't any the worse to go to Bamford's.'

I listlessly crumbled some dry toast on my plate. 'Well I

did the job all right, but I'd had a bit too much – no use denying it.'

Siegfried was in one of his encouraging moods. 'By God, James, those Bamfords are very strict Methodists. They're grand chaps but absolutely dead nuts against drink – if they thought you were under the influence of alcohol they'd never have you on the place again.' He ruthlessly bisected an egg yolk. 'I hope they didn't notice anything. Do you think they knew?'

'Oh maybe not. No, I shouldn't think so.' I closed my eyes and shivered as Siegfried pushed a forkful of sausage and fried bread into his mouth and began to chew briskly. My mind went back to the gentle hands replacing the monstrous cap on my head and I groaned inwardly.

Those Bamfords knew all right. Oh yes, they knew.

CHAPTER SEVEN

The silvery-haired old gentleman with the pleasant face didn't look the type to be easily upset but his eyes glared at me angrily and his lips quivered with indignation.

'Mr Herriot,' he said. 'I have come to make a complaint. I strongly object to your callousness in subjecting my dog to unnecessary suffering.'

'Suffering? What suffering?' I was mystified.

'I think you know, Mr Herriot. I brought my dog in a few days ago. He was very lame and I am referring to your treatment on that occasion.'

I nodded. 'Yes, I remember it well . . . but where does the suffering come in?'

'Well, the poor animal is going around with his leg dangling and I have it on good authority that the bone is fractured and should have been put in plaster immediately.' The old gentleman stuck his chin out fiercely.

'All right, you can stop worrying,' I said. 'Your dog has a radial paralysis caused by a blow on the ribs and if you are patient and follow my treatment he'll gradually improve. In fact I think he'll recover completely.'

'But he trails his leg when he walks.'

'I know – that's typical, and to the layman it does give the appearance of a broken leg. But he shows no sign of pain, does he?'

'No, he seems quite happy, but this lady seemed to be absolutely sure of her facts. She was adamant.'

'Lady?'

'Yes,' said the old gentleman. 'She is very clever with animals and she came round to see if she could help in my dog's convalescence. She brought some excellent condition powders with her.'

'Ah!' A blinding shaft pierced the fog in my mind. All was suddenly clear. 'It was Mrs Donovan, wasn't it?'

'Well . . . er, yes. That was her name.'

Old Mrs Donovan was a woman who really got around. No matter what was going on in Darrowby – weddings, funerals, house-sales – you'd find the dumpy little figure and walnut face among the spectators, the darting, black-button eyes taking everything in. And always, on the end of its lead, her terrier dog.

When I say 'old', I'm only guessing, because she appeared ageless; she seemed to have been around a long time but she could have been anything between fifty-five and seventy-five. She certainly had the vitality of a young woman because she must have walked vast distances in her dedicated quest to keep abreast of events. Many people took an uncharitable view of her acute curiosity but whatever the motivation, her activities took her into almost every channel of life in the town. One of these channels was our veterinary practice.

Because Mrs Donovan, among her other widely ranging interests, was an animal doctor. In fact I think it would be safe to say that this facet of her life transcended all the others.

She could talk at length on the ailments of small animals

and she had a whole armoury of medicines and remedies at her command, her two specialities being her miracle-working condition powders and a dog shampoo of unprecedented value for improving the coat. She had an uncanny ability to sniff out a sick animal and it was not uncommon when I was on my rounds to find Mrs Donovan's dark gipsy face poised intently over what I had thought was my patient while she administered calf's foot jelly or one of her own patent nostrums.

I suffered more than Siegfried because I took a more active part in the small animal side of our practice. I was anxious to develop this aspect and to improve my image in this field and Mrs Donovan didn't help at all. 'Young Mr Herriot,' she would confide to my clients, 'is all right with cattle and such like, but he don't know nothing about dogs and cats.'

And of course they believed her and had implicit faith in her. She had the irresistible mystic appeal of the amateur and on top of that there was her habit, particularly endearing in Darrowby, of never charging for her advice, her medicines, her long periods of diligent nursing.

Older folk in the town told how her husband, an Irish farm worker, had died many years ago and how he must have had a 'bit put away' because Mrs Donovan had apparently been able to indulge all her interests over the years without financial strain. Since she inhabited the streets of Darrowby all day and every day I often encountered her and she always smiled up at me sweetly and told me how she had been sitting up all night with Mrs So-and-so's dog that I'd been treating. She felt sure she'd be able to pull it through.

There was no smile on her face, however, on the day when she rushed into the surgery while Siegfried and I were having tea.

'Mr Herriot!' she gasped. 'Can you come? My little dog's been run over!'

I jumped up and ran out to the car with her. She sat in the passenger seat with her head bowed, her hands clasped tightly on her knees.

'He slipped his collar and ran in front of a car,' she murmured. 'He's lying in front of the school halfway up Cliffend Road. Please hurry.'

I was there within three minutes but as I bent over the dusty little body stretched on the pavement I knew there was nothing I could do. The fast-glazing eyes, the faint, gasping respirations, the ghastly pallor of the mucous membranes all told the same story.

'I'll take him back to the surgery and get some saline into him, Mrs Donovan,' I said. 'But I'm afraid he's had a massive internal haemorrhage. Did you see what happened exactly?'

She gulped. 'Yes, the wheel went right over him.'

Ruptured liver, for sure. I passed my hands under the little animal and began to lift him gently, but as I did so the breathing stopped and the eyes stared fixedly ahead.

Mrs Donovan sank to her knees and for a few moments she gently stroked the rough hair of the head and chest. 'He's dead, isn't he?' she whispered at last.

'I'm afraid he is,' I said.

She got slowly to her feet and stood bewilderedly among the little group of bystanders on the pavement. Her lips moved but she seemed unable to say any more.

I took her arm, led her over to the car and opened the door. 'Get in and sit down,' I said. 'I'll run you home. Leave everything to me.'

I wrapped the dog in my calving overall and laid him in the boot before driving away. It wasn't until we drew up outside Mrs Donovan's house that she began to weep silently. I sat there without speaking till she had finished. Then she wiped her eyes and turned to me.

'Do you think he suffered at all?'

'I'm certain he didn't. It was all so quick – he wouldn't know a thing about it.'

She tried to smile. 'Poor little Rex, I don't know what I'm going to do without him. We've travelled a few miles together, you know.'

'Yes, you have. He had a wonderful life, Mrs Donovan. And let me give you a bit of advice – you must get another dog. You'd be lost without one.'

She shook her head. 'No, I couldn't. That little dog meant too much to me. I couldn't let another take his place.'

'Well I know that's how you feel just now but I wish you'd think about it. I don't want to seem callous – I tell everybody this when they lose an animal and I know it's good advice.'

'Mr Herriot, I'll never have another one.' She shook her head again, very decisively. 'Rex was my faithful friend for many years and I just want to remember him. He's the last dog I'll ever have.'

I often saw Mrs Donovan around the town after this and I was glad to see she was still as active as ever, though she looked strangely incomplete without the little dog on its lead. But it must have been over a month before I had the chance to speak to her.

It was on the afternoon that Inspector Halliday of the RSPCA rang me.

'Mr Herriot,' he said, 'I'd like you to come and see an animal with me. A cruelty case.'

'Right, what is it?'

'A dog, and it's pretty grim. A dreadful case of neglect.' He gave me the name of a row of old brick cottages down by the river and said he'd meet me there.

Halliday was waiting for me, smart and business-like in his dark uniform, as I pulled up in the back lane behind the houses. He was a big, blond man with cheerful blue eyes but he didn't smile as he came over to the car.

'He's in here,' he said, and led the way towards one of the doors in the long, crumbling wall. A few curious people were hanging around and with a feeling of inevitability I recognized a gnome-like brown face. Trust Mrs Donovan, I thought, to be among those present at a time like this.

We went through the door into the long garden. I had found that even the lowliest dwellings in Darrowby had long strips of land at the back as though the builders had taken it for granted that the country people who were going to live in them would want to occupy themselves with the pursuits of the soil; with vegetable and fruit growing, even stock-keeping in a small way. You usually found a pig there, a few hens, often pretty beds of flowers.

But this garden was a wilderness. A chilling air of desolation hung over the few gnarled apple and plum trees standing among a tangle of rank grass as though the place had been forsaken by all living creatures.

Halliday went over to a ramshackle wooden shed with peeling paint and a rusted corrugated iron roof. He produced a key, unlocked the padlock and dragged the door partly open. There was no window and it wasn't easy to identify the jumble inside; broken gardening tools, an ancient mangle, rows of flower pots and partly-used paint tins. And right at the back, a dog sitting quietly.

I didn't notice him immediately because of the gloom and because the smell in the shed started me coughing, but as I drew closer I saw that he was a big animal, sitting very upright, his collar secured by a chain to a ring in the wall. I had seen some thin dogs but this advanced emaciation reminded me of my text books on anatomy; nowhere else did the bones of pelvis, face and rib cage stand out with such horrifying clarity. A deep, smoothed out hollow in the earth floor showed where he had lain, moved about, in fact lived for a very long time.

The sight of the animal had a stupefying effect on me; I only half took in the rest of the scene – the filthy shreds of sacking scattered nearby, the bowl of scummy water.

'Look at his back end,' Halliday muttered.

I carefully raised the dog from his sitting position and realized that the stench in the place was not entirely due to the piles of excrement. The hindquarters were a welter of pressure sores which had turned gangrenous and strips of sloughing tissue hung down from them. There were similar sores along the sternum and ribs. The coat, which seemed to be a dull yellow, was matted and caked with dirt.

The Inspector spoke again. 'I don't think he's ever been out of here. He's only a young dog – about a year old – but I understand he's been in this shed since he was an eight-week-old pup. Somebody out in the lane heard a whimper or he'd never have been found.'

I felt a tightening of the throat and a sudden nausea which wasn't due to the smell. It was the thought of this patient animal sitting starved and forgotten in the darkness and filth for a year. I looked again at the dog and saw in his eyes only a calm trust. Some dogs would have barked their heads off and soon been discovered, some would have become terrified and vicious, but this was one of the totally undemanding kind, the kind which had complete faith in people and accepted all their actions without complaint. Just an occasional whimper perhaps as he sat interminably in the empty blackness which had been his world and at times wondered what it was all about.

'Well, Inspector, I hope you're going to throw the book at whoever's responsible,' I said.

Halliday grunted. 'Oh, there won't be much done. It's a case of diminished responsibility. The owner's definitely simple. Lives with an aged mother who hardly knows what's going on either. I've seen the fellow and it seems he threw in a bit of food when he felt like it and that's about all he did. They'll fine him and stop him keeping an animal in the future but nothing more than that.'

'I see.' I reached out and stroked the dog's head and he immediately responded by resting a paw on my wrist. There was a pathetic dignity about the way he held himself erect, the calm eyes regarding me, friendly and unafraid. 'Well, you'll let me know if you want me in court.'

'Of course, and thank you for coming along.' Halliday hesitated for a moment. 'And now I expect you'll want to put this poor thing out of his misery right away.'

I continued to run my hand over the head and ears while I thought for a moment. 'Yes . . . yes, I suppose so. We'd never find a home for him in this state. It's the kindest thing to do. Anyway, push the door wide open will you so that I can get a proper look at him.'

In the improved light I examined him more thoroughly. Perfect teeth, well-proportioned limbs with a fringe of yellow hair. I put my stethoscope on his chest and as I listened to the slow, strong thudding of the heart the dog again put his paw on my hand.

I turned to Halliday, 'You know, Inspector, inside this bag of bones there's a lovely healthy Golden Retriever. I wish there was some way of letting him out.'

As I spoke I noticed there was more than one figure in the door opening. A pair of black pebble eyes were peering intently at the big dog from behind the Inspector's broad back. The other spectators had remained in the lane but Mrs Donovan's curiosity had been too much for her. I continued conversationally as though I hadn't seen her.

'You know, what this dog needs first of all is a good shampoo to clean up his matted coat.'

'Huh?' said Halliday.

'Yes. And then he wants a long course of some really strong condition powders.'

'What's that?' The Inspector looked startled.

'There's no doubt about it,' I said. 'It's the only hope for him, but where are you going to find such things? Really powerful enough, I mean.' I sighed and straightened up. 'Ah well, I suppose there's nothing else for it. I'd better put him to sleep right away. I'll get the things from my car.'

When I got back to the shed Mrs Donovan was already inside examining the dog despite the feeble remonstrances of the big man.

'Look!' she said excitedly, pointing to a name roughly scratched on the collar. 'His name's Roy.' She smiled up at me. 'It's a bit like Rex, isn't it, that name?'

'You know, Mrs Donovan, now you mention it, it is. It's very like Rex, the way it comes off your tongue.' I nodded seriously.

She stood silent for a few moments, obviously in the grip of a deep emotion, then she burst out.

'Can I have 'im? I can make him better, I know I can. Please, please let me have 'im!'

'Well I don't know,' I said. 'It's really up to the Inspector. You'll have to get his permission.'

Halliday looked at her in bewilderment, then he said: 'Excuse me, Madam,' and drew me to one side. We walked a few yards through the long grass and stopped under a tree.

'Mr Herriot,' he whispered, 'I don't know what's going on

here, but I can't just pass over an animal in this condition to anybody who has a casual whim. The poor beggar's had one bad break already – I think it's enough. This woman doesn't look a suitable person . . .'

I held up a hand. 'Believe me, Inspector, you've nothing to worry about. She's a funny old stick but she's been sent from heaven today. If anybody in Darrowby can give this dog a new life it's her.'

Halliday still looked very doubtful. 'But I still don't get it. What was all that stuff about him needing shampoos and condition powders?'

'Oh never mind about that. I'll tell you some other time. What he needs is lots of good grub, care and affection and that's just what he'll get. You can take my word for it.'

'All right, you seem very sure.' Halliday looked at me for a second or two then turned and walked over to the eager little figure by the shed.

I had never before been deliberately on the look out for Mrs Donovan: she had just cropped up wherever I happened to be, but now I scanned the streets of Darrowby anxiously day by day without sighting her. I didn't like it when Gobber Newhouse got drunk and drove his bicycle determinedly through a barrier into a ten foot hole where they were laying the new sewer and Mrs Donovan was not in evidence among the happy crowd who watched the council workmen and two policemen trying to get him out; and when she was nowhere to be seen when they had to fetch the fire engine to the fish and chip shop the night the fat burst into flames I became seriously worried.

Maybe I should have called round to see how she was getting on with that dog. Certainly I had trimmed off the necrotic tissue and dressed the sores before she took him away, but perhaps he needed something more than that. And yet at the time I had felt a strong conviction that the main thing was to get him out of there and clean him and feed him and nature would do the rest. And I had a lot of faith in Mrs Donovan – far more than she had in me – when it came to animal doctoring; it was hard to believe I'd been completely wrong.

It must have been nearly three weeks and I was on the point of calling at her home when I noticed her stumping briskly along the far side of the market place, peering closely into every shop window exactly as before. The only difference was that she had a big yellow dog on the end of the lead.

I turned the wheel and sent my car bumping over the cobbles till I was abreast of her. When she saw me getting out she stopped and smiled impishly but she didn't speak as I bent over Roy and examined him. He was still a skinny dog but he looked bright and happy, his wounds were healthy and granulating and there was not a speck of dirt in his coat or on his skin. I knew then what Mrs Donovan had been doing all this time; she had been washing and combing and teasing at that filthy tangle till she had finally conquered it.

As I straightened up she seized my wrist in a grip of surprising strength and looked up into my eyes.

'Now, Mr Herriot,' she said. 'Haven't I made a difference to this dog!'

'You've done wonders, Mrs Donovan,' I said. 'And you've been at him with that marvellous shampoo of yours, haven't you?'

She giggled and walked away and from that day I saw the two of them frequently, but at a distance, and something like two months went by before I had a chance to talk to her again. She was passing by the surgery as I was coming down the steps and again she grabbed my wrist.

'Mr Herriot,' she said, just as she had done before. 'Haven't I made a difference to this dog!'

I looked down at Roy with something akin to awe. He had grown and filled out and his coat, no longer yellow but a rich gold, lay in luxuriant shining swathes over the well-fleshed ribs and back. A new, brightly-studded collar glittered on his neck and his tail, beautifully fringed, fanned the air gently. He was now a Golden Retriever in full magnificence. As I stared at him he reared up, plunked his fore paws on my chest and looked into my face, and in his eyes I read plainly the same calm affection and trust I had seen back in that black, noisome shed.

'Mrs Donovan,' I said softly, 'he's the most beautiful dog in Yorkshire.' Then, because I knew she was waiting for it. 'It's those wonderful condition powders. Whatever do you put in them?'

'Ah, wouldn't you like to know!' She bridled and smiled up at me coquettishly and indeed she was nearer being kissed at that moment than for many years.

I suppose you could say that that was the start of Roy's second life. And as the years passed I often pondered on the beneficent providence which had decreed that an animal which had spent his first twelve months abandoned and unwanted, staring uncomprehendingly into that unchanging, stinking darkness, should be whisked in a moment into an existence of light and movement and love. Because I don't think any dog had it quite so good as Roy from then on.

His diet changed dramatically from odd bread crusts to best stewing steak and biscuit, meaty bones and a bowl of warm milk every evening. And he never missed a thing. Garden fêtes, school sports, evictions, gymkhanas – he'd be there. I was pleased to note that as time went on Mrs Donovan seemed to be clocking up an even greater daily mileage. Her expenditure on shoe leather must have been phenomenal, but of course it was absolute pie for Roy – a busy round in the morning, home for a meal then straight out again; it was all go.

Mrs Donovan didn't confine her activities to the town centre; there was a big stretch of common land down by the river where there were seats, and people used to take their dogs for a gallop and she liked to get down there fairly regularly to check on the latest developments on the domestic scene. I often saw Roy loping majestically over the grass among a pack of assorted canines, and when he wasn't doing that he was submitting to being stroked or patted or generally fussed over. He was handsome and he just liked people; it made him irresistible.

It was common knowledge that his mistress had bought a whole selection of brushes and combs of various sizes with which she laboured over his coat. Some people said she had a little brush for his teeth, too, and it might have been true, but he certainly wouldn't need his nails clipped – his life on the roads would keep them down.

Mrs Donovan, too, had her reward; she had a faithful companion by her side every hour of the day and night. But there was more to it than that; she had always had the compulsion to help and heal animals and the salvation of Roy was the high point of her life – a blazing triumph which never dimmed.

I know the memory of it was always fresh because many years later I was sitting on the sidelines at a cricket match and I saw the two of them; the old lady glancing keenly around her, Roy gazing placidly out at the field of play, apparently enjoying every ball. At the end of the match I watched them move away with the dispersing crowd; Roy would be about twelve then and heaven only knows how old Mrs Donovan must have been, but the big golden animal was trotting along effortlessly and his mistress, a little more bent perhaps and her head rather nearer the ground, was going very well.

When she saw me she came over and I felt the familiar tight grip on my wrist.

'Mr Herriot,' she said, and in the dark probing eyes the pride was still as warm, the triumph still as bursting new as if it had all happened yesterday.

'Mr Herriot, haven't I made a difference to this dog!'

CHAPTER EIGHT

'How would you like to officiate at Darrowby Show, James?' Siegfried threw the letter he had been reading on to the desk and turned to me.

'I don't mind, but I thought you always did it.'

'I do, but it says in that letter that they've changed the date this year and it happens I'm going to be away that weekend.'

'Oh well, fine. What do I have to do?'

Siegfried ran his eye down his list of calls. 'It's a sinecure, really. More a pleasant day out than anything else. You have to measure the ponies and be on call in case any animals are injured. That's about all. Oh and they want you to judge the Family Pets.'

'Family Pets?'

'Yes, they run a proper dog show but they have an expert judge for that. This is just a bit of fun – all kinds of pets. You've got to find a first, second and third.'

'Right,' I said. 'I think I should just about be able to manage that.'

'Splendid.' Siegfried tipped up the envelope in which the letter had come. 'Here are your car park and luncheon tickets for self and friend if you want to take somebody with you. Also your vet's badge. OK?'

The Saturday of the show brought the kind of weather that must have had the organizers purring with pleasure; a sky of wide, unsullied blue, hardly a whiff of wind and the kind of torrid, brazen sunshine you don't often find in North Yorkshire.

As I drove down towards the show ground I felt I was looking at a living breathing piece of old England; the group of tents and marquees vivid against the green of the riverside field, the women and children in their bright summer dresses, the cattle with their smocked attendants, a line of massive Shire horses parading in the ring.

I parked the car and made for the stewards' tent with its flag hanging limply from the mast. Tristan parted from me there. With the impecunious student's unerring eye for a little free food and entertainment he had taken up my spare tickets. He headed purposefully for the beer tent as I went in to report to the show secretary.

Leaving my measuring stick there I looked around for a while.

A country show is a lot of different things to a lot of different people. Riding horses of all kinds from small ponies to hunters were being galloped up and down and in one ring the judges hovered around a group of mares and their beautiful little foals.

In a corner four men armed with buckets and brushes were washing and grooming a row of young bulls with great concentration, twiddling and crimping the fuzz over the rumps like society hairdressers.

Wandering through the marquees I examined the bewildering variety of produce from stalks of rhubarb to bunches of onions, the flower displays, embroidery, jams, cakes, pies. And the children's section; a painting of 'The Beach at Scarborough' by Annie Heseltine, aged nine; rows of wobbling copperplate handwriting – 'A thing of beauty is a joy for ever', Bernard Peacock, aged twelve.

Drawn by the occasional gusts of melody I strolled across the grass to where the Darrowby and Houlton Silver Band was rendering *Poet and Peasant*. The bandsmen were of all ages from seventies down to one or two boys of about fourteen and most of them had doffed their uniform tunics as they sweated in the hot sun. Pint pots reposed under many of the chairs and the musicians refreshed themselves frequently with leisurely swigs.

I was particularly fascinated by the conductor, a tiny frail man who looked about eighty. He alone had retained his full uniform, cap and all, and he stood apparently motionless in front of the crescent of bandsmen, chin sunk on chest, arms hanging limply by his sides. It wasn't until I came right up to him that I realized his fingers were twitching in time with the music and that he was, in fact, conducting. And the more I watched him the more fitting it seemed that he should do it like that. The Yorkshireman's loathing of exhibitionism or indeed any outward show of emotion made it unthinkable that he should throw his arms about in the orthodox manner; no doubt he had spent weary hours rehearsing and coaching his players but here, when the results of his labours were displayed to the public he wasn't going to swank about it. Even the almost imperceptible twitching of the finger-ends had something guilty about it as if the old man felt he was being caught out in something shameful.

But my attention was jerked away as a group of people walked across on the far side of the band. It was Helen with Richard Edmundson and behind them Mr Alderson and Richard's father deep in conversation. The young man walked very close to Helen, his shining, plastered-down fair hair hovering possessively over her dark head, his face animated as he talked and laughed.

There were no clouds in the sky but it was as if a dark hand had reached across and smudged away the brightness of the sunshine. I turned quickly and went in search of Tristan.

I soon picked out my colleague as I hurried into the marquee with 'Refreshments' over the entrance. He was leaning with an elbow on the makeshift counter of boards and trestles chatting contentedly with a knot of cloth-capped locals, a Woodbine in one hand, a pint glass in the other. There was a general air of earthy bonhomie. Drinking of a more decorous kind would be taking place at the president's bar behind the stewards' headquarters with pink gins or sherry as the main tipple but here it was beer, bottled and draught, and the stout ladies behind the counter were working with the fierce concentration of people who knew they were in for a hard day.

'Yes, I saw her,' Tristan said when I gave him my news. 'In fact there she is now.' He nodded in the direction of the family group as they strolled past the entrance. 'I've had my eye on them for some time – I don't miss much from in here you know, Jim.'

'Ah well.' I accepted a half of bitter from him. 'It all looks pretty cosy. The two dads like blood brothers and Helen hanging on to that bloke's arm.'

Tristan squinted over the top of his pint at the scene outside and shook his head. 'Not exactly. He's hanging on to HER arm.' He looked at me judicially. 'There's a difference, you know.'

'I don't suppose it makes much difference to me either way,' I grunted.

'Well don't look so bloody mournful.' He took an effortless swallow which lowered the level in his glass by about six inches. 'What do you expect an attractive girl to do? Sit at home waiting for you to call? If you've been pounding on her door every night you haven't told me about it.'

'It's all right you talking. I think old man Alderson would set his dogs on me if I showed up there. I know he doesn't like me hanging around Helen and on top of that I've got the feeling he thinks I killed his cow on my last visit.'

'And did you?'

'No, I didn't. But I walked up to a living animal, gave it an injection and it promptly died, so I can't blame him.'

I took a sip at my beer and watched the Alderson party who had changed direction and were heading away from our retreat. Helen was wearing a pale blue dress and I was thinking how well the colour went with the deep brown of her hair and how I liked the way she walked with her legs swinging easily and her shoulders high and straight when the loudspeaker boomed across the show ground.

'Will Mr Herriot, Veterinary Surgeon, please report to the stewards immediately.'

It made me jump but at the same time I felt a quick stab of pride. It was the first time I had heard myself and my profession publicly proclaimed. I turned to Tristan. He was supposed to be seeing practice and this could be something interesting. But he was immersed in a story which he was trying to tell to a little stocky man with a fat, shiny face, and he was having difficulty because the little man, determined to get his full measure of enjoyment, kept throwing himself into helpless convulsions at the end of every sentence, and the finish was a long way away. Tristan took his stories very seriously; I decided not to interrupt him.

A glow of importance filled me as I hurried over the grass, my official badge with 'Veterinary Surgeon' in gold letters dangling from my lapel. A steward met me on the way.

'It's one of the cattle. Had an accident, I think.' He pointed to a row of pens along the edge of the field.

A curious crowd had collected around my patient which had been entered in the in-calf heifers class. The owner, a stranger from outside the Darrowby practice came up to me, his face glum.

'She tripped coming off the cattle wagon and went 'ead first into the wall. Knocked one of 'er horns clean off.'

The heifer, a bonny little light roan, was a pathetic sight. She had been washed, combed, powdered and primped for the big day and there she was with one horn dangling drunkenly down the side of her face and an ornamental fountain of bright arterial blood climbing gracefully in three jets from the broken surface high into the air.

I opened my bag. I had brought a selection of the things I might need and I fished out some artery forceps and suture material. The rational way to stop haemorrhage of this type is to grasp the bleeding vessel and ligate it, but it wasn't always as easy as that. Especially when the patient won't co-operate.

The broken horn was connected to the head only by a band of skin and I quickly snipped it away with scissors; then, with the farmer holding the heifer's nose I began to probe with my forceps for the severed vessels. In the bright sunshine it was surprisingly difficult to see the spurting blood and as the little animal threw her head about I repeatedly felt the warm spray across my face and heard it spatter on my collar.

It was when I was beginning to lose heart with my ineffectual groping that I looked up and saw Helen and her boy friend watching me from the crowd. Young Edmundson looked mildly amused as he watched my unavailing efforts but Helen smiled encouragingly as she caught my eye. I did my best to smile back at her through my bloody mask but I don't suppose it showed.

I gave it up when the heifer gave a particularly brisk toss which sent my forceps flying on to the grass. I did what I should probably have done at the beginning – clapped a pad of cotton wool and antiseptic powder on to the stump and secured it with a figure of eight bandage round the other horn.

'That's it, then,' I said to the farmer as I tried to blink the blood out of my eyes. 'The bleeding's stopped, anyway. I'd advise you to have her properly de-horned soon or she's going to look a bit odd.'

Just then Tristan appeared from among the spectators.

'What's got you out of the beer tent?' I enquired with a touch of bitterness.

'It's lunch time, old lad,' Tristan replied equably. 'But we'll have to get you cleaned up a bit first. I can't be seen with you in that condition. Hang on, I'll get a bucket of water.'

The show luncheon was so excellent that it greatly restored me. Although it was taken in a marquee the committee men's wives had somehow managed to conjure up a memorable cold spread. There was fresh salmon and home fed ham and slices of prime beef with mixed salads and apple pie and the big brimming jugs of cream you only see at farming functions. One of the ladies was a noted cheese maker and we finished with some delicious goat cheese and coffee. The liquid side was catered for too with a bottle of Magnet Pale Ale and a glass at every place.

I didn't have the pleasure of Tristan's company at lunch because he had strategically placed himself well down the table between two strict Methodists so that his intake of Magnet was trebled.

I had hardly emerged into the sunshine when a man touched me on the shoulder.

'One of the dog show judges wants you to examine a dog. He doesn't like the look of it.'

He led me to where a thin man of about forty with a small

dark moustache was standing by his car. He held a wire-haired fox terrier on a leash and he met me with an ingratiating smile.

'There's nothing whatever the matter with my dog,' he declared, 'but the chap in there seems very fussy.'

I looked down at the terrier. 'I see he has some matter in the corner of his eyes.'

The man shook his head vigorously. 'Oh no, that's not matter. I've been using some white powder on him and a bit's got into his eyes, that's all.'

'Hmm, well let's see what his temperature says, shall we?'

The little animal stood uncomplaining as I inserted the thermometer. When I took the reading my eyebrows went up.

'It's a hundred and four. I'm afraid he's not fit to go into the show.'

'Wait a minute.' The man thrust out his jaw. 'You're talking like that chap in there. I've come a long way to show this dog and I'm going to show him.'

'I'm sorry but you can't show him with a temperature of a hundred and four.'

'But he's had a car journey. That could put up his temperature.'

I shook my head. 'Not as high as that it couldn't. Anyway he looks sick to me. Do you see how he's half closing his eyes as though he's frightened of the light? It's possible he could have distemper.'

'What? That's rubbish and you know it. He's never been fitter!' The man's mouth trembled with anger.

I looked down at the little dog. He was crouching on the grass miserably. Occasionally he shivered, he had a definite photophobia and there was that creamy blob of pus in the corner of each eye. 'Has he been inoculated against distemper?'

'Well no, he hasn't, but why do you keep on about it?'

'Because I think he's got it now and for his sake and for the sake of the other dogs here you ought to take him straight home and see your own vet.'

He glared at me. 'So you won't let me take him into the show tent?'

'That's right. I'm very sorry, but it's out of the question.' I turned and walked away.

I had gone only a few yards when the loudspeaker boomed again. 'Will Mr Herriot please go to the measuring stand where the ponies are ready for him.'

I collected my stick and trotted over to a corner of the field where a group of ponies had assembled; Welsh, Dales, Exmoor, Dartmoor – all kinds of breeds were represented.

For the uninitiated, horses are measured in hands which consist of four inches and a graduated stick is used with a cross piece and a spirit level which rests on the withers, the highest point of the shoulders. I had done a fair bit of it in individual animals but this was the first time I had done the job at a show. With my stick at the ready I stood by the two wide boards which had been placed on the turf to give the animals a reasonably level standing surface.

A smiling young woman led the first pony, a smart chestnut, on to the boards.

'Which class?' I asked.

'Thirteen hands.'

I tried the stick on him. He was well under.

'Fine, next please.'

A few more came through without incident then there was a lull before the next group came up. The ponies were arriving on the field all the time in their boxes and being led over to me, some by their young riders, others by the parents. It looked as though I could be here quite a long time.

During one of the lulls a little man who had been standing near me spoke up.

'No trouble yet?' he asked.

'No, everything's in order,' I replied.

He nodded expressionlessly and as I took a closer look at him his slight body, dark, leathery features and high shoulders seemed to give him the appearance of a little brown gnome. At the same time there was something undeniably horsy about him.

'You'll 'ave some awkward 'uns,' he grunted. 'And they

allus say the same thing. They allus tell you the vet at some other show passed their pony.' His swarthy cheeks crinkled in a wry smile.

'Is that so?'

'Aye, you'll see.'

Another candidate, led by a beautiful blonde, was led on to the platform. She gave me the full blast of two big greenish eyes and flashed a mouthful of sparkling teeth at me.

'Twelve two,' she murmured seductively.

I tried the stick on the pony and worked it around, but try as I might I couldn't get it down to that.

'I'm afraid he's a bit big,' I said.

The blonde's smile vanished. 'Have you allowed half an inch for his shoes?'

'I have indeed, but you can see for yourself, he's well over.'

'But he passed the vet without any trouble at Hickley,' she snapped and out of the corner of my eye I saw the gnome nodding sagely.

'I can't help that,' I said. 'I'm afraid you'll have to put him into the next class.'

For a moment two green pebbles from the cold sea bed fixed me with a frigid glare then the blonde was gone taking her pony with her.

Next, a little bay animal was led on to the stand by a hard-faced gentleman in a check suit and I must say I was baffled by its behaviour. Whenever the stick touched the withers it sank at the knees so that I couldn't be sure whether I was getting the right reading or not. Finally I gave up and passed him through.

The gnome coughed. 'I know that feller.'

'You do?'

'Aye, he's pricked that pony's withers with a pin so many times that it drops down whenever you try to measure 'im.'

'Never!'

'Sure as I'm standing here.'

I was staggered, but the arrival of another batch took up my attention for a few minutes. Some I passed, others I had to banish to another class and the owners took it in different ways – some philosophically, a few with obvious annoyance. One or two of the ponies just didn't like the look of the stick at all and I had to dance around them as they backed away and reared.

The last pony in this group was a nice grey led by a bouncy man wearing a great big matey smile.

'How are you, all right?' he inquired courteously. 'This 'un's thirteen two.'

The animal went under the stick without trouble but after he had trotted away the gnome spoke up again.

'I know that feller, too.'

'Really?'

'Not 'alf. Weighs down 'is ponies before they're measured. That grey's been standing in 'is box for the last hour with a twelve stone sack of corn on 'is back. Knocks an inch off.'

'Good God! Are you sure?'

'Don't worry, I've seen 'im at it.'

My mind was beginning to reel just a little. Was the man making it all up or were there really these malign forces at work behind all this innocent fun?

'That same feller,' continued the gnome. 'I've seen 'im bring a pony to a show and get half an inch knocked off for shoes when it never 'ad no shoes on.'

I wished he'd stop. And just then there was an interruption. It was the man with the moustache. He sidled up to me and whispered confidentially in my ear.

'Now I've just been thinking. My dog must have got over his journey by now and I expect his temperature will be normal. I wonder if you'd just try him again. I've still got time to show him.'

I turned wearily. 'Honestly, it'll be a waste of time. I've told you, he's ill.'

'Please! Just as a favour.' He had a desperate look and a fanatical light flickered in his eye.

'All right.' I went over to the car with him and produced my thermometer. The temperature was still a hundred and four.

'Now I wish you'd take this poor little dog home,' I said. 'He shouldn't be here.'

For a moment I thought the man was going to strike me. 'There's nothing wrong with him!' he hissed, his whole face working with emotion.

'I'm sorry,' I said, and went back to the measuring stand.

A boy of about fifteen was waiting for me with his pony. It was supposed to be in the thirteen two class but was nearly one and a half inches over.

'Much too big, I'm afraid,' I said. 'He can't go in that class.'

The boy didn't answer. He put his hand inside his jacket and produced a sheet of paper. 'This is a veterinary certificate to say he's under thirteen two.'

'No good, I'm sorry,' I replied. 'The stewards have told me not to accept any certificates. I've turned down two others today. Everything has to go under the stick. It's a pity, but there it is.'

His manner changed abruptly. 'But you've GOT to accept it!' he shouted in my face. 'There doesn't have to be any measurements when you have a certificate.'

'You'd better see the stewards. Those are my instructions.'

'I'll see my father about this, that's what!' he shouted and led the animal away.

Father was quickly on the scene. Big, fat, prosperous-looking, confident. He obviously wasn't going to stand any nonsense from me.

'Now look here, I don't know what this is all about but you have no option in this matter. You have to accept the certificate.'

'I don't, I assure you,' I answered. 'And anyway, it's not as though your pony was slightly over the mark. He's miles over – nowhere near the height.'

Father flushed dark red. 'Well let me tell you he was passed through by the vet at . . .'

'I know, I know,' I said, and I heard the gnome give a short laugh. 'But he's not going through here.'

There was a brief silence then both father and son began to scream at me. And as they continued to hurl abuse I felt a hand on my arm. It was the man with the moustache again.

'I'm going to ask you just once more to take my dog's temperature,' he whispered with a ghastly attempt at a smile. 'I'm sure he'll be all right this time. Will you try him again?'

I'd had enough. 'No, I bloody well won't!' I barked. 'Will you kindly stop bothering me and take that poor animal home.'

It's funny how the most unlikely things motivate certain people. It didn't seem a life and death matter whether a dog got into a show or not but it was to the man with the moustache. He started to rave at me.

'You don't know your job, that's the trouble with you! I've come all this way and you've played a dirty trick on me. I've got a friend who's a vet, a proper vet, and I'm going to tell him about you, yes I am. I'm going to tell him about you!'

At the same time the father and son were still in full cry, snarling and mouthing at me and I became suddenly aware that I was in the centre of a hostile circle. The blonde was there too, and some of the others whose ponies I had outed and they were all staring at me belligerently, making angry gestures.

I felt very much alone because the gnome, who had seemed an ally, was nowhere to be seen. I was disappointed in the gnome; he was a big talker but had vanished at the first whiff of danger. As I surveyed the threatening crowd I moved my measuring stick round in front of me; it wasn't much of a weapon but it might serve to fend them off if they rushed me.

And just at that moment, as the unkind words were thick upon the air, I saw Helen and Richard Edmundson on the fringe of the circle, taking it all in. I wasn't worried about him but again it struck me as strange that it should be my destiny always to be looking a bit of a clown when Helen was around.

Anyway, the measuring was over and I felt in need of sustenance. I retreated and went to find Tristan.

CHAPTER NINE

The atmosphere in the beer tent was just what I needed. The hot weather had made the place even more popular than usual and it was crowded; many of the inhabitants had been there since early morning and the air was thick with earthy witticisms, immoderate laughter, cries of joy; and the nice thing was that nobody in there cared a damn about the heights of ponies or the temperatures of dogs.

I had to fight my way through the crush to reach Tristan who was leaning across the counter in earnest conversation with a comely young barmaid. The other serving ladies were middle-aged but his practised eye had picked this one out; glossy red hair, a puckish face and an inviting smile. I had been hoping for a soothing chat with him but he was unable to give me his undivided attention, so after juggling with a glass among the throng for a few minutes I left.

Out on the field the sun still blazed, the scent of the trampled grass rose into the warm air, the band was playing a selection from *Rose Marie* and peace began to steal into my soul. Maybe I could begin to enjoy the show now the pinpricks were over; there was only the Family Pets to judge and I was looking forward to that.

For about an hour I wandered among the pens of mountainous pigs and haughty sheep; the rows of Shorthorn cows with their classical wedge-shaped grace, their level udders and dainty feet.

I watched in fascination a contest which was new to me; shirt-sleeved young men sticking a fork into a a straw bale and hurling it high over a bar with a jerk of their thick brown arms.

Old Steve Bramley, a local farmer, was judging the heavy horses and I envied him his massive authority as he stumped, bowler-hatted and glowering around each animal, leaning occasionally on his stick as he took stock of the points. I couldn't imagine anyone daring to argue with him.

It was late in the afternoon when the loudspeaker called me to my final duty. The Family Pets contestants were arranged on wooden chairs drawn up in a wide circle on the turf. They were mainly children but behind them an interested ring of parents and friends watched me warily as I arrived.

The fashion for exotic pets was still in its infancy but I experienced a mild shock of surprise when I saw the variety of creatures on show. I suppose I must have had a vague mental picture of a few dogs and cats but I walked round the circle in growing bewilderment looking down at rabbits – innumerable rabbits of all sizes and colours – guinea pigs, white mice, several budgerigars, two tortoises, a canary, a kitten, a parrot, a mynah bird, a box of puppies, a few dogs and cats and a goldfish in a bowl. The smaller pets rested on their owners' knees, the others squatted on the ground.

How, I asked myself, was I going to come to a decision here? How did you choose between a parrot and a puppy, a budgie and a bulldog, a mouse and a mynah? Then as I circled it came to me; it couldn't be done. The only way was to question the children in charge and find which ones looked after their pets best, which of them knew most about their feeding and general husbandry. I rubbed my hands together and repressed a chuckle of satisfaction; I had something to work on now.

I don't like to boast, but I think I can say in all honesty that I carried out an exhaustive scientific survey of that varied group. From the outset I adopted an attitude of cold detachment, mercilessly banishing any ideas of personal preference. If I had been pleasing only myself I would have given first prize to a gleaming black Labrador sitting by a chair with massive composure and offering me a gracious paw every time I came near. And my second would have been a benevolent tabby – I have always had a thing about tabby cats – which rubbed its cheek against my hand as I talked to its owner. The pups, crawling over each other and grunting obesely, would probably have come third. But I put away these unworthy thoughts and pursued my chosen course.

I was distracted to some extent by the parrot which kept saying 'Hellow' in a voice of devastating refinement like a butler answering a telephone and the mynah which repeatedly adjured me to 'Shut door as you go out', in a booming Yorkshire baritone.

The only adult in the ring was a bosomy lady with glacial pop eyes and a white poodle on her knee. As I approached she gave me a challenging stare as though defying me to place her pet anywhere but first.

'Hello, little chap,' I said, extending my hand. The poodle responded by drawing its lips soundlessly back from its teeth and giving me much the same kind of look as its owner. I withdrew my hand hastily.

'Oh you needn't be afraid of him,' the lady said frigidly. 'He won't hurt you.'

I gave a light laugh. 'I'm sure he won't.' I held out my hand again. 'You're a nice little dog, aren't you?' Once more the poodle bared his teeth and when I persevered by trying to stroke his ears he snapped noiselessly, his teeth clicking together an inch from my fingers.

'He doesn't like you, I can see that. Do you, darling?' The lady put her cheek against the dog's head and stared at me distastefully as though she knew just how he felt.

'Shut door as you go out,' commanded the mynah gruffly from somewhere behind me.

I gave the lady my questionnaire and moved on.

And among the throng there was one who stood out; the little boy with the goldfish. In reply to my promptings he discoursed knowledgeably about his fish, its feeding, life history and habits. He even had a fair idea of the common diseases. The bowl, too, was beautifully clean and the water fresh; I was impressed.

When I had completed the circuit I swept the ring for the last time with a probing eye. Yes, there was no doubt about it; I had the three prize winners fixed in my mind beyond any question and in an order based on strictly scientific selection. I stepped out into the middle.

'Ladies and gentlemen,' I said, scanning the company with an affable smile.

'Hellow,' responded the parrot fruitily.

I ignored him and continued. 'These are the successful entrants. First, number six, the goldfish. Second, number fifteen, the guinea pig. And third, number ten, the white kitten.'

I half expected a little ripple of applause but there was none. In fact my announcement was greeted by a tight-lipped silence. I had noticed an immediate change in the atmosphere when I mentioned the goldfish. It was striking – a sudden cold wave which swept away the expectant smiles and replaced them with discontented muttering.

I had done something wrong, but what? I looked around helplessly as the hum of voices increased. 'What do you think of that, then?' 'Not fair, is it?' 'Wouldn't have thought it of him?' 'All them lovely rabbits and he hardly looked at them.'

I couldn't make it out, but my job was done, anyway. I pushed between the chairs and escaped to the open field.

'Shut door as you go out,' the mynah requested in deepest bass as I departed.

I sought out Tristan again. The atmosphere in the beer tent had changed, too. The drinkers were long since past their peak and the hilarious babel which had met me on my last visit had died to an exhausted murmur. There was a general air of satiation. Tristan, pint in hand, was being addressed with great solemnity by a man in a flat cap and braces. The man swayed slightly as he grasped Tristan's free hand and gazed into his eyes. Occasionally he patted him on the shoulder with the utmost affection. Obviously my colleague had been forging deep and lasting friendships in here while I was making enemies outside.

I sidled up to him and spoke into his ear. 'Ready to go soon, Triss?'

He turned slowly and looked at me. 'No, old lad,' he said,

articulating carefully. 'I'm afraid I shan't be coming with you. They're having a dance here on the showfield later and Doreen has consented to accompany me.' He cast a loving glance across the counter at the redhead who crinkled her nose at him.

I was about to leave when a snatch of conversation from behind made me pause.

'A bloody goldfish!' a voice saying disgustedly.

'Aye, it's a rum 'un, George,' a second voice replied.

There was a slurping sound of beer being downed.

'But tha knows, Fred,' the first voice said. 'That vet feller had to do it. Didn't 'ave no choice. He couldn't pass over t'squire's son.'

'Reckon you're right, but it's a bugger when you get graft and corruption in t'Family Pets.'

A heavy sigh, then 'It's the way things are nowadays, Fred. Everything's hulterior.'

'You're right there, George. It's hulterior, that's what it is.'

I fought down a rising panic. The Pelhams had been Lords of the Manor of Darrowby for generations and the present squire was Major Pelham. I knew him as a friendly farmer client, but that was all. I'd never heard of his son.

I clutched at Tristan's arm. 'Who is that little boy over there?'

Tristan peered out glassily across the sward. 'The one with the goldfish bowl, you mean?'

'That's right.'

'It's young Nigel Pelham, the squire's son.'

'Oh Gawd,' I moaned. 'But I've never seen him before. Where's he been?'

'Boarding school down south, I believe. On holiday just now.'

I stared at the boy again. Tousled fair hair, grey open-necked shirt, sunburned legs. Just like all the others.

George was at it again. 'Lovely dogs and cats there was, but squire's lad won it with a bloody goldfish.'

'Well, let's be right,' his companion put in. 'If that lad 'ad brought along a bloody stuffed monkey he'd still 'ave got fust prize with it.'

'No doubt about it, Fred. T'other kids might as well 'ave stopped at 'ome.'

'Aye, it's not like it used to be, George. Nobody does owt for nowt these days.'

'True, Fred, very true.' There was a gloomy silence punctuated by noisy gulpings. Then, in weary tones: 'Well you and me can't alter it. It's the kind of world we're living in today.'

I reeled out into the fresh air and the sunshine. Looking round at the tranquil scene, the long stretch of grass, the loop of pebbly river with the green hills rising behind, I had a sense of unreality. Was there any part of this peaceful cameo of rural England without its sinister undertones? As if by instinct I made my way into the long marquee which housed the produce section. Surely among those quiet rows of vegetables I would find repose.

The place was almost empty but as I made my way down the long lines of tables I came upon the solitary figure of old John William Enderby who had a little grocer's shop in the town.

'Well how are things?' I inquired.

'Nobbut middlin' lad,' the old man replied morosely.

'Why, what's wrong?'

'Well, ah got a second with me broad beans but only a highly commended for me shallots. Look at 'em.'

I looked. 'Yes, they're beautiful shallots, Mr Enderby.'

'Aye, they are, and nobbut a highly commended. It's a insult, that's what it is a insult.'

'But Mr Enderby . . . highly commended . . . I mean, that's pretty good isn't it?'

'No it isn't, it's a insult!'

'Oh bad luck.'

John William stared at me wide-eyed for a moment. 'It's not bad luck, lad, it's nowt but a twist.'

'Oh surely not!'

'Ah'm tellin' you. Jim Houlston got first with 'is shallots and judge is his wife's cousin.'

'Never!'

'It's true,' grunted John William, nodding solemnly. 'It's nowt but a twist.'

'Well I've never heard of such a thing!'

'You don't know what goes on, young man. Ah wasn't even placed with me taties. Frank Thompson got first wi' that lot.' He pointed to a tray of noble tubers.

I studied them. 'I must admit they look splendid potatoes.'

'Aye, they are, but Frank pinched 'em.'

'What?'

'Aye, they took first prize at Brisby show last Thursday and Frank pinched 'em off t'stand.'

I clutched at the nearby table. The foundations of my world were crumbling. 'That can't be true, Mr Enderby.'

'Ah'm not jokin' nor jestin',' declared John William. 'Them's self and same taties, ah'd know them anywhere. It's nowt but a . . .'

I could take no more. I fled.

Outside the evening sunshine was still warm and the whole field was awash with the soft light which, in the Dales, seems to stream down in a golden flood from the high tops. But it was as if the forces of darkness were pressing on me; all I wanted was to get home.

I hurried to the stewards' tent and collected my measuring stick, running a gauntlet of hostile stares from the pony people I had outed earlier in the day. They were still waving their certificates and arguing.

On the way to the car I had to pass several of the ladies who had watched me judge the pets and though they didn't exactly draw their skirts aside they managed to convey their message. Among the rows of vehicles I spotted the man with the moustache. He still hadn't taken his terrier away and his eyes, full of wounded resentment, followed my every step.

I was opening my door when Helen and her party, also apparently on the way home, passed about fifty yards away. Helen waved, I waved back, and Richard Edmundson gave me a nod before helping her into the front seat of a gleaming, silver Daimler. The two fathers got into the back.

As I settled into the seat of my little Austin, braced my feet against the broken floor boards and squinted through the cracked windscreen I prayed that just this once the thing would go on the starter. Holding my breath I pulled at the knob but the engine gave a couple of lazy turns then fell silent.

Fishing the starting handle from under the seat I crept out and inserted it in its hole under the radiator; and as I began the old familiar winding the silver monster purred contemptuously past me and away.

Dropping into the driver's seat again I caught sight of my face in the mirror and could see the streaks and flecks of blood still caked on my cheek and around the roots of my hair. Tristan hadn't done a very good job with his bucket of cold water.

I looked back at the emptying field and at the Daimler disappearing round a distant bend. It seemed to me that in more ways than one the show was over.

CHAPTER TEN

Ben Ashby the cattle dealer looked over the gate with his habitual deadpan expression. It always seemed to me that after a lifetime of buying cows from farmers he had developed a terror of showing any emotion which might be construed as enthusiasm. When he looked at a beast his face registered nothing beyond, occasionally, a gentle sorrow.

This was how it was this morning as he leaned on the top spar and directed a gloomy stare at Harry Sumner's heifer. After a few moments he turned to the farmer.

'I wish you'd had her in for me, Harry. She's too far away. I'm going to have to get over the top.' He began to climb stiffly upwards and it was then that he spotted Monty. The bull hadn't been so easy to see before as he cropped the grass among the group of heifers but suddenly the great head rose high about the others, the nose ring gleamed, and an ominous, strangled bellow sounded across the grass. And as he gazed at us he pulled absently at the turf with a fore foot.

Ben Ashby stopped climbing, hesitated for a second then returned to ground level.

'Aye well,' he muttered, still without changing expression. 'It's not that far away. I reckon I can see all right from here.'

Monty had changed a lot since the first day I saw him about two years ago. He had been a fortnight old then, a skinny, knock-kneed little creature, his head deep in a calf bucket.

'Well, what do you think of me new bull?' Harry Sumner had asked, laughing. 'Not much for a hundred quid is he?'

I whistled. 'As much as that?'

'Aye, it's a lot for a new-dropped calf, isn't it? But I can't think of any other way of getting into the Newton strain. I haven't the brass to buy a big 'un.'

Not all the farmers of those days were as farseeing as Harry and some of them would use any type of male bovine to get their cows in calf.

One such man produced a gaunt animal for Siegfried's inspection and asked him what he thought of his bull. Seigfried's reply of 'All horns and balls' didn't please the owner but I still treasure it as the most graphic description of the typical scrub bull of that period.

Harry was a bright boy. He had inherited a little place of about a hundred acres on his father's death and with his young wife had set about making it go. He was in his early twenties and when I first saw him I had been deceived by his almost delicate appearance into thinking that he wouldn't be up to the job; the pallid face, the large, sensitive eyes and slender frame didn't seem fitted for the seven days a week milking, feeding, mucking-out slog that was dairy farming. But I had been wrong.

The fearless way he plunged in and grabbed at the hind feet of kicking cows for me to examine and his clenched-teeth determination as he hung on to the noses of the big loose beasts at testing time made me change my mind in a hurry. He worked endlessly and tirelessly and it was natural that his drive should have taken him to the south of Scotland to find a bull.

Harry's was an Ayrshire herd – unusual among the almost universal shorthorns in the Dales – and there was no doubt an injection of the famous Newton blood would be a sure way of improving his stock.

'He's got prize winners on both his sire and dam's side.' the young farmer said. 'And a grand pedigree name, too. Newton Montmorency the Sixth – Monty for short.'

As though recognizing his name, the calf raised his head from the bucket and looked at us. It was a comic little face – wet-muzzled, milk slobbered halfway up his cheeks and dribbling freely from his mouth. I bent over into the pen and scratched the top of the hard little head, feeling the tiny horn buds no bigger than peas under my fingers. Limpid-eyed and unafraid, Monty submitted calmly to the caress for a few moments then sank his head again in the bucket.

I saw quite a bit of Harry Sumner over the next few weeks and usually had a look at his expensive purchase. And as the calf grew you could see why he had cost £100. He was in a pen with three of Harry's own calves and his superiority was evident at a glance; the broad forehead and wide-set eyes; the deep chest and short straight legs; the beautifully even line of the back from shoulder to tail head. Monty had class; and small as he was he was all bull.

He was about three months old when Harry rang to say he thought the calf had pneumonia. I was surprised because the weather was fine and warm and I knew Monty was in a draught-free building. But when I saw him I thought immediately that his owner's diagnosis was right. The heaving of the rib cage, the temperature of 105 degrees – it looked fairly straightforward. But when I got my stethoscope on his chest and listened for the pneumonic sounds I heard nothing. His lungs were perfectly clear. I went over him several times but there was not a squeak, not a râle, not the slightest sign of consolidation.

This was a facer. I turned to the farmer. 'It's a funny one, Harry. He's sick, all right, but his symptoms don't add up to anything recognizable.'

I was going against my early training because the first vet I ever saw practice with in my student days told me once: 'If you don't know what's wrong with an animal for God's sake don't admit it. Give it a name – call it McLuskie's Disease or Galloping Dandruff – anything you like, but give it a name.' But no inspiration came to me as I looked at the panting, anxious-eyed little creature.

Treat the symptoms. That was the thing to do. He had a temperature so I'd try to get that down for a start. I brought out my pathetic armoury of febrifuges; the injection of non-specific antiserum, the 'fever drink' of sweet spirit of nitre; but over the next two days it was obvious that the time-honoured remedies were having no effect.

On the fourth morning, Harry Sumner met me as I got out of my car. 'He's walking funny, this morning, Mr Herriot – and he seems to be blind.'

Blind! An unusual form of lead-poisoning – could that be it? I hurried into the calf pen and began to look round the walls, but there wasn't a scrap of paint anywhere and Monty had spent his entire life in there.

And anyway, as I looked at him I realized that he wasn't really blind; his eyes were staring and slightly upturned and he blundered unseeingly around the pen, but he blinked as I passed my hand in front of his face. To complete my bewilderment he walked with a wooden, stiff-legged gait almost like a mechanical toy and my mind began to snatch at diagnostic straws – tetanus, no – meningitis – no, no; I always tried to maintain the calm, professional exterior but I had to fight an impulse to scratch my head and stand gaping.

I got off the place as quickly as possible and settled down to serious thought as I drove away. My lack of experience didn't help, but I did have a knowledge of pathology and physiology and when stumped for a diagnosis I could usually work something out on rational grounds. But this thing didn't make sense.

That night I got out my books, notes from college, back numbers of the Veterinary Record and anything else I could find on the subject of calf diseases. Somewhere here there would surely be a clue. But the volumes on medicine and surgery were barren of inspiration and I had about given up hope when I came upon the passage in a little pamphlet on calf diseases. 'Peculiar, stilted gait, staring eyes with a tendency to gaze upwards, occasionally respiratory symptoms with high temperature.' The words seemed to leap out at me from the printed page and it was as though the unknown author was patting me on the shoulder and murmuring reassuringly: 'This is it, you see. It's all perfectly clear.'

I grabbed the phone and rang Harry Sumner. 'Harry, have you ever noticed Monty and those other calves in the pen licking each other?'

'Aye, they're allus at it, the little beggars. It's like a hobby with them. Why?'

'Well I know what's wrong with your bull. He's got a hair ball.'

'A hair ball? Where?'

'In the abomasum – the fourth stomach. That's what's setting up all those strange symptoms.'

'Well I'll go to hell. What do we do about it, then?'

'It'll probably mean an operation, but I'd like to try dosing him with liquid paraffin first. I'll put a pint bottle on the step for you if you'll come and collect it. Give him half a pint now and the same first thing in the morning. It might just grease the thing through. I'll see you tomorrow.'

I hadn't a lot of faith in the liquid paraffin. I suppose I suggested it for the sake of doing something while I played nervously with the idea of operating. And next morning the picture was as I expected; Monty was still rigid-limbed, still staring sightlessly ahead of him, and an oiliness round his rectum and down his tail showed that the paraffin had bypassed the obstruction.

'He hasn't had a bite now for three days,' Harry said. 'I doubt he won't stick it much longer.'

I looked from his worried face to the little animal trembling in the pen. 'You're right. We'll have to open him up straight away to have any hope of saving him. Are you willing to let me have a go?'

'Oh, aye, let's be at t'job – sooner the better.' He smiled at me. It was a confident smile and my stomach gave a lurch. His confidence could be badly misplaced because in those days abdominal surgery in the bovine was in a primitive state. There were a few jobs we had begun to tackle fairly regularly but removal of a hairball wasn't one of them and my knowledge of the procedure was confined to some rather small-print reading in the text books.

But this young farmer had faith in me. He thought I could do the job so it was no good letting him see my doubts. It was at times like this that I envied our colleagues in human medicine. When a surgical case came up they packed their patient off to a hospital but the vet just had to get his jacket off on the spot and make an operating theatre out of the farm buildings.

Harry and I busied ourselves in boiling up the instruments, setting out buckets of hot water and laying a clean bed of straw in an empty pen. Despite his weakness the calf took nearly sixty cc's of Nembutal into his vein before he was fully anaesthetized but finally he was asleep, propped on his back between two straw bales, his little hooves dangling above him. I was ready to start.

It's never the same as it is in the books. The pictures and diagrams look so simple and straightforward but it is a different thing when you are cutting into a living, breathing creature with the abdomen rising and falling gently and the blood oozing beneath your knife. The abomasum, I knew, was just down there, slightly to the right of the sternum but as I cut through the peritoneum there was this slippery mass of fat-streaked omentum obscuring everything; and as I pushed it aside one of the bales moved and Monty tilted to his left causing a sudden gush of intestines into the wound. I put the flat of my hand against the shining pink loops – it would be just great if my patient's insides started spilling out on to the straw before I had started.

'Pull him upright, Harry, and shove that bale back into place,' I gasped. The farmer quickly complied but the intestines weren't at all anxious to return to their place and kept intruding coyly as I groped for the abomasum. Frankly I was beginning to feel just a bit lost and my heart was thudding when I came upon something hard. It was sliding about beyond the wall of one of the stomachs – at the moment I wasn't sure which. I gripped it and lifted it into the wound. I had hold of the abomasum and that hard thing inside must be the hairball.

Repelling the intestines which had made another determined attempt to push their way into the act, I incised the stomach and had my first look at the cause of the trouble. It wasn't a ball at all, rather a flat plaque of densely-matted hair, mixed freely with strands of hay, sour curd and a shining covering of my liquid paraffin. The whole thing was jammed against the pyloric opening.

Gingerly I drew it out through the incision and dropped it in the straw. It wasn't till I had closed the stomach wound with gut, stitched up the muscle layer and had started on the skin that I realized that the sweat was running down my face. As I blew away a droplet from my nose end Harry broke the silence.

'It's a hell of a tricky job, isn't it?' he said. Then he laughed and thumped my shoulder. 'I bet you felt a bit queer the first time you did one of these!'

I pulled another strand of suture silk through and knotted it. 'You're right, Harry,' I said. 'How right you are.'

When I had finished we covered Monty with a horse rug and piled straw on top of that, leaving only his head sticking out. I bent over and touched a corner of the eye. Not a vestige of corneal reflex. God, he was deep – had I given him too much anaesthetic? And of course there'd be surgical shock, too. As I left I glanced back at the motionless little animal. He looked smaller than ever and very vulnerable under the bare walls of the pen.

I was busy for the rest of the day but that evening my thoughts kept coming back to Monty. Had he come out of it yet? Maybe he was dead. I hadn't the experience of previous cases to guide me and I simply had no idea of how a calf reacted to an operation like that. And I couldn't rid myself of the nagging consciousness of how much it all meant to Harry Sumner. The bull is half the herd, they say, and half of Harry's future herd was lying there under the straw – he wouldn't be able to find that much money again.

I jumped suddenly from my chair. It was no good, I had to find out what was happening. Part of me rebelled at the idea of looking amateurish and unsure of myself by going fussing back, but, I thought, I could always say I had returned to look for an instrument.

The farm was in darkness as I crept into the pen. I shone my torch on the mound of straw and saw with a quick thump of the heart that the calf had not moved. I dropped to my knees and pushed a hand under the rug; he was breathing anyway. But there was still no eye reflex – either he was dying or he was taking a hell of a time to come out.

In the shadows of the yard I looked across at the soft glow from the farmhouse kitchen. Nobody had heard me. I slunk over to the car and drove off with the sick knowledge that I was no further forward. I still didn't know how the job was going to turn out.

Next morning I had to go through the same thing again and as I walked stiffly across to the calf pen I knew for sure I'd see something this time. Either he'd be dead or better. I opened the outer door and almost ran down the passage. It was the third pen along and I stared hungrily into it.

Monty was sitting up on his chest. He was still under the rug and straw and he looked sorry for himself but when a bovine animal is on its chest I always feel hopeful. The tensions flowed from me in a great wave. He had survived the operation – the first stage was over; and as I knelt, rubbing the top of his head, I had the feeling that we were going to win.

And, in fact, he did get better, though I have always found it difficult to explain to myself scientifically why the removal of that pad of tangled fibres could cause such a dramatic improvement in so many directions. But there it was. His temperature did drop and his breathing returned to normal, his eyes did stop staring and the weird stiffness disappeared from his limbs.

But though I couldn't understand it, I was none the less delighted. Like a teacher with his favourite pupil I developed a warm proprietary affection for the calf and when I happened to be on the farm I found my feet straying unbidden to his pen. He always walked up to me and regarded me with friendly interest; it was as if he had a fellow feeling for me, too.

He was rather more than a year old when I noticed the change. The friendly interest gradually disappeared from his eyes and was replaced by a thoughtful, speculative look; and he developed a habit of shaking his head at me at the same time.

'I'd stop going in there, Mr Herriot, if I were you,' Harry said one day. 'He's getting big and I reckon he's going to be a cheeky bugger before he's finished.'

But cheeky was the wrong word. Harry had a long, trouble-free spell and Monty was nearly two years old when I saw him again. It wasn't a case of illness this time. One or two of Harry's cows had been calving before their time and it was typical of him that he should ask me to blood test his entire herd for Brucellosis.

We worked our way easily through the cows and I had a long row of glass tubes filled with blood in just over an hour.

'Well, that's the lot in here,' the farmer said. 'We only have bull to do and we're finished.' He led the way across the yard through the door into the calf pens and along a passage to the bull box at the end. He opened the half door and as I looked inside I felt a sudden sense of shock.

Monty was enormous. The neck with its jutting humps of muscle supported a head so huge that the eyes looked tiny. And there was nothing friendly in those eyes now; no expression at all, in fact, only a cold black glitter. He was standing sideways to me, facing the wall, but I knew he was watching me as he pushed his head against the stones, his great horns scoring the whitewash with slow, menacing deliberation. Occasionally he snorted from deep in his chest but apart from that he remained ominously still. Monty wasn't just a bull – he was a vast, brooding presence.

Harry grinned as he saw me staring over the door. 'Well, do you fancy popping inside to scratch his head? That's what you allus used to do.'

'No thanks.' I dragged my eyes away from the animal. 'But I wonder what my expectation of life would be if I did go in.'

'I reckon you'd last about a minute,' Harry said thoughtfully. 'He's a grand bull – all I ever expected – but by God he's a mean 'un. I never trust him an inch.'

'And how,' I asked without enthusiasm, 'am I supposed to get a sample of blood from him?'

'Oh I'll trap his head in yon corner.' Harry pointed to a metal yoke above a trough in an opening into the yard at the far side of the box. 'I'll give him some meal to 'tice him in.' He went back down the passage and soon I could see him out in the yard scooping meal into the trough.

The bull at first took no notice and continued to prod at the wall with his horns, then he turned with awesome slowness, took a few unhurried steps across the box and put his nose down to the trough. Harry, out of sight in the yard, pulled the lever and the yoke crashed shut on the great neck.

'All right,' the farmer cried, hanging on to the lever, 'I have 'im. You can go in now.'

I opened the door and entered the box and though the bull was held fast by the head there was still the uneasy awareness that he and I were alone in that small space together. And as I passed along the massive body and put my hand on the neck I sensed a quivering emanation of pent up power and rage. Digging my fingers into the jugular furrow I watched the vein rise up and poised my needle. It would take a good hard thrust to pierce that leathery skin.

The bull stiffened but did not move as I plunged the needle in and with relief I saw the blood flowing darkly into the syringe. Thank God I had hit the vein first time and didn't have to start poking around. I was withdrawing the needle and thinking that the job had been so simple after all when everything started to happen. The bull gave a tremendous bellow and whipped round at me with no trace of his former lethargy. I saw that he had got one horn out of the yoke and though he couldn't reach me with his head, his shoulder knocked me on my back with a terrifying revelation of unbelievable strength. I heard Harry shouting from outside and as I scrambled up and headed for the box door I saw that the madly plunging creature had almost got his second horn clear and when I reached the passage I heard the clang of the yoke as he finally freed himself.

Anybody who has travelled a narrow passage a few feet ahead of about a ton of snorting, pounding death will appreciate that I didn't dawdle. I was spurred on by the certain knowledge that if Monty caught me he would plaster me against the wall as effortlessly as I would squash a ripe plum, and though I was clad in a long oilskin coat and wellingtons I doubt whether an olympic sprinter in full running kit would have bettered my time.

I made the door at the end with a foot to spare, dived through and crashed it shut. The first thing I saw was Harry Sumner running round from the outside of the box. He was very pale. I couldn't see my face but it felt pale; even my lips were cold and numb.

'God, I'm sorry!' Harry said hoarsely. 'The yoke couldn't have closed properly – that bloody great neck of his. The lever just jerked out of my hand. Damn, I'm glad to see you – I thought you were a goner!'

I looked down at my hand. The blood-filled syringe was still tightly clutched there. 'Well I've got my sample anyway, Harry. And it's just as well, because it would take some fast talking to get me in there to try for another. I'm afraid you've just seen the end of a beautiful friendship.'

'Aye, the big sod!' Harry listened for a few moments to the thudding of Monty's horns against the door. 'And after all you did for him. That's gratitude for you.'

CHAPTER ELEVEN

I suppose if it hadn't been for the Tuberculin Testing Scheme I'd never have come to know Ewan and Ginny Ross.

Siegfried broached the matter to me one morning as I was making up some colic mixture in the dispensary.

'All this extra testing work is a bit much for a one-man practice, especially when it's an older man. Ewan Ross has been on the phone asking me if I could help him and we've thrashed out a plan which could benefit us both. But it depends on you.'

'What do you mean?'

'Well, would you be willing to go up to Scarburn and do his testing say three days a week? Ewan and I would split the proceeds and you'd get a little cut too.'

I screwed a cork into the last bottle. 'It's all right with me. I'd enjoy a bit of fresh country. It's real wild up there – about twenty-five miles away isn't it?'

'Just about. It is a bit bleak, but it's beautiful in fine weather. And I'm sure you'll get on with Ewan.'

'I've heard quite a lot about him.' I laughed. 'They say he'd rather settle down with a bottle than work.'

Siegfried turned a level gaze on me. 'They say a lot of things but he's a good friend of mine and just about the best veterinary surgeon I've ever seen.' He paused for a moment then went on. 'I want you to go up there tomorrow to meet him, then you can judge for yourself.'

As I drove out next morning I reflected on the snippets which had come through to me about Ewan Ross. I didn't know all that much about him; twenty-five miles was enough to make him remote from my own working area and in any case hard drinking and wild behaviour were the norm among the older members of the profession. The more recent graduates were a different type altogether; more scientifically orientated, more conscious of professional standards; but the men who had been on the go for twenty years or more, many of them ex-servicemen, were a hard-bitten, rugged lot of characters. Most of them had had a hell of a life, working single-handed through the years when times were hard, money short and the work at its roughest and I suppose they just had to erupt now and then.

Ewan Ross, it was said, would incarcerate himself in some village pub and go on a bender lasting days on end until his wife finally managed to winkle him out and entice him back to his practice. People said, too, that he liked to challenge big farm men in bars to 'take a hold' – to shake hands with him and have a test of grip which usually finished with the big man on the floor. There were tales, too, of brushes with the police – he'd lost his licence for a while for being drunk in charge of a car – and other things.

The scene beyond my car windows was changing all the time as I drove. The Dales country around Darrowby was softened by the trees which lined the valley floors and by the lush, level pastures by the rivers where they wandered among leisurely shallows. But this was the high Pennines, the harsh, wind-blown roof of England, almost treeless with only the endless miles of dry stone walls climbing and criss-crossing over the bald heights.

And driving into Scarburn, it occurred to me that this was just the sort of place some seedy character would want to hole up. It was only too easy to picture the broken-down vet and his harassed, blowsy wife. I had always thought Darrowby was quiet and a bit rough-hewn but it was a sophisticated metropolis compared to Scarburn.

On this windy, sunless day the grey horse-shoe of buildings grouped around the steeply sloping market place seemed in danger of sliding down the high fell on which it was perched. I drove past the ironmonger's, the Methodist Chapel, a draper's with a few dowdy clothes in the window, the Temperance Hotel; there was no attempt at adornment or softness anywhere and apart from a few muffled women battling against the wind the streets were empty.

I found the veterinary surgeon's plate on a small modern house about two hundred yards beyond the market place and knocked at the door. I had a fairly clear mental image by now of my colleague within; needing a shave, running to fat, the smell of whisky about him, and as the door opened I drew in my breath in anticipation.

A tallish, heavy-shouldered man stood there. The face, ruddy and handsome with pale blue friendly eyes, could have been that of a young man but for the swathes of silver in the sandy hair above it. The suit of soft brown tweed hung gracefully on his lean frame. He held out his hand.

'You'll be James Herriot. Come away in.' The voice had the lilt of the Scottish Highlands with something else in it.

He led the way into the kitchen where a woman was standing by the stove. 'Ginny,' he called. 'Come and meet Siegfried's right hand man, young Mr Herriot.'

Virginia Ross turned her head and looked at me.

'Hello,' she said. 'You're just in time for coffee.' And she gave me a crooked smile with one eyebrow slightly raised which had an extraordinary effect. Over the years I knew her she always looked at me like that – as though I was a quite pleasant but amusing object – and it always did the same thing to me. It's difficult to put into words but perhaps I can best describe it by saying that if I had been a little dog I'd have gone leaping and gambolling around the room wagging my tail furiously.

She would be about ten years younger than Ewan – somewhere in her early forties – but she had the kind of attractiveness that was ageless. She filled three mugs with coffee and I sat down at the table with the feeling that I was with friends. I couldn't count the times I have sat in that kitchen since that first day, drinking tea or coffee or if I happened in around lunch time, eating Ginny's delectable food. She was a cook with the magic touch; in fact as time went on I found she could do just about anything. She spoke several languages, had read everything, she painted and embroidered and as I said, she could cook. How she could cook! She must have had to work on a very tight budget but she managed to make a poem out of the simplest materials.

Ewan pushed away his mug and stood up. 'I've got to operate on a colt for umbilical hernia. Would you care to come along?'

'Yes,' I said. 'I'd like that very much.'

We went out to a small building alongside the house which was the surgery and dispensary. There is a fascination in seeing another man's set-up and I browsed happily along the shelves and tables. There isn't nearly so much fun in doing this nowadays because vets all use the same drugs – a narrow variation in the range of antibiotics, sulphonamides and steroids – but back there in 1939 we were still using the countless mystical remedies of the dark ages.

And Ewan's selection was even more primitive than ours at Darrowby, Physic balls, electuaries, red blister, stimulant draught, ammonia powders, cooling lotions, alterative mixture, Donovan's solution; and a lot of Ewan's own pet ideas with a whiff of black magic about them; like his paste of arsenic and soft soap which you smeared on a length of twine and tied around the necks of tumours where it was supposed to eat its way through.

As I wandered round I watched him preparing for the operation. He didn't seem to have a sterilizer but he was methodically boiling the instruments in a saucepan on a gas ring. Then he took them out with forceps and carefully wrapped them one by one in sheets of clean brown paper. He was a picture of unhurried calm.

It was the same when we got to the farm. Ewan paced about the field till he found a perfectly level spot where the grass was long and soft, then he pottered along, peering closely at the ground, throwing aside a few small stones which were lurking there. When he was satisfied he made a table out of a couple of straw bales, covered it with a clean sheet and laid out his instruments on it meticulously. Next to the bales he stationed a bucket of hot water, soap and towel and finally produced a beautiful soft white rope tied in a neat coil. Only then did he allow the colt to be led out.

I must have looked a bit open-mouthed because he grinned and said, 'I never start anything till I've set my stall out properly.'

What struck me was the difference from my boss in Darrowby. Siegfried would never have had the patience to go through all this procedure; his system was based on Napoleon's dictum of *'On s'engage et puis on voit'* and it usually involved a lot of yelling and rushing about. I had to admit that this was more peaceful.

But I really saw what Ewan was made of when he started to do the job. He was using the old-fashioned method of casting the horse by sidelines and trussing him up before administering the chloroform but he did it as I'd never seen it done before.

The patient was a shaggy little animal with the beginnings of feathers round his hooves; he was typical of the hundreds of cart colts we had to deal with every year and he trembled nervously as he looked around him.

Ewan seemed to pacify him immediately with a few soft words as he placed the rope around his neck then between the hind legs and back through the neck loop; and when the farm men pulled on the rope he stood by the head still talking so that the colt collapsed easily on to his grassy bed.

It was an education for me to watch him then, deftly tugging and knotting till the animal was positioned on his back with his legs tied together fore and hind and the operation area exposed. Once more Ewan had set his stall out properly.

He gave me the job of looking after the chloroform muzzle while he incised the skin, tucked away the hernia and neatly sutured the wound. He did it all with the firm, almost rough movements of the expert surgeon and as I watched the strong fingers at work I was reminded again, of the tales of 'take a hold'.

Even when he was finished and had thoroughly cleared away the last drop of blood and debris from the operation site he still was in no hurry. He washed and dried his instruments with great deliberation, wrapped them up again in the sheets of brown paper then sat down on the straw bales to wait for the colt to come round from the anaesthetic. As he sat there, perfectly relaxed, he pulled a cigarette paper from his pocket, tipped a stream of dark brown dusty tobacco into it from a little pouch, rolled the paper effortlessly with one hand, licked it, screwed up one end and thrust it into his mouth.

As the smoke curled round his ears he gave a few instructions in his soft Highland voice.

'Now just pull him on to his chest will you. That's right, put your knee behind his shoulder and let him rest there for a while. Don't hurry him, now, he'll get up when he's ready.'

He didn't leave for another twenty minutes when the colt gave a final effort and heaved himself to his feet where he stood shakily, looking around him in some bewilderment.

'Let him stand there awhile till he's steady on his legs,' Ewan said. 'Then you can walk him back to his box.'

He turned to me. 'Well now, there's not a bad little pub in this village. How about a beer before lunch?'

There was nobody but ourselves in the bar. Ewan took a contented sip of his half pint then pulled the small pouch again from his pocket. I watched him again as he rolled another cigarette with one hand.

I laughed. 'You know, I've only seen that done by cowboys on the pictures. Where did you learn the art?'

'Oh that?' Ewan gave his shy smile, 'In Canada, a long time ago. It was the only way I had of getting a smoke for years and I've never got out of the way of it.'

He obviously found difficulty in talking about himself but as we sat I was able to build a picture of his history. He was a farmer's son from West Sutherland and even as a small boy he had worked with horses and been fascinated by them. On leaving school he had, like many other restless Highlanders, sailed away to seek his fortune. First he tried Australia where he took a job riding the rabbit fences, then he moved to Canada and worked on a ranch for years, more or less living in the saddle. He came to England with the Canadian Expeditionary Force at the beginning of the war and served till 1918 in the cavalry. I suppose he must have recognized then that his life seemed to be inevitably bound up with horses so he enrolled with a lot of other ex-servicemen in the London Veterinary College. That was where he met Ginny.

He didn't go into details of how he had finally landed in

Scarburn and I didn't press him. But it seemed such a waste. You don't often find a top class horseman and a veterinary surgeon combined. Siegfried was such a one and I never thought I'd see a better. But Ewan Ross could beat them all. The extraordinary thing was that he had settled in a cattle and sheep district where his equine skills were seldom exploited. Certainly there were numbers of racing stables in the Pennines but Ewan made not the slightest attempt to gain a footing there; a 'horse specialist' in a big Bentley used to travel around doing most of the racing work and making a packet of money in the process. He wasn't a bad chap, either. But Ewan had forgotten more about horses than he'd ever know.

I suppose the simple explanation was that Ewan was devoid of ambition. He didn't want a big successful practice, he wasn't interested in being rich or famous. Even this morning when I talked to him about our plans in Darrowby I could see he was listening with polite attention, but it didn't mean a thing to him. No, Ewan would do enough work to keep going and beyond that he just didn't give a damn.

We stayed for something like half an hour in the bar and we'd drunk three glasses of beer apiece. I looked at my watch.

'I'd better be getting back down the hill to Darrowby,' I said. 'I've got a few things fixed for this afternoon.'

Ewan smiled. 'Oh, there's no hurry. We'll just have one for the road.' His voice was soft as usual but it had a sleepy quality now and I was surprised to see a slight glassiness in the pale blue eyes. There was no doubt about it – that small amount of drink had affected him.

'No thanks,' I said. 'I've really got to go.'

And as I drove back along the narrow dry-walled road that crawled its slow way among the fells I pondered on the strange fact; Ewan Ross couldn't drink. Or he had a certain proportion of alcohol in his bloodstream so that he was easily topped up. But I didn't think it was that; he just had a low threshold for the stuff. I had a conviction that he would have stayed in that pub if I had been agreeable; and who knows when he might have come out? Ewan's famous benders could all have started as simply.

Anyway, I was only guessing and I never did find out, because I always said 'No thanks' when he said 'We'll just have one for the road.' All the years I knew him I never saw him drunk or anything like it so I can't say anything about that other side of his life.

Strangely enough, circumstances took me through Scarburn just a few days afterwards. It was Sunday and the church was turning out and from my car I saw Ewan and Ginny, dressed in their best, walking down the street ahead of me. I didn't catch them up – just watching them till the straight-backed easy-striding man and the elegant woman turned the corner out of sight, and I thought as I was to think so often what marvellous-looking people were my two new friends.

CHAPTER TWELVE

'You know, there's maybe something in this Raynes ghost business after all.' Tristan pushed his chair back from the breakfast table, stretched out his legs more comfortably and resumed his study of the *Darrowby and Houlton Times*. 'It says here they've got a historian looking into it and this man has unearthed some interesting facts.'

Siegfried didn't say anything, but his eyes narrowed as his brother took out a Woodbine and lit it. Siegfried had given up smoking a week ago and he didn't want to watch anybody light up; particularly somebody like Tristan who invested even the smallest action with quiet delight, rich fulfilment. My boss's mouth tightened to a grim line as the young man unhurriedly selected a cigarette, flicked his lighter and dragged the smoke deep with a kind of ecstatic gasp.

'Yes,' Tristan continued, thin outgoing wisps mingling with his words. 'This chap points out that several of the monks were murdered at Raynes Abbey in the fourteenth century.'

'Well, so what?' snapped Siegfried.

Tristan raised his eyebrows. 'This cowled figure that's been seen so often lately near the abbey – why shouldn't it be the spirit of one of those monks?'

'Whaat? What's that you say?'

'Well, after all it makes you think, doesn't it? Who knows what fell deeds might have been ...?'

'What the hell are you talking about?' Siegfried barked.

Tristan looked hurt. 'That's all very well and you may laugh, but remember what Shakespeare said.' He raised a solemn finger. ' "There are more things in heaven and earth, Horatio, than are dreamt of in your ..." '

'Oh balls!' said Siegfried, bringing the discussion effectively to a close.

I took a last thankful swallow of coffee and put down my cup, I was pleased that the topic had petered out fairly peacefully because Siegfried was in an edgy condition. Up to last week he had been a dedicated puffer of pipe and cigarettes but he had also developed a classical smoker's cough and had suffered increasingly from violent stomach ache. At times his long thin face had assumed the appearance of a skull, the cheeks deeply sunken, the eyes smouldering far down in their sockets. And the doctor had said he must give up smoking.

Siegfried had obeyed, felt immediately better and was instantly seized with the evangelical zeal of the convert. But he didn't just advise people to give up tobacco; I have seen him several times strike a cigarette from the trembling fingers of farm workers, push his face to within inches of theirs and grind out menacingly, 'Now don't ever let me see you with one of those bloody things in your mouth again, do you hear?'

Even now there are grizzled men who tell me with a shudder, 'Nay, ah've never had a fag sin' Mr Farnon told me to stop, thirty years back. Nay, bugger it, the way 'e looked at me I durstn't do it!'

However the uncomfortable fact remained that his crusade hadn't the slightest effect on his brother. Tristan smoked almost continually but he never coughed and his digestion was excellent.

Siegfried looked at him now as he contentedly tapped off a little ash and took another blissful suck. 'You smoke too many of those bloody cigarettes!'

'So do you.'

'No I don't!' Siegfried retorted. 'I'm a non-smoker and it's time you were too! It's a filthy habit and you'll kill yourself the way you're going!'

Tristan gave him a benign look and again his words were floated out on the fine Woodbine mist. 'Oh I'm sure you're wrong. Do you know, I think it rather agrees with me.'

Siegfried got up and left the room. I sympathized with him for he was in a difficult position. Being *in loco parentis* he was in a sense providing his brother with the noxious weeds and his innate sense of propriety prevented him from abusing this position by dashing the things from Tristan's hands as he did with others. He had to fall back on exhortation and it was getting him nowhere. And there was another thing – he probably wanted to avoid a row this morning as Tristan was leaving on one of his mysterious trips back to the Veterinary College; in fact my first job was to take him down to the Great North Road where he was going to hitch a lift.

After I had left him there I set off on my rounds and, as I drove, my thoughts kept going back to the conversation at breakfast. A fair number of people were prepared to swear that they had seen the Raynes ghost and though it was easy to dismiss some of them as sensation mongers or drunkards the fact remained that others were very solid citizens indeed.

The story was always the same. There was a hill beyond Raynes village and at the top a wood came right up to the roadside. Beyond lay the abbey. People driving up the hill late at night said they had seen the monk in their headlights – a monk in a brown habit just disappearing into the wood. They believed the figure had been walking across the road but they weren't sure because it was always a little too far away. But they were adamant about the other part; they had seen a cowled figure, head bowed, go into that wood. There must have been something uninviting about the apparition because nobody ever said they had gone into the wood after it.

It was strange that after my thoughts had been on Raynes during the day I should be called to the village at one o'clock the following morning. Crawling from bed and climbing wearily into my clothes I couldn't help thinking of Tristan curled up peacefully in his Edinburgh lodgings far away from the troubles of practice. But I didn't feel too bad about getting up; Raynes was only three miles away and the job held no prospect of hard labour – a colic in a little boy's Shetland pony. And it was a fine night – very cold with the first chill of autumn but with a glorious full moon to light my way along the road.

They were walking the pony round the yard when I got there. The owner was the accountant at my bank and he gave me a rueful smile.

'I'm very sorry to get you out of bed, Mr Herriot, but I was hoping this bit of bellyache would go off. We've been parading round here for two hours. When we stop he tries to roll.'

'You've done the right thing,' I said. 'Rolling can cause a twist in the bowel.' I examined the little animal and was reassured. He had a normal temperature, good strong pulse, and listening at his flank I could hear the typical abdominal sounds of spasmodic colic.

What he needed was a good evacuation of the bowel, but I had to think carefully when computing the dose of arecoline for this minute member of the equine species. I finally settled on an eighth of a grain and injected it into the neck muscles. The pony stood for a few moments in the typical colic position, knuckling over and sinking down on one hind leg then the other and occasionally trying to lie down.

'Walk him on again slowly will you?' I was watching for the next stage and I didn't have long to wait; the pony's jaws began to champ and his lips to slobber and soon long dribbles of saliva hung down from his mouth. All right so far but I had to wait another fifteen minutes before he finally cocked his tail and deposited a heap of faeces on the concrete of the yard.

'I think he'll be OK now,' I said. 'So I'll leave you to it. Give me another ring if he's still in pain.'

Beyond the village the road curved suddenly out of sight of the houses then began the long straight climb to the abbey. Just up there at the limits of my headlights would be where the ghost was always seen – walking across the road and into the black belt of trees. At the top of the hill, on an impulse, I drew in to the side of the road and got out of the car. This was the very place. At the edge of the wood, under the brilliant moon, the smooth boles of the beeches shone with an eerie radiance and, high above, the branches creaked as they swayed in the wind.

I walked into the wood, feeling my way carefully with an arm held before me till I came out on the other side. Raynes Abbey lay before me.

I had always associated the beautiful ruin with summer days with the sun warming the old stones of the graceful arches, the chatter of voices, children playing on the cropped turf; but this was 2.30 AM in an empty world and the cold breath of the coming winter on my face. I felt suddenly alone.

In the cold glare everything was uncannily distinct. But there was a look of unreality about the silent rows of columns reaching into the dark sky and throwing their long pale shadows over the grass. Away at the far end I could see the monks' cells – gloomy black caverns deep in shadow – and as I looked an owl hooted, accentuating the heavy, blanketing silence.

A prickling apprehension began to creep over me, a feeling that my living person had no place here among these brooding relics of dead centuries. I turned quickly and began to hurry through the wood, bumping into the trees, tripping over roots and bushes, and when I reached my car I was trembling and more out of breath than I should have been. It was good to slam the door, turn the ignition and hear the familiar roar of the engine.

I was home within ten minutes and trotted up the stairs, looking forward to catching up on my lost sleep. Opening my bedroom door I flicked on the switch and felt a momentary surprise when the room remained in darkness. Then I stood frozen in the doorway.

By the window, where the moonlight flooded in, making a pool of silver in the gloom, a monk was standing. A monk in a brown habit, motionless, arms folded, head bowed. His face was turned from the light towards me but I could see nothing under the drooping cowl but a horrid abyss of darkness.

I thought I would choke. My mouth opened but no sound came. And in my racing mind one thought pounded above the others – there were such things as ghosts after all.

Again my mouth opened and a hoarse shriek emerged.

'Who in the name of God is that?'

The reply came back immediately in a sepulchral bass.

'Tristaan.'

I don't think I actually swooned, but I did collapse limply across my bed and lay there gasping, the blood thundering in my ears. I was dimly aware of the monk standing on a chair and screwing in the light bulb, giggling helplessly the while. Then he flicked on the switch and sat on my bed. With his cowl pushed back on his shoulders he lit a Woodbine and looked down at me, still shaking with laughter.

'Oh God, Jim, that was marvellous – even better than I expected.'

I stared up at him and managed a whisper. 'But you're in Edinburgh . . .'

'Not me, old lad. There wasn't much doing so I concluded my business and hitched straight back, I'd just got in when I saw you coming up the garden. Barely had time to get the bulb out and climb into my outfit – I couldn't miss the opportunity.'

'Feel my heart,' I murmured.

Tristan rested his hand on my ribs for a moment and as he felt the fierce hammering a fleeting concern crossed his face.

'Hell, I'm sorry, Jim.' Then he patted my shoulder reassuringly. 'But don't worry. If it was going to be fatal you'd have dropped down dead on the spot. And anyway, a good fright is very beneficial – acts like a tonic. You won't need a holiday this year.'

'Thanks,' I said. 'Thanks very much.'

'I wish you could have heard yourself.' He began to laugh again. 'That scream of terror . . . oh dear, oh dear!'

I hoisted myself slowly into a sitting position, pulled out the pillow, propped it against the bed head and leaned back against it. I still felt very weak.

I eyed him coldly. 'So you're the Raynes ghost.'

Tristan grinned in reply but didn't speak.

'You young devil! I should have known. But tell me, why do you do it? What do you get out of it?'

'Oh I don't know.' The young man gazed dreamily at the ceiling through the cigarette smoke. 'I suppose it's just getting the timing right so that the drivers aren't quite sure whether they've seen me or not. And then I get a hell of a kick out of hearing them revving up like mad and roaring off for home. None of them ever slows down.'

'Well, somebody once told me your sense of humour was overdeveloped,' I said. 'And I'm telling you it'll land you in the cart one of these days.'

'Not a chance. I keep my bike behind a hedge about a hundred yards down the road so that I can make a quick getaway if necessary. There's no problem.'

'Well, please yourself.' I got off the bed and made shakily for the door. 'I'm going downstairs for a tot of whisky, and just remember this.' I turned and glared at him. 'If you try that trick on me again I'll strangle you.'

A few days later at about eight o'clock in the evening I was sitting reading by the fireside in the big room at Skeldale House when the door burst open and Siegfried burst into the room.

'James,' he rapped out. 'Old Horace Dawson's cow has split its teat. Sounds like a stitching job. The old chap won't be able to hold the cow and he has no near neighbours to help him so I wonder if you'd come and give me a hand.'

'Sure, glad to.' I marked the place in my book, stretched

and yawned then got up from the chair. I noticed Siegfried's foot tapping on the carpet and it occurred to me, not for the first time, that the only thing that would satisfy him would be some kind of ejector seat on my chair which would hurl me straight through the door and into action on the word of command. I was being as quick as I could but I had the feeling as always – when I was writing something for him or operating under his eyes – that I wasn't going nearly fast enough. There were elements of tension in the knowledge that the mere fact of watching me rise from the chair and replace my book in the fireside alcove was an almost unbearable strain for him.

By the time I was halfway across the carpet he had disappeared into the passage. I followed at a trot and just made it into the street as he was starting the car. Grabbing the door I made a dive for the interior and felt the road whip away from under my foot as we took off into the darkness.

Fifteen minutes later we screeched to a halt in the yard behind a little smallholding standing on its own across a couple of fields. The engine had barely stopped before my colleague was out of the car and striding briskly towards the cow house. He called to me over his shoulder as he went.

'Bring the suture materials, James, will you . . . and the local and syringe . . . and that bottle of wound lotion . . .'

I heard the brief murmur of conversation from within then Siegfried's voice again, raised this time in an impatient shout.

'James! What are you doing out there? Can't you find those things?'

I had hardly got the boot open and I rummaged frantically among the rows of tins and bottles. I found what he required, galloped across the yard and almost collided with him as he came out of the building.

He was in mid shout. 'James! What the hell's keeping you . . . oh, you're there. Right, let's have the stuff . . . what have you been doing all this time?'

He had been right about Horace Dawson, a tiny frail man of about eighty who couldn't be expected to do any strong-arm stuff. Despite his age he had stubbornly refused to give up milking the two fat shorthorn cows which stood in the little cobbled byre.

Our patient had badly damaged a teat; either she or her neighbour must have stood on it because there was a long tear running almost full length with the milk running from it.

'It's a bad one, Horace,' Siegfried said. 'You can see it goes right into the milk channel. But we'll do what we can for her – it'll need a good few stitches in there.'

He bathed and disinfected the teat then filled a syringe with local anaesthetic.

'Grab her nose, James,' he said, then spoke gently to the farmer. 'Horace, will you please hold her tail for me. Just catch it by the very end, that's the way . . . lovely.'

The little man squared his shoulders. 'Aye, ah can do that fine, Mr Farnon.'

'Good lad, Horace, that's splendid, thank you. Now stand well clear.' He bent over and as I gripped the animal's nose he inserted the needle above the top extremity of the wound.

There was an instant smacking sound as the cow registered her disapproval by kicking Siegfried briskly halfway up his wellington boot. He made no sound but breathed deeply and flexed his knee a couple of times before crouching down again.

'Cush pet,' he murmured soothingly as he stuck the needle in again.

This time the cloven foot landed on his forearm, sending the syringe winging gracefully through the air till it came to rest, by a piece of good fortune, in the hay-rack. Siegfried straightened up, rubbed his arm thoughtfully, retrieved his syringe and approached the patient again.

For a few moments he scratched around the root of her tail and addressed her in the friendliest manner. 'All right, old lady, it isn't very nice, is it?'

When he got down again he adopted a new stance, burrowing with his head into the cow's flank and stretching his long arms high he managed despite a few more near misses to infiltrate the tissues round the wound with local. Then he proceeded to thread a needle unhurriedly, whistling tunelessly under his breath.

Mr Dawson watched him admiringly. 'Ah know why you're such a good feller wi' animals, Mr Farnon. It's because you're so patient – I reckon you're t'patientest man ah've ever seen.'

Siegfried inclined his head modestly and recommenced work. And it was more peaceful now. The cow couldn't feel a thing as my colleague put in a long, even row of stitches, pulling the lips of the wound firmly together.

When he had finished he put an arm round the old man's shoulders.

'Now, Horace, if that heals well the teat will be as good as new. But it won't heal if you pull at it, so I want you to use this tube to milk her.' He held up a bottle of spirit in which a teat syphon gleamed.

'Very good,' said Mr Dawson firmly. 'Ah'll use it.'

Siegfried wagged a playful finger in his face. 'But you've got to be careful, you know. You must boil the tube every time before use and keep it always in the bottle or you'll finish up with mastitis. Will you do that?'

'Mr Farnon,' the little man said, holding himself very erect. 'Ah'll do exactly as you say.'

'That's my boy, Horace.' Siegfried gave him a final pat on the back before starting to pick up his instruments. 'I'll pop back in about two weeks to take the stitches out.'

As we were leaving, the vast form of Claude Blenkiron loomed suddenly in the byre door. He was the village policeman, though obviously off duty judging by the smart check jacket and slacks.

'I saw you had summat on, Horace, and I wondered if you wanted a hand.'

'Nay, thank ye, Mr Blenkiron. It's good of ye but you're ower late. We've done t'job,' the old man replied.

Siegfried laughed. 'Wish you'd arrived half an hour ago, Claude. You could have tucked this cow under your arm while I stitched her.'

The big man nodded and a slow smile spread over his face. He looked the soul of geniality but I felt, as always, that there was a lot of iron behind that smile. Claude was a well-loved character in the district, a magnificent athlete who bestowed lavish help and friendship on all who needed it on his beat. But though he was a sturdy prop to the weak and the elderly he was also a merciless scourge of the ungodly.

I had no first hand knowledge but there were rumours that Claude preferred not to trouble the magistrates with trivialities but dispensed his own form of instant justice. It was said that he kept a stout stick handy and acts of hooliganism and vandalism were rapidly followed by a shrill yowling down some dark alley. Second offenders were almost unknown and in fact his whole district was remarkably law-abiding. I looked again at the smiling face. He really was the most pleasant-looking man but as I say there was something else there and nothing would ever have induced me to pick a fight with him.

'Right, then,' he said. 'I was just on me way into Darrowby so I'll say goodnight, gentlemen.'

Siegfried put a hand on his arm. 'Just a moment, Claude, I want to go on to see another of my cases. I wonder if you'd give Mr Herriot a lift into the town.'

'I'll do that with pleasure, Mr Farnon,' the policeman replied and beckoned me to follow him.

In the darkness outside I got into the passenger seat of a little Morris Eight and waited for a few moments while Claude squeezed his bulk behind the wheel. As we set off he began to talk about his recent visit to Bradford where he had been taking part in a wrestling match.

We had to go through Raynes village on the way back and as we left the houses behind and began the ascent to the abbey he suddenly stopped talking. Then he startled me as he snapped upright in his seat and pointed ahead.

'Look, look there, it's that bloody monk!'

'Where? Where?' I feigned ignorance but I had seen it all right – the cowled, slow-pacing figure heading for the wood.

Claude's foot was on the boards and the car was screaming up the hill. At the top he swung savagely on to the roadside grass so that the headlights blazed into the depth of the wood and as he leapt from the car there was a fleeting moment when his quarry was in full view; a monk, skirts hitched high, legging it with desperate speed among the trees.

The big man reached into the back of the car and pulled out what looked like a heavy walking stick. 'After the bugger!' he shouted, plunging eagerly forward.

I panted after him. 'Wait a minute, what are you going to do if you catch him?'

'I'm goin' to come across his arse with me ash plant,' Claude said with chilling conviction and galloped ahead of me till he disappeared from the circle of light. He was making a tremendous noise, beating against the tree trunks and emitting a series of intimidating shouts.

My heart bled for the hapless spectre blundering in the darkness with the policeman's cries dinning in his ears. I waited with tingling horror for the final confrontation and the tension increased as time passed and I could still hear Claude in full cry; 'Come out of there, you can't get away! Come on, show yourself!' while his splintering blows echoed among the trees.

I did my own bit of searching but found nothing. The monk did indeed seem to have disappeared and when I finally returned to the car I found the big man already there.

'Well that's a rum 'un, Mr Herriot,' he said. 'I can't find 'im and I can't think where he's got to. I was hard on his heels when I first spotted him and he didn't get out of the wood because I can see over the fields in the moonlight. I've 'ad a scout round the abbey too, but he isn't there. He's just bloody vanished.'

I was going to say something like, 'Well, what else would you expect from a ghost?' but the huge hand was still swinging that stick and I decided against it.

'Well I reckon we'd better get on to Darrowby,' the policeman grunted, stamping his feet on the frosty turf. I shivered. It was bitterly cold with an east wind getting up and I was glad to climb back into the car.

In Darrowby I had a few companionable beers with

Claude at his favourite haunt, the Black Bull, and it was ten thirty when I got into Skeldale House. There was no sign of Tristan and I felt a twinge of anxiety.

It must have been after midnight when I was awakened by a faint scuffling from the next room. Tristan occupied what had been the long, narrow 'dressing room' in the grand days when the house was young. I jumped out of bed and opened the communicating door.

Tristan was in pyjamas and he cuddled two hot water bottles to his bosom. He turned his head and gave me a single haggard glance before pushing one of the bottles well down the bed. Then he crawled between the sheets and lay on his back with the second bottle clasped across his chest and his eyes fixed on the ceiling. I went over and looked down at him in some concern. He was shaking so much that the whole bed vibrated with him.

'How are you, Triss?' I whispered.

After a few moments a faint croak came up. 'Frozen to the bloody marrow, Jim.'

'But where the heck have you been?'

Again the croak. 'In a drainpipe.'

'A drainpipe!' I stared at him. 'Where?'

The head rolled feebly from side to side on the pillow. 'Up at the wood. Didn't you see the pipes by the roadside?'

A great light flashed. 'Of course, yes! They're going to put a new sewer into the village, aren't they?'

'That's right,' Tristan whispered. 'When I saw that big bloke pounding into the wood I cut straight back and dived into one of the pipes. God only knows how long I was in there.'

'But why didn't you come out after we left?'

A violent shudder shook the young man's frame and he closed his eyes briefly. 'I couldn't hear a thing in there. I was jammed tight with my cowl over my ears and there was a ninety mile an hour wind screaming down the pipe. I didn't hear the car start and I daren't come out in case that chap was still standing there with his bloody great shillelagh.' He took hold of the quilt with one hand and picked at it fitfully.

'Well never mind, Triss,' I said. 'You'll soon get warmed up and you'll be all right after a night's sleep.'

Tristan didn't appear to have heard. 'They're horrible things, drainpipes, Jim.' He looked up at me with hunted eyes. 'They're full of muck and they stink of cats' pee.'

'I know, I know.' I put his hand back inside the quilt and pulled the sheets up round his chin. 'You'll be fine in the morning.' I switched off the light and tiptoed from the room. As I closed the door I could still hear his teeth chattering.

Clearly it wasn't only the cold that was bothering him; he was still in a state of shock. And no wonder. The poor fellow had been enjoying a little session of peaceful haunting with never a care in the world when without warning there was a scream of brakes a blaze of light and that giant bounding into the middle of it like the demon king. It had all been too much.

Next morning at the breakfast table Tristan was in poor shape. He looked very pale, he ate little and at intervals his body was racked by deep coughing spasms.

Siegfried looked at him quizzically. 'I know what's done this to you. I know why you're sitting there like a zombie, coughing your lungs up.'

His brother stiffened in his chair and a tremor crossed his face. 'You do?'

'Yes, I hate to say I told you so, but I did warn you, didn't I? It's all those bloody cigarettes!'

Tristan never did give up smoking but the Raynes ghost was seen no more and remains an unsolved mystery to this day.

CHAPTER THIRTEEN

The arrangement with Ewan Ross had worked out very well. It meant a lot of driving for me; twenty-five miles to Scarburn, then a full day round the farms in that area followed by the run back to Darrowby at night, but I enjoyed working up there on the airy summit of Yorkshire and meeting a fresh community of farmers who, like all hillmen, seemed to vie with each other in hospitality. In their rough, flagged kitchens I ate superb meals which belied their modest description of 'a bit o' dinner' and it was almost routine for me to bring home a parcel of butter, a few eggs, sometimes an exquisite piece of spare rib.

Of course I realize I was lucky. At the commencement of the Tuberculin Testing Scheme there was a nice incentive bonus on the milk or on the numbers of cattle and I appeared on the farms almost as a bringer of bounty. In later years when attestation became universal the stock owners came to regard the tests as a necessary nuisance, but, as I say, I was lucky – I was in on the honeymoon period.

The arrangement suited Siegfried, too. Certainly he had to work hard on the days when I was away but it brought in some welcome revenue to the practice.

And best of all it suited Ewan, because without doing a single thing or even thinking about it he had a Ministry cheque on his breakfast table every quarter. This was absolutely tailored to his personality because nothing would ever have induced him to spend hours in routine work, then go home and fill in forms with long columns of descriptions and ages and measurements.

When he had to do a job he did it magnificently. And he did it with such care – always boiling up before he left the house and wrapping syringes and instruments in his strips of clean brown paper of which he must have had an endless supply. But if he could get away with it he stayed at home. In fact, after lunch every day he took off his shoes, put on his slippers and got down by the fireside. Once he was there it took something spectacular to shift him.

I have seen him sitting there smoking while Ginny answered the phone to farmers who wanted his services.

'Och, it'll do tomorrow,' he would say.

Not for him the sweat of fighting the clock, the panic of urgent calls coming in from opposite directions, the tightening ball of tension in the stomach when the work began to pile up. No, no, he put on his slippers, rolled cigarettes and let it all flow past him.

He had only a mild interest in the work we did in Darrowby but he was fascinated by the funny things that happened to us. He dearly loved to listen to my accounts of the various contretemps at Skeldale House and, strangely, he wanted to hear them again and again almost as a child would. Often, as he lay back in his chair with the smoke rising from his twisted little cigarette he would say suddenly in his soft Highland-Canadian voice.

'Tell me about the rubber suit.'

I must have told him that tale twenty times before but it made no difference. He would gaze fixedly at me as I went through the story again and though his expression hardly changed his shoulders would begin to shake silently and the pale blue eyes to brim with tears.

Looking back I often wonder who was right – Ewan or all the successful vets who gave themselves ulcers dashing round in circles. I do know that he enjoyed a deference from his clients which I never encountered elsewhere. Perhaps there is a lesson somewhere in the fact that he received grateful thanks if he went to an animal the same day he was called, whereas Siegfried and I who tried to get to a case within twenty minutes were greeted with 'what kept you?' if we took half an hour.

There was another advantage to Ewan in having me to do his testing; he was able to pass on occasional private jobs to me while I was on the farms and as the weeks passed he began to use me more and more as a general assistant. It became commonplace for the farmers to say, 'Oh, and Mr Ross said would you take some nan-berries off a stirk's belly while you're here,' or 'Will you inject some calves for scour? Mr Ross rang and said you were coming.' One morning I was startled to find a couple of strapping two-year-old horses waiting for me to castrate standing before I commenced the day's work.

If the farmers had any objection to a young stranger doing their work they never voiced it. Whatever Ewan did or arranged was right with them; in fact there didn't seem to be much they wouldn't do for him.

This was brought home to me forcibly one night. I had had a particularly rough day in the Scarburn district. Herds which I thought had about twenty animals turned out to have fifty or sixty and these were scattered around in little buildings miles apart on the fell-sides. There was only one way to get to them – you walked; and while this might have been enjoyable in good weather it had been a lowering late autumn day with a gusting wind scouring the flattened grass and almost piercing my bones like the first quick gleam of winter's teeth. It had almost stupefied me.

And on top of that I had had a wider than usual selection of Ewan's private jobs; a couple of cleansings, a farrowing, a few pregnancy diagnoses; all jacket-off jobs which left my arms raw and painful. I must have tested about four hundred unyielding bovines, elbowing and squeezing between their craggy bodies, and it seemed almost too much that just when I was turning away from the very last cow of the day she should kick me resoundingly just behind the knee. This farewell gesture dropped me in a moaning heap on the byre floor and it was some minutes before I was able to hobble away.

The journey back to Darrowby had seemed interminable and it didn't help at all when I got home and found that Siegfried was out and there were a few more calls left for me in our own practice. When I finally crawled into bed I had nothing left to offer.

It was just after midnight when the bedside phone rang. With a feeling of disbelief I recognized Ewan's voice – what the devil could he possibly want with me at this hour?

'Hello, Jim, sorry to disturb you.' The words seemed to reach out and caress me.

'That's all right, Ewan, what can I do for you?' I said trying to sound casual but gripping the sheets tightly with my free hand.

Ewan paused for a moment. 'Well now I'm in a wee bit of bother here. It's a calving.'

The window rattled as the wind buffeted the glass. 'A calving?' I quavered.

'Yes, a big cow with a great long pelvis and the calf's head is back. I've been trying for an hour but I'm damned if I can reach it – my arm's not long enough.'

'Ah yes, I've a very short arm myself,' I babbled. 'I know just how you feel. I'm no good when it comes to jobs like that.'

A soft chuckle came over the line. 'Oh, I don't want your arm, Jim, it's that embryotome I want.'

'Embryotome?'

'That's right. Remember you were telling me what a wonderful instrument it was.'

Why couldn't I keep my big mouth shut? My mind began to hunt round desperately for a way of escape.

'But Ewan, you'd kill the calf. An embryotome isn't indicated in a case like this.'

'This calf's dead and stinking, Jim. All I want is to get its head off to save the cow.'

I was trapped. I didn't say anything more but lay quivering, waiting for the terrible words which I knew were coming.

They came all right. 'Just slip out here and do it for me will you, Jim?'

As I tottered from my bed I became aware immediately that the knee where I had been kicked had stiffened up and I could hardly bend it. In the darkness of the garden the dead leaves crunched softly under my feet and when I reached the yard the wind roared in the elms, tearing the last leaves from the branches and hurling them past my face like driven snow flakes.

Huddled over the wheel, my head nodding with weariness, I drove out of the town. My destination was Hutton House, a farm about five miles on the other side of Scarburn, and I muttered feebly to myself as I peered through the windscreen.

'Just slip out here!' he says. 'Just slip out thirty bloody miles over narrow twisting roads and get down on your belly and knock your guts out!' Damn Ewan Ross, and damn his Highland charm and his Highland indolence. I was like a bloody little shuttlecock – back and forth, back and forth. And I was absolutely whacked and my arms were sore and my knee ached. Almost whimpering with self pity I bemoaned my lot. This country vetting was a mug's game. I should have been a doctor, my mother always wanted me to be a doctor, and I wouldn't have to drive thirty miles to a cold cow house but just pop round the corner into a nice warm bedroom and pat the hand of some sweet old lady and dole out a few pills then back within minutes to my bed – my deep, deep, soft, soft bed...

I lurched suddenly into wakefulness as the car careered straight for the roadside wall. Gripping the wheel tightly, feeling the wind pulling against the steering, I decided that the main thing was not to fall asleep. It wasn't easy; there was a numbing sameness about the miles of walls, the endless strip of road rolling out before me, but finally, after about an hour, I chugged into Scarburn and for a few moments my headlights swept across the unheeding tight-shut face of the little town. Then the last five miles with the engine fighting against the rising ground before I drew up outside the gate of Hutton House.

I should say the first gate because there were four along the track leading to the pin point of light high on the fell-side. And at each gate the wind, whipping straight from the north, tugged fiercely at the car door as I got out and each time as I turned away from the headlights the fields were lost in the blackness and there was only the cold glitter of stars in a clean-swept sky.

At last the huddle of farm buildings lay before me and I drove up to the chink of brightness which came from the byre door. Even here in the yard the wind tore at me as I wrestled with the boot. Gasping, I lifted out my wellingtons, bottle of antiseptic and the accursed embryotome and hurried over to the low building.

Inside, all was peace; a delicious warmth rising from the low row of somnolent cows, my patient propped on her chest between two bales, Mr Hugill, the stooping, wrinkled farmer and Ewan sitting comfortably cross-legged, smoking one of his funny cigarettes. He was sitting in a chair, too – they had even brought a chair out here for him – and in the light of the big oil lamp he looked across at me without speaking for a moment then he gave me his shy smile.

'Jim, it's good of you to come. I've had a damn hard try but I know when I'm beat. I can tell you you're a sight for sore eyes walking in that door.'

Mr Hugill chuckled. 'Aye, we're badly in need of a bit o'young blood on t'job.'

Suddenly I stopped feeling sorry for myself. I didn't care about the long journey, about being winkled from my delectable bed. But I didn't feel much like young blood as I stripped off, knelt down gingerly on my stiff knee and thrust an arm, chafed red and tingling from the antiseptic, into the cow.

I realized straight away what Ewan meant. This cow did have a hell of a long pelvis. The calf's feet were in the passage and the head was tucked away back along the ribs somewhere. I had to surmise this because at full stretch I could just reach the cleft made by the flexion of the neck. There was no chance of straightening it out, so my task was clear; I had to get an embryotomy wire down that cleft and round the neck so that I could cut off the head.

This was one of those calvings without the true savour; without the rewarding sight of a new living creature at the finish. But sometimes it happened like this. The calf I was feeling had been dead for about twenty-four hours judging by the sweetish smell and the emphysematous crackling under the skin, and had to be regarded simply as a piece of inanimate tissue which had to be removed or the mother would surely die of septicaemia or have to be slaughtered. As though divining my thoughts the cow laid her head along her side, looked at me and moaned softly. She had the bonny white face of the Hereford Cross and she looked sick; she wanted rid of that thing inside her more than anybody.

The usual procedure is to pass a cord round the part to be cut off and then pull the wire through; but it isn't as easy as that. It is one thing pushing it into a tight space but quite another thing finding it at the other side. Fortunately some intelligent chap who clearly knew what calving was all about had come up with a simple invention – a heavy lead weight with a small hole at one end for the cord and a bigger one at the other end for your finger.

I fished my weight out now and again pushed an arm alongside the dry legs and up to the cleft in the neck. By straining to the limit I managed to force the weight forward and felt it fall down into the cleft. I came out of the cow now and carefully soaped my arm. This was the moment of truth. If I could get hold of the weight on the underside of the neck and pull it through with the cord attached the rest was easy. The job was over in fact. If I couldn't reach it all was lost.

Again down on the cobbles and again the long reach between the calf's legs and the clinging vaginal wall right forward beneath the twisted neck where my lead weight just had to be. It wasn't there. Digging my toes between the stones on the floor I fought for another inch and managed to pass my fingers up into the cleft. Still nothing. The weight hadn't fallen through – it was stuck up there, probably a fraction above my groping fingers; and my hopes were stuck with it.

I went back to the bucket and soaped the other arm. Sometimes that worked. But the result was the same; a desperate fumbling at nothing. Not for the first time I cursed the accident of anatomy which had given me a short arm. Siegfried with his slender build and long reach would have been putting his jacket on by now, all ready to go home.

But there was nothing else for it but to fight on – and I wasn't in shape for fighting. Even a man in peak condition can't spend much time inside a cow without having the blood squeezed relentlessly from his arm by the uterine contractions, but when he starts as I did from a point of maximum fragility it is really no contest. It took only about a minute for my arm to be reduced to something like a stalk of asparagus with useless twitching fingers on the end. I had to keep changing round faster and faster till I was flopping on the cobbles like a stranded fish. And all the time it was getting worse in there; drier, more clinging, everything closing down till I could hardly move, never mind get my hand on that precious lead weight.

I must have gone on like this for the best part of an hour before the futility of it became plain. I had to try something else. Hoisting myself on to my knees I turned round.

'Mr Hugill, would you please bring me some warm water in another bucket.'

As the farmer hurried from the byre I turned to Ewan.

'It's that bloody weight,' I said. 'I expected it to fall straight down but it hasn't. The bend in the neck must be so tight the thing can't get through. I'm going to pump some water in to see if it'll open things up a bit.'

Ewan looked with compassion at my sweating face and sagging jaw, at the caked dirt and slime and bits of straw sticking to my chest. 'Right, Jim,' he said. 'That sounds like a good idea.'

I didn't enjoy my visit out to the car. Standing stripped to the waist in total darkness in the teeth of a north wind is an overrated pastime but it made a change from the cobbles. I fumbled a pump and rubber tube from the boot and returned to the byre at a trot.

Ewan operated the pump as I pushed the tube forward over the dried-out legs, playing the water from side to side and especially into that bend in the neck.

When I had finished I came out of the cow quickly, dropped the tube and, slightly breathless, soaped my arm again. This was really it this time. That water would give me more room, but only for a few seconds.

Lying down again I inserted my arm and it was like a different world – lots of space, everything moist and moveable. My fingers trembled as they inched forward under that neck and, hallelujah, the weight was there, the smooth, metallic, beautiful edge of the thing just projecting from among the hair. I could twiddle it with the end of my fingers and I felt it gradually coming down till the hole was within reach and I thrust my finger through it with savage relief and lay like that for a few moments smiling stupidly down at the wet stones and knowing I had won.

The rest was routine. Joining the cord to the wire and pulling it round the neck; threading the wire through the shining steel tubes of the embryotome which protected the vaginal wall from the cutting edge; the few minutes of steady sawing till the sudden lack of resistance told that the head was off and the obstruction removed.

After that, Ewan and I took a leg apiece and delivered the calf without difficulty, the head followed and the job was done. Swilling myself down with the last of the water I looked at the cow; she had had a long tussle but nothing to do her any harm; no hard pulling, no internal damage. She should be all right. And as though trying to reassure me she hunched her hind legs under her, gave a heave and got to her feet.

'By Gaw, that's a good sign,' Mr Hugill said.

The cow turned her fine white face towards me for a moment, straddled her legs, strained a couple of times, and the placenta welled in multi-coloured entirety from her vulva and plopped into the channel.

'And that's a better sign,' Ewan murmured. He looked at his watch. 'Nearly three o'clock.' Then he turned to the farmer. 'Is your missus up, Mr Hugill?'

The old man didn't seem surprised at the question, in fact he seemed to be expecting it. 'Aye, she's up, right enough, Mr Ross?'

'And is the fire on?'

'Aye, there's a real good fire, Mr Ross,' he replied eagerly.

'Splendid!' Ewan said, rubbing his hands. 'Well, I think we'll have some boiled eggs.' He looked over at me. 'Boiled eggs all right for you, Jim?'

'Boiled eggs?' The concept was difficult to grasp at this hour.

'Yes, just the thing for you after your hard work.'

'Oh well, right, just as you say.'

Ewan became very brisk. 'Fine, we'll have boiled eggs, Mr Hugill, and some tea of course, and maybe a little toast.' He rubbed his chin thoughtfully like a diner at his favourite restaurant pondering over the menu. 'Oh and a few scones would be very nice.'

'Very good, Mr Ross, I'll go in and tell t'missus.' The farmer nodded happily and scuttled away.

Ten minutes later, walking into the farmhouse kitchen, I felt strangely disembodied. Maybe it was because my physical state had progressed from mere exhaustion to something like coma, but the whole thing seemed unreal. The brasses of hearth and mantelpiece glinting in the flames from a crackling wood fire, the table under a hissing tilly lamp laden with its burden of scones, crusty bread, ham and egg pie, curd tarts, fruit cake; it all looked like something from a dream. And it was funny, but the most incredible objects of all were the boiled eggs, brown and massive, top heavy in their china cradles, two for Ewan at the top of the table and two for me down the side.

Mrs Hugill, stout and beaming, poured our tea, then she and her husband sat down on either side of the fire and waited with evident interest for us to go into action. Ewan with total lack of self consciousness began busily to knock the tops off his eggs and slap butter on the toast. I followed mechanically, noting even through the mists that the eggs had a creamy savour which you maybe only found when the hens spent their lives pecking around a 1,500 foot high farmyard, and that the tang of yeast was strong in the homemade bread even though I mumbled it with a dry mouth and numb lips. The tea, too, would have been excellent but for the fact that I added salt to it instead of sugar; just sat and watched myself pouring salt from the little spoon first on to my egg plate then into my tea. It tasted different, but I don't recommend it.

All the time the call of home and bed was getting stronger

but Ewan was in no hurry. Speaking through a mouthful of ham and egg pie he addressed his hostess.

'Mrs Hugill, now I know why you always win the prizes at Scarburn show with your baking.'

As the good lady giggled with pleasure I struggled to my feet. 'I second that, Mrs Hugill, I've really enjoyed it, but it's time I was away. I've a long way to go.

Ewan swallowed, wiped his lips and smiled across the table. 'Well I can't thank you enough, Jim. You've saved the situation. I couldn't have done what you've done tonight even if I'd had your magic embryotome.'

'Oh that's all right, it's been a pleasure.' I made my way to the door and took a last look back at the scene which I still could scarcely believe; the farmer and his wife nodding and waving from the bright fireside, Ewan, in lordly state at the head of the table, hacking vigorously at a large Wensleydale cheese.

I hardly noticed the run back. In a comfortable state of suspended animation I sat with half-closed eyes fixed on the road ahead. There was none of the apprehension of the journey out, none of the moaning and griping, just the warm satisfaction that a good cow would be pulling hay from its rack tomorrow instead of hanging from the butcher's hook. Only a little thing, nothing world-shaking about it, but good.

When I drove into the yard at Skeldale House the gale had blown itself out leaving a deep litter of leaves shining brilliant gold in the headlights and I scuffed my way through them, ankle deep, feeling the still air cool on my face in the darkness. Bed was an unbelievable haven and as I floated away my last emotion was a feeling of wonder at the things the farmers would do for Ewan Ross.

My clients had shown me many kindnesses in the past and I had a lot of future still ahead of me, but I doubted whether anybody would ever give me boiled eggs at three o'clock in the morning.

CHAPTER FOURTEEN

It was the chance to start my public speaking career; a definite opportunity which I knew I should grasp, yet I shrank from it.

'Oh I don't know,' I said to the curate, 'I've never done anything of the sort before. Maybe you'd better look for somebody else.'

The curate beamed on me. He was in his thirties and had always struck me as being a saintly man since he obviously saw no evil in anything or anybody.

'Oh come now, Mr Herriot. I'm sure you'd manage splendidly and the youth club are longing to hear you. A lot of my young people are from farming families and they'd be quite fascinated to have a vet speak to them.'

'Well it's very nice of you to say so, Mr Blenkinsopp.' But I had a mental image of the packed church hall, the rows of faces looking up at me, and I began to sweat at the very thought. 'I tell you what – if they want to hear a vet I'll get Mr Farnon to give them a talk. He's very good.'

The curate squeezed my arm. 'But Mr Herriot, it's you I want. You are very young and the boys and girls would have something in common with you from the start. And you'd only have to speak for about half an hour and then there would be questions and a lively discussion.'

'Oh I don't think I'd better,' I muttered though inwardly I writhed at the shame of being scared to get up in front of an audience. 'Maybe some other time, but I really don't feel I could do it just at present.'

Mr Blenkinsopp sighed. 'Ah well, just as you wish, but I know the club members will be disappointed. And Miss Alderson, too.'

'Miss Alderson?'

'Yes, Helen helps me run the club. In fact it was she who suggested you as a speaker.'

'She did?'

'Yes, indeed.'

'She attends all the meetings, I suppose?' I said.

'Oh of course. I'm sure she was looking forward to seeing you at our next get-together.'

'Mm . . . well . . . I wonder. Maybe I'd better have a bash at it.'

'Splendid!' The curate's face shone with pleasure. 'You have plenty of time – it's not till three weeks on Tuesday.'

'Well done, James.' Siegfried said at lunch. 'I'm glad you've grasped the nettle. All professional men have to get used to public speaking and the sooner you begin the better. And it helps our image – one has to wave the flag a little now and then.'

'I suppose so.' I fiddled with my napkin for a moment. 'But I haven't much idea about what to say. Have you any suggestions?'

'Thank you, Mrs Hall, that looks wonderful.' Siegfried said to our housekeeper as she impassively placed a large steak and kidney pie in front of him. Then he turned to me again. 'Well, James, you've been asked to speak as a vet so you've got to deal with veterinary matters. If they're farmers' sons and daughters they'll lap it up.'

'Yes, but that's a big subject. What exactly do you mean?'

My employer attacked the pie resolutely and a heavenly steam escaped as his knife pierced the crust. 'Pass your plate, James.' He mounded on meat and pastry then pushed a tureen of mashed potatoes towards me. 'I know it's a big subject so you've got to pick out some attractive and interesting aspects.'

'I don't think I'd know where to start,' I said. 'I wish you'd sort of sketch something out for me.'

Siegfried chewed thoughtfully for a few moments. 'Everybody has their own ideas about these things, of course, but if

I were you I'd start off with something to catch their attention – some provocative remark or question – then I'd paint a broad tapestry of the profession, including its history, and in between I'd shove in some practical things, maybe about first aid in animals.'

'First aid, eh?'

'Yes, that's right.' My employer was warming to his subject. 'How to stop haemorrhage, how to deal with emergencies when the vet isn't available. How about puncturing the rumen in a bloated cow? That would make them sit up.'

'It would, wouldn't it? Yes, I think I'll do that.' I made a few mental notes. 'But how about the opening remark you mentioned? Any ideas about that?'

Siegfried carefully transported an extra boiled leek from its bed of white sauce on to his plate. For perhaps a minute he stared ahead of him in silence then without warning he crashed his fist down on the table, making me bite my tongue painfully.

'I've got it, James! Not a shadow of a doubt about it.' He held up a finger and intoned, 'WHAT DOES MRCVS MEAN TO YOU? There's your opening line – how about that?'

'Gosh, it's good!' I gazed at him admiringly. 'What does MRCVS mean to you? I really like that.'

'There you are, then,' he said, chewing smugly, 'and you must deliver it in loud, ringing tones. You'll have them on the edge of their seats right from the start, and gasping to hear more. A good beginning is vital.'

'Well thanks, Siegfried, you've been a big help. I think I can get the material together now but the only thing is, can I put it over? I've never spoken in public – what if I dry up as soon as I get on my feet? What if I can't remember a thing?'

'Oh there's no possibility of that, but I know how you feel and I'll give you one more piece of advice.' He pointed solemnly at me with his fork. 'Since it's your first time you ought to get the whole thing word perfect. Practise it day by day till you can recite it like poetry, then you'll be all right.'

'OK,' I said. 'I'll do that, too.'

Siegfried leaned back and laughed. 'Good lad! And in the meantime, stop worrying. You're going to knock 'em cold, James, I just know you are.'

I took his advice literally and over the next three weeks as I drove along the frost-bound roads my lips were continually moving as I harangued my imaginary audience. Several times I saw roadside workers look up in surprise as my declamations boomed out at them through the open windows, and I got to the stage where every syllable, every inflection tripped effortlessly off my tongue in perfect order.

In fact, it all began to sound so good to me that in a fearful sort of way I began to look forward to the big night. How many would be there to hear me? Fifty? Sixty? Maybe even a hundred? Well, let 'em all come. And Helen would be there. Maybe my stock wasn't so high in that direction but it wouldn't do any harm if she were to see me hold the mass of young people in my thrall, the youthful faces upturned eagerly to me, drinking in my every word.

My confidence grew steadily as the days passed and when the fateful Tuesday evening finally arrived I was in a state of pallid resolution. No panic. A certain tension and dryness of the mouth, but above all a cold determination to make good.

Before I left for the church hall I bathed, put on my best suit and inspected my face carefully in the mirror. It wouldn't do if I had a piece of cow muck sticking on an eyebrow in front of all that throng.

I was glad I didn't have far to walk because there had been a fall of snow that morning followed by a few hours of icy rain and the streets were deep in slush. As I opened the hall door and stepped inside, the curate met me with a radiant smile.

'Ah, Mr Herriot, here you are! So kind of you to come. Our young people can hardly wait to hear you.'

We were in a narrow lobby with doors on either side and from somewhere I could hear music and laughter. But I didn't pay much attention because Helen was coming down the stairs at the far end.

She laughed and for a moment her eyes held mine with that warm, interested, kind look which was part of her. It was a funny thing but whenever I met Helen she looked at me like that. I hadn't had a lot of luck in my contacts with her but afterwards there was no difference; it was always the same calm, friendly smile.

Of course she was a kind girl, Helen, that was it. This was probably the way she looked at everybody – with that soft flame kindling in her eyes' blue depths and the full lips parted over the white teeth. And there was the way her mouth went into little upturned folds in the corners . . . and how her dark hair fell softly across the white of her cheek . . .

But Mr Blenkinsopp was giving a series of little coughs. I dragged my attention back to him.

'Come in and see our club room before you start,' he said, opening one of the doors. 'I think you'll agree that it's a pleasant place for them to come on these wintry evenings.'

We went inside. A gramophone was playing and some pretty teenage girls were fox-trotting together to the music. A few lads lounged about while two others were playing billiards on a miniature table in the corner. The curate gazed fondly at the scene, the music stopped, the record was changed for a waltz and the dancing began again. It struck me as strange that it didn't seem to occur to any of the boys to dance with those attractive girls.

I looked at the two billiard players. They would be about fifteen or sixteen and were obviously devotees of the cinema. There was something of the Bowery pool room in their scowling attitude, the cigarettes dangling from their lips, the way they squinted through the smoke as they bent to play a shot, the tough, deadpan chalking of the cues, the contemptuous gangsterish disregard of the other occupants of the room.

The curate clapped his hands. 'Come now, boys and girls, it's time you joined the others in the hall. Mr Herriot is ready to talk to you now.'

The room emptied rapidly as the young people went through a door in the far corner. Soon there only remained the gangsters at the billiard table; they didn't appear to have heard. The curate called on them several times more but they took no notice. Finally Helen went over and whispered tensely at them and at length they threw down their cues and with a single malevolent glance in my direction they slouched from the room.

This then was the moment of truth when I would face my audience after the weeks of preparation. I took a deep breath and followed the others into the hall and on to the platform. Perched on a shaky chair between Helen and Mr Blenkinsopp I surveyed the scene.

It wasn't a big hall – it would probably have held a hundred if it had been full. But it wasn't full tonight, in fact the main feature about it was space. I made a quick count of the audience; there were twelve. They were disposed in little knots among the empty chairs. Halfway up clustered the six teenage girls, then a few rows behind, a very fat boy holding a bag of potato crisps and near him a thin, dispirited-looking youth with sleepy eyes. Right on the back row, against the wall, the two gangsters lounged in attitudes of studied boredom. What surprised me most, however, was the sight of two tiny girls, mere tots of about four, right in the middle of the front row, a long way from anybody else. One sported a big pink bow in her hair while the other wore pigtails. Their little legs swinging, they looked up at me incuriously.

I turned to Helen. 'Who are those two?'

'Oh, they like to come with their big sisters now and again,' she replied. 'They love it and they're very good. They won't be any trouble.'

I nodded stupidly, still trying to adjust my mind to the fact that these were the people who were going to receive my searching exposition on veterinary science. None of them seemed to be showing the slightest interest in me except for one very pretty little thing in the centre of the teenage group who gazed up at me with shining eyes as though she couldn't wait for me to begin.

Mr Blenkinsopp stood up and made a charming introductory speech. As he spoke, the gangsters at the back giggled, wrestled and dug at each other's ribs; the girls, with the exception of the little darling in the centre peeped back at the fighting pair in admiration.

At last I heard the curate's final words. 'And now I have great pleasure in asking Mr Herriot to address you.'

I got slowly to my feet and gazed over the twelve. The gangsters were still wrestling, the fat boy put a crisp in his mouth and began to crunch it loudly, down in the front, tot number one was sucking her thumb while the other, rocking her head from side to side, appeared to be singing to herself.

I felt a moment of wild panic. Should I change the entire plan and just talk casually about a few trivial points? But I couldn't. I had the whole thing off parrot-like and I'd have to deliver it as I had learned it. There was no way out.

With an effort I steadied myself and cleared my throat. 'What does MRCVS mean to you?' I cried.

It seemed to startle Mr Blenkinsopp because he jumped slightly in his chair, but the audience remained totally unmoved. MRCVS appeared to mean not a thing to them. I ploughed ahead, sketching out the history of the Royal College, painstakingly illustrating its development from the early days of farriery. Nobody was listening except the little pet in the centre but I was in the groove and couldn't stop.

'A supplemental Royal Charter was granted in 1932,' I pronounced after about ten minutes' hard going and just then the thin boy yawned. I had labelled him as an ineffectual sort of lad but he certainly could yawn; it was a stretching, groaning, voluptuous paroxysm which drowned my words and it went on and on till he finally lay back, bleary and exhausted by the effort. His companion munched his crisps stolidly.

By the time I had been holding forth for twenty minutes I seemed to be standing listening to myself with a kind of wonder. 'After qualification,' I was saying, 'the main avenues open to the new graduate are general practice and work under the Ministry of Agriculture and Fisheries. The latter is mainly concerned with preventive medicine and with the implementation of the laws governing the notifiable diseases.'

The gangsters punched each other fiercely with stifled laughter, the fat boy had another crisp, tot one drew ecstatically on her thumb while her other hand fondled a lock of her hair. Tot two stuck her legs straight out and admired her little white socks and red shoes. Only the dear girl in the middle paid any attention.

I began to break out in a light perspiration. The thing was taking a lot longer than I had thought to get through, and I had the growing conviction that I must be looking more and more of a chump in Helen's eyes as time went on.

I had rehearsed a few light sallies designed to send my audience into convulsions of laughter as a contrast to the absorbing, serious stuff, but even those who were listening failed to change expression at my shafts of wit. Except, of course, for the little treasure in the middle who pealed back at me sweetly every time.

But I stuck to it grimly. Surely I'd get through to them when I came to the practical bit about first aid.

'All right,' I said, 'you've got a calf with a nasty cut on its leg. The blood is pouring out and you can't get hold of a vet. If you just leave it the blood will all run out and the calf will die. What are you going to do?'

Nobody seemed to care much either way except for tot two. She obviously didn't like the turn things were taking and she stared up at me, her lower lip protruding and trembling.

I went on to explain about tourniquets and pressure pads and then moved on to a discussion of bloat.

'This cow is blown up ready to burst,' I proceeded. 'You've got to do something or she could drop down dead any second.'

I glanced apprehensively at tot two. Her lip was sticking out more every second and was now like a soup plate, but it was no good, I had to go on.

'You must get a knife like a carving knife and stick it straight into the stomach,' I declaimed desperately. 'Now I'll tell you just where to stick it in . . .'

But tot two had had enough. She threw back her head and bawled heartily till her big sister hurried down a few rows and led her away in floods of tears, her pigtails dangling forlornly. Tot one was undisturbed, utterly engrossed as she was with her thumb and the wisp of hair she was rub-rub-rubbing.

Anyway I was getting towards the last lap now.

'The future of the profession, I am convinced, will be less and less involved with the problems of the individual animal,' I went on, addressing myself now exclusively to the little sweetheart in the centre who kept her eyes fixed on me with open admiration. The thin boy went into another of his mighty yawns while his companion finished his last crisp and crumpled the bag noisily.

'We must also consider the emergence of small animal work in any of our plans for the future. Over the past few years the increase in this field has been . . .'

But I had to pause as there was a major disturbance at the back. The jolly feud between the gangsters had flared into ugly warfare. Fists flew, blood streamed, a few ripe oaths rocketed over the company. After a couple of minutes the combatants drew apart and sat glaring and snarling at each other as they dabbed their wounds.

'Whatever the uncertainties and despite the depressed state of agriculture I feel there will always be a place for the veterinary surgeon in our national economy.' That was it. I sat down and Helen, the curate and the little charmer in the middle applauded enthusiastically.

Mr Blenkinsopp rose, beaming delightedly around him. He congratulated me on my splendid talk and said how much they'd all enjoyed it and finished by saying he would now throw the meeting open for questions.

I settled back in my chair. So this was to be the lively discussion he had talked about. I hunted around anxiously from face to face but my audience stared back, dead-eyed; for the first time all evening there was dead silence.

The minutes ticked away and I felt the tension building in me, but at last there was a stirring in the middle of the hall. It was my darling girl; God bless and keep her, she was going to say something. I felt a sudden glow at the knowledge that my words had stimulated a response in at least one young mind.

She sat up in her seat, moistened her lips and smiled at me, bright eyed. She was indeed going to ask a question and as it turned out it was the only one of the evening. I leaned forward expectantly as she began to speak.

'Mr Herriot, I 'ave a little dog what's moultin'. What can I do for 'im?'

CHAPTER FIFTEEN

Probably the most dramatic occurrence in the history of veterinary practice was the disappearance of the draught horse. It is an almost incredible fact that this glory and mainstay of the profession just melted quietly away within a few years. And I was one of those who were there to see it happen.

When I first came to Darrowby the tractor had already begun to take over, but tradition dies hard in the agricultural world and there were still a lot of horses around. Which was just as well because my veterinary education had been geared to things equine with everything else a poor second. It had been a good scientific education in many respects but at times I wondered if the people who designed it still had a mental picture of the horse doctor with his top hat and frock coat busying himself in a world of horse-drawn trams and brewers' drays.

We learned the anatomy of the horse in great detail then that of the other animals much more superficially. It was the same with the other subjects; from animal husbandry with such insistence on a thorough knowledge of shoeing that we developed into amateur blacksmiths – right up to medicine and surgery where it was much more important to know about glanders and strangles than canine distemper. Even as we were learning, we youngsters knew it was ridiculous, with the draught horse already cast as a museum piece and the obvious potential of cattle and small animal work.

Still, after we had absorbed a vast store of equine lore it was a certain comfort that there were still a lot of patients on which we could try it out. I should think in my first two years I treated farm horses nearly every day and though I never was and never will be an equine expert there was a strange thrill in meeting with the age-old conditions whose names rang down almost from medieval times. Quittor, fistulous withers, poll evil, thrush, shoulder slip – vets had been wrestling with them for hundreds of years using very much the same drugs and procedures as myself. Armed with my firing iron and box of blister I plunged determinedly into what had always been the surging mainstream of veterinary life.

And now, in less than three years the stream had dwindled, not exactly to a trickle but certainly to the stage where the final dry-up was in sight. This meant, in a way, a lessening of the pressures on the veterinary surgeon because there is no doubt that horse work was the roughest and most arduous part of our life.

So that today, as I looked at the three-year-old gelding, it occurred to me that this sort of thing wasn't happening as often as it did. He had a long tear in his flank where he had caught himself on barbed wire and it gaped open whenever he moved. There was no getting away from the fact that it had to be stitched.

The horse was tied by the head in his stall, his right side against the tall wooden partition. One of the farm men, a hefty six footer, took a tight hold of the head collar and leaned back against the manger as I puffed some iodoform into the wound. The horse didn't seem to mind, which was a comfort because he was a massive animal emanating an almost tangible vitality and power. I threaded my needle with a length of silk. lifted one of the lips of the wound and passed it through. This was going to be no trouble, I thought as I lifted the flap at the other side and pierced it, but as I was drawing the needle through, the gelding made a convulsive leap and I felt as though a great wind had whistled across the front of my body. Then, strangely, he was standing there against the wooden boards as if nothing had happened.

On the occasions when I have been kicked I have never seen it coming. It is surprising how quickly those great muscular legs can whip out. But there was no doubt he had had a good go at me because my needle and silk was nowhere to be seen, the big man at the head was staring at me with wide eyes in a chalk white face and the front of my clothing was in an extraordinary state. I was wearing a gaberdine mac and it looked as if somebody had taken a razor blade and painstakingly cut the material into narrow strips which hung down in ragged strips to ground level. The great iron-shod hoof had missed my legs by an inch or two but my mac was a write-off.

I was standing there looking around me in a kind of stupor when I heard a cheerful hail from the doorway.

'Now then, Mr Herriot, what's he done at you?' Cliff Tyreman, the old horseman, looked me up and down with a mixture of amusement and asperity.

'He's nearly put me in hospital, Cliff,' I replied shakily. 'About the closest near miss I've ever had. I just felt the wind of it.'

'What were you tryin' to do?'

'Stitch that wound, but I'm not going to try any more. I'm off to the surgery to get a chloroform muzzle.'

The little man looked shocked. 'You don't need no choloform. I'll haud him and you'll have no trouble.'

'I'm sorry, Cliff.' I began to put away my suture materials, scissors and powder. 'You're a good bloke, I know, but he's had one go at me and he's not getting another chance. I don't want to be lame for the rest of my life.'

The horseman's small, wiry frame seemed to bunch into a ball of aggression. He thrust forward his head in a characteristic posture and glared at me. 'I've never heard owt as daft in me life.' Then he swung round on the big man who was still hanging on to the horse's head, the ghastly pallor of his face now tinged with a delicate green. 'Come on out o' there, Bob! You're that bloody scared you're upsetting t'oss. Come on out of it and let me have 'im!'

Bob gratefully left the head and, grinning sheepishly moved with care along the side of the horse. He passed Cliff on the way and the little man's head didn't reach his shoulder.

Cliff seemed thoroughly insulted by the whole business. He took hold of the head collar and regarded the big animal with the disapproving stare of a schoolmaster at a naughty child. The horse, still in the mood for trouble, laid back his ears and began to plunge about the stall, his huge feet clattering ominously on the stone floor, but he came to rest quickly as the little man uppercutted him furiously in the ribs.

'Get stood up straight there, ye big bugger. What's the matter with ye?' Cliff barked and again he planted his tiny fist against the swelling barrel of the chest, a puny blow which the animal could scarcely have felt but which reduced him to quivering submission. 'Try to kick, would you, eh? I'll bloody fettle you!' He shook the head collar and fixed the horse with a hypnotic stare as he spoke. Then he turned to me. 'You can come and do your job, Mr Herriot, he won't hurt tha.'

I looked irresolutely at the huge, lethal animal. Stepping open-eyed into dangerous situations is something vets are called upon regularly to do and I suppose we all react differently. I know there were times when an over-vivid imagination made me acutely aware of the dire possibilities and now my mind seemed to be dwelling voluptuously on the frightful power in those enormous shining quarters, on the unyielding flintiness of the spatulate feet with their rims of metal. Cliff's voice cut into my musings.

'Come on, Mr Herriot, I tell ye he won't hurt tha.'

I reopened my box and tremblingly threaded another needle. I didn't seem to have much option; the little man wasn't asking me, he was telling me. I'd have to try again.

I couldn't have been a very impressive sight as I shuffled forwards, almost tripping over the tattered hula-hula skirt which dangled in front of me, my shaking hands reaching out once more for the wound, my heart thundering in my ears. But I needn't have worried. It was just as the little man had said; he didn't hurt me. In fact he never moved. He seemed to be listening attentively to the muttering which Cliff was directing into his face from a few inches' range. I powdered and stitched and clipped as though working on an anatomical specimen. Chloroform couldn't have done it any better.

As I retreated thankfully from the stall and began again to put away my instruments the monologue at the horse's head began to change its character. The menacing growl was replaced by a wheedling, teasing chuckle.

'Well, ye see, you're just a daft awd bugger, getting yourself all airigated over nowt. You're a good lad, really, aren't ye, a real good lad.' Cliff's hand ran caressingly over the neck and the towering animal began to nuzzle his cheek, as completely in his sway as any Labrador puppy.

When he had finished he came slowly from the stall, stroking the back, ribs, belly and quarters, even giving a playful tweak at the tail on parting while what had been a few minutes ago an explosive mountain of bone and muscle submitted happily.

I pulled a packet of Gold Flake from my pocket. 'Cliff, you're a marvel. Will you have a cigarette?'

'It 'ud be like givin' a pig a strawberry,' the little man replied, then he thrust forth his tongue on which reposed a half-chewed gobbet of tobacco. 'It's allus there. Ah push it in fust thing every mornin' soon as I get out of bed and there it stays. You'd never know, would you?'

I must have looked comically surprised because the dark eyes gleamed and the rugged little face split into a delighted grin. I looked at that grin – boyish, invincible – and reflected on the phenomenon that was Cliff Tyreman.

In a community in which toughness and durability was the norm he stood out as something exceptional. When I had first seen him nearly three years ago barging among cattle, grabbing their noses and hanging on effortlessly, I had put him down as an unusually fit middle-aged man; but he was in fact nearly seventy. There wasn't much of him but he was formidable; with his long arms swinging, his stumping, pigeon-toed gait and his lowered head he seemed always to be butting his way through life.

'I didn't expect to see you today,' I said. 'I heard you had pneumonia.'

He shrugged. 'Aye, summat of t'sort. First time I've ever been off work since I was a lad.'

'And you should be in your bed now, I should say.' I looked at the heaving chest and partly open mouth. 'I could hear you wheezing away when you were at the horse's head.'

'Nay, I can't stick that nohow. I'll be right in a day or two.' He seized a shovel and began busily clearing away the heap of manure behind the horse, his breathing loud and stertorous in the silence.

Harland Grange was a large, mainly arable farm in the low country at the foot of the Dale, and there had been a time when this stable had had a horse standing in every one of the long row of stalls. There had been over twenty with at least twelve regularly at work, but now there were only two, the young horse I had been treating and an ancient grey called Badger.

Cliff had been head horseman and when the revolution came he turned to tractoring and other jobs around the farm with no fuss at all. This was typical of the reaction of thousands of other farm workers throughout the country; they didn't set up a howl at having to abandon the skills of a lifetime and start anew – they just got on with it. In fact, the younger men seized avidly upon the new machines and proved themselves natural mechanics.

But to the old experts like Cliff, something had gone. He would say: 'It's a bloody sight easier sitting on a tractor – it used to play 'ell with me feet walking up and down them fields all day.' But he couldn't lose his love of horses; the fellow feeling between working man and working beast which had grown in him since childhood and was in his blood for ever.

My next visit to the farm was to see a fat bullock with a piece of turnip stuck in his throat but while I was there, the farmer, Mr Gilling, asked me to have a look at old Badger.

'He's had a bit of a cough lately. Maybe it's just his age, but see what you think.'

The old horse was the sole occupant of the stable now. 'I've sold the three year old,' Mr Gilling said. 'But I'll still keep the old 'un – he'll be useful for a bit of light carting.'

I glanced sideways at the farmer's granite features. He looked the least sentimental of men but I knew why he was keeping the old horse. It was for Cliff.

'Cliff will be pleased, anyway,' I said.

Mr Gilling nodded. 'Aye, I never knew such a feller for 'osses. He was never happier than when he was with them.' He gave a short laugh. 'Do you know, I can remember years ago when he used to fall out with his missus he'd come down to this stable of a night and sit among his 'osses. Just sit here for hours on end looking at 'em and smoking. That was before he started chewing tobacco.'

'And did you have Badger in those days?'

'Aye, we bred him. Cliff helped at his foaling – I remember the little beggar came arse first and we had a bit of a job pullin' him out.' He smiled again. 'Maybe that's why he was always Cliff's favourite. He always worked Badger himself – year in year out – and he was that proud of 'im that if he had to take him into the town for any reason he'd plait ribbons into his mane and hang all his brasses on him first.' He shook his head reminiscently.

The old horse looked round with mild interest as I went up to him. He was in his late twenties and everything about him suggested serene old age; the gaunt projection of the pelvic bones, the whiteness of face and muzzle, the sunken eye with its benign expression. As I was about to take his temperature he gave a sharp, barking cough and it gave me the first clue to his ailment. I watched the rise and fall of his breathing for a minute or two and the second clue was there to be seen; further examination was unnecessary.

'He's broken winded, Mr Gilling,' I said. 'Or he's got pulmonary emphysema to give it its proper name. Do you see that double lift of the abdomen as he breathes out? That's because his lungs have lost their elasticity and need an extra effort to force the air out.'

'What's caused it, then?'

'Well it's to do with his age, but he's got a bit of cold on him at the moment and that's brought it out.'

'Will he get rid of it in time?' the farmer asked.

'He'll be a bit better when he gets over his cold, but I'm afraid he'll never be quite right. I'll give you some medicine to put in his drinking water which will alleviate his symptoms.' I went out to the car for a bottle of the arsenical expectorant mixture which we used then.

It was about six weeks later that I heard from Mr Gilling again. He rang me about seven o'clock one evening.

'I'd like you to come out and have a look at old Badger,' he said.

'What's wrong? Is it his broken wind again?'

'No, it's not that. He's still got the cough but it doesn't seem to bother him much. No, I think he's got a touch of colic. I've got to go out but Cliff will attend to you.'

The little man was waiting for me in the yard. He was carrying an oil lamp. As I came up to him I exclaimed in horror.

'Good God, Cliff, what have you been doing to yourself?' His face was a patchwork of cuts and scratches and his nose, almost without skin, jutted from between two black eyes.

He grinned through the wounds, his eyes dancing with merriment. 'Came off me bike t'other day. Hit a stone and went right over handlebars, arse over tip.' He burst out laughing at the very thought.

'But damn it, man, haven't you been to a doctor? You're not fit to be out in that state.'

'Doctor? Nay, there's no need to bother them fellers. It's nowt much.' He fingered a gash on his jaw. 'Ah lapped me chin up for a day in a bit o' bandage, but it's right enough now.'

I shook my head as I followed him into the stable. He hung up the oil lamp then went over to the horse.

'Can't reckon t'awd feller up,' he said. 'You'd think there wasn't much ailing him but there's summat.'

There were no signs of violent pain but the animal kept transferring his weight from one hind foot to the other as if he did have a little abdominal discomfort. His temperature was normal and he didn't show symptoms of anything else.

I looked at him doubtfully. 'Maybe he has a bit of colic. There's nothing else to see, anyway. I'll give him an injection to settle him down.'

'Right you are, maister, that's good.' Cliff watched me get my syringe out then he looked around him into the shadows at the far end of the stable.

'Funny seeing only one 'oss standing here. I remember when there was a great row of 'em and the barfins and bridles hangin' there on the stalls and the rest of the harness behind them all shinin' on t'wall.' He transferred his plug of tobacco to the other side of his mouth and smiled. 'By gaw, I were in here at six o'clock every morning feedin' them and gettin' them ready for work and ah'll tell you it was a sight to see us all goin' off ploughing at the start o' the day. Maybe six pairs of 'osses setting off with their harness jinglin' and the ploughmen sittin' sideways on their backs. Like a regular procession it was.'

I smiled. 'It was an early start, Cliff.'

'Aye, by Gaw, and a late finish. We'd bring the 'osses home at night and give 'em a light feed and take their harness off, then we'd go and have our own teas and we'd be back 'ere again afterwards, curry-combing and dandy-brushin' all the sweat and dirt off 'em. Then we'd give them a right good stiff feed of chop and oats and hay to set 'em up for the next day.'

'There wouldn't be much left of the evening then, was there?'

'Nay, there wasn't. It was about like work and bed, I reckon, but it never bothered us.'

I stepped forward to give Badger the injection, then

paused. The old horse had undergone a slight spasm, a barely perceptible stiffening of the muscles, and as I looked at him he cocked his tail for a second then lowered it.

'There's something else here,' I said. 'Will you bring him out of his stall, Cliff, and let me see him walk across the yard.'

And watching him clop over the cobbles I saw it again; the stiffness, the raising of the tail. Something clicked in my mind, I walked over and rapped him under the chin and as the membrana nictitans flicked across his eye then slid slowly back I knew.

I paused for a moment. My casual little visit had suddenly become charged with doom.

'Cliff,' I said. 'I'm afraid he's got tetanus.'

'Lockjaw, you mean?'

'That's right. I'm sorry, but there's no doubt about it. Has he had any wounds lately – especially in his feet?'

'Well he were dead lame about a fortnight ago and blacksmith let some matter out of his hoof. Made a right big 'ole.'

There it was. 'It's a pity he didn't get an anti-tetanus shot at the time,' I said. I put my hand into the animal's mouth and tried to prise it open but the jaws were clamped tightly together. 'I don't suppose he's been able to eat today.'

'He had a bit this morning but nowt tonight. What's the lookout for him, Mr Herriot?'

What indeed? If Cliff had asked me the same question today I would have been just as troubled to give him an answer. The facts are that seventy to eighty per cent of tetanus cases die and whatever you do to them in the way of treatment doesn't seem to make a whit of difference to those figures. But I didn't want to sound entirely defeatist.

'It's a very serious condition as you know, Cliff, but I'll do all I can. I've got some antitoxin in the car and I'll inject that into his vein and if the spasms get very bad I'll give him a sedative. As long as he can drink there's a chance for him because he'll have to live on fluids – gruel would be fine.'

For a few days Badger didn't get any worse and I began to

hope. I've seen tetanus horses recover and it is a wonderful experience to come in one day and find that the jaws have relaxed and the hungry animal can once more draw food into its mouth.

But it didn't happen with Badger. They had got the old horse into a big loose box where he could move around in comfort and each day as I looked over the half door I felt myself willing him to show some little sign of improvement; but instead, after the first few days he began to deteriorate. A sudden movement or the approach of any person would throw him into a violent spasm so that he would stagger stiff-legged round the box like a big wooden toy, his eyes terrified, saliva drooling from between his fiercely clenched teeth. One morning I was sure he would fall and I suggested putting him in slings. I had to go back to the surgery for the slings and it was just as I was entering Skeldale House that the phone rang.

It was Mr Gilling. 'He's beat us to it, I'm afraid. He's flat out on the floor and I doubt it's a bad job, Mr Herriot. We'll have to put him down, won't we?'

'I'm afraid so.'

'There's just one thing. Mallock will be taking him away but old Cliff says he doesn't want Mallock to shoot 'im. Wants you to do it. Will you come?'

I got out the humane killer and drove back to the farm, wondering at the fact that the old man should find the idea of my bullet less repugnant than the knacker man's. Mr Gilling was waiting in the box and by his side Cliff, shoulders hunched, hands deep in his pockets. He turned to me with a strange smile.

'I was just saying to t'boss how grand t'awd lad used to look when I got 'im up for a show. By Gaw you should have seen him with 'is coat polished and the feathers on his legs scrubbed as white as snow and a big blue ribbon round his tail.'

'I can imagine it, Cliff,' I said. 'Nobody could have looked after him better.'

He took his hands from his pockets, crouched by the prostrate animal and for a few minutes stroked the white-flecked neck and pulled at the ears while the old sunken eye looked at him impassively.

He began to speak softly to the old horse but his voice was steady, almost conversational, as though he was chatting to a friend.

'Many's the thousand miles I've walked after you, awd lad, and many's the talk we've had together. But I didn't have to say much to tha, did I? I reckon you knew every move I made, everything I said. Just one little word and you always did what ah wanted you to do.'

He rose to his feet. 'I'll get on with me work now, boss,' he said firmly, and strode out of the box.

I waited awhile so that he would not hear the bang which signalled the end of Badger, the end of the horses of Harland Grange and the end of the sweet core of Cliff Tyreman's life.

As I was leaving I saw the little man again. He was mounting the iron seat of a roaring tractor and I shouted to him above the noise.

'The boss says he's going to get some sheep in and you'll be doing a bit of shepherding. I think you'll enjoy that.'

Cliff's undefeated grin flashed out as he called back to me.

'Aye, I don't mind learnin' summat new. I'm nobbut a lad yet!'

CHAPTER SIXTEEN

This was a different kind of ringing. I had gone to sleep as the great bells in the church tower down the street pealed for the Christmas midnight mass, but this was a sharper, shriller sound.

It was difficult at first to shake off the mantle of unreality in which I had wrapped myself last night. Last night –

Christmas Eve. It had been like a culmination of all the ideas I had ever held about Christmas – a flowering of emotions I had never experienced before. It had been growing in me since the afternoon call to a tiny village where the snow lay deep on the single street and on the walls and on the ledges of the windows where the lights on the tinselled trees glowed red and blue and gold; and as I left it in the dusk I drove beneath the laden branches of a group of dark spruce as motionless as though they had been sketched against the white background of the fields. And when I reached Darrowby it was dark and around the market place the little shops were bright with decorations and the light from the windows fell in a soft yellow wash over the trodden snow of the cobbles. People, anonymously muffled, were hurrying about, doing their last minute shopping, their feet slithering over the rounded stones.

I had known many Christmases in Scotland but they had taken second place to the New Year celebrations; there had been none of this air of subdued excitement which started days before with folks shouting good wishes and coloured lights winking on the lonely fell-sides and the farmers' wives plucking the fat geese, the feathers piled deep around their feet. And for fully two weeks you heard the children piping carols in the street then knocking on the door for sixpences. And best of all, last night the Methodist choir had sung out there, filling the night air with rich, thrilling harmony.

Before going to bed and just as the church bells began, I closed the door of Skeldale House behind me and walked again into the market place. Nothing stirred now in the white square stretching smooth and cold and empty under the moon, and there was a Dickensian look about the ring of houses and shops put together long before anybody thought of town planning; tall and short, fat and thin, squashed in crazily around the cobbles, their snow-burdened roofs jagged and uneven against the frosty sky.

As I walked back, the snow crunching under my feet, the bells clanging, the sharp air tingling in my nostrils, the wonder and mystery of Christmas enveloped me in a great wave. Peace on earth, goodwill towards men; the words became meaningful as never before and I saw myself suddenly as a tiny particle in the scheme of things; Darrowby, the farmers, the animals and I seemed for the first time like a warm, comfortable entity. I hadn't been drinking but I almost floated up the stairs of Skeldale House to my bedroom.

The temperature up there was about the same as in the street. It was always like that and I had developed the habit of hurling off my clothes and leaping into bed before the freezing air could get at me, but tonight my movements were leisurely and when I finally crawled between the sheets I was still wallowing in my Yuletide euphoria. There wouldn't be much work tomorrow; I'd have a long lie – maybe till nine – and then a lazy day, a glorious hiatus in my busy life. As I drifted into sleep it was as though I was surrounded by the smiling faces of my clients looking down at me with an all-embracing benevolence; and strangely I fancied I could hear singing, sweet and haunting, just like the Methodist choir – God Rest Ye Merry Gentlemen . . .

But now there was this other bell which wouldn't stop. Must be the alarm. But as I pawed at the clock the noise continued and I saw that it was six o'clock. It was the phone of course. I lifted the receiver.

A metallic voice, crisp and very wideawake, jarred in my ear. 'Is that the vet?'

'Yes, Herriot speaking,' I mumbled.

'This is Brown, Willet Hill. I've got a cow down with milk fever. I want you here quick.'

'Right, I'll see to it.'

'Don't take ower long.' Then a click at the far end.

I rolled on to my back and stared at the ceiling. So this was Christmas Day. The day when I was going to step out of the world for a spell and luxuriate in the seasonal spirit. I hadn't bargained for this fellow jerking me brutally back to reality. And not a word of regret or apology. No 'sorry to get you out of bed', or anything else, never mind 'Merry Christmas'. It was just a bit hard.

Mr Brown was waiting for me in the darkness of the farmyard. I had been to his place a few times before and as my headlights blazed on him I was struck, as always, by his appearance of perfect physical fitness. He was a gingery man of about forty with high cheekbones set in a sharp-featured clear-skinned face. Red hair peeped from under a check cap and a faint auburn down covered his cheeks, his neck, the backs of his hands. It made me feel a bit more sleepy just to look at him.

He didn't say good morning but nodded briefly then jerked his head in the direction of the byre. 'She's in there' was all he said.

He watched in silence as I gave the injections and it wasn't until I was putting the empty bottles into my pocket that he spoke.

'Don't suppose I'll have to milk her today?'

'No,' I replied. 'Better leave the bag full.'

'Anything special about feedin'?'

'No, she can have anything she likes when she wants it.' Mr Brown was very efficient. Always wanted to know every detail.

As we crossed the yard he halted suddenly and turned to face me. Could it be that he was going to ask me in for a nice hot cup of tea?

'You know,' he said, as I stood ankle deep in the snow, the frosty air nipping at my ears. 'I've had a few of these cases lately. Maybe there's summat wrong with my routine. Do you think I'm steaming up my cows too much?'

'It's quite possible.' I hurried towards the car. One thing I wasn't going to do was deliver a lecture on animal husbandry at this moment.

My hand was on the door handle when he said 'I'll give you another ring if she's not up by dinner time. And there's one other thing – that was a hell of a bill I had from you fellers last month, so tell your boss not to be so savage with 'is pen.' Then he turned and walked quickly towards the house.

Well that was nice, I thought as I drove away. Not even thanks or goodbye, just a complaint and a promise to haul me away from my roast goose if necessary. A sudden wave of anger surged in me. Bloody farmers! There were some miserable devils among them. Mr Brown had doused my festive feelings as effectively as if he had thrown a bucket of water over me.

As I mounted the steps of Skeldale House the darkness had paled to a shivery grey. Mrs Hall met me in the passage. She was carrying a tray.

'I'm sorry,' she said. 'There's another urgent job. Mr Farnon's had to go out, too. But I've got a cup of coffee and some fried bread for you. Come in and sit down – you've got time to eat it before you go.'

I sighed. It was going to be just another day after all. 'What's this about, Mrs Hall?' I asked, sipping the coffee.

'It's old Mr Kirby,' she replied. 'He's in a right state about his nanny goat.'

'Nanny goat!'

'Aye, he says she's choking.'

'Choking! How the heck can she be choking?' I shouted.

'I'm sure I don't know. And I wish you wouldn't shout at me, Mr Herriot. It's not my fault.'

'I'm sorry, Mrs Hall, I'm really sorry.' I finished the coffee sheepishly. My feeling of goodwill was at a very low ebb.

Mr Kirby was a retired farmer, but he had sensibly taken a cottage with a bit of land where he kept enough stock to occupy his time – a cow, a few pigs and his beloved goats. He had always had goats, even when he was running his dairy herd; he had a thing about them.

The cottage was in a village high up the Dale. Mr Kirby met me at the gate.

'Ee, lad,' he said. 'I'm right sorry to be bothering you this early in the morning and Christmas an' all, but I didn't have no choice. Dorothy's real bad.'

He led the way to a stone shed which had been converted into a row of pens. Behind the wire of one of them a large white Saanen goat peered out at us anxiously and as I watched her she gulped, gave a series of retching coughs, then stood trembling, saliva drooling from her mouth.

The farmer turned to me, wide-eyed. 'You see, I had to

get you out, didn't I? If I left her till tomorrow she'd be a goner.'

'You're right, Mr Kirby,' I replied. 'You couldn't leave her. There's something in her throat.'

We went into the pen and as the old man held the goat against the wall I tried to open her mouth. She didn't like it very much and as I prised her jaws apart she startled me with a loud, long-drawn human-sounding cry. It wasn't a big mouth but I have a small hand and, as the sharp back teeth tried to nibble me, I poked a finger deep into the pharynx.

There was something there all right. I could just touch it but I couldn't get hold of it. Then the animal began to throw her head about and I had to come out; I stood there, saliva dripping from my hand, looking thoughtfully at Dorothy.

After a few moments I turned to the farmer. 'You know, this is a bit baffling. I can feel something in the back of her throat, but it's soft – like cloth. I'd been expecting to find a bit of twig, or something sharp sticking in there – it's funny what a goat will pick up when she's pottering around outside. But if it's cloth, what the heck is holding it there? Why hasn't she swallowed it down?'

'Aye, it's a rum 'un, isn't it?' The old man ran a gentle and along the animal's back. 'Do you think she'll get rid of it herself? Maybe it'll just slip down?'

'No, I don't. It's stuck fast, God knows how, but it is. And I've got to get it out soon because she's beginning to blow up. Look there.' I pointed to the goat's left side, bulged by the tympanitic rumen, and as I did so, Dorothy began another paroxysm of coughs which seemed almost to tear her apart.

Mr Kirby looked at me with a mute appeal, but just at that moment I didn't see what I could do. Then I opened the door of the pen. 'I'm going to get my torch from the car. Maybe I can see something to explain this.'

The old man held the torch as I once more pulled the goat's mouth open and again heard the curious child-like wailing. It was when the animal was in full cry that I noticed something under the tongue – a thin, dark band.

'I can see what's holding the thing now,' I cried. 'It's

hooked round the tongue with string or something.' Carefully I pushed my forefinger under the band and began to pull.

It wasn't string. It began to stretch as I pulled carefully at it . . . like elastic. Then it stopped stretching and I felt a real resistance . . . whatever was in the throat was beginning to move. I kept up a gentle traction and very slowly the mysterious obstruction came sliding up over the back of the tongue and into the mouth, and when it came within reach I let go the elastic, grabbed the sodden mass and hauled it forth. It seemed as if there was no end to it – a long snake of dripping material nearly two feet long – but at last I had it out on to the straw of the pen.

Mr Kirby seized it and held it up and as he unravelled the mass wonderingly he gave a sudden cry.

'God 'elp us, it's me summer drawers!'

'Your what?'

'Me summer drawers. Ah don't like them long johns when weather gets warmer and I allus change into these little short 'uns. Missus was havin' a clearout afore the end of t'year and she didn't know whether to wash 'em or mek 'em into dusters. She washed 'em at t'finish and Dorothy must have got 'em off the line.' He held up the tattered shorts and regarded them ruefully. 'By Gaw, they've seen better days, but I reckon Dorothy's fettled them this time.'

Then his body began to shake silently, a few low giggles escaped from him and finally he gave a great shout of laughter. It was an infectious laugh and I joined in as I watched him. He went on for quite a long time and when he had finished he was leaning weakly against the wire netting.

'Me poor awd drawers,' he gasped, then leaned over and patted the goat's head. 'But as long as you're all right, lass, I'm not worried.'

'Oh, she'll be OK.' I pointed to her left flank. 'You can see her stomach's going down already.' As I spoke, Dorothy belched pleasurably and began to nose interestedly at her hay rack.

The farmer gazed at her fondly. 'Isn't that grand to see! She's ready for her grub again. And if she hadn't got her tongue round the elastic that lot would have gone right down and killed her.'

'I really don't think it would, you know,' I said. 'It's amazing what ruminants can carry around in their stomachs. I once found a bicycle tyre inside a cow when I was operating for something else. The tyre didn't seem to be bothering her in the least.'

'I see.' Mr Kirby rubbed his chin. 'So Dorothy might have wandered around with me drawers inside her for years.'

'It's possible. You'd never have known what became of them.'

'By gaw, that's right.' Mr Kirby said, and for a moment I thought he was going to start giggling again, but he mastered himself and seized my arm. 'But I don't know what I'm keeping you out here for, lad. You must come in and have a bit o' Christmas cake.'

Inside the tiny living-room of the cottage I was ushered to the best chair by the fireside where two rough logs blazed and crackled.

'Bring cake out for Mr Herriot, mother,' the farmer cried as he rummaged in the pantry. He reappeared with a bottle of whisky at the same time as his wife bustled in carrying a cake thickly laid with icing and ornamented with coloured spangles, toboggans, reindeers.

Mr Kirby unscrewed the stopper. 'You know, mother, we're lucky to have such men as this to come out on a Christmas mornin' to help us.'

'Aye, we are that.' The old lady cut a thick slice of the cake and placed it on a plate by the side of an enormous wedge of Wensleydale cheese.

Her husband meanwhile was pouring my drink. Yorkshiremen are amateurs with whisky and there was something delightfully untutored in the way he was sloshing it into the glass as if it was lemonade; he would have filled it to the brim if I hadn't stopped him.

Drink in hand, cake on knee, I looked across at the farmer and his wife who were sitting in upright kitchen chairs watching me with quiet benevolence. The two faces had something in common – a kind of beauty. You would find faces like that only in the country; deeply wrinkled and weathered, clear-eyed, alight with a cheerful serenity.

I raised my glass. 'A happy Christmas to you both.'

The old couple nodded and replied smilingly. 'And the same to you, Mr Herriot.'

'Aye, and thanks again, lad,' said Mr Kirby. 'We're right grateful to you for runnin' out here to save awd Dorothy. We've maybe mucked up your day for you but it would've mucked up ours if we'd lost the old lass, wouldn't it, mother?'

'Don't worry, you haven't spoiled anything for me.' I said. 'In fact you've made me realize again that it really is Christmas.' And as I looked around the little room with the decorations hanging from the low-beamed ceiling I could feel the emotions of last night surging slowly back, a warmth creeping through me that had nothing to do with the whisky.

I took a bite of the cake and followed it with a moist slice of cheese. When I had first come to Yorkshire I had been aghast when offered this unheard-of combination, but time had brought wisdom and I had discovered that the mixture when chewed boldly together was exquisite; and, strangely, I had also found that there was nothing more suitable for washing it finally over the tonsils than a draught of raw whisky.

'You don't mind t'wireless, Mr Herriot?' Mrs Kirby asked. 'We always like to have it on Christmas morning to hear t'old hymns but I'll turn it off if you like.'

'No please leave it, it sounds grand.' I turned to look at the old radio with its chipped wooden veneer, the ornate scroll-work over the worn fabric; it must have been one of the earliest models and it gave off a tinny sound, but the singing of the church choir was none the less sweet ... 'Hark the Herald Angels Sing' – flooding the little room, mingling with the splutter of the logs and the soft voices of the old people.

They showed me a picture of their son, who was a policeman over in Houlton and their daughter who was married to a neighbouring farmer. They were bringing their grand-children up for Christmas dinner as they always did and Mrs

Kirby opened a box and ran a hand over the long row of crackers. The choir started on 'Once in Royal David's City', I finished my whisky and put up only feeble resistance as the farmer plied the bottle again. Through the small window I could see the bright berries of a holly tree pushing through their covering of snow.

It was really a shame to have to leave here and it was sadly that I drained my glass for the second time and scooped up the last crumbs of cake and icing from my plate.

Mr Kirby came out with me and at the gate of the cottage he stopped and held out his hand.

'Thank ye lad, I'm right grateful,' he said. 'And all the very best to you.'

For a moment the rough dry palm rasped against mine, then I was in the car, starting the engine. I looked at my watch; it was still only half past nine but the first early sunshine was sparkling from a sky of palest blue.

Beyond the village the road climbed steeply then curved around the rim of the valley in a wide arc, and it was here that you came suddenly upon the whole great expanse of the Plain of York spread out almost at your feet. I always slowed down here and there was always something different to see, but today the vast chequerboard of fields and farms and woods stood out with a clarity I had never seen before. Maybe it was because this was a holiday and down there no factory chimney smoked, no lorries belched fumes, but the distance was magically foreshortened in the clear, frosty air and I felt I could reach out and touch the familiar landmarks far below.

I looked back at the enormous white billows and folds of the fells, crowding close, one upon another into the blue distance, every crevice uncannily defined, the highest summits glittering where the sun touched them. I could see the village with the Kirbys' cottage at the end. I had found Christmas and peace and goodwill and everything back there.

Farmers? They were the salt of the earth.

CHAPTER SEVENTEEN

Marmaduke Skelton was an object of interest to me long before our paths crossed. For one thing I hadn't thought people were ever called Marmaduke outside of books and for another he was a particularly well-known member of the honourable profession of unqualified animal doctors.

Before the Veterinary Surgeons' Act of 1948 anybody who fancied his chance at it could dabble in the treatment of animal disease. Veterinary students could quite legally be sent out to cases while they were seeing practice, certain members of the lay public did a bit of veterinary work as a sideline while others did it as a full time job. These last were usually called 'quacks'.

The disparaging nature of the term was often unjust because, though some of them were a menace to the animal population, others were dedicated men who did their job with responsibility and humanity and after the Act were brought into the profession's fold as Veterinary Practitioners.

But long before all this there were all sorts and types among them. The one I knew best was Arthur Lumley, a charming little ex-plumber who ran a thriving small animal practice in Brawton, much to the chagrin of Mr Angus Grier MRCVS. Arthur used to drive around in a small van. He always wore a white coat and looked very clinical and efficient, and on the side of the van in foot-high letters which would have got a qualified man a severe dressing down from the Royal College was the legend, 'Arthur Lumley MKC, Canine and Feline Specialist'. The lack of 'letters' after their name was the one thing which differentiated these men from qualified vets in the eyes of the general public and I was interested to see that Arthur did have an academic attainment. However the degree of MKC was unfamiliar to me and he was somewhat cagey when I asked him about it; I did find out eventually what it stood for: Member of the Kennel Club.

Marmaduke Skelton was of a vastly different breed. I had been working long enough round the Scarburn district to become familiar with some of the local history and it seemed that when Mr and Mrs Skelton were producing a family in the early 1900s they must have thought their offspring were destined for great things; they named their four sons Marmaduke, Sebastian, Cornelius and, incredibly, Alonzo. The two middle brothers drove lorries for the Express Dairy and Alonzo was a small farmer; one of my vivid memories is the shock of surprise when I was filling up the forms after his tuberculin test and asked him for his first name. The exotic appellation pronounced in gruff Yorkshire was so incongruous that I thought he was pulling my leg; in fact I was going to make a light comment but something in his eye prompted me to leave it alone.

Marmaduke, or Duke as he was invariably called, was the colourful member of the family. I had heard a lot about him on my visits to Scarburn farms; he was a 'right good hand' at calving, foaling and lambing, and 'as good as any vitnery' in the diagnosis and treatment of animals' ailments. He was also an expert castrator, docker and pig-killer. He made a nice living at his trade and, of course, in Ewan Ross he had the ideal professional opposition; a veterinary surgeon who worked only when he felt like it and who didn't bother to go to a case unless he was in the mood. Much as the farmers liked and in many cases revered Ewan, they were often forced to fall back on Duke's services.

If Duke had confined his activities to treating his patients I don't think Ewan would ever have spared him a thought; but Skelton liked to enliven his farm visits with sneers about the old Scotch vet who had never been much good and was definitely getting past it now. Maybe even that didn't get very far under Ewan's skin but at the mention of his rival's name his mouth would harden a little and a ruminative expression creep into the blue eyes.

And it wasn't easy to like Duke. There were the tales you

heard about his savage brawls and about how he knocked his wife and children around when the mood was on him. I didn't find his appearance engaging either when I first saw him swaggering across Scarburn market place; a black bull of a man, a shaggy Heathcliffe with fierce, darting eyes and a hint of braggadocio in the bright red handkerchief tied round his neck.

But on this particular afternoon I wasn't thinking about Duke Skelton, in fact I wasn't thinking about anything much as I sprawled in a chair by the Rosses' fireside. I had just finished one of Ginny's lunches; something with the unassuming name of fish pie but in truth a magical concoction in which the humble haddock was elevated to unimagined heights by the admixture of potatoes, tomatoes, eggs, macaroni and things only Ginny knew. Then the apple crumble and the chair close to the fire with the heat from the flames beating on my face.

The thoughts I had were slumbrous ones; that this house and the people in it had come to have a magnetic attraction for me; that if this had been a big successful practice the phone would have been dinging and Ewan would be struggling into his coat as he chewed his last bite. And an unworthy thought as I glanced through the window at the white garden and the snow-burdened trees; that if I didn't hurry back to Darrowby, Siegfried might do double the work and finish the lot before I got home.

Playing with the soothing picture of the muffled figure of my boss battling round the farms I watched Ginny placing a coffee cup by her husband's elbow. Ewan smiled up into her face and just then the phone rang.

Like most vets I am bell-happy and I jumped, but Ewan didn't. He began quietly to sip his coffee as Ginny picked up the receiver and he didn't change expression when his wife came over and said, 'It's Tommy Thwaite. One of his cows has put its calf bed out.'

These dread tidings would have sent me leaping round the room but Ewan took a long swallow at his coffee before replying.

'Thank you, dear. Will you tell him I'll have a look at her shortly.'

He turned to me and began to tell me something funny which had happened to him that morning and when he had finished he went into his characteristic laugh – showing nothing apart from a vibration of the shoulders and a slight popping of the eyes. Then he relaxed in his chair and recommenced his leisurely sipping.

Though it wasn't my case my feet were itching. A bovine prolapsed uterus was not only an urgent condition but it held such grim promise of hard labour that I could never get it over quickly enough. Some were worse than others and I was always in a hurry to find out what was in store.

Ewan, however, appeared to be totally incurious. In fact he closed his eyes and I thought for a moment he was settling down for a post prandial nap. But it was only a gesture of resignation at the wrecking of his afternoon's repose and he gave a final stretch and got up.

'Want to come with me, Jim?' he asked in his soft voice.

I hesitated for a moment then, callously abandoning Siegfried to his fate, I nodded eagerly and followed Ewan into the kitchen.

He sat down and pulled on a pair of thick woollen oversocks which Ginny had been warming by the stove, then he put on his wellingtons, a short overcoat, yellow gloves and a check cap. As he strolled along the narrow track which had been dug through the garden snow he looked extraordinarily youthful and debonair.

He didn't go into his dispensary this time and I wondered what equipment he would use, thinking at the same time of Siegfried's words: 'Ewan has his own way of doing everything.'

At the farm Mr Thwaite trotted over to meet us. He was understandably agitated but there was something else; a nervous rubbing of the hands, an uneasy giggle as he watched my colleague opening the car boot.

'Mr Ross,' he blurted out at last, 'I don't want you to be upset, but I've summat to tell you.' He paused for a moment. 'Duke Skelton's in there with my cow.'

Ewan's expression did not flicker. 'Oh, right. Then you won't need me.' He closed the boot, opened the door and got back into the car.

'Hey, hey, I didn't mean you to go away!' Mr Thwaite ran round and cried through the glass. 'Duke just happened to be in t'village and he said he'd help me out.'

'Fine,' Ewan said, winding down the window, 'I don't mind in the least. I'm sure he'll do a good job for you.'

The farmer screwed up his face in misery. 'But you don't understand. He's been in there for about an hour and a half and he's no further forward. He's not doin' a bit o' good and he's about buggered an' all. I want you to take over, Mr Ross.'

'No, I'm sorry.' Ewan gave him a level stare. 'I couldn't possibly interfere. You know how it is, Tommy. He's begun the job – I've got to let him finish.' He started the engine.

'No, no, don't go!' shouted Mr Thwaite, beating the car roof with his hands. 'Duke's whacked, I tell ye. If you drive away now ah'm going to lose one of ma best cows. You've got to help me, Mr Ross!' He seemed on the verge of tears.

My colleague looked at him thoughtfully as the engine purred. Then he bent forward and turned off the ignition. 'All right, I'll tell you what – I'll go in there and see what he says. If he wants me to help, then I will.'

I followed him into the byre and as we paused just inside the door Duke Skelton looked up from his work. He had been standing head down, one hand resting on the rump of a massive cow, his mouth hanging open, his great barrel chest heaving. The thick hair over his shoulders and ribs was matted with blood from the huge everted uterus which dangled behind the animal. Blood and filth streaked his face and covered his arms and as he stared at us from under his shaggy brows he looked like something from the jungle.

'Well now, Mr Skelton,' Ewan mumured conversationally. 'How are you getting on?'

Duke gave him a quick malevolent glance. 'Ah'm doin' all right.' The words rumbled from deep down through his gaping lips.

Mr Thwaite stepped forward, smiling ingratiatingly.

'Come on, Duke, you've done your best. I think you should let Mr Ross give you a 'and now.'

'Well ah don't.' The big man's jaw jutted suddenly. 'If I was lookin' for help I wouldn't want 'IM.' He turned away and seized the uterus. Hoisting it in his arms he began to push at it with fierce concentration.

Mr Thwaite turned to us with an expression of despair and opened his mouth to lament again, but Ewan silenced him with a raised hand, pulling a milking stool from a corner and squatted down comfortably against a wall. Unhurriedly he produced his little pouch and, one-handed, began to make a cigarette; as he licked the paper, screwed up the end and applied a match he gazed with blank eyes at the sweating, struggling figure a few feet from him.

Duke had got the uterus about halfway back. Grunting and gasping, legs straddled, he had worked the engorged mass inch by inch inside the vulva till he had just about enough cradled in his arms for one last push; and as he stood there taking a breather with the great muscles of his shoulders and arms rigid his immense strength was formidably displayed. But he wasn't as strong as that cow. No man is as strong as a cow and this cow was one of the biggest I had ever seen with a back like a table top and rolls of fat round her tail-head.

I had been in this position myself and I knew what was coming next. I didn't have to wait long. Duke took a long wheezing breath and made his assault, heaving desperately, pushing with arms and chest, and for a second or two he seemed to be winning as the mass disappeared steadily inside. Then the cow gave an almost casual strain and the whole thing welled out again till it hung down bumping against the animal's hocks.

As Duke almost collapsed against her pelvis in the same attitude as when we first came in I felt pity for the man. I found him uncharming but I felt for him. That could easily be me standing there; my jacket and shirt hanging on that nail, my strength ebbing, my sweat mingling with the blood. No man could do what he was trying to do. You could push back a calf bed with the aid of an epidural anaesthetic to stop the straining or you could sling the animal up to a beam with a block and tackle; you couldn't just stand there and do it from scratch as this chap was trying to do.

I was surprised Duke hadn't learned that with all his experience; but apparently it still hadn't dawned on him even now because he was going through all the motions of having another go. This time he got even further – a few more inches inside before the cow popped it out again. The animal appeared to have a sporting streak because there was something premeditated about the way she played her victim along before timing her thrust at the very last moment. Apart from that she seemed somewhat bored by the whole business; in fact with the possible exception of Ewan she was the calmest among us.

Duke was trying again. As he bent over wearily and picked up the gory organ I wondered how often he had done this since he arrived nearly two hours ago. He had guts, there was no doubt. But the end was near. There was a frantic urgency about his movements as though he knew himself it was his last throw and as he yet again neared his goal his grunts changed to an agonized whimpering, an almost tearful sound as though he were appealing to the recalcitrant mass, beseeching it to go away inside and stay away, just this once.

And when the inevitable happened and the poor fellow, panting and shaking, surveyed once more the ruin of his hopes I had the feeling that somebody had to do something.

Mr Thwaite did it. 'You've had enough, Duke,' he said. 'For God's sake come in the house and get cleaned up. Missus'll give you a bit o' dinner and while you're having it Mr Ross'll see what he can do.'

The big man, arms hanging limp by his sides, chest heaving, stared at the farmer for a few seconds then he turned abruptly and snatched his clothes from the wall.

'Aw right,' he said and began to walk slowly towards the door. He stopped opposite Ewan but didn't look at him. 'But ah'll tell you summat, Maister Thwaite. If ah can't put that calf bed back this awd bugger never will.'

Ewan drew on his cigarette and peered up at him impassively. He didn't follow him with his eyes as he left the byre but leaned back against the wall, puffed out a thin plume of smoke and watched it rise and disappear among the shadows in the roof.

Mr Thwaite was soon back. 'Now, Mr Ross,' he said a little breathlessly, 'I'm sorry about you havin' to wait but we can get on now. I expect you'll be needin' some fresh hot water and is there anything else you want?'

Ewan dropped his cigarette on the cobbles and ground it with his foot. 'Yes, you can bring me a pound of sugar.'

'What's that?'

'A pound of sugar.'

'A pound of . . . right, right . . . I'll get it.'

In no time at all the farmer returned with an unopened paper bag. Ewan split the top with his finger, walked over to the cow and began to dust the sugar all over the uterus. Then he turned to Mr Thwaite again.

'And I'll want a pig stool, too. I expect you have one.'

'Oh aye, we have one, but what the hangment . . . ?'

Ewan cocked a gentle eye at him. 'Bring it in, then. It's time we got this job done.'

As the farmer disappeared at a stiff gallop I went over to my colleague. 'What's going on, Ewan? What the devil are you chucking that sugar about for?'

'Oh it draws the serum out of the uterus. You can't beat it when the thing's engorged like that.'

'It does?' I glanced unbelievingly at the bloated organ. 'And aren't you going to give her an epidural . . . and some pituitrin . . . and a calcium injection?'

'Och no,' Ewan replied with his slow smile. 'I never bother about those things.'

I didn't get the chance to ask him what he wanted with the pig stool because just then Mr Thwaite trotted in with one under his arm.

Most farms used to have them. They were often called 'creels' and the sides of bacon were laid on them at pig-killing time. This was a typical specimen – like a long low table with four short legs and a slatted concave top. Ewan took hold of it and pushed it carefully under the cow just in front of the udder while I stared at it through narrowed eyes. I was getting out of my depth.

Ewan then walked unhurriedly out to his car and returned with a length of rope and two objects wrapped in the inevitable brown paper. As he draped the rope over the partition, pulled on a rubber parturition gown and began to open the parcels I realized I was once again watching Ewan setting out his stall.

From the first parcel he produced what looked like a beer tray but which I decided couldn't possibly be; but when he said, 'Here, hold this a minute, Jim,' and I read the emblazoned gold scroll, 'John Smith's Magnet Pale Ale' I had to change my mind. It was a beer tray.

He began to unfold the brown paper from the other object and my brain reeled a little as he fished out an empty whisky bottle and placed it on the tray. Standing there with my strange burden I felt like the stooge in a conjuring act and I wouldn't have been a bit surprised if my colleague had produced a live rabbit next.

But all he did was to fill the whisky bottle with some of the clean hot water from the bucket.

Next he looped the rope round the cow's horns, passed it round the body a couple of times then leaned back and pulled. Without protest the big animal collapsed gently on top of the pig stool and lay there with her rear end stuck high in the air.

'Right now, we can start,' Ewan murmured, and as I threw down my jacket and began to tear off my tie he turned to me in surprise.

'Here, here, what do you think you're doing?'

'Well I'm going to give you a hand, of course.'

One corner of his mouth twitched upwards. 'It's kind of you, Jim, but there's no need to get stripped off. This will only take a minute. I just want you and Mr Thwaite to keep the thing level for me.'

He gently hoisted the organ which to my fevered imagination had shrunk visibly since the sugar, on to the beer tray and gave the farmer and me an end each to hold.

Then he pushed the uterus back.

He did literally only take a minute or not much more. Without effort, without breaking sweat or exerting visible pressure he returned that vast mass to where it belonged while the cow, unable to strain or do a thing about it, just lay there with an aggrieved expression on her face. Then he took his whisky bottle, passed it carefully into the vagina and disappeared up to arm's length where he began to move his shoulder vigorously.

'What the hell are you doing now?' I whispered agitatedly into his ear from my position at the end of the beer tray.

'I'm rotating each horn to get it back into place and pouring a little hot water from the bottle into the ends of the horns to make sure they're completely involuted.'

'Oh, I see.' I watched as he removed the bottle, soaped his arms in the bucket and began to take off his overall.

'But aren't you going to stitch it in?' I blurted out.

Ewan shook his head. 'No, Jim. If you put it back properly it never comes out again.'

He was drying his hands when the byre door opened and Duke Skelton slouched in. He was washed and dressed, with his red handkerchief knotted again round his neck and he glared fierce-eyed at the cow which, tidied up and unperturbed, looked now just like all the other cows in the row. His lips moved once or twice before he finally found his voice.

'Aye, it's all right for some people,' he snarled. 'Some people with their bloody fancy injections and instruments! It's bloody easy that way, isn't it.' Then he swung round and was gone.

As I heard his heavy boots clattering across the yard it struck me that his words were singularly inapt. What was there even remotely fancy about a pig stool, a pound of sugar, a whisky bottle and a beer tray?

CHAPTER EIGHTEEN

'I work for cats.'

That was how Mrs Bond introduced herself on my first visit, gripping my hand firmly and thrusting out her jaw defiantly as though challenging me to make something of it. She was a big woman with a strong, high-cheekboned face and a commanding presence and I wouldn't have argued with her anyway, so I nodded gravely as though I fully understood and agreed, and allowed her to lead me into the house.

I saw at once what she meant. The big kitchen-living-room had been completely given over to cats. There were cats on the sofas and chairs and spilling in cascades on to the floor, cats sitting in rows along the window sills and right in the middle of it all, little Mr Bond, pallid, wispy-moustached, in his shirt sleeves reading a newspaper.

It was a scene which was going to become very familiar. A lot of the cats were obviously uncastrated Toms because the atmosphere was vibrant with their distinctive smell – a fierce pungency which overwhelmed even the sickly wisps from the big saucepans of nameless cat food bubbling on the stove. And Mr Bond was always there, always in his shirt sleeves and reading his paper, a lonely little island in a sea of cats.

I had heard of the Bonds, of course. They were Londoners who for some obscure reason had picked on North Yorkshire for their retirement. People said they had a 'bit o' brass' and they had bought an old house on the outskirts of Darrowby where they kept themselves to themselves – and the cats. I had heard that Mrs Bond was in the habit of taking in strays and feeding them and giving them a home if they wanted it and this had predisposed me in her favour, because in my experience the unfortunate feline species seemed to be fair game for every kind of cruelty and neglect. They shot cats, threw things at them, starved them and set their dogs on them for fun. It was good to see somebody taking their side.

My patient on this first visit was no more than a big kitten, a terrified little blob of black and white crouching in a corner.

'He's one of the outside cats,' Mrs Bond boomed.

'Outside cats?'

'Yes. All these you see here are the inside cats. The others are the really wild ones who simply refuse to enter the house. I feed them of course but the only time they come indoors is when they are ill.'

'I see.'

'I've had frightful trouble catching this one. I'm worried about his eyes – there seemed to be a skin growing over them, and I do hope you can do something for him. His name, by the way, is Alfred.'

'Alfred? Ah yes, quite.' I advanced cautiously on the little half-grown animal and was greeted by a waving set of claws and a series of open-mouthed spittings. He was trapped in his corner or he would have been off with the speed of light.

Examining him was going to be a problem. I turned to Mrs Bond. 'Could you let me have a sheet of some kind? An old ironing sheet would do. I'm going to have to wrap him up.'

'Wrap him up?' Mrs Bond looked very doubtful but she disappeared into another room and returned with a tattered sheet of cotton which looked just right.

I cleared the table of an amazing variety of cat feeding dishes, cat books, cat medicines and spread out the sheet, then I approached my patient again. You can't be in a hurry in a situation like this and it took me perhaps five minutes of wheedling and 'Puss-pussing' while I brought my hand nearer and nearer. When I got as far as being able to stroke his cheek I made a quick grab at the scruff of his neck and finally bore Alfred, protesting bitterly and lashing out in all directions, over to the table. There, still holding tightly to his scruff, I laid him on the sheet and started the wrapping operation.

This is something which has to be done quite often with obstreperous felines and, although I say it, I am rather good at it. The idea is to make a neat, tight roll, leaving the relevant piece of cat exposed; it may be an injured paw, perhaps the tail, and in this case of course the head. I think it was the beginning of Mrs Bond's unquestioning faith in me when she saw me quickly enveloping that cat till all you could see of him was a small black and white head protruding from an immovable cocoon of cloth. He and I were now facing each other, more or less eyeball to eyeball, and Alfred couldn't do a thing about it.

As I say, I rather pride myself on this little expertise and even today my veterinary colleagues have been known to remark: 'Old Herriot may be limited in many respects but by God he can wrap a cat.'

As it turned out, there wasn't a skin growing over Alfred's eyes. There never is.

'He's got a paralysis of the third eyelid, Mrs Bond. Animals have this membrane which flicks across the eye to protect it. In this case it hasn't gone back, probably because the cat is in low condition – maybe had a touch of cat flu or something else which has weakened him. I'll give him an injection of vitamins and leave you some powder to put in his food if you could keep him in for a few days. I think he'll be all right in a week or two.'

The injection presented no problems with Alfred furious but helpless inside his sheet and I had come to the end of my first visit to Mrs Bond's.

It was the first of many. The lady and I established an immediate rapport which was strengthened by the fact that I was always prepared to spend time over her assorted charges; crawling on my stomach under piles of logs in the outhouses to reach the outside cats, coaxing them down from trees, stalking them endlessly through the shrubbery. But from my point of view it was rewarding in many ways.

For instance there was the diversity of names she had for her cats. True to her London upbringing she had named many of the Toms after the great Arsenal team of those days. There was Eddie Hapgood, Cliff Bastin, Ted Drake,

Wilf Copping, but she did slip up in one case because Alex James had kittens three times a year with unfailing regularity.

Then there was her way of calling them home. The first time I saw her at this was on a still summer evening. The two cats she wanted me to see were out in the garden somewhere and I walked with her to the back door where she halted, clasped her hands across her bosom, closed her eyes and gave tongue in a mellifluous contralto.

'Bates, Bates, Bates, Ba-hates.' She actually sang out the words in a reverent monotone except for a delightful little lilt on the 'Ba-hates'. Then once more she inflated her ample rib cage like an operatic prima donna and out it came again, delivered with the utmost feeling.

'Bates, Bates, Bates, Ba-hates.'

Anyway it worked, because Bates the cat came trotting from behind a clump of laurel. There remained the other patient and I watched Mrs Bond with interest.

She took up the same stance, breathed in, closed her eyes, composed her features into a sweet half-smile and started again.

'Seven-times-three, Seven-times-three, Seven-times-three-hee.' It was set to the same melody as Bates with the same dulcet rise and fall at the end. She didn't get the quick response this time, though, and had to go through the performance again and again, and as the notes lingered on the still evening air the effect was startlingly like a muezzin calling the faithful to prayer.

At length she was successful and a fat tortoiseshell slunk apologetically along the wall-side into the house.

'By the way, Mrs Bond,' I asked, making my voice casual. 'I didn't quite catch the name of that last cat.'

'Oh, Seven-times-three?' She smiled reminiscently. 'Yes, she is a dear. She's had three kittens seven times running, you see, so I thought it rather a good name for her, don't you?'

'Yes, yes, I do indeed. Splendid name, splendid.'

Another thing which warmed me towards Mrs Bond was her concern for my safety. I appreciated this because it is a rare trait among animal owners. I can think of the trainer after one of his racehorses had kicked me clean out of a loose box examining the animal anxiously to see if it had damaged its foot; the little old lady dwarfed by the bristling, teeth-bared Alsatian saying: 'You'll be gentle with him won't you and I hope you won't hurt him – he's very nervous'; the farmer, after an exhausting calving which I feel certain has knocked about two years off my life expectancy, grunting morosely: 'I doubt you've tired that cow out, young man.'

Mrs Bond was different. She used to meet me at the door with an enormous pair of gauntlets to protect my hands against scratches and it was an inexpressible relief to find that somebody cared. It became part of the pattern of my life; walking up the garden path among the innumerable slinking, wild-eyed little creatures which were the outside cats, the ceremonial acceptance of the gloves at the door, then the entry into the charged atmosphere of the kitchen with little Mr Bond and his newspaper just visible among the milling furry bodies of the inside cats. I was never able to ascertain Mr Bond's attitude to cats – come to think of it he hardly ever said anything – but I had the impression he could take them or leave them.

The gauntlets were a big help and at times they were a veritable godsend. As in the case of Boris. Boris was an enormous blue-black member of the outside cats and my bête noire in more senses than one. I always cherished a private conviction that he had escaped from a zoo; I had never seen a domestic cat with such sleek, writhing muscles, such dedicated ferocity. I'm sure there was a bit of puma in Boris somewhere.

It had been a sad day for the cat colony when he turned up. I have always found it difficult to dislike any animal; most of the ones which try to do us a mischief are activated by fear, but Boris was different; he was a malevolent bully and after his arrival the frequency of my visits increased because of his habit of regularly beating up his colleagues. I was forever stitching up tattered ears, dressing gnawed limbs.

We had one trial of strength fairly early. Mrs Bond

wanted me to give him a worm dose and I had the little tablet all ready held in forceps. How I ever got hold of him I don't quite know, but I hustled him on to the table and did my wrapping act at lightning speed, swathing him in roll upon roll of stout material. Just for a few seconds I thought I had him as he stared up at me, his great brilliant eyes full of hate. But as I pushed my loaded forceps into his mouth he clamped his teeth viciously down on them and I could feel claws of amazing power tearing inside the sheet. It was all over in moments. A long leg shot out and ripped its way down my wrist. I let go my tight hold of the neck and in a flash Boris sank his teeth through the gauntlet into the ball of my thumb and was away. I was left standing there stupidly, holding the fragmented worm tablet in a bleeding hand and looking at the bunch of ribbons which had once been my wrapping sheet. From then on Boris loathed the very sight of me and the feeling was mutual.

But this was one of the few clouds in a serene sky. I continued to enjoy my visits there and life proceeded on a tranquil course except, perhaps, for some legpulling from my colleagues. They could never understand my willingness to spend so much time over a lot of cats. And of course this fitted in with the general attitude because Siegfried didn't believe in people keeping pets of any kind. He just couldn't understand their mentality and propounded his views to anybody who cared to listen. He himself, of course, kept five dogs and two cats. The dogs, all of them, travelled everywhere with him in the car and he fed dogs and cats every day with his own hands – wouldn't allow anybody else to do the job. In the evening all seven animals would pile themselves round his feet as he sat in his chair by the fire. To this day he is still as vehemently anti-pet as ever, though another generation of waving dogs' tails almost obscures him as he drives around and he also has several cats, a few tanks of tropical fish and a couple of snakes.

Tristan saw me in action at Mrs Bond's on only one occasion. I was collecting some long forceps from the instrument cupboard when he came into the room.

'Anything interesting, Jim?' he asked.

'No, not really. I'm just off to see one of the Bond cats. It's got a bone stuck between its teeth.'

The young man eyed me ruminatively for a moment. 'Think I'll come with you. I haven't seen much small animal stuff lately.'

As we went down the garden at the cat establishment I felt a twinge of embarrassment. One of the things which had built up my happy relationship with Mrs Bond was my tender concern for her charges. Even with the wildest and the fiercest I exhibited only gentleness, patience and solicitude; it wasn't really an act, it came quite naturally to me. However I couldn't help wondering what Tristan would think of my cat bedside manner.

Mrs Bond in the doorway had summed up the situation in a flash and had two pairs of gauntlets waiting. Tristan looked a little surprised as he received his pair but thanked the lady with typical charm. He looked still more surprised when he entered the kitchen, sniffed the rich atmosphere and surveyed the masses of furry creatures occupying almost every available inch of space.

'Mr Herriot, I'm afraid it's Boris who has the bone in his teeth,' Mrs Bond said.

'Boris!' My stomach lurched. 'How on earth are we going to catch him?'

'Oh I've been rather clever,' she replied. 'I've managed to entice him with some of his favourite food into a cat basket.'

Tristan put his hand on a big wicker cage on the table. 'In here, is he?' he asked casually. He slipped back the catch and opened the lid. For something like a third of a second the coiled creature within and Tristan regarded each other tensely, then a sleek black body exploded silently from the basket past the young man's left ear on to the top of a tall cupboard.

'Christ!' said Tristan. 'What the hell was that?'

'That,' I said, 'was Boris, and now we've got to get hold of him again.' I climbed on to a chair, reached slowly on to the top of the cupboard top and started 'Puss-puss-puss'ing in my most beguiling tone.

After about a minute Tristan appeared to think he had a better idea; he made a sudden leap and grabbed Boris's tail. But only briefly, because the big cat freed himself in an instant and set off on a whirlwind circuit of the room; along the tops of cupboards and dressers, across the curtains, careering round and round like a wall of death rider.

Tristan stationed himself at a strategic point and as Boris shot past he swiped at him with one of the gauntlets.

'Missed the bloody thing!' he shouted in chagrin. 'But here he comes again . . . take that, you black sod! Damn it, I can't nail him!'

The docile little inside cats, startled by the scattering of plates and tins and pans and by Tristan's cries and arm wavings, began to run around in their turn, knocking over whatever Boris had missed. The noise and confusion even got through to Mr Bond because just for a moment he raised his head and looked around him in mild surprise at the hurtling bodies before returning to his newspaper.

Tristan, flushed with the excitement of the chase had really begun to enjoy himself. I cringed inwardly as he shouted over to me happily.

'Send him on, Jim, I'll get the bugger next time round!'

We never did catch Boris. We just had to leave the piece of bone to work its own way out, so it wasn't a successful veterinary visit. But Tristan as we got back into the car smiled contentedly.

'That was great, Jim. I didn't realize you had such fun with your pussies.'

Mrs Bond on the other hand, when I next saw her, was rather tight-lipped over the whole thing.

'Mr Herriot,' she said, 'I hope you aren't going to bring that young man with you again.'

CHAPTER NINETEEN

I always liked having a student with us. These young men had to see at least six months' practice on their way through college and most of their vacations were spent going round with a vet.

We, of course, had our own resident student in Tristan but he was in a different category. I often envied him his remarkable brain because he didn't have to be taught anything – he seemed to know things, to absorb knowledge without apparent effort or indeed without showing interest. If you took Tristan to a case he usually spent his time on the farm sitting in the car reading his *Daily Mirror* and smoking Woodbines.

There were all types among the others – some from the country some from the towns, some dull-witted, some bright – but as I say, I liked having them.

For one thing they were good company in the car. A big part of a country vet's life consists of solitary driving and it was a relief to be able to talk to somebody. It was wonderful, too, to have a gate-opener. Some of the outlying farms were approached through long, gated roads – one which always struck terror into me had eight gates – and it is hard to convey the feeling of sheer luxury when somebody else leaped out and opened them.

And there was another little pleasure; asking the students questions. My own days of studying and examinations were still fresh in my memory and on top of that I had all the vast experience of nearly three years of practice. It gave me a feeling of power to drop casual little queries about the cases we saw and watch the lads squirm as I had so recently squirmed myself. I suppose that even in those early days I was forming a pattern for later life; unknown to myself I was falling into the way of asking a series of my own pet questions as all examiners are liable to do and many years later I overheard one youngster asking another: 'Has he grilled you on the causes of fits in calves yet? Don't worry, he will.' That made me feel suddenly old but there was compensation on another occasion when a newly qualified ex-student rushed up to me and offered to buy me all the beer I could drink. 'You know what the examiner asked me in the final oral? The causes of fits in calves! By God I paralysed him – he had to beg me to stop talking.'

And students were useful in other ways. They ran and got things out of the car boot, they pulled a rope at calvings, they were skilled assistants at operations, they were a repository for my worries and doubts; it isn't too much to say that during their brief visits they revolutionized my life.

So this Easter I waited on the platform of Darrowby station with pleasant anticipation. This lad had been recommended by one of the Ministry officials. 'A really first class chap. Final year London – several times gold medallist. He's seen mixed and town practice and thought he ought to have a look at some of the real rural stuff. I said I'd give you a ring. His name is Richard Carmody.'

Veterinary students came in a variety of shapes and sizes but there were a few features most of them had in common and I already had a mental picture of an eager-faced lad in tweed jacket and rumpled slacks carrying a rucksack. He would probably jump on to the platform as soon as the train drew up. But this time there was no immediate sign of life and a porter had begun to load a stack of egg boxes into the guard's van before one of the compartment doors opened and a tall figure descended in leisurely manner.

I was doubtful about his identity but he seemed to place me on sight. He walked over, held out a hand and surveyed me with a level gaze.

'Mr Herriot?'

'Yes . . . er . . . yes. That's right.'

'My name is Carmody.'

'Ah yes, good. How are you?' We shook hands and I took in the fine check suit and tweedy hat, the shining brogues and pigskin case. This was a very superior student, in fact a highly impressive young man. About a couple of years younger than myself but with a mature air in the set of his broad shoulders and the assurance on his strong, high-coloured face.

I led him across the bridge out on to the station yard. He didn't actually raise his eyebrows when he saw my car but he shot a cold glance at the mud-spattered vehicle, at the cracked windscreen and smooth tyres; and when I opened the door for him I thought for a moment he was going to wipe the seat before sitting down.

At the surgery I showed him round. I was only the assistant but I was proud of our modest set-up and most people were impressed by their first sight of it. But Carmody said, 'Hm', in the little operating room, 'Yes, I see', in the dispensary, and 'Quite' at the instrument cupboard. In the stockroom he was more forthcoming. He reached out and touched a packet of our beloved Adrevan worm medicine for horses.

'Still using this stuff, eh?' he said with a faint smile.

He didn't go into any ecstasies but he did show signs of approval when I took him out through the french windows into the long, high-walled garden where the daffodils glowed among the unkempt tangle and the wisteria climbed high over the old bricks of the tall Georgian house. In the cobbled yard at the foot of the garden he looked up at the rooks making their din high in the overhanging elms and he gazed for a few moments through the trees to where you could see the bare ribs of the fells still showing the last white runnels of winter.

'Charming,' he murmured. 'Charming.'

I was glad enough to see him to his lodgings that evening. I felt I needed time to readjust my thinking.

When we started out next morning I saw he had discarded his check suit but was still very smart in a hacking jacket and flannels.

'Haven't you any protective clothing?' I asked.

'I've got these.' He indicated a spotless pair of wellingtons in the back of the car.

'Yes, but I mean an oilskin or a coat of some kind. Some of our jobs are pretty dirty.'

He smiled indulgently. 'Oh, I'm sure I'll be all right. I've been round the farms before, you know.'

I shrugged my shoulders and left it at that.

Our first visit was to a lame calf. The little animal was limping round its pen, holding up a fore leg and looking very woebegone. The knee was visibly swollen and as I palpated it there seemed to be a lumpiness in the fluid within as if there might be a flocculus of pus among it. The temperature was a hundred and four.

I looked up at the farmer. 'This is joint ill. He probably got an infection through his navel soon after birth and it's settled in his knee. We'll have to take care of him because his internal organs such as the liver and lungs can be affected. I'll give him an injection and leave you some tablets for him.'

I went out to the car and when I came back Carmody was bending over the calf, feeling at the distended knee and inspecting the navel closely. I gave my injection and we left.

'You know,' Carmody said as we drove out of the yard, 'that wasn't joint ill.'

'Really?' I was a bit taken aback. I didn't mind students discussing the pros and cons of my diagnoses as long as they didn't do it in front of the farmer, but I had never had one tell me bluntly that I was wrong. I made a mental note to try to keep this fellow away from Siegfried; one remark like that and Siegfried would hurl him unhesitatingly out of the car, big as he was.

'How do you make that out, then?' I asked him.

'Well there was only the one joint involved and the navel was perfectly dry. No pain or swelling there. I should say he just sprained that knee.'

'You may be right, but wouldn't you say the temperature was a bit high for a sprain?'

Carmody grunted and shook his head slightly. Apparently he had no doubts.

A few gates cropped up in the course of our next batch of calls and Carmody got out and opened them just like any ordinary being except that he did it with a certain leisurely elegance. Watching his tall figure as he paced across, his head held high, the smart hat set at just the right angle, I had to admit again that he had enormous presence. It was remarkable at his age.

Shortly before lunch I saw a cow that the farmer had said on the phone might have TB. 'She's gone down t'nick ever since she calved, guv'nor. I doubt she's a screw, but you'd better have a look at her, anyroad.'

As soon as I walked into the byre I knew what the trouble was. I have been blessed with an unusually sensitive nose and the sickly sweet smell of ketone hit me right away. It has always afforded me a childish pleasure to be able to say suddenly in the middle of a tuberculin test, 'There's a cow in here about three weeks calved that isn't doing very well,' and watch the farmer scratch his head and ask me how I knew.

I had another little triumph today. 'Started going off her cake first didn't she?' and the farmer nodded assent. 'And the flesh has just melted off her since then?'

'That's right,' the farmer said, 'I've never seen a cow go down as quick.'

'Well you can stop worrying, Mr Smith. She hasn't got TB, she's got slow fever and we'll be able to put her right for you.'

Slow fever is the local term for acetonaemia and the farmer smiled in relief. 'Damn. I'm glad! I thowt she was dog meat. I nearly rang Mallock this morning.'

I couldn't reach for the steroids which we use today, but I injected six ounces of glucose and 100 units of insulin intravenously – it was one of my pet remedies and might make modern vets laugh. But it used to work. The cow, dead-eyed and gaunt, was too weak to struggle as the farmer held her nose.

When I had finished I ran my hand over the jutting bones, covered, it seemed, only by skin.

'She'll soon fatten up now,' I said. 'But cut her down to

once a day milking – that's half the battle. And if that doesn't work, stop milking her entirely for two or three days.'

'Yes, I reckon she's putting it in t'bucket instead of on her back.'

'That's it exactly, Mr Smith.'

Carmody didn't seem to appreciate this interchange of home-spun wisdom and fidgeted impatiently. I took my cue and headed for the car.

'I'll see her in a couple of days,' I cried as we drove away, and waved to Mrs Smith who was looking out from the farmhouse doorway. Carmody however raised his hat gravely and held it a few inches above his head till we had left the yard, which was definitely better. I had noticed him doing this at every place we had visited and it looked so good that I was playing with the idea of starting to wear a hat so that I could try it too.

I glanced sideways at my companion. Most of a morning's work done and I hadn't asked him any questions. I cleared my throat.

'By the way, talking about that cow we've just seen, can you tell me something about the causes of acetonaemia?'

Carmody regarded me impassively. 'As a matter of fact I can't make up my mind which theory I endorse at the moment. Stevens maintains it is the incomplete oxidation of fatty acids, Sjollema leans towards liver intoxication and Janssen implicates one of the centre of the autonomic nervous system. My own view is that if we could only pin-point the exact cause of the production of diacetic acid and beta-oxybutyric acid in the metabolism we'd be well on the way to understanding the problem. Don't you agree?'

I closed my mouth which had begun to hang open.

'Oh yes, I do indeed . . . it's that oxy . . . that old beta-oxy . . . yes, that's what it is, without a doubt.' I slumped lower in my seat and decided not to ask Carmody any more questions; and as the stone walls flipped past the windows I began to face up to the gradually filtering perception that this was a superior being next to me. It was depressing to ponder on the fact that not only was he big, good-looking, completely sure of himself but brilliant as well. Also, I thought bitterly, he had every appearance of being rich.

We rounded the corner of a lane and came up to a low huddle of stone buildings. It was the last call before lunch and the gate into the yard was closed.

'We might as well go through,' I murmured. 'Do you mind?'

The student heaved himself from the car, unlatched the gate and began to bring it round. And he did it as he seemed to do everything: coolly, unhurriedly, with natural grace. As he passed the front of the car I was studying him afresh, wondering again at his style, his massive composure, when, apparently from nowhere, an evil looking little black cur dog glided silently out, sank its teeth with dedicated venom into Carmody's left buttock and slunk away.

Not even the most monolithic dignity can survive being bitten deeply and without warning in the backside. Carmody screamed, leaped in the air clutching his rear, then swarmed to the top of the gate with the agility of a monkey. Squatting on the top spar, his natty hat tipped over one eye, he glared about him wildly.

'What the hell?' he yelled. 'What the bloody hell?'

'It's all right,' I said, hurrying towards him and resisting the impulse to throw myself on the ground and roll about. 'It was just a dog.'

'Dog? What dog? Where?' Carmody's cries took on a frantic note.

'It's gone – disappeared. I only saw it for a couple of seconds.' And indeed, as I looked around it was difficult to believe that that flitting little black shadow had ever existed.

Carmody took a bit of coaxing down from the top of the gate and when he finally did reach ground level he limped over and sat down in the car instead of seeing the case. And when I saw the tattered cloth on his bottom I couldn't blame him for not risking a further attack. If it had been anybody else I'd have told him to drop his pants so that I could slap on some iodine but in this instance I somehow couldn't bring myself to do it. I left him sitting there.

CHAPTER TWENTY

When Carmody turned up for the afternoon round he had completely recovered his poise. He had changed his flannels and adopted a somewhat lopsided sitting position in the car but apart from that the dog episode might never have happened. In fact we had hardly got under way when he addressed me with a touch of arrogance.

'Look, I'm not going to learn much just watching you do things. Do you think I could carry out injections and the like? I want actual experience with the animals themselves.'

I didn't answer for a moment but stared ahead through the maze of fine cracks on the windscreen. I couldn't very well tell him that I was still trying to establish myself with the farmers and that some of them had definite reservations about my capabilities. Then I turned to him.

'OK. I'll have to do the diagnosing but whenever possible you can carry on from there.'

He soon had his first taste of action. I decided that a litter of ten weeks old pigs might benefit from an injection of E coli antiserum and handed him the bottle and syringe. And as he moved purposefully among the little animals I thought with gloomy satisfaction that though I may not be au fait with all the small print in the text books I did know better than to chase pigs into the dirty end of the pen to catch them. Because with Carmody in close pursuit the squealing creatures leaped from their straw bed and charged in a body towards a stagnant lake of urine against the far wall. And as the student grabbed at their hind legs the pigs scrabbled among the filth, kicking it back over him in a steady shower. He did finally get them all injected but at the end his smart outfit was liberally spattered and I had to open the windows wide to tolerate his presence in the car.

The next visit was to a big arable farm in the low country, and it was one of the few places where they had hung on to their horses; the long stable had several stalls in use and the names of the horses on the wall above; Boxer, Captain, Bobby, Tommy, and the mares Bonny and Daisy. It was Tommy the old cart horse we had to see and his trouble was a 'stoppage'.

Tommy was an old friend of mine; he kept having mild bouts of colic with constipation and I often wondered if he had a faecolith lurking about in his bowels somewhere. Anyway, six drachms of Istin in a pint of water invariably restored him to normal health and I began automatically to shake up the yellow powder in a drenching bottle. Meanwhile the farmer and his man turned the horse round in his stall, ran a rope under his nose band, threw it over a beam in the stable roof and pulled the head upwards.

I handed the bottle to Carmody and stepped back. The student looked up and hesitated. Tommy was a big horse and the head, pulled high, was far beyond reach; but the farm man pushed a ramshackle kitchen chair wordlessly forward and Carmody mounted it and stood swaying precariously.

I watched with interest. Horses are awkward things to drench at any time and Tommy didn't like Istin, even though it was good for him. On my last visit I had noticed that he was becoming very clever at holding the bitter mixture at the back of his throat instead of swallowing it. I had managed to foil him by tapping him under the chin just as he was toying with the idea of coughing it out and he had gulped it down with an offended look. But it was more and more becoming a battle of wits.

Carmody never really had a chance. He started off well enough by grasping the horse's tongue and thrusting the bottle past the teeth, but Tommy outwitted him effortlessly by inclining his head and allowing the liquid to flow from the far side of his mouth.

'It's coming out t'other side, young man!' the farmer cried with some asperity.

The student gasped and tried to direct the flow down the throat but Tommy had summed him up immediately as an amateur and was now in complete command of the situation. By judicious rolling of the tongue and a series of little coughs and snorts he kept ridding himself of most of the medicine and I felt a pang of pity at the sight of Carmody weaving about on the creaking chair as the yellow fluid cascaded over his clothes.

At the end, the farmer squinted into the empty bottle.

'Well I reckon t'oss got SOME of it,' he muttered sourly.

Carmody eyed him impassively for a moment, shook a few ounces of Istin solution from somewhere up his sleeve and strode out of the stable.

At the next farm I was surprised to detect a vein of sadism in my makeup. The owner, a breeder of pedigree Large White pigs, was exporting a sow abroad and it had to be subjected to various tests including a blood sample for Brucellosis. Extracting a few cc's of blood from the ear vein of a struggling pig is a job which makes most vets shudder and it was clearly a dirty trick to ask a student to do it, but the memory of his coldly confident request at the beginning of the afternoon seemed to have stilled my conscience. I handed him the syringe with scarcely a qualm.

The pigman slipped a noose into the sow's mouth and drew it tight over the snout and behind the canine teeth. This common method of restraint isn't at all painful but the sow was one of those who didn't like any form of mucking about. She was a huge animal and as soon as she felt the rope she opened her mouth wide in a long-drawn, resentful scream. The volume of sound was incredible and she kept it up effortlessly without any apparent need to draw breath. Conversation from then on was out of the question and I watched in the appalling din as Carmody put an elastic tourniquet at the base of the sow's ear, swabbed the surface with spirit and then poked with his needle at the small blood vessel. Nothing happened. He tried again but the syringe remained obstinately empty. He had a few more attempts then, as I felt the top of my head was going to come loose I wandered from the pen into the peace of the yard.

I took a leisurely stroll round the outside of the piggery, pausing for a minute or two to look at the view at the far end where the noise was comparatively faint. When I returned to the pen the screaming hit me again like a pneumatic drill and Carmody, sweating and slightly pop-eyed, looked up from the ear where he was still jabbing fruitlessly. It seemed to me that everybody had had enough. Using sign language I indicated to the student that I'd like to have a go and by a happy chance my first effort brought a dark welling of blood into the syringe. I waved to the pigman to remove the rope and the moment he did so the big sow switched off the noise magically and began to nose, quite unperturbed, among the straw.

'Nothing very exciting at the next place,' I kept the triumph out of my voice as we drove away. 'Just a bullock with a tumour on its jaw. But it's an interesting herd – all Galloways, and this group we're going to see have been wintered outside. They're the toughest animals in the district.'

Carmody nodded. Nothing I said seemed to rouse much enthusiasm in him. For myself this herd of untamed black cattle always held a certain fascination; contacts with them were always coloured by a degree of uncertainty – sometimes you could catch them to examine them, sometimes you couldn't.

As we approached the farm I could see a bunch of about thirty bullocks streaming down the scrubby hillside on our right. The farm men were driving them down through the scattered gorse bushes and the sparse groups of trees to where the stone walls met in a rough V at the front.

One of them waved to me. 'We're going to try to get a rope on 'im down in the corner while he's among his mates. He's a wick bugger – you'd never get near him in t'field.'

After a lot of shouting and waving and running about the bullocks were finally cornered and they stood in a tight, uneasy pack, their shaggy black polls bobbing among the steam rising from their bodies.

'There he is! You can see the thing on his face.' A man pointed to a big beast about the middle of the bunch and began to push his way towards him. My admiration for the Yorkshire farm worker rose another notch as I watched him squeezing between the plunging, kicking animals. 'When I get the rope on his head you'll all have to get on t'other end – one man'll never hold 'im.' He gasped as he fought his way forward.

He was obviously an expert because as soon as he got within reach he dropped the halter on to the bullock's head with practised skill. 'Right!' he shouted. 'Give me a hand with him. We have 'im now.'

But as he spoke the beast gave a great bellow and began to charge from the pack. The man cried out despairingly and disappeared among the hairy bodies. The rope whipped free out of reach of everybody. Except Carmody. As the bullock shot past him he grabbed the trailing rope with a reflex action and hung on.

I watched, fascinated, as man and beast careered across the field. They were travelling away from me towards the far slope, the animal head down, legs pistoning, going like a racehorse, the student also at full speed but very upright, both hands on the rope in front of him, a picture of resolution.

The men and I were helpless spectators and we stood in a silent group as the beast turned left suddenly and disappeared behind a clump of low trees. It was gone for only a few moments but it seemed a long time and when it reappeared it was going faster than ever, hurtling over the turf like a black thunderbolt. Carmody, incredibly, was still there on the end of the rope and still very upright but his strides had increased to an impossible length till he seemed to be touching the ground only every twenty feet or so.

I marvelled at his tenacity but obviously the end was near. He took a last few soaring, swooping steps then he was down on his face. But he didn't let go. The bullock, going better than ever, had turned towards us now, dragging the inert form apparently without effort, and I winced as I saw it was headed straight for a long row of cow pats.

It was when Carmody was skidding face down through the third heap of muck that I suddenly began to like him. And when he finally did have to release his hold and lay for a moment motionless on the grass I hurried over to help him up. He thanked me briefly then looked calmly across the field at a sight which is familiar to every veterinary surgeon – his patient thundering out of sight across the far horizon.

The student was almost unrecognizable. His clothes and face were plastered with filth except where the saffron streaks of the Istin showed up like war paint, he smelt abominably, he had been bitten in the backside, nothing had really gone right for him all day yet he was curiously undefeated. I smiled to myself. It was no good judging this bloke by ordinary standards; I could recognize the seeds of greatness when I saw them.

Carmody stayed with us for two weeks and after that first day I got on with him not so badly. Of course it wasn't the same relationship as with other students; there was always a barrier of reserve. He spent a lot of time squinting down the practice microscope at blood films, skin scrapings, milk smears, and by the end of each day he had collected a fresh supply of samples from the cases he had seen. He would come and drink a polite beer with me after an evening call but there was none of the giggling over the day's events as with the other young lads. I had the feeling always that he would rather have been writing up his case book and working out his findings.

But I didn't mind. I found an interest in being in contact with a truly scientific mind. He was as far removed as he could be from the traditional studious swot – his was a cold, superior intellect and there was something rewarding in watching him at work.

I didn't see Carmody again for over twenty years. I picked out his name in the Record when he qualified with top marks then he disappeared into the great world of research for a while to emerge with a PhD and over the years he added a string of further degrees and qualifications. Every now and then an unintelligible article would appear in the professional journals under his name and it became commonplace when reading scientific papers to see references to what Dr Carmody had said on the subject.

When I finally did see him he was the guest of honour at a professional banquet, an international celebrity heavy with honours. From where I was sitting at the far end of one of the side tables I listened to his masterly speech with a feeling of inevitability; the wide grasp of his subject, the brilliant exposition – I had seen it all coming those many years ago.

Afterwards when we had left the tables he moved among us and I gazed with something like awe at the majestic figure approaching. Carmody had always been big, but with the tail coat tight across the massive shoulders and the vast expanse of gleaming shirt front stretched over the curving abdomen he was almost overpowering. As he passed he stopped and looked at me.

'It's Herriot, isn't it?' the handsome, high-coloured face still had that look of calm power.

'Yes, it is. It's good to see you again.'

We shook hands. 'And how is the practice at Darrowby?'

'Oh, as usual,' I replied. 'Bit too busy at times. We could do with some help if ever you felt like it.'

Carmody nodded gravely. 'I'd like that very much. It would be good for me.'

He was about to move on when he paused. 'Perhaps you'd let me know any time you want a pig bled.' For a moment we looked into each other's eyes and I saw a small flame flicker briefly in the frosty blue. Then he was gone.

As I looked at the retreating back a hand gripped my arm. It was Brian Miller, a happily obscure practitioner like myself.

'Come on, Jim, I'll buy you a drink,' he said.

We went into the bar and ordered two beers.

'That Carmody!' Brian said. 'The man's got a tremendous brain, but by God he's a cold fish.'

I sipped at the beer and looked thoughtfully into my glass for a few seconds.

'Oh I don't know,' I said. 'He certainly gives that impression, but Carmody's all right.'

CHAPTER TWENTY-ONE

The big room at Skeldale House was full. It seemed to me that this room with its graceful alcoves, high, carved ceiling and french windows lay at the centre of our life in Darrowby. It was where Siegfried, Tristan and I gathered when the day's work was done, toasting our feet by the white wood fireplace with the glass-fronted cupboard on top, talking over the day's events. It was the heart of our bachelor existence, sitting there in a happy stupor, reading, listening to the radio, Tristan usually flipping effortlessly through the *Daily Telegraph* crossword.

It was where Siegfried entertained his friends and there was a constant stream of them – old and young, male and female. But tonight it was Tristan's turn and the pack of young people with drinks in their hands were there at his invitation. And they wouldn't need much persuasion. Though just about the opposite of his brother in many ways he had the same attractiveness which brought the friends running at the crook of a finger.

The occasion was the Daffodil Ball at the Drovers' Arms and we were dressed in our best. This was a different kind of function from the usual village institute hop with the farm lads in their big boots and music from a scraping fiddle and piano. It was a proper dance with a popular local band – Lenny Butterfield and his Hot Shots – and was an annual affair to herald the arrival of spring.

I watched Tristan dispensing the drinks. The bottles of whisky, gin and sherry which Siegfried kept in the fireplace cupboard had taken some severe punishment but Tristan himself had been abstemious. An occasional sip from a glass of light ale perhaps, but nothing more. Drinking, to him, meant the bulk intake of draught bitter; all else was mere vanity and folly. Dainty little glasses were anathema and even now when I see him at a party where everybody is holding small drinks Tristan somehow contrives to have a pint in his hand.

'Nice little gathering, Jim,' he said, appearing at my elbow. 'A few more blokes than girls but that won't matter much.'

I eyed him coldly. I knew why there were extra men. It was so that Tristan wouldn't have to take the floor too often. It fitted in with his general dislike of squandering energy that he was an unenthusiastic dancer; he didn't mind walking a girl round the floor now and again during the evening but he preferred to spend most of the time in the bar.

So, in fact, did a lot of the Darrowby folk. When we arrived at the Drovers the bar was congested while only a dedicated few circled round the ballroom. But as time went on more and more couples ventured out and by ten o'clock the dance floor was truly packed.

And I soon found I was enjoying myself. Tristan's friends were an effervescent bunch; likeable young men and attractive girls; I just couldn't help having a good time.

Butterfield's famed band in their short red jackets added greatly to the general merriment. Lenny himself looked about fifty-five and indeed all four of the Hot Shots ensemble were rather elderly, but they made up for their grey hairs by sheer vivacity. Not that Lenny's hair was grey; it was dyed a determined black and he thumped the piano with dynamic energy, beaming out at the company through his horn-rimmed glasses, occasionally bawling a chorus into the microphone by his side, announcing the dances, making throaty wisecracks. He gave value for money.

There was no pairing off in our party and I danced with all the girls in turn. At the peak of the evening I was jockeying my way around the floor with Daphne and the way she was constructed made it a rewarding experience. I never have been one for skinny women but I suppose you could say that Daphne's development had strayed a little too far in the other direction. She wasn't fat, just lavishly endowed.

Battling through the crush, colliding with exuberant neighbours, bouncing deliciously off Daphne, with everybody singing as they danced and the Hot Shots pouring out an insistent boom-boom beat, I felt I hadn't a care in the world. And then I saw Helen.

She was dancing with the inevitable Richard Edmundson, his shining gold head floating above the company like an emblem of doom. And it was uncanny how in an instant my cosy little world disintegrated leaving a chill gnawing emptiness.

When the music stopped I returned Daphne to her friends and went to find Tristan. The comfortable little bar in the Drovers was overflowing and the temperature like an oven. Through an almost impenetrable fog of cigarette smoke I discerned my colleague on a high stool holding court with a group of perspiring revellers. Tristan himself looked cool and, as always, profoundly content. He drained his glass, smacked his lips gently as though it had been the best pint of beer he'd ever tasted, then, as he reached across the counter and courteously requested a refill he spotted me struggling towards him.

When I reached his stool he laid an affable hand on my shoulder, 'Ah, Jim, nice to see you. Splendid dance, this, don't you think?'

I didn't bring up the fact that I hadn't seen him on the floor yet, but making my voice casual I mentioned that Helen was there.

Tristan nodded benignly. 'Yes, saw her come in. Why don't you go and dance with her?'

'I can't do that. She's with a partner – young Edmundson.'

'Not at all.' Tristan surveyed his fresh pint with a critical eye and took an exploratory sip. 'She's with a party, like us. No partner.'

'How do you know that?'

'I watched all the fellows hang their coats out there while the girls went upstairs. No reason at all why you shouldn't have a dance with her.'

'I see.' I hesitated for a few moments then made my way back to the ballroom.

But it wasn't as easy as that. I had to keep doing my duty with the girls in our group and whenever I headed for Helen she was whisked away by one of her men friends before I got near her. At times I fancied she was looking over at me but I couldn't be sure; the only thing I knew for certain was that I wasn't enjoying myself any more; the magic and gaiety had gone and I felt a rising misery at the thought that this was going to be another of my frustrating contacts with Helen when all I could do was look at her hopelessly. Only this time was worse – I hadn't even spoken to her.

I was almost relieved when the manager came up and told me there was a call for me. I went to the phone and spoke to Mrs Hall. There was a bitch in trouble whelping and I had to go. I looked at my watch – after midnight, so that was the end of the dance for me.

I stood for a moment listening to the muffled thudding from the dance floor then slowly pulled on my coat before going into say good-bye to Tristan's friends. I exchanged a few words with them, waved, then turned back and pushed the swing door open.

Helen was standing there, about a foot away from me. Her hand was on the door, too. I didn't wonder whether she was going in or out but stared dumbly into her smiling blue eyes.

'Leaving already, Jim?' she said.

'Yes, I've got a call, I'm afraid.'

'Oh what a shame. I hope it's nothing very serious.'

I opened my mouth to speak, but her dark beauty and the very nearness of her suddenly filled my world and a wave of hopeless longing swept over and submerged me. I slid my hand a few inches down the door and gripped hers as a drowning man might, and wonderingly I felt her fingers come round and entwine themselves tightly in mine.

And in an instant there was no band, no noise, no people, just the two of us standing very close in the doorway.

'Come with me,' I said.

Helen's eyes were very large as she smiled that smile I knew so well.

'I'll get my coat,' she murmured.

This wasn't really me, I thought, standing on the hall carpet watching Helen trotting quickly up the stairs, but I had to believe it as she reappeared on the landing pulling on her coat. Outside, on the cobbles of the market place my car, too, appeared to be taken by surprise because it roared into life at the first touch of the starter.

I had to go back to the surgery for my whelping instruments and in the silent moonlit street we got out and opened the big white door to Skeldale House.

And once in the passage it was the most natural thing in the world to take her in my arms and kiss her gratefully and unhurriedly. I had waited a long time for this and the minutes flowed past unnoticed as we stood there, our feet on the black and red eighteenth-century tiles, our heads almost touching the vast picture of the Death of Nelson which dominated the entrance.

We kissed again at the first bend of the passage under the companion picture of the Meeting of Wellington and Blucher at Waterloo. We kissed at the second bend by the tall cupboard where Siegfried kept his riding coats and boots. We kissed in the dispensary in between searching for my instruments. Then we tried it out in the garden and this was the best of all with the flowers still expectant in the moonlight and the fragrance of the moist earth and grass rising about us.

I have never driven so slowly to a case. About ten miles an hour with Helen's head on my shoulder and all the scents of spring drifting in through the open window. And it was like sailing from stormy seas into a sweet, safe harbour, like coming home.

The light in the cottage window was the only one showing in the sleeping village, and when I knocked at the door Bert Chapman answered. Bert was a council roadman – one of the breed for whom I felt an abiding affinity.

The council men were my brethren of the roads. Like me they spent most of their lives on the lonely by-ways around

Darrowby and I saw them most days of the week, repairing the tarmac, cutting back the grass verges in the summer, gritting and snow ploughing in the winter. And when they spotted me driving past they would grin cheerfully and wave as if the very sight of me had made their day. I don't know whether they were specially picked for good nature but I don't think I have ever met a more equable body of men.

One old farmer remarked sourly to me once. 'There's no wonder the buggers are 'appy, they've got nowt to do.' An exaggeration, of course, but I knew how he felt; compared with farming every other job was easy.

I had seen Bert Chapman just a day or two ago, sitting on a grassy bank, his shovel by his side, a vast sandwich in his hand. He had raised a corded forearm in salute, a broad smile bisecting his round, sun-reddened face. He had looked eternally carefree but tonight his smile was strained.

'I'm sorry to bother you this late, Mr Herriot,' he said as he ushered us into the house, 'but I'm gettin' a bit worried about Susie. Her pups are due and she's been making a bed for them and messing about all day but nowt's happened. I was goin' to leave her till morning but about midnight she started panting like 'ell – I don't like the look of her.'

Susie was one of my regular patients. Her big, burly master was always bringing her to the surgery, a little shame-faced at his solicitude, and when I saw him sitting in the waiting room looking strangely out of place among the ladies with their pets, he usually said 'T'missus asked me to bring Susie.' But it was a transparent excuse.

'She's nobbut a little mongrel, but very faithful,' Bert said, still apologetic, but I could understand how he felt about Susie, a shaggy little ragamuffin whose only wile was to put her paws on my knees and laugh up into my face with her tail lashing. I found her irresistible.

But she was a very different character tonight. As we went into the living room of the cottage the little animal crept from her basket, gave a single indeterminate wag of her tail then stood miserably in the middle of the floor, her ribs heaving. As I bent to examine her she turned a wide panting mouth and anxious eyes up to me.

I ran my hand over her abdomen. I don't think I have ever felt a more bloated little dog; she was as round as a football, absolutely bulging with pups, ready to pop, but nothing was happening.

'What do you think?' Bert's face was haggard under his sunburn and he touched the dog's head briefly with a big calloused hand.

'I don't know yet, Bert,' I said. 'I'll have to have a feel inside. Bring me some hot water, will you?'

I added some antiseptic to the water, soaped my hand and with one finger carefully explored the vagina. There was a pup there, all right; my finger tip brushed across the nostrils, the tiny mouth and tongue; but he was jammed in that passage like a cork in a bottle.

Squatting back on my heels I turned to the Chapmans.

'I'm afraid there's a big pup stuck fast. I have a feeling that if she could get rid of this chap the others would come away. They'd probably be smaller.'

'Is there ony way of shiftin' him, Mr Herriot?' Bert asked.

I paused for a moment. 'I'm going to put forceps on his head and see if he'll move. I don't like using forceps but I'm going to have one careful try and if it doesn't work I'll have to take her back to the surgery for a caesarean.'

'An operation?' Bert said hollowly. He gulped and glanced fearfully at his wife. Like many big men he had married a tiny woman and at this moment Mrs Chapman looked even smaller than her four foot eleven inches as she huddled in her chair and stared at me with wide eyes.

'Oh I wish we'd never had her mated,' she wailed, wringing her hands. 'I told Bert five year old was too late for a first litter but he wouldn't listen. And now we're maybe going to lose 'er.'

I hastened to reassure her. 'No, she isn't too old, and everything may be all right. Let's just see how we get on.'

I boiled the instrument for a few minutes on the stove then kneeled behind my patient again. I poised the forceps for a moment and at the flash of steel a grey tinge crept under Bert's sunburn and his wife coiled herself into a ball in her chair. Obviously they were non-starters as assistants so Helen held Susie's head while I once more reached in towards the pup. There was desperately little room but I managed to direct the forceps along my finger till they touched the nose. Then very gingerly I opened the jaws and pushed them forward with the very gentlest pressure until I was able to clamp them on either side of the head.

I'd soon know now. In a situation like this you can't do any pulling, you can only try to ease the thing along. This I did and I fancied I felt just a bit of movement; I tried again and there was no doubt about it, the pup was coming towards me. Susie, too, appeared to sense that things were taking a turn for the better. She cast off her apathy and began to strain lustily.

It was no trouble after that and I was able to draw the pup forth almost without resistance.

'I'm afraid this one'll be dead,' I said, and as the tiny creature lay across my palm there was no sign of breathing. But, pinching the chest between thumb and forefinger I could feel the heart pulsing steadily and I quickly opened his mouth and blew softly down into his lungs.

I repeated this a few times then laid the pup on his side in the basket. I was just thinking it was going to be no good when the little rib cage gave a sudden lift, then another and another.

'He's off!' Bert exclaimed happily. 'That's champion! We want these puppies alive tha knows. They're by Jack Dennison's terrier and he's a grand 'un.'

'That's right,' Mrs Chapman put in. 'No matter how many she has, they're all spoken for. Everybody wants a pup out of Susie.'

'I can believe that,' I said. But I smiled to myself. Jack Dennison's terrier was another hound of uncertain ancestry, so this lot would be a right mixture. But none the worse for that.

I gave Susie half a cc of pituitrin. 'I think she needs it after pushing against that fellow for hours. We'll wait and see what happens now.'

And it was nice waiting. Mrs Chapman brewed a pot of tea and began to slap butter on to home-made scones. Susie, partly aided by my pituitrin, pushed out a pup in a self-satisfied manner about every fifteen minutes. The pups themselves soon set up a bawling of surprising volume for such minute creatures. Bert, relaxing visibly with every minute, filled his pipe and regarded the fast-growing family with a grin of increasing width.

'Ee, it is kind of you young folks to stay with us like this.' Mrs Chapman put her head on one side and looked at us worriedly. 'I should think you've been dying to get back to your dance all this time.'

I thought of the crush at the Drovers. The smoke, the heat, the nonstop boom-boom of the Hot Shots and I looked around the peaceful little room with the old-fashioned black grate, the low, varnished beams, Mrs Chapman's sewing box, the row of Bert's pipes on the wall. I took a firmer grasp of Helen's hand which I had been holding under the table for the last hour.

'Not at all, Mrs Chapman,' I said. 'We haven't missed it in the least.' And I have never been more sincere.

It must have been about half past two when I finally decided that Susie had finished. She had six fine pups which was a good score for a little thing like her and the noise had abated as the family settled down to feast on her abundant udder.

I lifted the pups out one by one and examined them. Susie didn't mind in the least but appeared to be smiling with modest pride as I handled her brood. When I put them back with her she inspected them and sniffed them over busily before rolling on to her side again.

'Three dogs and three bitches,' I said. 'Nice even litter.'

Before leaving I took Susie from her basket and palpated her abdomen. The degree of deflation was almost unbelievable; a pricked balloon could not have altered its shape more spectacularly and she had made a remarkable metamorphosis to the lean, scruffy little extrovert I knew so well.

When I released her she scurried back and curled herself

round her new family who were soon sucking away with total absorption.

Bert laughed. 'She's fair capped wi' them pups.' He bent over and prodded the first arrival with a horny forefinger. 'I like the look o' this big dog pup. I reckon we'll keep this 'un for ourselves, mother. He'll be company for t'awd lass.'

It was time to go. Helen and I moved over to the door and little Mrs Chapman with her fingers on the handle looked up at me.

'Well, Mr Herriot,' she said, 'I can't thank you enough for comin' out and putting our minds at rest. I don't know what I've done wi' this man of mine if anything had happened to his little dog.'

Bert grinned sheepishly. 'Nay,' he muttered. 'Ah was never really worried.'

His wife laughed and opened the door and as we stepped out into the silent scented night she gripped my arm and looked up at me roguishly.

'I suppose this is your young lady,' she said.

I put my arm round Helen's shoulders.

'Yes,' I said firmly, 'this is my young lady.'

CHAPTER TWENTY-TWO

It was almost as though I were looking at my own cows because as I stood in the little new byre and looked along the row of red and roan backs I felt a kind of pride.

'Frank,' I said. 'They look marvellous. You wouldn't think they were the same animals.'

Frank Metcalfe grinned. 'Just what I was thinking meself. It's wonderful what a change of setting'll do for livestock.'

It was the cows' first day in the new byre. Previously I had seen them only in the old place – a typical Dales cowhouse, centuries old with a broken cobbled floor and gaping holes where the muck and urine lay in pools, rotting wooden partitions between the stalls and slit windows as though the place had been built as a fortress. I could remember Frank sitting in it milking, almost invisible in the gloom, the cobwebs hanging in thick fronds from the low roof above him.

In there, the ten cows had looked what they were – a motley assortment of ordinary milkers – but today they had acquired a new dignity and style.

'You must feel it's been worth all your hard work,' I said, and the young farmer nodded and smiled. There was a grim touch about the smile as though he was reliving for a moment the hours and weeks and months of back-breaking labour he had put in there. Because Frank Metcalfe had done it all himself. The rows of neat, concreted standings, the clean, level sweep of floor, the whitewashed, cement-rendered walls all bathed in light from the spacious windows had been put there by his own two hands.

'I'll show you the dairy,' Frank said.

We went into a small room which he had built at one end and I looked admiringly at the gleaming milk cooler, the spotless sinks and buckets, the strainer with its neat pile of filter pads.

'You know,' I said. 'This is how milk should be produced. All those mucky old places I see every day on my rounds – they nearly make my hair stand on end.'

Frank leaned over and drew a jet of water from one of the taps. 'Aye, you're right. It'll all be like this and better one day and it'll pay the farmers better too. I've got me TT licence now and the extra fourpence a gallon will make a hell of a difference. I feel I'm ready to start.'

And when he did start, I thought, he'd go places. He seemed to have all the things it took to succeed at the hard trade of farming – intelligence, physical toughness, a love of the land and animals and the ability to go slogging on endlessly when other people were enjoying their leisure. I felt these qualities would overcome his biggest handicap which was simply that he didn't have any money.

Frank wasn't a farmer at all to start with. He was a steel

worker from Middlesbrough. When he had first arrived less than a year ago with his young wife to take over the isolated small holding at Bransett I had been surprised to learn that he hailed from the city because he had the dark, sinewy look of the typical Dalesman – and he was called Metcalfe.

He had laughed when I mentioned this. 'Oh, my great grandfather came from these parts and I've always had a hankering to come back.'

As I came to know him better I was able to fill in the gaps in that simple statement. He had spent all his holidays up here as a small boy and though his father was a foreman in the steelworks and he himself had served his time at the trade the pull of the Dales had been like a siren song welling stronger till he had been unable to resist it any longer. He had worked on farms in his spare time, read all he could about agriculture and finally had thrown up his old life and rented the little place high in the fells at the end of a long, stony track.

With its primitive house and tumbledown buildings it seemed an unpromising place to make a living and in any case I hadn't much faith in the ability of townspeople to suddenly turn to farming and make a go of it; in my short experience I had seen quite a few try and fail. But Frank Metcalfe had gone about the job as though he had been at it all his life, repairing the broken walls, improving the grassland, judiciously buying stock on his shoe-string budget; there was no sign of the bewilderment and despair I had seen in so many others.

I had mentioned this to a retired farmer in Darrowby and the old man chuckled. 'Aye, you've got to have farmin' inside you. There's very few people as can succeed at it unless it's in their blood. It matters nowt that young Metcalfe's been brought up in a town, he's still got it in 'im – he's got it through the titty, don't you see, through the titty.'

Maybe he was right, but whether Frank had it through the titty or through study and brains he had transformed the holding in a short time. When he wasn't milking, feeding, mucking out, he was slaving at that little byre, chipping stones, mixing cement, sand and dust clinging to the sweat on his face. And now, as he said, he was ready to start.

As we came out of the dairy he pointed to another old building across the yard. 'When I'm straightened out I aim to convert that into another byre. I've had to borrow a good bit but now I'm TT I should be able to clear it off in a couple of years. Sometime in the future if all goes well I might be able to get a bigger place altogether.'

He was about my own age and a natural friendship had sprung up between us. We used to sit under the low beams of his cramped living room with its single small window and sparse furniture and as his young wife poured cups of tea he liked to talk of his plans. And, listening to him, I always felt that a man like him would do well not only for himself but for farming in general.

I looked at him now as he turned his head and gazed for a few moments round his domain. He didn't have to say: 'I love this place, I feel I belong here.' It was all there in his face, in the softening of his eyes as they moved over the huddle of grass fields cupped in a hollow of the fells. These fields, clawed by past generations from the rough hillside and fighting their age-old battle with heather and bracken, ran up to a ragged hem of cliff and scree and above you could just see the lip of the moor – a wild land of bog and peat hag. Below, the farm track disappeared round the bend of a wooded hill. The pastures were poor and knuckles of rock pushed out in places through the thin soil, but the clean, turf-scented air and the silence must have been like a deliverance after the roar and smoke of the steel-works.

'Well we'd better see that cow, Frank,' I said. 'The new byre nearly made me forget what I came for.'

'Aye, it's this red and white 'un. My latest purchase and she's never been right since I got her. Hasn't come on to her milk properly and she seems dozy, somehow.'

The temperature was a hundred and three and as I put the thermometer away I sniffed. 'She smells a bit, doesn't she?'

'Aye,' Frank said. 'I've noticed that myself.'

'Better bring me some hot water, then. I'll have a feel inside.'

The uterus was filled with a stinking exudate and as I withdrew my arm there was a gush of yellowish, necrotic material. 'Surely she must have had a bit of a discharge,' I said.

Frank nodded. 'Yes, she has had, but I didn't pay much attention – a lot of them do it when they're clearing up after calving.'

I drained the uterus by means of a rubber tube and irrigated it with antiseptic, then I pushed in a few acriflavine pessaries. 'That'll help to clean her up, and I think she'll soon be a lot better in herself, but I'm going to take a blood sample from her.'

'Why's that?'

'Well it may be nothing, but I don't like the look of that yellow stuff. It consists of decayed cotyledones – you know, the berries on the calf bed – and when they're that colour it's a bit suspicious of Brucellosis.'

'Abortion, you mean?'

'It's possible, Frank. She may have calved before her time or she may have calved normally but still been infected. Anyway the blood will tell us. Keep her isolated in the meantime.'

A few days later at breakfast time in Skeldale House I felt a quick stab of anxiety as I opened the lab report and read that the agglutination test on the blood had given a positive result. I hurried out to the farm.

'How long have you had this cow?' I asked.

'Just over three weeks,' the young farmer replied.

'And she's been running in the same field as your other cows and the in-calf heifers?'

'Yes, all the time.'

I paused for a moment. 'Frank, I'd better tell you the implications. I know you'll want to know what might happen. The source of infection in Brucellosis is the discharges of an infected cow and I'm afraid this animal of yours will have thoroughly contaminated that pasture. Any or all of your animals may have picked up the bug.'

'Does that mean they'll abort?'

'Not necessarily. It varies tremendously. Many cows carry

their calves through despite infection.' I was doing my best to sound optimistic.

Frank dug his hands deep into his pockets. His thin, dark-complexioned face was serious. 'Damn, I wish I'd never seen the thing. I bought her at Houlton market – God knows where she came from, but it's too late to talk like that now. What can we do about the job?'

'The main thing is to keep her isolated and away from the other stock. I wish there was some way to protect the others but there isn't much we can do. There are only two types of vaccine – live ones which can only be given to empty cows and yours are all in-calf, and dead ones which aren't reckoned to be of much use.'

'Well I'm the sort that doesn't like to just sit back and wait. The dead vaccine won't do any harm if it doesn't do any good, will it?'

'No.'

'Right, let's do 'em all with it and we'll hope for the best.'

Hoping for the best was something vets did a lot of in the thirties. I vaccinated the entire herd and we waited.

Nothing happened for a full eight weeks. Summer lengthened into autumn and the cattle were brought inside. The infected cow improved, her discharge cleared up and she began to milk a bit better. Then Frank rang early one morning.

'I've found a dead calf laid in the channel when I went in to milk. Will you come?'

It was a thinly-haired seven months foetus that I found. The cow looked sick and behind her dangled the inevitable retained placenta. Her udder which, if she had calved normally would have been distended with milk, the precious milk which Frank depended on for his livelihood, was almost empty.

Obsessed by a feeling of helplessness I could only offer the same old advice; isolate, disinfect – and hope.

A fortnight later one of the in-calf heifers did it – she was a pretty little Jersey cross which Frank had hoped would push up his butter fat percentage – and a week after that one of the cows slipped a calf in her sixth month of pregnancy.

It was when I was visiting this third case that I met Mr Bagley. Frank introduced him somewhat apologetically. 'He says he has a cure for this trouble, Jim. He wants to talk to you about it.'

In every sticky situation there is always somebody who knows better than the vet. Subconsciously I suppose I had been waiting for a Mr Bagley to turn up and I listened patiently.

He was very short with bandy legs in cloth leggings, and he looked up at me intently. 'Young man, I've been through this on ma own farm and ah wouldn't be here today if I hadn't found the remedy.'

'I see, and what was that, Mr Bagley?'

'I have it 'ere.' The little man pulled a bottle from his jacket pocket. 'It's a bit mucky – it's been stood in t'cow house window for a year or two.'

I read the label. 'Professor Driscoll's Abortion Cure. Give two tablespoonsful to each cow in the herd in a pint of water and repeat on the following day.' The professor's face took up most of the label. He was an aggressive-looking, profusely whiskered man in a high Victorian collar and he glared out at me belligerently through a thick layer of dust. He wasn't so daft, either, because lower down the bottle I read. 'If an animal has aborted a dose of this mixture will prevent further trouble.' He knew as well as I did that they didn't often do it more than once.

'Yes,' Mr Bagley said. 'That's the stuff. Most of my cows did it on me but I kept goin' with the medicine and they were right as a bobbin next time round.'

'But they would be in any case. They develop an immunity you see.'

Mr Bagley put his head on one side and gave a gentle unbelieving smile. And who was I to argue, anyway? I hadn't a thing to offer.

'OK, Frank,' I said wearily. 'Go ahead – like my vaccine, I don't suppose it can do any harm.'

A fresh bottle of Driscoll's cure was purchased and little Mr Bagley supervised the dosing of the herd. He was cock-a-hoop when, three weeks later, one of the cows calved bang on time.

'Now then, what do you say, young man? Ma stuff's working already, isn't it?'

'Well I expected some of them to calve normally,' I replied and the little man pursed his lips as though he considered me a bad loser.

But I wasn't really worried about what he thought; all I felt was an unhappy resignation. Because this sort of thing was always happening in those days before the modern drugs appeared. Quack medicines abounded on the farms and the vets couldn't say a lot about them because their own range of pharmaceuticals was pitifully inadequate.

And in those diseases like abortion which had so far defeated all the efforts of the profession at control the harvest for the quack men was particularly rich. The farming press and country newspapers were filled with confident advertisements of red drenches, black draughts, pink powders which were positively guaranteed to produce results. Professor Driscoll had plenty of competition.

When shortly afterwards another cow calved to time Mr Bagley was very nice about it. 'We all 'ave to learn, young man, and you haven't had much practical experience. You just hadn't heard of my medicine and I'm not blaming you, but I think we're on top of t'job now.'

I didn't say anything. Frank was beginning to look like a man who could see a gleam of hope and I wasn't going to extinguish it by voicing my doubts. Maybe the outbreak had run its course – these things were unpredictable.

But the next time I heard Frank on the phone all my gloomy forebodings were realized. 'I want you to come out and cleanse three cows.'

'Three!'

'Aye, they did it one after the other – bang, bang, bang. And all before time. It's an absolute bugger, Jim – I don't know what I'm going to do.'

He met me as I got out of the car at the top of the track.

He looked ten years older, his face pale and haggard as though he hadn't slept. Mr Bagley was there, too, digging a hole in front of the byre door.

'What's he doing?' I asked.

Frank looked down at his boots expressionlessly. 'He's burying one of the calves. He says it does a lot of good if you put it in front of the door.' He looked at me with an attempt at a smile. 'Science can do nowt for me so we might as well try a bit of black magic.'

I felt a few years older myself as I picked my way round the deep grave Mr Bagley was digging. The little man looked up at me as I passed. 'This is a very old remedy,' he explained. 'Ma medicine seems to be losing its power so we'll have to try summat stronger. The trouble is,' he added with some asperity. 'I was called in on this case far too late.'

I removed the putrefying afterbirths from the three cows and got off the place as soon as possible. I felt such a deep sense of shame that I could hardly meet Frank's eye. And it was even worse on my next visit a fortnight later because as I walked across the yard I was conscious of a strange smell polluting the sweet hill air. It was a penetrating, acrid stink and though it rang a bell somewhere I couldn't quite identify it. As Frank came out of the house he saw me sniffing and looking round.

'Not very nice is it?' he said with a tired smile. 'I don't believe you've met our goat.'

'You've got a goat?'

'Well, we've got the loan of one – an old Billy. I don't see him around right now but by God you can always smell him. Mr Bagley dug 'im up somewhere – says he did one of his neighbours a world of good when he was having my trouble. Burying the calves wasn't doing any good so he thought he'd better bring on the goat. It's the smell that does the trick, he says.'

'Frank, I'm sorry,' I said. 'It's still going on, then?'

He shrugged his shoulders. 'Aye, two more since I saw you. But I'm past worrying now, Jim, and for God's sake stop looking so bloody miserable yourself. You can't do anything, I know that. Nobody can do anything.'

Driving home, I brooded on his words. Contagious Bovine Abortion has been recognized for centuries and I had read in old books of the filthy scourge which ravaged and ruined the ancient farmers just as it was doing to Frank Metcalfe today. The experts of those days said it was due to impure water, improper feeding, lack of exercise, sudden frights. They did note, however, that other cows which were allowed to sniff at the foetuses and afterbirth were likely to suffer the same fate themselves. But beyond that it was a black tunnel of ignorance.

We modern vets, on the other hand, knew all about it. We knew it was caused by a Gram negative bacillus called Brucella abortus whose habits and attributes we had studied till we knew its every secret; but when it came to helping a farmer in Frank's situation we were about as much use as our colleagues of old who wrote those quaint books. True, dedicated researchers were working to find a strain of the bacillus which would form a safe and efficient vaccine to immunize cattle in calfhood and as far back as 1930 a certain strain 19 had been developed from which much was hoped. But even now it was still in the experimental stage. If Frank had had the luck to be born twenty years later the chances are that those cows he bought would have all been vaccinated and protected by that same strain 19. Nowadays we even have an efficient dead vaccine for the pregnant cows.

Best of all there is now a scheme under way for the complete eradication of Brucellosis and this has brought the disease to the notice of the general public. People are naturally interested mainly in the public health aspect and they have learned about the vast spectrum of illnesses which the infected milk can cause in humans. But few townsmen know what Brucellosis can do to farmers.

The end of Frank's story was not far away. Autumn was reaching into winter and the frost was sparkling on the steps of Skeldale House when he called one night to see me. We went into the big room and I opened a couple of bottles of beer.

'I thought I'd come and tell you, Jim,' he said in a matter of fact tone. 'I'm having to pack up.'

'Pack up?' Something in me refused to accept what he was saying.

'Aye, I'm going back to me old job in Middlesbrough. There's nowt else to do.'

I looked at him helplessly. 'It's as bad as that, is it?'

'Well just think.' He smiled grimly. 'I have three cows which calved normally out of the whole herd. The rest are a mucky, discharging, sickly lot with no milk worth talking about. I've got no calves to sell or keep as replacements. I've got nowt.'

I hesitated. 'There's no hope of raising the wind to get you over this?'

'No, Jim. If I sell up now I'll just about be able to pay the bank what I owe them. The rest I borrowed from my old man and I'm not goin' back to him for more. I promised him I'd return to the steelworks if this didn't work out and that's what I'm goin' to do.'

'Oh hell, Frank,' I said. 'I can't tell you how sorry I am. You haven't had a scrap of luck all the way through.'

He looked at me and smiled with no trace of self pity. 'Aye well,' he said. 'These things happen.'

I almost jumped at the words. 'These things happen!' That's what farmers always said after a disaster. That old man in Darrowby had been right. Frank really did have it through the titty.

And in truth he wasn't the only man to be bankrupted in this way. What had hit Frank was called an 'abortion storm' and the same sort of thing had driven a legion of good men to the wall. Some of them hung on, tightened their belts, spent their life savings and half starved till the storm abated and they could start again. But Frank had no savings to see him through; his venture had been a gamble from the beginning and he had lost.

I never heard of him again. At first I thought he might write, but then I realized that once the agonizing break had been made it had to be complete.

From some parts of the northern Pennines you can see away over the great sprawl of Teesside and when the fierce glow from the blast furnaces set the night sky alight I used to think of Frank down there and wonder how he was getting on. He'd make a go of it all right, but how often did his mind turn to the high-blown green hollow where he had hoped to build something worth while and to live and bring up his children?

Some people called Peters bought the little farm at Bransett after he left. Strangely enough they were from Teesside, too, but Mr Peters was a wealthy director of the ICI and used the place only as a weekend retreat. It was ideal for the purpose because he had a young family all keen on riding and the fields were soon being grazed by an assortment of horses and ponies. In the summer Mrs Peters used to spend months on end up there with the children. They were nice people who cared for their animals and I was a frequent visitor.

The dwelling house was renovated almost out of recognition and I drank coffee instead of tea in the living-room which had become a place of grace and charm with an antique table, chintz covers and pictures on the walls. The old outbuildings were converted into loose boxes with shining, freshly painted doors.

The only thing which got no attention was Frank's little new byre; it was used as a storage place for corn and bedding for the horses.

I always felt a tug at my heart when I looked in there at the thick dust on the floor, the windows almost opaque with dirt, the cobwebs everywhere, the rusting water bowls, the litter of straw bales, peat moss and sacks of oats where once Frank's cows had stood so proudly.

It was all that was left of a man's dream.

CHAPTER TWENTY-THREE

After the night of the Daffodil Ball I just seemed to drift naturally into the habit of dropping in to see Helen on an occasional evening. And before I knew what was happening I had developed a pattern; around eight o'clock my feet began to make of their own accord for Heston Grange. Of course I fought the impulse – I didn't go every night; there was my work which often occupied me round the clock, there was a feeling of propriety, and there was Mr Alderson.

Helen's father was a vague little man who had withdrawn into himself to a great extent since his wife's death a few years ago. He was an expert stockman and his farm could compare with the best, but a good part of his mind often seemed to be elsewhere. And he had acquired some little peculiarities; when things weren't going well he carried on long muttered conversations with himself but when he was particularly pleased about something he was inclined to break into a loud, tuneless humming. It was a penetrating sound and on my professional visits I could often locate him by tracking down this characteristic droning among the farm buildings.

At first when I came to see Helen I'm sure he never even noticed me – I was just one of the crowd of young men who hung around his daughter; but as time went on and my visits became more frequent he suddenly seemed to become conscious of me and began to regard me with an interest which deepened rapidly into alarm. I couldn't blame him, really. He was devoted to Helen and it was natural that he should desire a grand match for her. Richard Edmundson represented just that. His family were rich, powerful people and Richard was very keen indeed. Compared to him, an unknown, impecunious young vet was a poor bargain.

When Mr Alderson was around, my visits were uncomfortable affairs, and it was a pity because I instinctively liked him. He had an amiable, completely inoffensive nature which was very appealing and under other conditions we would have got along very well. But there was no getting round the fact that he resented me. And it wasn't because he wanted to hang on to Helen – he was an unselfish man and anyway, he had an excellent housekeeper in his sister who had been recently widowed and had come to live with the Aldersons. Auntie Lucy was a redoubtable character and was perfectly capable of running the household and looking after the two younger children. It was just that he had got used to the comfortable assumption that one day his daughter would marry the son of his old friend and have a life of untroubled affluence; and he had a stubborn streak which rebelled fiercely against any prospect of change.

So it was always a relief when I got out of the house with Helen. Everything was right then; we went to the little dances in the village institutes, we walked for miles along the old grassy mine tracks among the hills, or sometimes she came on my evening calls with me. There wasn't anything spectacular to do in Darrowby but there was a complete lack of strain, a feeling of being self-sufficient in a warm existence of our own that made everything meaningful and worthwhile.

Things might have gone on like this indefinitely but for a conversation I had with Siegfried. We were sitting in the big room at Skeldale House as we often did before bedtime, talking over the day's events when he laughed and slapped his knee.

'I had old Harry Forster in tonight paying his bill. He was really funny – sat looking round the room and saying "It's a nice little nest you have here, Mr Farnon, a nice little nest," and then, very sly "It's time there was a bird in this nest, you know, there should be a little bird in here." '

I laughed too. 'Well, you should be used to it by now. You're the most eligible bachelor in Darrowby. People are always having a dig at you – they won't be happy till they've got you married off.'

'Wait a minute, not so fast.' Siegfried eyed me thoughtfully. 'I don't think for a moment that Harry was talking about me, it was you he had in mind.'

'What do you mean?'

'Well just think. Didn't you say you had run into the old boy one night when you were walking over his land with Helen. He'd be on to a thing like that in a flash. He thinks it's time you were hitched up, that's all.'

I lay back in my chair and gave myself over to laughter. 'Me! Married! That'll be the day. Can you imagine it? Poor old Harry.'

Siegfried leaned forward. 'What are you laughing at, James? He's quite right – it's time you were married.'

'What's that?' I looked at him incredulously. 'What are you on about now?'

'It's quite simple,' he said. 'I'm saying you ought to get married, and soon.'

'Oh come on Siegfried, you're joking!'

'Why should I be?'

'Well damn it, I'm only starting my career, I've no money, no nothing, I've never even thought about it.'

'You've never even ... well tell me this, are you courting Helen Alderson or aren't you?'

'Well I'm ... I've been ... oh I suppose you could call it that.'

Siegfried settled back comfortably on his chair, put his finger tips together and assumed a judicial expression. 'Good, good. You admit you're courting the girl. Now let us take it a step further. She is, from my own observation, extremely attractive – in fact she nearly causes a traffic pile-up when she walks across the cobbles on market day. It's common knowledge that she is intelligent, equable and an excellent cook. Perhaps you would agree with this?'

'Of course I would,' I said, nettled at his superior air. 'But what's this all about? Why are you going on like a High Court judge?'

'I'm only trying to establish my point, James, which is that you seem to have an ideal wife lined up and you are doing nothing about it. In fact, not to put a too fine point on it, I wish you'd stop playing around and let us see a little action.'

'But it's not as simple as that,' I said, my voice rising, 'I've told you already I'd have to be a lot better off, and anyway, give me a chance, I've only been going to the house for a few weeks – surely you don't start thinking of getting married as soon as that. And there's another thing – her old man doesn't like me.'

Siegfried put his head on one side and I gritted my teeth as a saintly expression began to settle on his face. 'Now my dear chap, don't get angry, but there's something I have to tell you for your own good. Caution is often a virtue, but in your case you carry it too far. It's a little flaw in your character and it shows in a multitude of ways. In your wary approach to problems in your work, for instance – you are always too apprehensive, proceeding fearfully step by step when you should be plunging boldly ahead. You keep seeing dangers when there aren't any – you've got to learn to take a chance, to lash out a bit. As it is, you are confined to a narrow range of activity by your own doubts.'

'The original stick-in-the-mud in fact, eh?'

'Oh come now, James, I didn't say that, but while we're talking, there's another small point I want to bring up. I know you won't mind my saying this. Until you get married I'm afraid I shall fail to get the full benefit of your assistance in the practice because frankly you are becoming increasingly besotted and bemused to the extent that I'm sure you don't know what you're doing half the time.'

'What the devil are you talking about? I've never heard such . . .'

'Kindly hear me out, James. What I'm saying is perfectly true – you're walking about like a man in a dream and you've developed a disturbing habit of staring into space when I'm talking to you. There's only one cure, my boy.'

'And it's a simple little cure, isn't it!' I shouted. 'No money, no home, but leap into matrimony with a happy cry. There's not a thing to worry about!'

'Ah-ah, you see, there you go again, looking for

difficulties.' He gave a little laugh and gazed at me with pitying affection. 'No money you say. Well one of these days you'll be a partner here. Your plate will be out on those railings in front of the house, so you'll never be short of your daily bread. And as regards a home – look at all the empty rooms in this house. You could set up a private suite upstairs without any trouble. So that's just a piffling little detail.'

I ran my hand distractedly through my hair. My head was beginning to swim. 'You make it all sound easy.'

'But it IS easy!' Siegfried shot upright in his chair. 'Go out and ask that girl without further delay and get her into church before the month is out!' He wagged a finger at me. 'Learn to grasp the nettle of life, James. Throw off your hesitant ways and remember:' He clenched his fist and struck an attitude. 'There is a tide in the affairs of men which, taken at the flood . . .'

'OK, OK,' I said, rising wearily from my chair, 'That's enough, I get the message. I'm going to bed now.'

And I don't suppose I am the first person to have had his life fundamentally influenced by one of Siegfried's chance outbursts. I thought his opinions ridiculous at the time but he planted a seed which germinated and flowered almost overnight. There is no doubt he is responsible for the fact that I was the father of a grown-up family while I was still a young man, because when I brought the subject up with Helen she said yes she'd like to marry me and we set our eyes on an early date. She seemed surprised at first – maybe she had the same opinion of me as Siegfried and expected it would take me a few years to get off the ground.

Anyway, before I had time to think much more about it everything was neatly settled and I found I had made a magical transition from jeering at the whole idea to making plans for furnishing our prospective bedsitter at Skeldale House.

It was a blissful time with only one cloud on the horizon; but that cloud bulked large and forbidding. As I walked hand in hand with Helen, my thoughts in the air, she kept bringing me back to earth with an appealing look.

'You know, Jim, you'll really have to speak to Dad. It's time he knew.'

CHAPTER TWENTY-FOUR

I had been warned long before I qualified that country practice was a dirty, stinking job. I had accepted the fact and adjusted myself to it but there were times when this side of my life obtruded itself and became almost insupportable. Like now, when even after a long hot bath I still smelt.

As I hoisted myself from the steaming water I sniffed at my arm and there it was; the malodorous memory of that horrible cleansing at Tommy Dearlove's striking triumphantly through all the soap and antiseptic almost as fresh and pungent as it had been at four o'clock this afternoon. Nothing but time would move it.

But something in me rebelled at the idea of crawling into bed in this state and I looked with something like desperation along the row of bottles on the bathroom shelf. I stopped at Mrs Hall's bath salts, shining violent pink in their big glass jar. This was something I'd never tried before and I tipped a small handful into the water round my feet. For a moment my head swam as the rising steam was suddenly charged with an aggressive sweetness then on an impulse I shook most of the jar's contents into the bath and lowered myself once more under the surface.

For a long time I lay there smiling to myself in triumph as the oily liquid lapped around me. Not even Tommy Dearlove's cleansing could survive this treatment.

The whole process had a stupefying effect on me and I was half asleep even as I sank back on the pillow. There followed a few moments of blissful floating before a delicious slumber claimed me. And when the bedside phone boomed in my ear the sense of injustice and personal affront was even stronger than usual. Blinking sleepily at the clock which said 1.15 AM I lifted the receiver and mumbled into it, but I was jerked suddenly wide awake when I recognized Mr Alderson's voice. Candy was calving and something was wrong. Would I come right away.

There has always been a 'this is where I came in' feeling about a night call. And as my lights swept the cobbles of the deserted market place it was there again; a sense of returning to fundamentals, of really being me. The silent houses, the tight drawn curtains, the long, empty street giving way to the stone walls of the country road flipping endlessly past on either side. At these times I was usually in a state of suspended animation, just sufficiently awake to steer the car in the right direction, but tonight I was fully alert, my mind ticking over anxiously.

Because Candy was something special. She was the house cow, a pretty little Jersey and Mr Alderson's particular pet. She was the sole member of her breed in the herd but whereas the milk from the Shorthorns went into the churns to be collected by the big dairy, Candy's rich yellow offering found its way on to the family porridge every morning or appeared heaped up on trifles and fruit pies or was made into butter, a golden creamy butter to make you dream.

But apart from all that, Mr Alderson just liked the animal. He usually stopped opposite her on his way down the byre and began to hum to himself and gave her tail head a brief scratch as he passed. And I couldn't blame him because I sometimes wish all cows were Jerseys; small, gentle, doe-eyed creatures you could push around without any trouble; with padded corners and fragile limbs. Even if they kicked you it was like a love tap compared with the clump from a craggy Friesian.

I just hoped it would be something simple with Candy, because my stock wasn't high with Mr Alderson and I had a nervous conviction that he wouldn't react favourably if I started to make a ham-fisted job of calving his little favourite. I shrugged away my fears; obstetrics in the Jersey were usually easy.

Helen's father was an efficient farmer. As I pulled up in the yard I could see into the lighted loose box where two buckets of water were steaming in readiness for me. A towel was draped over the half door and Stan and Bert, the two long-serving cowmen, were standing alongside their boss. Candy was lying comfortably in deep straw. She wasn't straining and there was nothing visible at the vulva but the cow had a preoccupied, inward look as though all was not well with her.

I closed the door behind me. 'Have you had a feel inside her, Mr Alderson?'

'Aye, I've had me hand in and there's nowt there.'

'Nothing at all?'

'Not a thing. She'd been on for a few hours and not showing so I popped me hand in and there's no head, no legs, nowt. And not much room, either. That's when I rang you.'

This sounded very strange. I hung my jacket on a nail and began thoughtfully to unbutton my shirt. It was when I was pulling it over my head that I noticed Mr Alderson's nose wrinkling. The farm men, too, began to sniff and look at each other wonderingly. Mrs Hall's bath salts, imprisoned under my clothing had burst from their bondage in a sickly wave, filling the enclosed space with their strident message. Hurriedly I began to wash my arms in the hope that the alien odour might pass away but it seemed to get worse, welling from my warm skin, competing incongruously with the honest smells of cow, hay and straw. Nobody said anything. These men weren't the type to make the ribald remark which would have enabled me to laugh the thing off. There was no ambiguity about this scent; it was voluptuously feminine and Bert and Stan stared at me open-mouthed. Mr Alderson, his mouth turned down at the corners, his nostrils still twitching, kept his eyes fixed on the far wall.

Cringing inwardly I knelt behind the cow and in a moment my embarrassment was forgotten. The vagina was empty; a smooth passage narrowing rapidly to a small, ridged opening just wide enough to admit my hand. Beyond

I could feel the feet and head of a calf. My spirits plummeted. Torsion of the uterus. There was going to be no easy victory for me here.

I sat back on my heels and turned to the farmers. 'She's got a twisted calf bed. There's a live calf in there all right but there's no way out for it – I can barely get my hand through.'

'Aye, I thought it was something peculiar.' Mr Alderson rubbed his chin and looked at me doubtfully. 'What can we do about it, then?'

'We'll have to try to correct the twist by rolling the cow over while I keep hold of the calf. It's a good job there's plenty of us here.'

'And that'll put everything right, will it?'

I swallowed. I didn't like these jobs. Sometimes rolling worked and sometimes it didn't and in those days we hadn't quite got round to performing caesareans on cows. If I was unsuccessful I had the prospect of telling Mr Alderson to send Candy to the butcher. I banished the thought quickly.

'It'll put everything right,' I said. It had to. I stationed Bert at the front legs, Stan at the hind and the farmer holding the cow's head on the floor. Then I stretched myself on the hard concrete, pushed in a hand and grasped the calf's foot.

'Now roll her,' I gasped, and the men pulled the legs round in a clockwise direction. I held fiercely to the little feet as the cow flopped on to her other side. Nothing seemed to be happening inside.

'Push her on to her chest,' I panted.

Stan and Bert expertly tucked the legs under the cow and rolled her on to her brisket and as she settled there I gave a yell of pain.

'Get her back, quick! We're going the wrong way!' The smooth band of tissue had tightened on my wrist in a numbing grip of frightening power. For a moment I had the panicky impression that I'd never get out of there again.

But the men worked like lightning. Within seconds Candy

was stretched out on her original side, the pressure was off my arm and we were back where we started.

I gritted my teeth and took a fresh grip on the calf's foot. 'OK, try her the other way.'

This time the roll was anti-clockwise and we went through 180 degrees without anything happening. I only just kept my grasp on the foot – the resistance this time was tremendous. Taking a breather for a few seconds I lay face down while the sweat sprang out on my back, sending out fresh exotic vapours from the bath salts.

'Right. One more go!' I cried and the men hauled the cow further over.

And oh it was beautiful to feel everything magically unravelling and my arm lying free in a wide uterus with all the room in the world and the calf already beginning to slide towards me.

Candy summed up the situation immediately and for the first time gave a determined heaving strain. Sensing victory just round the corner she followed up with another prolonged effort which popped the calf wet and wriggling into my arms.

'By gum, it was quick at t'finish,' Mr Alderson murmured wonderingly. He seized a wisp of hay and began to dry off the little creature.

Thankfully I soaped my arms in one of the buckets. After every delivery there is a feeling of relief but in this case it was overwhelming. It no longer mattered that the loose box smelt like a ladies' hairdressing salon, I just felt good. I said goodnight to Bert and Stan as they returned to their beds, giving a final incredulous sniff as they passed me. Mr Alderson was pottering about, having a word with Candy then starting again on the calf which he had already rubbed down several times. He seemed fascinated by it. And I couldn't blame him because it was like something out of Disney; a pale gold fawn, unbelievably tiny with large dark limpid eyes and an expression of trusting innocence. It was a heifer, too.

The farmer lifted it as if it were a whippet dog and laid it by the mother's head. Candy nosed the little animal over, rumbling happily in her throat, then she began to lick it. I watched Mr Alderson. He was standing, hands clasped behind him, rocking backwards and forwards on his heels, obviously enchanted by the scene. Any time now, I thought. And I was right; the tuneless humming broke out, even louder than usual, like a joyful paean.

I stiffened in my wellingtons. There would never be a better time. After a nervous cough I spoke up firmly.

'Mr Alderson,' I said and he half turned his head. 'I would like to marry your daughter.'

The humming was switched off abruptly and he turned slowly till he was facing me. He didn't speak but his eyes searched my face unhappily. Then he bent stiffly, picked up the buckets one by one, tipped out the water and made for the door.

'You'd better come in the house,' he said.

The farmhouse kitchen looked lost and forsaken with the family abed. I sat in a high backed wooden chair by the side of the empty hearth while Mr Alderson put away his buckets, hung up the towel and washed his hands methodically at the sink, then he pottered through to the parlour and I heard him bumping and clinking about in the sideboard. When he reappeared he bore a tray in front of him on which a bottle of whisky and two glasses rattled gently. The tray lent the simple procedure an air of formality which was accentuated by the heavy cut crystal of the glasses and the virgin, unopened state of the bottle.

Mr Alderson set the tray down on the kitchen table which he dragged nearer to us before settling in the chair at the other side of the fireplace. Nobody said anything. I waited in the lengthening silence while he peered at the cap of the bottle like a man who had never seen one before then unscrewed it with slow apprehension as though he feared it might blow up in his face.

Finally he poured out two measures with the utmost gravity and precision, ducking his head frequently to compare the levels in the two glasses, and with a last touch of ceremony proffered the laden tray.

I took my drink and waited expectantly.

Mr Alderson looked into the lifeless fireplace for a minute or two then he directed his gaze upwards at the oil painting of the paddling cows which hung above the mantelpiece. He pursed his lips as though about to whistle but appeared to change his mind and without salutation took a gulp of his whisky which sent him into a paroxysm of coughing from which it took him some time to recover. When his breathing had returned to normal he sat up straight and fixed me with streaming eyes. He cleared his throat and I felt a certain tension.

'Aye well,' he said, 'it's grand hay weather.'

I agreed with him and he looked round the kitchen with the interested stare of a total stranger. Having completed his inspection he took another copious swallow from his glass, grimaced, closed his eyes, shook his head violently a few times, then leaned forward.

'Mind you,' he said, 'a night's rain would do a lot o' good.'

I gave my opinion that it undoubtedly would and the silence fell again. It lasted even longer this time and my host kept drinking his whisky as though he was getting used to it. And I could see that it was having a relaxing effect; the strained lines on his face were beginning to smooth out and his eyes were losing their hunted look.

Nothing more was said until he had replenished our glasses, balancing the amounts meticulously again. He took a sip at his second measure then he looked down at the rug and spoke in a small voice.

'James,' he said, 'I had a wife in a thousand.'

I was so surprised I hardly knew what to say. 'Yes, I know,' I murmured. 'I've heard a lot about her.'

Mr Alderson went on, still looking down, his voice full of gentle yearning.

'Yes, she was the grandest lass for miles around and the bonniest.' He looked up at me suddenly with the ghost of a smile. 'Nobody thought she'd ever have a feller like me, you know. But she did.' He paused and looked away. 'Aye, she did.'

He began to tell me about his dead wife. He told me

calmly, without self pity, but with a wistful gratitude for the happiness he had known. And I discovered that Mr Alderson was different from a lot of the farmers of his generation because he said nothing about her being a 'good worker'. So many of the women of those times seemed to be judged mainly on their working ability and when I had first come to Darrowby I had been shocked when I commiserated with a newly widowed old man. He had brushed a tear from his eye and said, 'Aye, she was a grand worker.'

But Mr Alderson said only that his wife had been beautiful, that she had been kind, and that he had loved her very much. He talked about Helen, too, about the things she had said and done when she was a little girl, about how very like her mother she was in every way. He never said anything about me but I had the feeling all the time that he meant it to concern me; and the very fact that he was talking so freely seemed a sign that the barriers were coming down.

Actually he was talking a little too freely. He was halfway down his third huge whisky and in my experience Yorkshiremen just couldn't take the stuff. I had seen burly ten pint men from the local pub keel over after a mere sniff at the amber fluid and little Mr Alderson hardly drank at all. I was getting worried.

But there was nothing I could do, so I let him ramble on happily. He was lying right back in his chair now, completely at ease, his eyes, alight with his memories, gazing somewhere above my head. In fact I am convinced he had forgotten I was there because after one long passage he dropped his eyes, caught sight of me and stared for a moment without recognition. When he did manage to place me it seemed to remind him of his duties as a host. But as he reached again for the bottles he caught sight of the clock on the wall.

'Well dang it, it's four o'clock. We've been here long enough. It's hardly worth goin' to bed, but I suppose we'd better have an hour or two's sleep.' He tipped the last of the whisky down his throat, jumped briskly to his feet, looked around him for a few moments in a business-like sort of way then pitched head first with a sickening clatter among the fire irons.

Frozen with horror, I started forward to help the small figure scrabbling on the hearth but I needn't have worried because he bounced back to his feet in a second or two and looked me in the eye as if nothing had happened.

'Well, I'd better be off,' I said. 'Thanks for the drink.' There was no point in staying longer as I realized that the chances of Mr Alderson saying 'Bless you, my son' or anything like that were remote. But I had a comforting impression that all was going to be well.

As I made my way to the door the farmer made a creditable attempt to usher me out but his direction was faulty and he tacked helplessly away from me across the kitchen floor before collapsing against a tall dresser. From under a row of willow pattern dinner plates his face looked at me with simple bewilderment.

I hesitated then turned back. 'I'll just walk up the stairs with you, Mr Alderson,' I said in a matter of fact voice and the little man made no resistance as I took his arm and guided him towards the door in the far corner.

As we creaked our way upstairs he stumbled and would have gone down again had I not grabbed him round the waist. As I caught him he looked up at me and grunted 'Thanks, lad,' and we grinned at each other for a moment before restarting the climb.

I supported him across the landing to his bedroom door and he stood hesitating as though about to say something. But finally he just nodded to me a couple of times before ducking inside.

I waited outside the door, listening in some anxiety to the bumps and thumps from within; but I relaxed as a loud, tuneless humming came through the panels. Everything most certainly was going to be all right.

CHAPTER TWENTY-FIVE

'Well, do you want t'job or don't you?'

Walt Barnett towered over me in the surgery doorway and his eyes flickered from my head to my feet and up again without expression. The cigarette dangling from his lower lip seemed to be a part of him as did the brown trilby hat and the shining navy blue serge suit stretched tightly over his bulky form. He must have weighed nearly twenty stone and with his red beefy brutal mouth and overbearing manner he was undeniably formidable.

'Well, er . . . yes. Of course we want the job,' I replied. 'I was just wondering when we could fit it in.' I went over to the desk and began to look through the appointment book. 'We're pretty full this week and I don't know what Mr Farnon has fixed for the week after. Maybe we'd better give you a ring.'

The big man had burst in on me without warning or greeting and barked, 'I 'ave a fine big blood 'oss to geld. When can you do 'im?'

I had looked at him hesitantly for a few moments, taken aback partly by the arrogance of his approach, partly by his request. This wasn't good news to me; I didn't like castrating fine big blood 'osses – I much preferred the ordinary cart colts and if you came right down to it I had a particular preference for Shetland ponies. But it was all part of living and if it had to be done it had to be done.

'You can give me a ring if you like, but don't be ower long about it.' The hard unsmiling stare still held me. 'And I want a good job doin', think on!'

'We always try to do a good job, Mr Barnett,' I said, fighting a rising prickle of resentment at his attitude.

'Aye well I've heard that afore and I've had some bloody

balls-ups,' he said. He gave me a final truculent nod, turned and walked out, leaving the door open.

I was still standing in the middle of the room seething and muttering to myself when Siegfried walked in. I hardly saw him at first and when he finally came into focus I found I was glowering into his face.

'What's the trouble, James?' he asked. 'A little touch of indigestion, perhaps?'

'Indigestion? No ... no ... Why do you say that?'

'Well you seemed to be in some sort of pain, standing there on one leg with your face screwed up.'

'Did I look like that? Oh it was just our old friend Walt Barnett. He wants us to cut a horse for him and he made the request in his usual charming way – he really gets under my skin, that man.'

Tristan came in from the passage. 'Yes, I was out there and I heard him. He's a bloody big lout.'

Siegfried rounded on him. 'That's enough! I don't want to hear that kind of talk in here.' Then he turned back to me. 'And really, James, even if you were upset I don't think it's an excuse for profanity.'

'What do you mean?'

'Well, some of the expletives I heard you muttering there were unworthy of you.' He spread his hands in a gesture of disarming frankness. 'Heaven knows I'm no prude but I don't like to hear such language within these walls.' He paused and his features assumed an expression of deep gravity. 'After all, the people who come in here provide us with our bread and butter and they should be referred to with respect.'

'Yes, but ...'

'Oh I know some are not as nice as others but you must never let them irritate you. You've heard the old saying, "The customer is always right." Well I think it's a good working axiom and I always abide by it myself.' He gazed solemnly at Tristan and me in turn. 'So I hope I make myself clear. No swearing in the surgery – particularly when it concerns the clients.'

'It's all right for you!' I burst out heatedly. 'But you didn't hear Barnett. I'll stand so much, but . . .'

Siegfried put his head on one side and a smile of ethereal beauty crept over his face. 'My dear old chap, there you go again, letting little things disturb you. I've had to speak to you about this before, haven't I? I wish I could help you, I wish I could pass on my own gift of remaining calm at all times.'

'What's that you said?'

'I said I wanted to help you, James, and I will.' He held up a forefinger. 'You've probably often wondered why I never get angry or excited.'

'Eh?'

'Oh I know you have – you must have. Well I'll let you into a little secret.' His smile took on a roguish quality. 'If a client is rude to me I simply charge him a little more. Instead of getting all steamed up like you do I tell myself that I'm putting ten bob extra on the bill and it works like magic.'

'Is that so?'

'Yes indeed, my boy.' He thumped my shoulder then became very serious. 'Of course I realize that I have an advantage right at the start – I have been blessed with a naturally even temperament while you are blown about in all directions by every little wind of circumstance. But I do think that this is something you could cultivate, so work at it, James, work at it. All this fretting and fuming is bad for you – your whole life would change if you could just acquire my own tranquil outlook.'

I swallowed hard. 'Well thank you, Siegfried,' I said. 'I'll try.'

Walt Barnett was a bit of a mystery man in Darrowby. He wasn't a farmer, he was a scrap merchant, a haulier, a dealer in everything from linoleum to second hand cars, and there was only one thing the local people could say for certain about him – he had brass, lots of brass. They said everything he touched turned to money.

He had bought a decaying mansion a few miles outside the town where he lived with a downtrodden little wife and where he kept a floating population of livestock; a few bullocks, some pigs and always a horse or two. He employed all the vets in the district in turn, probably because he didn't think much of any of us; a feeling which, I may say, was mutual. He never seemed to do any physical work and could be seen most days of the week shambling around the streets of Darrowby, hands in pockets, cigarette dangling, his brown trilby on the back of his head, his huge body threatening to burst through that shiny navy suit.

After my meeting with him we had a busy few days and it was on the following Thursday that the phone rang in the surgery. Siegfried lifted it and immediately his expression changed. From across the floor I could clearly hear the loud hectoring tones coming through the receiver and as my colleague listened a slow flush spread over his cheeks and his mouth hardened. Several times he tried to put in a word but the torrent of sound from the far end was unceasing. Finally he raised his voice and broke in but instantly there was a click and he found himself speaking to a dead line.

Siegfried crashed the receiver into its rest and swung round. 'That was Barnett – playing hell because we haven't rung him.' He stood staring at me for a few moments, his face dark with anger.

'The bloody bastard!' he shouted. 'Who the hell does he think he is? Abusing me like that, then hanging up on me when I try to speak!'

For a moment he was silent then he turned to me. 'I'll tell you this, James, he wouldn't have spoken to me like that if he'd been in this room with me.' He came over to me and held out his hands, fingers crooked menacingly. 'I'd have wrung his bloody neck, big as he is! I would have, I tell you, I'd have strangled the bugger!'

'But Siegfried,' I said. 'What about your system?'

'System? What system?'

'Well, you know the trick you have when people are unpleasant – you put something on the bill, don't you?'

Siegfried let his hands fall to his sides and stared at me for some time, his chest rising and falling with his emotion. Then he patted me on the shoulder and turned away towards the window where he stood looking out at the quiet street.

When he turned back to me he looked grim but calmer. 'By God, James, you're right. That's the answer. I'll cut Barnett's horse for him but I'll charge him a tenner.'

I laughed heartily. In those days the average charge for castrating a horse was a pound, or if you wanted to be more professional, a guinea.

'What are you laughing at?' my employer inquired sourly.

'Well ... at your joke. I mean, ten pounds ... ha-ha-ha!'

'I'm not joking, I'm going to charge him a tenner.'

'Oh come on, Siegfried, you can't do that.'

'You just watch me,' he said. 'I'm going to sort that bugger.'

Two mornings later I was going through the familiar motions of preparing for a castration; boiling up the emasculator and laying it on the enamel tray along with the scalpel, the roll of cotton wool, the artery forceps, the tincture of iodine, the suture materials, the tetanus antitoxin and syringes. For the last five minutes Siegfried had been shouting at me to hurry.

'What the hell are you doing through there, James? Don't forget to put in an extra bottle of chloroform. And bring the sidelines in case he doesn't go down. Where have you hidden those spare scalpel blades, James?'

The sunshine streamed across the laden tray, filtering through the green tangle of the wisteria which fell untidily across the surgery window. Reminding me that it was May and that there was nowhere a May morning came with such golden magic as to the long garden at Skeldale House; the high brick walls with their crumbling mortar and ancient stone copings enfolding the sunlight in a warm clasp and spilling it over the untrimmed lawns, the banks of lupins and bluebells, the masses of fruit blossom. And right at the top the rooks cawing in the highest branches of the elms.

Siegfried, chloroform muzzle looped over one shoulder, made a final check of the items on the tray then we set off. In less than half an hour we were driving through the lodge gates of the old mansion then along a mossy avenue which wandered among pine and birch trees up to the house which looked out from its wooded background over the rolling miles of fell and moor.

Nobody could have asked for a more perfect place for the operation; a high-walled paddock deep in lush grass. The two-year-old, a magnificent chestnut, was led in by two characters who struck me as typical henchmen for Mr Barnett. I don't know where he had dug them up but you didn't see faces like that among the citizens of Darrowby. One was a brown goblin who, as he conversed with his companion, repeatedly jerked his head and winked one eye as though they were sharing some disreputable secret. The other had a head covered with ginger stubble surmounting a countenance of a bright scrofulous red which looked as though a piece would fall off if you touched it; and deep in the livid flesh two tiny eyes darted.

The two of them regarded us unsmilingly and the dark one spat luxuriously as we approached.

'It's a nice morning,' I said.

Ginger just stared at me while Winker nodded knowingly and closed one eye as if I had uttered some craftiness which appealed to him.

The vast hunched figure of Mr Barnett hovered in the background, cigarette drooping, the bright sunshine striking brilliant shafts of light from the tight sheen of the navy suit.

I couldn't help comparing the aspect of the trio of humans with the natural beauty and dignity of the horse. The big chestnut tossed his head then stood looking calmly across the paddock, the large fine eyes alight with intelligence, the noble lines of the face and neck blending gently into the grace and power of the body. Observations I had heard about the higher and lower animals floated about in my mind.

Siegfried walked around the horse, patting him and talking to him, his eyes shining with the delight of the fanatic.

'He's a grand sort, Mr Barnett,' he said.

The big man glowered at him. 'Aye well, don't spoil 'im, that's all. I've paid a lot o' money for that 'oss.'

Siegfried gave him a thoughtful look then turned to me.

'Well, let's get on. We'll drop him over there on that long grass. Are you ready, James?'

I was ready, but I'd be a lot more at ease if Siegfried would just leave me alone. In horse work I was the anaesthetist and my colleague was the surgeon. And he was good; quick, deft, successful. I had no quarrel with the arrangement; he could get on with his job and let me do mine. But there was the rub; he would keep butting into my territory and I found it wearing.

Anaesthesia in the large animals has a dual purpose; it abolishes pain and acts as a means of restraint. It is obvious that you can't do much with these potentially dangerous creatures unless they are controlled.

That was my job. I had to produce a sleeping patient ready for the knife and very often I thought it was the most difficult part. Until the animal was properly under I always felt a certain tension and Siegfried didn't help in this respect. He would hover at my elbow, offering advice as to the quantity of chloroform and he could never bear to wait until the anaesthetic had taken effect. He invariably said, 'He isn't going to go down, James.' Then, 'Don't you think you should strap a foreleg up?'

Even now, thirty years later, when I am using such intravenous drugs as thiopentone he is still at it. Stamping around impatiently as I fill my syringe, poking over my shoulder with a long forefinger into the jugular furrow. 'I'd shove it in just there, James.'

I stood there irresolute, my employer by my side, the chloroform bottle in my pocket, the muzzle dangling from my hand. It would be wonderful, I thought, if just once I could be on my own to get on with it. And, after all, I had worked for him for nearly three years – surely I knew him well enough to be able to put it to him.

I cleared my throat. 'Siegfried, I was just wondering. Would you care to go and sit down over there for a few minutes till I get him down?'

'What's that?'

'Well I thought it would be a good idea if you left me to it. There's a bit of a crowd round the horse's head – I don't want him excited. So why don't you relax for a while. I'll give you a shout when he's down.'

Siegfried raised a hand. 'My dear chap, anything you say. I don't know what I'm hanging around here for anyway. I never interfere with your end as you well know.' He turned about and, tray under arm, marched off to where he had parked his car on the grass about fifty yards away. He strode round behind the Rover and sat down on the turf, his back against the metal. He was out of sight.

Peace descended. I became suddenly aware of the soft warmth of the sun on my forehead, of the bird song echoing among the nearby trees. Unhurriedly I fastened on the muzzle under the head collar and produced my little glass measure.

This once I had plenty of time. I'd start him off with just a couple of drachms to get him used to the smell of it without frightening him. I poured the clear fluid on to the sponge.

'Walk him slowly round in a circle,' I said to Ginger and Winker. 'I'm going to give him a little bit at a time, there's no hurry. But keep a good hold of that halter shank in case he plays up.'

There was no need for my warning. The two-year-old paced round calmly and fearlessly and every minute or so I trickled a little extra on to the sponge. After a while his steps became laboured and he began to sway drunkenly as he walked. I watched him happily; this was the way I liked to do it. Another little dollop would just about do the trick. I measured out another half ounce and walked over to the big animal.

His head nodded sleepily as I gave it to him. 'You're just about ready aren't you, old lad,' I was murmuring when the peace was suddenly shattered.

'He isn't going to go down, you know, James!' It was a booming roar from the direction of the car and as I whipped round in consternation I saw a head just showing over the bonnet. There was another cry.

'Why don't you strap up a . . .?'

At that moment the horse lurched and collapsed quietly on the grass and Siegfried came bounding knife in hand from his hiding place like a greyhound.

'Sit on his head!' he yelled. 'What are you waiting for, he'll be up in a minute! And get that rope round that hind leg! And bring my tray! And fetch the hot water!' He panted up to the horse then turned and bawled into Ginger's face, 'Come on, I'm talking to you. MOVE!'

Ginger went off at a bow-legged gallop and cannoned into Winker who was rushing forward with the bucket. Then they had a brief but frenzied tug of war with the rope before they got it round the pastern.

'Pull the leg forward,' cried my employer, bending over the operation site, then a full blooded bellow, 'Get the bloody foot out of my eye, will you! What's the matter with you, you wouldn't pull a hen off its nest the way you're going.'

I knelt quietly at the head, my knee on the neck. There was no need to hold him down; he was beautifully out, his eyes blissfully closed as Siegfried worked with his usual lightning expertise. There was a mere few seconds of silence broken only by the tinkling of instruments as they fell back on the tray, then my colleague glanced along the horse's back. 'Open the muzzle, James.'

The operation was over.

I don't think I've ever seen an easier job. By the time we had washed our instruments in the bucket the two-year-old was on his feet, cropping gently at the grass.

'Splendid anaesthetic, James,' said Siegfried, drying off the emasculator. 'Just right. And what a grand sort of horse.'

We had put our gear back in the boot and were ready to leave when Walt Barnett heaved his massive bulk over towards us. He faced Siegfried across the bonnet of the car.

'Well that were nowt of a job,' he grunted, slapping a cheque book down on the shining metal, 'How much do you want?'

There was an arrogant challenge in the words and, faced with the dynamic force, the sheer brutal presence of the man, most people who were about to charge a guinea would have changed their minds and said a pound.

'Well, I'm askin' yer,' he repeated. 'How much do you want?'

'Ah yes,' said Siegfried lightly. 'That'll be a tenner.'

The big man put a meaty hand on the cheque book and stared at my colleague. 'What?'

'That'll be a tenner,' Siegfried said again.

'Ten pounds?' Mr Barnett's eyes opened wider.

'Yes,' said Siegfried, smiling pleasantly. 'That's right. Ten pounds.'

There was a silence as the two men faced each other across the bonnet. The bird song and the noises from the wood seemed abnormally loud as the seconds ticked away and nobody moved. Mr Barnett was glaring furiously and I looked from the huge fleshy face which seemed to have swollen even larger across to the lean, strong-jawed, high-cheekboned profile of my employer. Siegfried still wore the remains of a lazy smile but down in the grey depths of his eye a dangerous light glinted.

Just when I was at screaming point the big man dropped his head suddenly and began to write. When he handed the cheque over he was shaking so much that the slip of paper fluttered as though in a high wind.

'Here y'are, then,' he said hoarsely.

'Thank you so much.' Siegfried read the cheque briefly then stuffed it carelessly into a side pocket. 'Isn't it grand to have some real May weather, Mr Barnett. Does us all good. I'm sure.'

Walt Barnett mumbled something and turned away. As I got into the car I could see the great expanse of navy blue back moving ponderously towards the house.

'He won't have us back, anyway,' I said.

Siegfried started the engine and we moved away. 'No, James, I should think he'd get his twelve bore out if we ventured down this drive again. But that suits me – I think I can manage to get through the rest of my life without Mr Barnett.'

Our road took us through the little village of Baldon and Siegfried slowed down outside the pub, a yellow-washed building standing a few yards back from the road with a wooden sign reading The Cross Keys and a large black dog sleeping on the sunny front step.

My boss looked at his watch. 'Twelve fifteen – they'll just have opened. A cool beer would be rather nice wouldn't it. I don't think I've been in this place before.'

After the brightness outside, the shaded interior was restful, with only stray splinters of sunshine filtering through the curtains on to the flagged floor, the fissured oak tables, the big fireplace with its high settle.

'Good morning to you, landlord,' boomed my employer, striding over to the bar. He was in his most ducal mood and I felt it was a pity he didn't have a silver-knobbed stick to rap on the counter.

The man behind the counter smiled and knuckled a forelock in the approved manner. 'Good morning to you, sir, and what can I get for you gentlemen?'

I half expected Siegfried to say, 'Two stoups of your choicest brew, honest fellow,' but instead he just turned to me and murmured 'I think two halves of bitter, eh James?'

The man began to draw the beer.

'Won't you join us?' Siegfried inquired.

'Thank ye sir, I'll 'ave a brown ale with you.'

'And possibly your good lady, too?' Siegfried smiled over at the landlord's wife who was stacking glasses at the end of the counter.

'That's very kind of you, I will.' She looked up, gulped, and an expression of wonder crept over her face. Siegfried hadn't stared at her – it had only been a five second burst from the grey eyes – but the bottle rattled against the glass as she poured her small port and she spent the rest of the time gazing at him dreamily.

'That'll be five and sixpence,' the landlord said.

'Right.' My employer plunged a hand into his bulging side pocket and crashed down on the counter an extraordinary mixture of crumpled bank notes, coins, veterinary instruments, thermometers, bits of string. He stirred the mass with a forefinger, flicking out a half crown and two florins across the woodwork.

'Wait a minute!' I exclaimed. 'Aren't those my curved scissors? I lost them a few days . . .'

Siegfried swept the pile out of sight into his pocket.

'Nonsense! What makes you think that?'

'Well, they look exactly like mine. Unusual shape – lovely long, flat blades. I've been looking everywhere . . .'

'James!' He drew himself up and faced me with frozen hauteur. 'I think you've said enough. I may be capable of stooping to some pretty low actions but I'd like to believe that certain things are beneath me. And stealing a colleague's curved scissors is one of them.'

I relapsed into silence. I'd have to bide my time and take my chance later. I was fairly sure I'd recognized a pair of my dressing forceps in there too.

In any case, something else was occupying Siegfried's mind. He narrowed his eyes in intense thought then delved into his other pocket and produced a similar collection which he proceeded to push around the counter anxiously.

'What's the matter?' I asked.

'That cheque I've just taken. Did I give it to you?'

'No, you put it in that pocket. I saw you.'

'That's what I thought. Well it's gone.'

'Gone?'

'I've lost the bloody thing!'

I laughed. 'Oh you can't have. Go through your other pockets – it must be on you somewhere.'

Siegfried made a systematic search but it was in vain.

'Well James,' he said at length. 'I really have lost it, but

I've just thought of a simple solution. I will stay here and have one more beer while you slip back to Walt Barnett and ask him for another cheque.'

CHAPTER TWENTY-SIX

Considering we spent our honeymoon tuberculin testing it was a big success. It compared favourably, at any rate, with the experiences of a lot of people I know who celebrated this milestone in their lives by cruising for a month on sunny seas and still wrote it off as a dead loss. For Helen and me it had all the ingredients; laughter, fulfilment and camaraderie, and yet it only lasted a week. And, as I say, we spent it tuberculin testing.

The situation had its origins one morning at the breakfast table when Siegfried, red-eyed after a bad night with a colicky mare, was opening the morning mail. He drew his breath in sharply as a thick roll of forms fell from an official envelope.

'God almighty! Look at all that testing!' He smoothed out the forms on the table cloth and read feverishly down the long list of farm premises. 'And they want us to start this lot around Ellerthorpe next week without fail – it's very urgent.' He glanced at me for a moment. 'That's when you're getting married, isn't it?'

I shifted uncomfortably in my chair. 'Yes, I'm afraid it is.'

Siegfried snatched a piece of toast from the rack and began to slap butter on it. 'Well this is just great isn't it? The practice going mad, a week's testing right at the top of the Dale, away in the back of beyond, and your wedding smack in the middle of it. You'll be drifting gaily off on your honeymoon without a care in the world while I'm rushing around here nearly disappearing up my own backside!' He bit a piece from the toast and began to chew it worriedly.

'I'm sorry, Siegfried,' I said. 'I didn't mean to land you in the cart like this. I couldn't know the practice was going to get so busy right now and I never expected them to throw all this testing at us.'

Siegfried paused in his chewing and pointed a finger at me. 'That's just it, James, that's your trouble – you don't look ahead. You just go belting straight on without a thought. Even when it comes to a bloody wedding you're not worried – oh no, let's get on with it, to hell with the consequences.' He paused to cough up a few crumbs which he had inhaled in his agitation. 'In fact I can't see what all the hurry is – you've got all the time in the world to get married, you're just a boy. And another thing – you hardly know this girl, you've only been seeing her regularly for a few weeks.'

'But wait a minute, you said . . .'

'No, let me finish, James. Marriage is a very serious step, not to be embarked upon without long and serious thought. Why in God's name does it have to be next week? Next year would have been soon enough and you could have enjoyed a nice long engagement. But no, you've got to rush in and tie the knot and it isn't so easily untied you know.'

'Oh hell, Siegfried, this is too bad! You know perfectly well it was you who . . .'

'One moment more. Your precipitate marital arrangements are going to cause me a considerable headache but believe me I wish you well. I hope all turns out for the best despite your complete lack of foresight, but at the same time I must remind you of the old saying: "Marry in haste, repent at leisure." '

I could stand no more. I leaped to my feet, thumped a fist on the table and yelled at him.

'But damn it, it was your idea! I was all for leaving it for a bit but you . . .'

Siegfried wasn't listening. He had been cooling off all the time and now his face broke into a seraphic smile. 'Now, now, now, James, you're getting excited again. Sit down and calm yourself. You mustn't mind my speaking to you like this – you are very young and it's my duty. You haven't done anything wrong at all; I suppose it's the most natural thing in the world for people of your age to act without thinking ahead, to jump into things with never a thought of the morrow. It's just the improvidence of youth.' Siegfried was about six years older than me but he had donned the mantle of the omniscient greybeard without effort.

I dug my fingers into my knees and decided not to pursue the matter. I had no chance anyway, and besides, I was beginning to feel a bit worried about clearing off and leaving him snowed under with work. I got up and walked to the window where I watched old Will Varley pushing a bicycle up the street with a sack of potatoes balanced on the handlebars as I had watched him a hundred times before. Then I turned back to my employer. I had had one of my infrequent ideas

'Look, Siegfried, I wouldn't mind spending my honeymoon round Ellerthorpe. It's wonderful up there at this time of the year and we could stay at the Wheat Sheaf. I could do the testing from there.'

He looked at me in astonishment. 'Spend it at Ellerthorpe? And testing? It's impossible – what would Helen say?'

'She wouldn't mind. In fact she could do the writing for me. We were only going off touring in the car so we haven't made any plans, and anyway it's funny, but Helen and I have often said we'd like to stay at the Wheat Sheaf some time – there's something about that little pub.'

Siegfried shook his head decisively. 'No, James I won't hear of it. In fact you're beginning to make me feel guilty. I'll get through the work all right so forget about it and go away and have a good time.'

'No, I've made up my mind. I'm really beginning to like the idea.' I scanned the list quickly. 'I can start testing at Allen's and do all those smaller ones around there on Tuesday, get married on Wednesday and go back for the second injection and readings on Thursday and Friday. I can knock hell out of that list by the end of the week.'

Siegfried looked at me as though he was seeing me for the first time. He argued and protested but for once I got my way. I fished the Ministry notification cards from the desk drawer and began to make the arrangements for my honeymoon.

On Tuesday at 12 noon I had finished testing the Allens' huge herd scattered for miles over the stark fells at the top of the Dale and was settling down with the hospitable folk for the inevitable 'bit o' dinner'. Mr Allen was at the head of the scrubbed table, and facing me were his two sons, Jack, aged about twenty, and Robbie, about seventeen. The young men were superbly fit and tough and I had been watching all morning in something like awe as they man-handled the wild, scattered beasts, chasing and catching tirelessly hour after hour. I had stared incredulously as Jack had run down a galloping heifer on the open moor, seized its horns and borne it slowly to the ground for me to inject; it struck me more than once that it was a pity that an Olympic selector was unlikely to stray into this remote corner of high Yorkshire – he would have found some world-beating material.

I always had to stand a bit of legpulling from Mrs Allen, a jolly talkative woman; on previous visits she had ribbed me mercilessly about being a slowcoach with the girls, the disgrace of having nothing better than a housekeeper to look after me. I knew she would start on me again today but I bided my time; I had a devastating riposte up my sleeve. She had just opened the oven door, filling the room with a delectable fragrance, and as she dumped a huge slab of roast ham on the table she looked down at me with a smile.

'Now then, Mr Herriot, when are we going to get you married off? It's time you found a nice girl, you know I'm always at you but you take not a bit o' notice.' She giggled as she bustled back to the cooking range for a bowl of mashed poatoes.

I waited until she returned before I dropped my bombshell. 'Well, as a matter of fact, Mrs Allen,' I said airily, 'I've decided to accept your advice. I'm getting married tomorrow.'

The good woman, mounding mashed potatoes on to my plate, stopped with her spoon in mid-air. 'Married tomorrow?' Her face was a study in blank astonishment.

'That's right. I thought you'd be pleased.'

'But . . . but . . . you're coming back here to read the test on Thursday and Friday.'

'Well of course. I have to finish the test, haven't I? I'll be bringing my wife with me – I'm looking forward to introducing her to you.'

There was a silence. The young men stared at me, Mr Allen stopped sawing at the ham and regarded me stolidly, then his wife gave an uncertain laugh.

'Oh come on, I don't believe it. You're kidding us. You'd be off on your honeymoon if you were getting married tomorrow.'

'Mrs Allen,' I said with dignity. 'I wouldn't joke about a serious matter like that. Let me repeat – tomorrow is my wedding day and I'll be bringing my wife along on Thursday to see you.'

Completely deflated, she heaped our plates and we all fell to in silence. But I knew she was in agony; she kept darting little glances at me and it was obvious she was dying to ask me more. The boys too, seemed intrigued; only Mr Allen, a tall, quiet man who, I'm sure wouldn't have cared if I'd been going to rob a bank tomorrow, ploughed calmly through his food.

Nothing more was said until I was about to leave, then Mrs Allen put a hand on my arm.

'You really don't mean it, do you?' Her face was haggard with strain.

I got into the car and called out through the window. 'Goodbye and thank you, Mrs Allen. Mrs Herriot and I will be along first thing on Thursday.'

I can't remember much about the wedding. It was a 'quiet do' and my main recollection is of desiring to get it all over with as soon as possible. I have only one vivid memory; of

Siegfried, just behind me in the church booming 'Amen' at regular intervals throughout the ceremony – the only time I have ever heard a best man do this.

It was an incredible relief when Helen and I were ready to drive away and when we were passing Skeldale House Helen grasped my hand.

'Look!' she cried excitedly. 'Look over there!'

Underneath Siegfried's brass plate which always hung slightly askew on the iron railings was a brand new one. It was of the modern bakelite type with a black background and bold white letters which read 'J. Herriot MRCVS Veterinary Surgeon', and it was screwed very straight and level on the metal.

Siegfried had said something about 'You'll see my wedding present on the way out.' And here it was. Not many people got a partnership as a gift, but it had happened to me and was the crowning point of three years of magnanimity.

I looked back down the street to try to see Siegfried but we had said our goodbyes and I would have to thank him later. So I drove out of Darrowby with a feeling of swelling pride because I knew what the plate meant – I was a man with a real place in the world. The thought made me slightly breathless. In fact we were both a little dizzy and we cruised for hours around the countryside, getting out when we felt like it, walking among the hills, taking no account of time. It must have been nine o'clock in the evening and darkness coming in fast when we realized we had gone far out of our way.

We had to drive ten miles over a desolate moor on the fell top and it was very dark when we rattled down the steep, narrow road into Ellerthorpe. The Wheat Sheaf was an unostentatious part of the single long village street, a low grey stone building with no light over the door, and as we went into the slightly musty-smelling hallway the gentle clink of glasses came from the public bar on our left. Mrs Burn, the elderly widow who owned the place, appeared from a back room and scrutinized us unemotionally.

'We've met before, Mrs Burn,' I said and she nodded. I

apologized for our lateness and was wondering whether I dare ask for a few sandwiches at this time of night when the old lady spoke up, quite unperturbed.

'Nay,' she said, 'it's right. We've been expecting you and your supper's waiting.' She led us to the dining-room where her niece, Beryl, served a hot meal in no time. Thick lentil soup, followed by what would probably be called a goulash these days but which was in fact simply a delicious stew with mushrooms and vegetables obviously concocted by a culinary genius. We had to say no to the gooseberry pie and cream.

It was like that all the time at the Wheat Sheaf. The whole place was aggressively unfashionable; needing a lick of paint, crammed with hideous Victorian furniture, but it was easy to see how it had won its reputation. It didn't have stylish guests, but fat, comfortable men from the industrial West Riding brought their wives at the weekends and did a bit of fishing or just took in the incomparable air between the mealtimes which were the big moments of the day. There was only one guest while we were there and he was a permanent one – a retired draper from Darlington who was always at the table in good time, a huge white napkin tucked under his chin, his eyes gleaming as he watched Beryl bring in the food.

But it wasn't just the home-fed ham, the Wensleydale cheese, the succulent steak and kidney pies, the bilberry tarts and mountainous Yorkshire puddings which captivated Helen and me. There was a peace, a sleepy insinuating charm about the old pub which we always recall with happiness. I still often pass the Wheat Sheaf, and as I look at its ancient stone frontage, quite unaltered by the passage of a mere thirty years, the memories are still fresh and warm; our footsteps echoing in the empty street when we took our last walk at night, the old brass bedstead almost filling the little room, the dark rim of the fells bulking against the night sky beyond our window, faint bursts of laughter from the farmers in the bar downstairs.

I particularly enjoyed too, our very first morning when I

took Helen to do the test at Allen's. As I got out of the car I could see Mrs Allen peeping round the curtains in the kitchen window. She was soon out in the yard and her eyes popped when I brought my bride over to her. Helen was one of the pioneers of slacks in the Dales and she was wearing a bright purple pair this morning which would in modern parlance knock your eye out. The farmer's wife was partly shocked, partly fascinated but she soon found that Helen was of the same stock as herself and within seconds the two women were chattering busily. I judged from Mrs Allen's vigorous head-nodding and her ever widening smile that Helen was putting her out of her pain by explaining all the circumstances. It took a long time and finally Mr Allen had to break into the conversation.

'If we're goin', we'll have to go,' he said gruffly and we set off to start the second day of the test.

We began on a sunny hillside where a group of young animals had been penned. Jack and Robbie plunged in among the beasts while Mr Allen took off his cap and courteously dusted the top of the wall.

'Your missus can sit 'ere,' he said.

I paused as I was about to start measuring. My missus! It was the first time anybody had said that to me. I looked over at Helen as she sat cross-legged on the rough stones, her notebook on her knee, pencil at the ready, and as she pushed back the shining hair from her forehead she caught my eye and smiled; and as I smiled back at her I became aware suddenly of the vast, swelling glory of the Dales around us, and of the Dales scent of clover and warm grass, more intoxicating than any wine. And it seemed that my first three years at Darrowby had been leading up to this moment, that the first big step of my life was being completed right here with Helen smiling at me and the memory, fresh in my mind, of my new plate hanging in front of Skeldale House.

I might have stood there indefinitely, in a sort of trance, but Mr Allen cleared his throat in a marked manner and I turned back to the job in hand.

'Right,' I said, placing my calipers against the beast's neck. 'Number thirty-eight, seven millimetres and circumscribed,' I called out to Helen. 'Number thirty-eight, seven, C.'

'Thirty-eight, seven, C,' my wife repeated as she bent over her book and started to write.

Every Living Thing

WITH ILLUSTRATIONS BY

VICTOR AMBRUS

To my revered and elderly friends,
Polly and Bodie

Be fruitful and multiply, and replenish the earth and subdue it: and have dominion over the fish of the sea and over the fowl of the air, and over every living thing that moveth upon the earth.

I

I am never at my best in the early morning, especially the cold mornings you get in the Yorkshire spring when a piercing March wind sweeps down from the fells, finding its way inside clothing, nipping at noses and ears. It was a cheerless time, and a particularly bad time to be standing in this cobbled farmyard watching a beautiful horse dying because of my incompetence.

It had started at eight o'clock. Mr Kettlewell telephoned as I was finishing my breakfast.

'I 'ave a fine big cart 'oss here and he's come out in spots.'

'Really? What kind of spots?'

'Well, round and flat, and they're all over 'im.'

'And it started quite suddenly?'

'Aye, he were right as rain last night.'

'All right, I'll have a look at him right away.' I nearly rubbed my hands. Urticaria. It usually cleared up spontaneously, but an injection hastened the process and I had a new antihistamine drug to try out – it was said to be specific for this sort of thing. Anyway, it was the kind of situation where it was easy for the vet to look good. A nice start to the day.

In the fifties, the tractor had taken over most of the work on the farms, but there was still a fair number of draught horses around, and when I arrived at Mr Kettlewell's place I realised that this one was something special.

The farmer was leading him from a loose box into the yard. A magnificent Shire, all of eighteen hands, with a noble head which he tossed proudly as he paced towards me. I appraised him with something like awe, taking in the swelling curve of the neck, the deep-chested body, the powerful limbs abundantly feathered above the massive feet.

'What a wonderful horse!' I gasped. 'He's enormous!'

Mr Kettlewell smiled with quiet pride. 'Aye, he's a right smasher. I only bought 'im last month. I do like to have a good 'oss about.'

He was a tiny man, elderly but sprightly, and one of my favourite farmers. He had to reach high to pat the huge neck and was nuzzled in return. 'He's kind, too. Right quiet.'

'Ah well, it's worth a lot when a horse is good-natured as well as good-looking.' I ran my hand over the typical plaques in the skin. 'Yes, this is urticaria, all right.'

'What's that?'

'Sometimes it's called nettle rash. It's an allergic condition. He may have eaten something unusual, but it's often difficult to pinpoint the cause.'

'Is it serious?'

'Oh no. I have an injection that'll soon put him right. He's well enough in himself, isn't he?'

'Aye, right as a bobbin.'

'Good. Sometimes it upsets an animal, but this fellow's the picture of health.'

As I filled my syringe with the antihistamine I felt that I had never spoken truer words. The big horse radiated health and well-being.

He did not move as I gave the injection, and I was about to put my syringe away when I had another thought. I had always used a proprietary preparation for urticaria and it had invariably worked. Maybe it would be a good idea to supplement the antihistamine, just to make sure. I wanted a good, quick cure for this splendid horse.

I trotted back to my car to fetch the old standby and injected the usual dose. Again the big animal paid no attention and the farmer laughed.

'By gaw, he doesn't mind, does 'e?'

I pocketed the syringe. 'No, I wish all our patients were like him. He's a grand sort.'

This, I thought, was vetting at its best. An easy, trouble-free case, a nice farmer and a docile patient who was a picture of equine beauty, a picture I could have looked at all day. I didn't want to go away although other calls were waiting. I just stood there, half listening to Mr Kettlewell's chatter about the imminent lambing season.

'Ah well,' I said at length, 'I must be on my way.' I was turning to go when I noticed that the farmer had fallen silent.

The silence lasted for a few moments, then, 'He's dotherin' a bit,' he said.

I looked at the horse. There was the faintest tremor in the muscles of the limbs. It was hardly visible, but as I watched, it began to spread upwards, bit by bit, until the skin over the neck, body and rump began to quiver. It was very slight, but there was no doubt it was gradually increasing in intensity.

'What is it?' said Mr Kettlewell.

'Oh, just a little reaction. It'll soon pass off.' I was trying to sound airy, but I wasn't so sure.

With agonising slowness the trembling developed into a generalised shaking of the entire frame and this steadily increased in violence as the farmer and I stood there in silence. I seemed to have been there a long time, trying to look calm and unworried, but I couldn't believe what I was seeing. This sudden inexplicable transition – there was no reason for it. My heart began to thump and my mouth turned dry as the shaking was replaced by great shuddering spasms which racked the horse's frame, and his eyes, so serene a short while ago, started from his head in terror, while foam began to drop from his lips. My mind raced. Maybe I shouldn't have mixed those injections, but it couldn't have this fearful effect. It was impossible.

As the seconds passed, I felt I couldn't stand much more of this. The blood hammered in my ears. Surely he would start to recover soon – he couldn't get worse.

I was wrong. Almost imperceptibly the huge animal began to sway. Only a little at first, then more and more until he was tilting from side to side like a mighty oak in a gale. Oh, dear God, he was going to go down and that would be the end. And that end had to come soon. Even the cobbles seemed to shake under my feet as the great horse crashed to the ground. For a few moments he lay there, stretched on his side, his feet pedalling convulsively, then he was still.

Well, that was it. I had killed this magnificent horse. It was impossible, unbelievable that a few minutes ago that animal had been standing there in all his strength and beauty and I had come along with my clever new medicines and now there he was, dead.

What was I going to say? I'm terribly sorry, Mr Kettlewell, I just can't understand how this happened. My mouth opened, but nothing came out, not even a croak. And, as though looking at a picture from the outside I became aware of the square of farm buildings with the dark, snow-streaked fells rising behind under a lowering sky, of the biting wind, the farmer and myself, and the motionless body of the horse.

I felt chilled to the bone and miserable, but I had to say my piece. I took a long, quavering breath and was about to speak when the horse raised his head slightly. I said nothing, nor did Mr Kettlewell, as the big animal eased himself onto his chest, looked around him for a few seconds then got to his feet. He shook his head, then walked across to his master. The recovery was just as quick, just as incredible, as the devastating collapse, and he showed no ill effects from his crashing fall onto the cobbled yard.

The farmer reached up and patted the horse's neck. 'You know, Mr Herriot, them spots have nearly gone!'

I went over and had a look. 'That's right. You can hardly see them now.'

Mr Kettlewell shook his head wonderingly. 'Aye, well, it's a wonderful new treatment. But I'll tell tha summat. I hope you don't mind me sayin' this, but,' he put his hand on my arm and looked up into my face, 'ah think it's just a bit drastic.'

I drove away from the farm and pulled up the car in the lee of a dry-stone wall. A great weariness had descended upon me. This sort of thing wasn't good for me. I was getting on in years now – well into my thirties – and I couldn't stand these shocks like I used to. I tipped the driving mirror down and had a look at myself. I was a bit pale, but not as ghastly white as I felt. Still, the feeling of guilt and bewilderment persisted, and with it the recurring thought that there must be easier ways of earning a living than as a country veterinary surgeon. Twenty-four hours a day, seven days a week, rough, dirty and peppered with traumatic incidents like that near catastrophe back there. I leaned back against the seat and closed my eyes.

When I opened them a few minutes later, the sun had broken through the clouds, bringing the green hillsides and the sparkling ridges of snow to vivid life, painting the rocky outcrops with gold. I wound down the window and breathed in the cold clean air drifting down, fresh and tangy, from the moorland high above. A curlew cried, breaking the enveloping silence, and on the grassy bank by the roadside I saw the first primroses of spring.

Peace began to steal through me. Maybe I hadn't done anything wrong with Mr Kettlewell's horse. Maybe antihistamines did sometimes cause these reactions. Anyway, as I started the engine and drove away, the old feeling began to well up in me and within moments it was running strong: it was good to be able to work with animals in this thrilling countryside; I was lucky to be a vet in the Yorkshire Dales.

2

There is no doubt that a shock to the system heightens the perception, because as I drove away from Mr Kettlewell's with my heart still fluttering to begin the rest of my morning round, it was as though I were seeing everything for the first time. In my daily work I was always aware of the beauty around me and had never lost the sense of wonder which had filled me when I had had my first sight of Yorkshire, but this morning the magic of the Dales was stronger than ever.

My eyes strayed again and again over the towering flanks of the fells, taking in the pattern of walled green fields won from the yellow moorland grass, and I gazed up at the high tops with the thrill of excitement which always came down to me from that untrodden land.

After visiting the isolated farm, I couldn't resist pulling my car off the unfenced road and climbing with my beagle, Dinah, to the high country which beckoned me. The snow had disappeared almost overnight leaving only runnels of white lying behind the walls and it was as though all the scents of the earth and growing things had been imprisoned and were released now by the spring sunshine in waves of a piercing sweetness. When I reached the summit I was breathless and gulped the crystal air greedily as though I could never get enough of it.

Here there was no evidence of the hand of man and I walked with my dog among miles of heather, peat hags and bog pools with the black waters rippling and the tufts of rushes bending and swaying in the eternal wind.

As the cloud shadows, racing on the wind, flew over me, trailing ribbons of shade and brightness over the endless browns and greens, I felt a rising exhilaration at just being up there on the roof of Yorkshire. It was an empty landscape where no creature stirred and it was silent except for the cry of a distant bird, yet I felt a further surge of excitement in the solitude, a tingling sense of the nearness of all creation.

As always, the siren song of the lonely uplands tempted me to stay, but the morning was wearing on and I had several more farms to visit.

It was with a lingering feeling of fulfilment that I finished my last call and headed for Darrowby, the town where I lived. Its square church tower had been pushing above the tumbled roofs of the little town as I came down the dale and soon I was driving through the cobbled market place with the square of fretted roofs above the shops and pubs which served its three thousand inhabitants.

In the far corner I turned down Trengate, the street where our surgery was, and drew up at the three storeys of mellow brick and climbing ivy of Skeldale House, my work place and happy home where my wife, Helen, and I had brought up our children.

The memories came back of the unforgettable times when my partner, Siegfried Farnon, and his inimitable brother, Tristan, had lived and laughed there with me in our bachelor days, but they were both married and lived with their families in their own homes. Tristan had joined the Ministry of Agriculture, but Siegfried was still my partner and for the thousandth time I thanked heaven that both the brothers were still my close friends.

My son, Jimmy, was ten now and daughter, Rosie, was six, and they were at school, but Siegfried was coming down the steps, stuffing bottles into his pockets.

'Ah, James,' he cried, 'I've just taken a message for you. One of your most esteemed clients – Mrs Bartram. Puppy is in need of your services.' He was grinning as he spoke.

I smiled ruefully in reply. 'Oh, fine. You didn't fancy going there yourself, did you?'

'No, no, my boy. Wouldn't dream of depriving you of the pleasure.' He waved cheerfully and climbed into his car.

I looked at my watch. I still had half an hour before lunch and Puppy was only walking distance away. I got my bag and set off.

The heavenly aroma of fish and chips drifted out on the spring air and I felt a quick stab of hunger as I looked through the shop window at the white-coated figures with their wire scoops, lifting out the crisply battered haddocks and laying them out to drain by the golden mounds of chips.

The lunchtime trade was brisk and the queue moved steadily round the shop, gathering up the newspaper-wrapped parcels, some customers hurrying home with them, others shaking on salt and vinegar before an alfresco meal in the street.

I always had my gastric juices titillated when I visited Mrs Bartram's dog in the flat above the fish and chip shop and I took another rewarding breath as I went down the alley and climbed the stairs.

Mrs Bartram was in her usual chair in the kitchen; fat, massive, deadpan, the invariable cigarette dangling from her lips. She was throwing chips from a bag in her lap to her dog, Puppy, sitting opposite. He caught them expertly one after the other.

Puppy belied his name. He was an enormous, shaggy creature of doubtful ancestry and with a short temper. I always treated him with respect.

'He's still rather fat, Mrs Bartram,' I said. 'Haven't you tried to change his diet as I advised? Remember I said he shouldn't really be fed solely on fish and chips.'

She shrugged and a light shower of ash fell on her blouse. 'Oh aye, ah did for a bit. I cut out the chips and just gave 'im fish every day, but he didn't like it. Loves his chips, 'e does.'

'I see.' I couldn't say too much about the diet because I had the feeling that Mrs Bartram herself ate very little else and it would have been tactless to point out that big chunks of battered fried fish didn't constitute a slimming regime, because her figure, like her dog's, bore witness to the fact.

In fact, as I looked at the two, they had a great similarity sitting there, bolt upright, facing each other. Both huge, immobile, but giving an impression of latent power.

Fat dogs are often lazy and good-natured, but a long succession of postmen, newsboys and door-to-door salesmen had had to take desperate evasive action as Puppy turned suddenly into a monster baying at their heels, and I had one vivid memory of a brush vendor cycling unhurriedly down the alley with his wares dangling from the handle bars, slowing down outside the flat, then, as Puppy catapulted into the street, taking off like the winner of the Tour de France.

'Well, what's the trouble, Mrs Bartram?' I asked, changing the subject.

'It's 'is eye. Keeps runnin'.'

'Ah yes, I see.' The big dog's left eye was almost completely closed, and a trickle of discharge made a dark track down the hair of his face. It made his appearance even more sinister. 'There's some irritation there, probably an infection.'

It would have been nice to find the cause. There could be a foreign body in there or just a spot of conjunctivitis. I reached out my hand to pull the eyelid down but Puppy, without moving, fixed me with his good eye and drew his lips back from a row of formidable teeth.

I withdrew my hand. 'Yes . . . yes . . . I'll have to give you some antibiotic ointment and you must squeeze a little into his eye three times a day. You'll be able to do that, won't you.'

'Course, I will. He's as gentle as an awd sheep.' Expressionlessly, she lit another cigarette from the old one and drew the smoke down deeply. 'Ah can do anything with 'im.'

'Good, good.' As I rummaged in my bag for the ointment I

had the old feeling of defeat, but there was nothing else for it. It was always long-range treatment with Puppy. I had never tried anything silly like taking his temperature; to be honest, I'd never laid a finger on him in my life.

I heard from Mrs Bartram again two weeks later. Puppy's eye was no better; in fact, it was worse.

I hurried round to the flat, inhaling the delicious vapours from the shop as I went down the alley. Puppy was in the same position as before, upright, facing his mistress and there was no doubt there was an increased discharge from the eye. But this time I fancied I could see something else and I leaned forward, peering closely into the dog's face as a faint but menacing growl warned me not to take any more liberties. And it was there, all right, the cause of the trouble. A tiny papilloma growing from the margin of the eyelid and rubbing on the cornea.

I turned to Mrs Bartram. 'He's got a little growth in there. It's irritating his eye and causing the discharge.'

'Growth?' The lady's face seldom registered any emotion, but one eyebrow twitched upward and the cigarette trembled briefly in her mouth. 'Ah don't like the sound 'o that.'

'Oh, it's quite benign,' I said. 'Nothing to worry about. I'll be able to remove it easily and he'll be perfectly all right afterwards.'

I spoke lightly because indeed these things were quite common and a little injection of local anaesthetic and a quick snip with a pair of curved scissors did the trick effortlessly, but as I looked at the big dog regarding me coldly with his one eye I felt a twinge of anxiety. Things might not be so easy with Puppy.

My misgivings proved to be well founded when Mrs Bartram brought him round to the surgery next morning and left him in the small consulting room. He would obviously have to be sedated before we could do anything and among the rush of new drugs were excellent tranquillisers like acetylpromazine. There was, however, the small matter of one of us grasping that leonine head while the other lifted a fold of skin and inserted the needle. Puppy made it very clear that such things were not on the agenda. Being on strange ground and feeling threatened he came roaring, open-mouthed, at Siegfried and me as soon as we tried to enter the room. We retreated hastily and locked the door.

'Dog catcher?' suggested Siegfried without conviction.

I shook my head. The dog catcher was a snare of soft flex on the end of a long pole and was a handy instrument to slip over a difficult dog's head and steady it while the injection was made, but with Puppy it would be like trying to lasso a grizzly bear. If we ever managed to get the loop over his head it would be the prelude to a fearsome wrestling match.

However, we'd had tough dogs before and we had a little trick in reserve.

'Looks like one for the nembutal,' Siegfried murmured and I nodded agreement. For unapproachable cases we kept a supply of succulent minced beef in the fridge. It was a delicacy which no dog could resist and it was a simple matter to break a few capsules of Nembutal among the meat and wait while the animal drifted into a state of blissful somnolence. It always worked.

However, it was time-consuming. Removing the tiny growth should have been a few minutes' job but we'd have to wait for twenty minutes or so until the stuff took effect. I tried not to think of the urgent cases all over the countryside needing our attention as I prepared the medicated mince.

The consulting room looked onto the garden through a sash window which was open a few inches at the bottom. I threw the meat through this aperture and the two of us went into the office to prepare for our rounds.

When we came back we expected to find Puppy slumbering peacefully, but when we peered in he threw himself at the window, snarling like a starving wolf. On the floor the meat lay untouched.

'Look at that!' I cried. 'I don't believe it. No dog's ever refused that lovely stuff before!'

Siegfried slapped his forehead. 'What a damn nuisance! Do you think he can smell the nembutal? Better try him with a bigger proportion of mince.'

I made up another supply and threw it again through the opening. We retreated to allay the dog's suspicions, but when we crept up ten minutes later the picture hadn't changed. Puppy had not eaten a single mouthful.

'What the hell are we going to do?' Siegfried burst out. 'It's going to be lunch time before we get out!'

It was indeed getting on towards lunch time because a gentle breeze was carrying the first fragrance from the fish and chip shop down the street.

'Just hang on for a minute,' I said. 'I think I know the answer.'

I galloped along Trengate and returned with a bag of chips. It was the work of a moment to insert a capsule in a chip and flick it through the aperture. Puppy was on it like flash and swallowed it without hesitation. Another chip, another capsule, and so on until he had received the requisite dose.

Even as we watched, the big dog's ferocity was gradually replaced by an amiable goofiness and when he took a few uncertain steps then flopped on to his side we knew we had won. When we finally unlocked the door and entered the room, Puppy was in a happy trance and we performed the operation in a couple of minutes.

He was still dopey and unusually peaceful when his mistress called to collect him later that day. When she brought him into the office, his huge head was level with my desk and he almost smiled at me as I sat down.

'We've removed that little thing, Mrs Bartram,' I said. 'His eye will be fine now, but I'm prescribing a course of Lincocin tablets to stop any further infection.'

As I reached for a pen to write the instructions I glanced at some of the other labels I had written. In those days, before injections became the general procedure, many of our medicines were given by mouth. The instructions on the other labels were varied: 'Mixture for bullock. To be given in a pint of treacle water.' 'Drench for calf. To be given in half a pint of flour gruel.'

I poised my pen for a moment, then, for the first time in my life, I wrote, 'Tablets for dog. One to be given three times daily inserted in chips.'

3

My throat was killing me. Three successive nocturnal lambings on the windswept hillsides in my shirt-sleeves had left me with the beginnings of a cold and I felt in urgent need of a packet of Geoff Hatfield's cough drops. An unscientific treatment, perhaps, but I had a childish faith in those powerful little candies which exploded in the mouth, sending a blast of medicated vapour surging through the bronchial tubes.

The shop was down a side alley, almost hidden away, and it was so tiny – not much more than a cubby hole – that there was hardly room for the sign, GEOFFREY HATFIELD, CONFECTIONER above the window. But it was full. It was always full, and, this being market day, it was packed out.

The little bell went 'ching' as I opened the door and squeezed into the crush of local ladies and farmers' wives. I'd have to wait for a while but I didn't mind, because watching Mr Hatfield in action was one of the rewarding things in my life.

I had come at a good time, too, because the proprietor was in the middle of one of his selection struggles. He had his back to me, the silver-haired, leonine head nodding slightly on the broad shoulders as he surveyed the rows of tall glass sweet jars against the wall. His hands, clasped behind him, tensed and relaxed repeatedly as he fought his inner battle, then he took a few strides along the row, gazing intently at each jar in turn. It struck me that Lord Nelson pacing the quarterdeck of the *Victory*, wondering how best to engage the enemy, could not have displayed a more portentous concentration.

The tension in the little shop rose palpably as he reached up a hand, then withdrew it with a shake of the head, but a sigh went up from the assembled ladies as, with a final grave nod and a squaring of the shoulders, he extended both arms, seized a jar and swung round to face the company. His large, Roman senator face, was crinkled into a benign smile.

'Now, Mrs Moffat,' he boomed at a stout matron, and holding out the glass vessel with both hands, inclining it slightly with all the grace and deference of a Cartier jeweller displaying a diamond necklace, 'I wonder if I can interest you in this.'

Mrs Moffat, clutching her shopping basket, peered closely at the paper-wrapped confections in the jar. 'Well, ah don't know . . .'

'If I remember rightly, madam, you indicated that you were seeking something in the nature of a Russian caramel, and I can thoroughly recommend these little sweetmeats. Not quite a Russian, but nevertheless a very nice, smooth-eating toffee.' His expression became serious, expectant.

The fruity tones rolling round his description made me want to grab the sweets and devour them on the spot, and they seemed to have the same effect on the lady. 'Right, Mr Hatfield,' she said eagerly, 'I'll 'ave half a pound.'

The shopkeeper gave a slight bow. 'Thank you so much, madam, I'm sure you will not regret your choice.' His features relaxed into a gracious smile and, as he lovingly trickled the toffees on to his scales before bagging them with a professional twirl, I felt a renewed desire to get at the things.

Mr Hatfield, leaning forward with both hands on the counter, kept his gaze on his customer until he had bowed her out of the shop with a courteous, 'Good day to you, madam', then he turned to face the congregation. 'Ah, Mrs Dawson, how very nice to see you. And what is your pleasure this morning?'

The lady, obviously delighted, beamed at him. 'I'd like some of them fudge chocolates I 'ad last week, Mr Hatfield. They were lovely. Have you still got some?'

'Indeed I have, madam, and I am delighted that you approve of my recommendation. Such a deliciously creamy flavour. Also, it so happens that I have just received a consignment in a special presentation box for Easter. He lifted one from the shelf and balanced it on the palm of his hand. 'Really pretty and attractive, don't you think?'

Mrs Dawson nodded rapidly. 'Oh aye, that's real bonny. I'll take a box and there's summat else I want. A right big bag of nice boiled sweets for the family to suck at. Mixed colours, you know. What 'ave you got?'

Mr Hatfield steepled his fingers, gazed at her fixedly and took a long, contemplative breath. He held this pose for several seconds then he swung round, clasped his hands behind him, and recommenced his inspection of the jars.

That was my favourite bit and, as always, I was enjoying it. It was a familiar scene. The tiny, crowded shop, the proprietor wrestling with his assignment and Alfred sitting at the far end of the counter.

Alfred was Geoff's cat and he was always there, seated upright and majestic on the polished boards near the curtained doorway which led to the Hatfield sitting room. As usual, he seemed to be taking a keen interest in the proceedings, his gaze moving from his master's face to the customer's and though it may have been my imagination I felt that his expression registered a grave involvement in the negotiations and a deep satisfaction at the outcome. He never left his place or encroached on the rest of the counter, but occasionally one or other of the ladies would stroke his cheek and he would respond with a booming purr and a gracious movement of the head towards them.

It was typical that he never yielded to any unseemly display of emotion. That would have been undignified, and dignity was an unchanging part of him. Even as a kitten he had never indulged in immoderate playfulness. I had neutered him three years earlier – for which he appeared to bear me no ill will – and he had grown into a massive, benevolent tabby. I looked at him now, sitting in his place. Vast, imperturbable, at peace with his world. There was no doubt he was a cat of enormous presence.

And it had always struck me forcibly that he was exactly like his master in that respect. They were two of a kind and it was no surprise that they were such devoted friends.

When it came to my turn I was able to reach Alfred and I tickled him under his chin. He liked that and raised his head high while the purring rumbled up from the furry rib cage until it resounded throughout the shop.

Even collecting my cough drops had its touch of ceremony. The big man behind the counter sniffed gravely at the packet then clapped his hand a few times against his chest. 'You can smell the goodness, Mr Herriot, the beneficial vapours. These will have you right in no time.' He bowed and smiled and I could swear that Alfred smiled with him.

I squeezed my way out through the ladies and as I walked down the alley I marvelled for the umpteenth time at the phenomenon of Geoffrey Hatfield. There were several other sweet shops in Darrowby, big double-fronted places with their wares attractively displayed in the windows, but none of them did anything like the trade of the poky establishment I had just left. There was no doubt that it was all due to Geoff's unique selling technique and it was certainly not an act on his part, it was born of a completely sincere devotion to his calling, a delight in what he was doing.

His manner and 'posh' diction gave rise to a certain amount of ribald comment from men who had left the local school with him at the age of fourteen, and in the pubs he was often referred to as 'the bishop', but it was good-natured stuff because he was a well-liked man. And, of course, the ladies adored him and flocked to bask in his attentions.

*

About a month later I was in the shop again to get some of Rosie's favourite liquorice all-sorts and the picture was the same – Geoffrey smiling and booming, Alfred in his place, following every move, the pair of them radiating dignity and well-being. As I collected my sweets, the proprietor whispered in my ear.

'I'll be closing for lunch at twelve noon, Mr Herriot. Would you be so kind as to call in and examine Alfred?'

'Yes, of course.' I looked along the counter at the big cat. 'Is he ill?'

'Oh, no, no . . . but I just feel there's something not right.'

Later I knocked at the closed door and Geoffrey let me into the shop, empty for once, then through the curtained doorway into his sitting room. Mrs Hatfield was at a table, drinking tea. She was a much earthier character than her husband. 'Now then, Mr Herriot, you've come to see t'little cat.'

'He isn't so little,' I said, laughing. And indeed, Alfred looked more massive than ever seated by the fire, looking calmly into the flames. When he saw me he got up, stalked unhurriedly over the carpet and arched his back against my legs. I felt strangely honoured.

'He's really beautiful, isn't he?' I murmured. I hadn't had a close look at him for some time and the friendly face with the dark stripes running down to the intelligent eyes appealed to me as never before. 'Yes,' I said, stroking the fur which shone luxuriantly in the flickering firelight, 'you're a big beautiful fellow.'

I turned to Mr Hatfield. 'He looks fine to me. What is it that's worrying you?'

'Oh, maybe it's nothing at all. His appearance certainly has not altered in the slightest, but for over a week now I've noticed that he is not quite so keen on his food, not quite so lively. He's not really ill . . . he's just different.'

'I see. Well, let's have a look at him.' I went over the cat carefully. Temperature was normal, mucous membranes a healthy pink. I got out my stethoscope and auscultated heart and lungs – nothing abnormal to hear. Palpation of the abdomen produced no clue.

'Well, Mr Hatfield,' I said, 'there doesn't seem to be anything obviously wrong with him. He's maybe a bit run down, but he doesn't look it. Anyway, I'll give him a vitamin injection. That should buck him up. Let me know in a few days if he's no better.'

'Thank you indeed, sir. I am most grateful. You have set my mind at rest.' The big man reached out a hand to his pet. The confident resonance of his voice was belied by the expression of concern on his face. Seeing them together made me sense anew the similarity of man and cat – human and animal, yes, but alike in their impressiveness.

I heard nothing about Alfred for a week and assumed that he had returned to normal, but then his master telephoned. 'He's just the same, Mr Herriot. In fact, if anything, he has deteriorated slightly. I would be obliged if you would look at him again.'

It was just as before. Nothing definite to see even on close examination. I put him on to a course of mixed minerals and vitamin tablets. There was no point in launching into treatment with our new antibiotics – there was no elevation of temperature, no indication of any infectious agent.

I passed the alley every day – it was only about a hundred yards from Skeldale House – and I fell into the habit of stopping and looking in through the little window of the shop. Each day, the familiar scene presented itself; Geoff bowing and smiling to his customers and Alfred sitting in his place at the end of the counter. Everything seemed right, and yet . . . there *was* something different about the cat.

I called in one evening and examined him again. 'He's losing weight,' I said.

Geoffrey nodded. 'Yes, I do think so. He is still eating fairly well, but not as much as before.'

'Give him another few days on the tablets,' I said, 'and if he's no better I'll have to get him round to the surgery and go into this thing a bit more deeply.'

I had a nasty feeling there would be no improvement and there wasn't, so one evening I took a cat cage round to the shop. Alfred was so huge that there was a problem fitting him into the container, but he didn't resist as I bundled him gently inside.

At the surgery I took a blood sample from him and X-rayed

him. The plate was perfectly clear and when the report came back from the laboratory it showed no abnormality.

In a way, it was reassuring, but that did not help because the steady decline continued. The next few weeks were something like a nightmare. My anxious peering through the shop window became a daily ordeal. The big cat was still in his place, but he was getting thinner and thinner until he was almost unrecognisable. I rang the changes with every drug and treatment I could think of, but nothing did any good. I had Siegfried examine him, but he thought as I did. The progressive emaciation was the sort of thing you would expect from an internal tumour, but further X-rays still showed nothing. Alfred must have been thoroughly fed up of all the pushing around, the tests, the kneading of his abdomen, but at no time did he show any annoyance. He accepted the whole thing placidly as was his wont.

There was another factor which made the situation much worse. Geoff himself was wilting under the strain. His comfortable coating of flesh was dropping steadily away from him, the normally florid cheeks were pale and sunken and, worse still, his dramatic selling style appeared to be deserting him. One day I left my viewpoint at the window and pushed my way into the press of ladies in the shop. It was a harrowing scene. Geoff, bowed and shrunken, was taking the orders without even a smile, pouring the sweets listlessly into their bags and mumbling a word or two. Gone was the booming voice and the happy chatter of the customers and a strange silence hung over the company. It was just like any other sweet shop.

Saddest sight of all was Alfred, still sitting bravely upright in his place. He was unbelievably gaunt, his fur had lost its bloom and he stared straight ahead, dead-eyed, as though nothing interested him any more. He was like a feline scarecrow.

I couldn't stand it any longer. That evening I went round to see Geoff Hatfield.

'I saw your cat today,' I said, 'and he's going rapidly downhill. Are there any new symptoms?'

The big man nodded dully. 'Yes, as a matter of fact. I was going to ring you. He's been vomiting a bit.'

I dug my nails into my palms. 'There it is again. Everything points to something abnormal inside him and yet I can't find a thing.' I bent down and stroked Alfred. 'I hate to see him like this. Look at his fur. It used to be so glossy.'

'That's right,' replied Geoff, 'he's neglecting himself. He never washes himself now. It's as though he can't be bothered. And before, he was always at it – lick, lick lick for hours on end.'

I stared at him. His words had sparked something in my mind. 'Lick, lick lick.' I paused in thought. 'Yes . . . when I think about it, no cat I ever knew washed himself as much as Alfred . . .' The spark suddenly became a flame and I jerked upright in my chair.

'Mr Hatfield,' I said, 'I want to do an exploratory laparotomy!'

'What do you mean?'

'I think he's got a hair-ball inside him and I want to operate to see if I'm right.'

'Open him up, you mean?'

'That's right.'

He put a hand over his eyes and his chin sank onto his chest. He stayed like that for a long time, then he looked at me with haunted eyes. 'Oh, I don't know. I've never thought of anything like that.'

'We've got to do something or this cat is going to die.'

He bent and stroked Alfred's head again and again, then without looking up he spoke in a husky voice. 'All right, when?'

'Tomorrow morning.'

Next day, in the operating room, as Siegfried and I bent over the sleeping cat, my mind was racing. We had been doing much more small-animal surgery lately, but I had always known what to expect. This time I felt as though I was venturing into the unknown.

I incised through skin, abdominal muscles and peritoneum and when I reached forward towards the diaphragm I could feel a doughy mass inside the stomach. I cut through the stomach wall and my heart leaped. There it was, a large, matted hair-ball, the cause of all the trouble. Something which wouldn't show up on an X-ray plate.

Siegfried grinned. 'Well, now we know!'

'Yes,' I said as the great waves of relief swept over me. 'Now we know.'

And there was more. After I had evacuated and stitched the stomach, I found other, smaller hair-balls, bulging the intestine along its length. These had all to be removed and the bowel wall stitched in several places. I didn't like this. It meant a bigger trauma and shock to my patient, but finally all was done and only a neat row of skin sutures was visible.

When I returned Alfred to his home, his master could hardly bear to look at him. At length he took a timid glance at the cat, still sleeping under the anaesthetic. 'Will he live?' he whispered.

'He has a good chance,' I replied. 'He has had some major surgery and it might take him some time to get over it, but he's young and strong. He should be all right.'

I could see Geoff wasn't convinced, and that was how it was over the next few days. I kept visiting the little room behind the shop to give the cat penicillin injections and it was obvious that Geoff had made up his mind that Alfred was going to die.

Mrs Hatfield was more optimistic, but she was worried about her husband.

'Eee, he's given up hope,' she said. 'And it's all because Alfred just lies in his bed all day. I've tried to tell 'im that it'll be a bit o' time before the cat starts runnin' around, but he won't listen.'

She looked at me with anxious eyes. 'And, you know, it's gettin' him down, Mr Herriot. He's a different man. Sometimes I wonder if he'll ever be the same again.'

I went over and peeped past the curtain into the shop. Geoff was there, doing his job like an automaton. Haggard, unsmiling, silently handing out the sweets. When he did speak it was in a listless monotone and I realised with a sense of shock that his voice had lost all its old timbre. Mrs Hatfield was right. He was a different man. And, I thought, if he stayed different, what would happen to his clientele? So far they had remained faithful, but I had a feeling they would soon start to drift away.

It was a week before the picture began to change for the better. I entered the sitting room, but Alfred wasn't there.

Mrs Hatfield jumped up from her chair. 'He's a lot better, Mr Herriot,' she said eagerly. 'Eating well and seemed to want to go into t'shop. He's in there with Geoff now.'

Again I took a surreptitious look past the curtain. Alfred was back in his place, skinny but sitting upright. But his master didn't look any better.

I turned back into the room. 'Well, I won't need to come any more, Mrs Hatfield. Your cat is well on the way to recovery. He should soon be as good as new.' I was quite confident about this, but I wasn't so sure about Geoff.

At this point, the rush of spring lambing and post lambing troubles overwhelmed me as it did every year, and I had little time to think about my other cases. It must have been three weeks before I visited the sweet shop to buy some chocolates for Helen. The place was packed and as I pushed my way inside all my fears came rushing back and I looked anxiously at man and cat.

Alfred, massive and dignified again, sat like a king at the far end of the counter. Geoff was leaning on the counter with both hands, gazing closely into a lady's face. 'As I understand you, Mrs Hird, you are looking for something in the nature of a softer sweetmeat.' The rich voice reverberated round the little shop. 'Could you perhaps mean a Turkish Delight?'

'Nay, Mr Hatfield, it wasn't that . . .'

His head fell on his chest and he studied the polished boards of the counter with fierce concentration. Then he looked up and pushed his face nearer to the lady's. 'A pastille, possibly . . .?'

'Nay . . . nay.'

'A truffle? A soft caramel? A peppermint cream?'

'No, nowt like that.'

He straightened up. This was a tough one. He folded his arms across his chest and as he stared into space and took the long inhalation I remembered so well I could see that he was a big man again, his shoulders spreading wide, his face ruddy and well fleshed.

Nothing having evolved from his cogitations, his jaw jutted and he turned his face upwards, seeking further inspiration from the ceiling. Alfred, I noticed, looked upwards, too.

There was a tense silence as Geoff held this pose, then a smile crept slowly over his noble features. He raised a finger. 'Madam,' he said, 'I do fancy I have it. Whitish, you said . . . sometimes pink . . . rather squashy. May I suggest to you . . . marshmallow?'

Mrs Hird thumped the counter. 'Aye, that's it, Mr Hatfield. I just couldn't think of t'name.'

'Ha-ha, I thought so,' boomed the proprietor, his organ tones rolling to the roof. He laughed, the ladies laughed, and I was positive that Alfred laughed, too.

All was well again. Everybody in the shop was happy – Geoff, Alfred, the ladies and, not least, James Herriot.

4

'You call yourself a vet, but you're nowt but a robber!'

Mrs Sidlow, her fierce little dark eyes crackling with fury, spat out the words and as I looked at her, taking in the lank, black hair framing the haggard face with its pointed chin, I thought, not for the first time, how very much she resembled a witch. It was easy to imagine her throwing a leg over a broomstick and zooming off for a quick flip across the moon.

'All t'country's talkin' about you and your big bills,' she continued. 'I don't know how you get away with it, it's daylight robbery – robbin' the poor farmers and then you come out here bold as brass in your flash car.'

That was what had started it. Since my old vehicle was dropping to bits I had lashed out on a second-hand Austin 10. It had done twenty thousand miles but had been well maintained and looked like new with its black bodywork shining in the sun and the very sight of it had sparked off Mrs Sidlow.

The purchase of a new car was invariably greeted with a bit of leg pulling by most of the farmers. 'Job must be payin' well,' they would say with a grin. But it was all friendly, with never a hint of the venom which seemed to be part of the Sidlow ménage.

The Sidlows hated vets. Not just me, but all of them and that was quite a few because they had tried every practice for miles around and had found them all wanting. The trouble was that Mr Sidlow himself was quite simply the only man in the district who knew anything about doctoring sick animals – his wife and all his grown-up family knew this as an article of faith and whenever illness struck any of his cattle, it was natural that father took over. It was only when he had exhausted his supply of secret remedies that the vet was called in. I personally had seen only dying animals on that farm and had been unable to bring them back to life, so the Sidlows were invariably confirmed in their opinion of me along with the rest of my profession.

Today I had been viewing with the old feeling of hopelessness an emaciated little beast huddled in a dark corner of the fold yard taking its last few breaths after a week of pneumonia while the family stood around breathing hostility, shooting the usual side glances at me from their glowering faces. I had been trailing wearily back to my car on the way out when Mrs Sidlow had spotted me from the kitchen window and catapulted into the yard.

'Aye, it's awright for you,' she went on. 'We 'ave to work hard to make a livin' on this spot and then such as you come and take our money away from us without doin' anythin' for it. Ah know what it is, your idea is to get rich quick!'

Only my long training that the customer is always right stopped me from barking back. Instead I forced a smile.

'Mrs Sidlow,' I said, 'I assure you that I'm anything but rich. In fact, if you could see my bank balance, you would see what I mean.'

'You're tellin' me you haven't much money?'

'That's right.'

She waved towards the Austin and gave me another searing glare. 'So this fancy car's just a lot o' show on nowt!'

I had no answer. She had me both ways – either I was a fat cat or a stuck-up poseur.

As I drove away up the rising road I looked back at the farm with its substantial house and wide sprawl of buildings. There were five hundred lush acres down there, lying in the low country at the foot of the dale. The Sidlows were big, prosperous farmers with none of the worries of the hill men who struggled to exist on the bleak smallholdings higher up, and it was difficult to understand why my imagined affluence should be such an affront to them.

It occurred to me, too, that this latest attack had come at a time when my finances were at their lowest ebb. As I changed gear I caught a glimpse of pink flesh through the knee of my old corduroys. Oh hell, these trousers had just about had it as indeed had a lot of my clothes, but the needs of two growing children came a long way before my own. Not that there was any point in going round my work looking like a male fashion plate – I had one of the roughest, dirtiest jobs in the world and could only aim at reasonable respectability – and I always had the comforting knowledge that I did have one 'good suit' which had lasted for many years simply because it was hardly ever worn.

But it was indeed strange that I should be perpetually hard up. Siegfried and I had built up a good, successful practice. I worked nearly all the time, seven days a week, in the evenings and often during the night and it was hard work, too – rolling about on cobbled floors fighting with tough calvings to the point of exhaustion, getting kicked, crushed, trodden on and sprayed with muck. Often, I spent days with every muscle in my body aching. But I still had only a niggling and immovable overdraft of £1,000 to show for it all.

Of course, much of my time was spent driving a car. You didn't get paid for that, and maybe it was the reason for my situation. Yet the driving, the work and the whole rich life was spent out in this glorious countryside. I really loved all of it and it was only when I was accused of being a kind of agricultural con man that the contradiction came home to me.

As the road climbed higher I began to see the church tower and roofs of Darrowby and, at last, on the edge of the town, the gates of Mrs Pumphrey's beautiful home lay beckoning. I looked at my watch – twelve noon. Long practice had enabled me to time my visits here just before lunch when I could escape the rigours of country practice and wallow for a little while in the hospitality of the elderly widow who had brightened my life for so long.

As my tyres crunched on the gravel of the drive I smiled as Tricki Woo appeared at the window to greet me. He was old now, but he could still get up there to his vantage point and his Pekingese face was split as always by a panting grin of welcome.

Mounting the steps between the twin pillars of the doorway, I could see that he had left the window and I heard his joyous barking in the hall. Ruth, the long-serving maid, answered my ring, beaming with pleasure as Tricki flung himself at my knees.

'Eee, he's glad to see you Mr 'erriot,' she said and, laying a hand on my arm, 'we all are!'

She ushered me into the gracious drawing room where Mrs Pumphrey was sitting in an armchair by the fire. She raised her white head from her book and cried out in delight. 'Ah, Mr Herriot, how very very nice! Tricki, isn't it wonderful to have Uncle Herriot visiting again!'

She waved me to the armchair opposite. 'I have been expecting you for Tricki's check-up, but before you examine him you must sit down and warm yourself. It is so terribly cold. Ruth, my dear, will you bring Mr Herriot a glass of sherry. You will say yes, won't you, Mr Herriot.'

I murmured my thanks. I always said yes to the very special sherry which came in enormous glasses and was deeply heartening at all times but on cold days in particular. I sank into the cushions and stretched my legs towards the flames which leaped in the fireplace, and as I took my first sip and Ruth deposited a plate of tiny biscuits by my side while the little dog climbed on to my knee, the last of the hostile Sidlow vibes slipped gently away from me.

'Tricki has been awfully well since your last visit, Mr Herriot,' Mrs Pumphrey said. 'I know he is always going to be a little stiff with his arthritis but he does get around so well, and his little heart cough is no worse. And, best of all,' she clasped her hands together and her eyes widened, 'he hasn't gone flop-bott at all. Not once! So perhaps you won't have to squeeze the poor darling.'

'Oh no, I won't. Certainly not. I only do that if he really needs it.' I had been squeezing Tricki Woo's bottom for many years because of his anal gland trouble so graphically named by his mistress and the little animal had never resented it. I stroked his head as Mrs Pumphrey went on.

'There is something very interesting I must tell you. As you know, Tricki has always been deeply knowledgeable about horse racing, a wonderful judge of form, and wins nearly all his bets. Well now,' she raised a finger and spoke in a confidential murmur, 'just recently he has become very interested in greyhound racing!'

'Is that so?'

'Yes, indeed, he has begun to cover the meetings at the Middlesbrough greyhound track and has instructed me to place bets for him and, you know, he has won quite a lot of money already!'

'Gosh!'

'Yes, only this morning Crowther, my chauffeur, collected twelve pounds from the bookmaker after last evening's races.'

'Well, well, how wonderful.' My heart bled for Honest Joe Prendergast, the local turf accountant who must be suffering after losing money on horse-racing to a dog for years and then having to pay out on the greyhounds, too. 'Quite remarkable.'

'Isn't it, isn't it!' Mrs Pumphrey gave me a radiant smile, then she became serious. 'But I do wonder, Mr Herriot, just what is responsible for this new interest. What is your opinion?'

I shook my head gravely. 'Difficult to say. Very difficult.'

'However, I have a theory,' she said. 'Do you think perhaps that as he grows older he is more drawn to animals of his own species and prefers to bet on doggy runners like greyhounds?'

'Could be . . . could be . . .'

'And, after all, you would think with this affinity it would give him more insight and a better chance of winning.'

'Well, yes, that's possible. That's another point.'

Tricki, well aware that we were talking about him, waved his fine tail and looked up at me with his wide grin and lolling tongue.

I settled deeper in the cushions as the sherry began to send warm tendrils through my system. This was a happily familiar situation, listening to Mrs Pumphrey's recitals of Tricki Woo's activities. She was a kind, highly intelligent and cultivated lady, admired by all and a benefactress to innumerable charities. She sat on committees and her opinion was sought on many important matters, but where her dog was concerned her conversation never touched on weighty topics, but was filled with strange and wondrous things.

She leaned forward in her chair. 'There is something else I would like to talk to you about, Mr Herriot. You know that a Chinese restaurant has set up in Darrowby?'

'Yes, very nice, too.'

She laughed. 'But who would have thought it? A Chinese restaurant in a little place like Darrowby – it's amazing!'

'Very unexpected, I agree. But this last year or two they have been popping up all over Britain.'

'Yes, but what I want to discuss with you is that this has affected Tricki.'

'What!'

'Yes, he has been most upset over the whole business.'

'How on earth . . . ?'

'Well, Mr Herriot,' she frowned and gazed at me, solemn faced, 'I told you many years ago and you have always known that Tricki is descended from a long line of Chinese Emperors.'

'Yes, yes, of course.'

'Well, I think I can explain the whole problem if I start at the beginning.'

I took a long swallow at my sherry with the pleasant sensation that I was floating away in a dream world. 'Please do.'

'When the restaurant first opened,' she went on, 'there was a surprising amount of resentment among some of the local people. They criticized the food and the very nice little Chinese man and his wife, and put it about that there was no place for such a restaurant in Darrowby and that it should not be patronised. Now it so happened that when Tricki and I were out on our little walks, he overheard these remarks in the street, and he was furious.'

'Really?'

'Yes, quite affronted. I can tell when he feels like this. He stalks about with an insulted expression and it is so difficult to placate him.'

'Dear me, I'm sorry.'

'And after all, one can fully understand how he felt when he heard his own people being denigrated.'

'Quite, quite, absolutely – only natural.'

'However . . . however, Mr Herriot,' she raised a finger again and gave me a knowing smile, 'the clever darling suggested the cure himself.'

'He did?'

'Yes, he told me that we ourselves should start to frequent the restaurant and sample their food.'

'Ah.'

'And that is what we did. I had Crowther drive us there for lunch and we did enjoy it so much. Also, we found we could take the food home all nice and hot in little boxes – what fun! Now that we have started, Crowther often pops out in the evening and brings us our supper and, you know, the restaurant seems quite busy now. I feel we have really helped.'

'I'm sure you have,' I said, and I meant it. The Lotus Garden, tucked in a corner of the market place, wasn't much more than a shop front with four small tables inside and the sight of the gleaming black length of the limousine and liveried chauffeur parked frequently at its door must have given it a tremendous lift. I was struggling unsuccessfully to picture the locals peering through the window at Mrs Pumphrey and Tricki eating at one of those tiny tables when she went on.

'I'm so glad you think so. And we have enjoyed it so much. Tricki adores the char sui and my favourite is the chow mein. The little Chinese man is teaching us how to use the chop sticks, too.'

I put down my empty glass and dusted the tasty biscuit crumbs from my jacket. I hated to interrupt these sessions and return to reality, but I looked at my watch. 'I'm so glad things turned out so nicely, Mrs Pumphrey, but I think I'd better give the little chap his check-up.'

I lifted Tricki on to a settee and palpated his abdomen thoroughly. Nothing wrong there. Then I fished out my stethoscope and listened to his heart and lungs. There was the heart murmur I knew about and some faint bronchitic sounds which I expected. In fact I was totally familiar with all my old friend's internal workings after treating him over the years. Teeth now – maybe could do with another scale next time. Eyes with the beginnings of the lens opacity of the old dog, but not too bad at all.

I turned to Mrs Pumphrey. Tricki was on prednoleucotropin for his arthritis and oxytet for the bronchitis but I never elaborated on his ailments to her – too many medical terms upset her. 'He's really wonderful for his age, Mrs Pumphrey. You have his tablets to use when necessary and you know where I am if ever you need me. Just one thing. You have been very good with his diet lately so don't give him too many titbits – not even extra char sui!'

She giggled and gave me a roguish look. 'Oh, please don't scold me, Mr Herriot. I promise I'll be good.' She paused for a moment. 'I must mention one more thing with regard to Tricki's arthritis. You know that Hodgkin has been throwing rings for him for years?'

'Yes, I do.' Her words raised an image of the dour old gardener under duress casting the rubber rings on the lawn while the little dog, barking in delight, brought them back to him again. Hodgkin, who clearly didn't like dogs, invariably looked utterly fed up and his lips always seemed to be moving as he muttered either to himself or Tricki.

'Well, I thought in view of Tricki's condition that Hodgkin was throwing the rings too far and I told him to throw them for just a few feet. The little darling would have just as much fun with much less exertion.'

'I see.'

'Unfortunately,' here her expression became disapproving, 'Hodgkin has been rather mean about it.'

'In what way?'

'I wouldn't have known anything about it,' she said, lowering her voice, 'but Tricki confided in me.'

'Did he really?'

'Yes, he told me that Hodgkin had complained bitterly that it meant he had to bend down a lot more often to pick up the rings and that he had arthritis too. I wouldn't have minded,' her voice sank to a whisper, 'but Tricki was deeply shocked; he said Hodgkin used the word "bloody" several times.'

'Oh dear, dear, yes, I see the difficulty.'

'It has made the whole thing so embarrassing for Tricki. What do you think I should do?'

I nodded sagely and after some cogitation gave my opinion. 'I do think, Mrs Pumphrey, that it would be a good idea to have the throwing sessions less often and for a shorter time. After all, both Tricki and Hodgkin are no longer young.'

She gazed at me for a few moments, then smiled fondly. 'Oh, thank you, Mr Herriot, I'm sure you are right, as always. I shall follow your advice.'

I was about to make my farewells when Mrs Pumphrey put a hand on my arm. 'Before you go, Mr Herriot, I would like you to see something.'

She led the way to a room off the hall and opened the doors of a massive wardrobe. I looked at a long row of opulent suits – I had never seen so many outside a shop.

'These,' she said, running her hand slowly along jackets of all kinds, dark and dressy, light and tweed, 'belonged to my late husband.' For a few moments she was silent as she fingered one sleeve after another, then she became suddenly brisk and turned to me with a bright smile. 'He did love good clothes and went to London for all his suits. Now this one,' she reached up and lifted down a jacket and trousers of Lovat tweed, 'this one was made by one of the best tailors in Savile Row. Ooh, it's so heavy, will you hold it, please?' She gasped as she laid it on my outstretched arm and I, too, was amazed at its weight.

'Yes,' she went on, 'it is the most beautiful country suit and, do you know, he never wore it.' She shook her head and her eyes softened as she stroked the lapels. 'No, he never did. He died a few days after it was made and he was so looking forward to it. He was such an outdoor man, but he did like to be smartly dressed.' Then she said somewhat abruptly, looking up at me with a resolute expression, 'Now, Mr Herriot, would you like to have this suit?'

'Eh?'

'I wish you would have it. I'm sure it would be of great use to you and it is being wasted just hanging here in this wardrobe.'

I didn't know what to say, but my mind went back to various pauses in our conversation by the fire when I had noticed her eyes lingering briefly on the fringe of material on my frayed cuff as I raised my glass, and at my threadbare knees.

As I stood silent she looked suddenly worried. 'Perhaps I am embarrassing you?'

'Oh, no, no, no, not at all. It's very kind of you. I'm sure I'd love to have it.'

'Oh, I am glad.' She clapped her hands. 'It will be just right for you, quite the correct thing for a country vet. I'd so much like to think of you wearing it.'

'Right . . . right . . .' I said, still a little bemused. 'Thank you very much.' I laughed. 'Such a nice surprise.'

'Good, good,' she said, laughing too. Then she called across the hall. 'Ruth, Ruth, will you bring one of those big sheets of brown paper to put round this suit, there's a dear.'

As the maid hurried off, Mrs Pumphrey put her head on one side. 'There's just one thing, Mr Herriot. My husband was rather a large man. Some alterations will be necessary.'

'Oh, that's all right,' I said, 'I can see to that.'

As I walked over the gravel to my car weighed down with my parcel, I mused on the upturn in my day. A couple of hours ago I had slunk away like a pariah from a farm after a visit steeped in censure and dislike and with a final tongue-lashing thrown in, and look at me now. Mrs Pumphrey and Ruth were smiling and waving from the doorway. Tricki was back at his window, laughing his head off as he barked his farewell, the curtains moving with the wagging of his tail. My stomach glowed with sherry and savoury biscuits and I had a handsome free suit in my arms.

Not for the first time I thanked providence for the infinite variety of veterinary practice.

5

'Look at this, Helen!' I cried as I pulled off the brown paper back in Skeldale House. 'Mrs Pumphrey's given me a suit!'

My wife gasped as my new acquisition was unveiled. 'It's beautiful, Jim. So expensive-looking!'

'Isn't it just. I could never afford one like this.'

We looked down at the sumptuous tweed with its faint, scarcely discernible pattern of brownish threads among the Lovat green and Helen held up the jacket to examine it more closely.

'Gosh, it's so thick and heavy, I can hardly lift it! I've never seen such cloth – you'll never feel cold wearing this. Aren't you going to try it on? There's time before lunch – I'll just pop through to the kitchen and see that nothing's boiling over.'

I hurried to our bedroom and, bubbling with anticipation, removed my trousers and pulled on the new ones, then I donned the jacket and looked in the mirror. I really didn't have to look – I realised from the start that my hopes were dashed. The trousers rested in concertina-like folds round my ankles while the jacket sleeves hung several inches below my hands. The late Mr Pumphrey hadn't just been large, he must have been a giant.

I was observing myself sadly when I heard muffled sounds from the doorway. Helen was leaning against the wall laughing helplessly as she pointed a shaking finger in my direction. 'Oh dear,' she gasped. 'I'm sorry, but oh, ha-ha-ha!'

'Okay,' I said. 'I know, I know, it's a washout.' Then I caught sight of myself again in the mirror and couldn't fight back a wry smile. 'You're right, I do look funny, but what a disappointment. It's such a marvellous suit – I thought I was going to be Darrowby's best-dressed man. What the heck are we going to do with the thing?'

Helen dried her eyes and came over to me. 'Oh, it's such a shame, but wait a minute.' She tucked the sleeves up until my hands were revealed then knelt and rolled up a few folds of trousers. Then she stood back to view the result. 'Do you know, I really think it could be altered to fit you.'

'Oh come on, it's unthinkable. I'm drowned in it.' I glowered again at my reflection.

My wife shook her head vigorously. 'I'm not so sure. Looking at you now, I can just imagine how splendid it could be. Anyway, I'm going to take it round to Mr Bendelow and see if I can sweetheart him into doing it quickly.'

I grinned at the thought of our local tailor stirring himself. 'That would be a miracle.'

'You never know,' Helen said. 'I'm going to try, anyway.'

Later that day she came to me with the news that Mr Bendelow had been so dazzled by the quality of the material and the cut that he had promised a rush job.

The excitement over the suit was forgotten as I had an urgent call immediately after lunch.

Ted Newcombe's voice on the phone was strained and shaking. 'It's Clover – she's on calvin' and there's just a head and nowt else. I've had a go, but I can't reach the legs – it's a whopper of a calf. And it's the one I badly want – you remember?'

'Yes, I do remember, of course.'

'Can you get 'ere quick, Mr Herriot?'

'I'm leaving now.'

Clover was his best heifer and had been served by a premium bull. To a hill farmer like Ted, it would be a disaster if he lost the calf. I shouted to Helen and ran out to the car.

Ted's smallholding was a grey smudge high on a hillside near the top of the dale. There was no road to it and my car bumped its way up the grassy slope with my drugs and instruments rattling and clinking behind me. The flagged yard and thick-walled buildings were hundreds of years old; in fact, coupled with its inaccessibility, it was the sort of place where only hard-up people like Ted would dream of trying to make a living. The rent was low and it was all he could afford.

He was coming out of the byre as I drew up, Tall and thin, about my own age, father of a boy and girl who walked down that hill every day and then the two miles to the village school. He looked worried, but managed a grin.

'Nice car, Mr Herriot!' He gave the gleaming bonnet a mock polish with his sleeve but, as was typical of him, that was as far as the mickey-taking went.

I followed him into the little byre and I realised why he didn't feel much like joking. The smile was wiped off my own face immediately I looked at the beautiful heifer groaning and heaving, with an enormous muzzle just peeping from her vulva as she strained.

No vet likes to see that. It wasn't just a case of sorting out a malpresentation, it meant that a huge calf was finding it impossible to find a way out.

'I've 'ad a go,' Ted said as I stripped off and began to wash my arms in the buckets of steaming water. 'But there's no legs – feet are miles away. I remember you tellin' me once to push back the head to reach the feet but I've tried and she's ower strong for me.'

I nodded. The farmer hadn't much flesh on his bones, but he had a stringy power in his arms and I knew what he meant. 'Nobody's as strong as a big beast like that, Ted.'

'And all the time I'm wonderin' if t'calf's still alive. He's been squeezed in there for a hell of a long time.'

That was my worry, too. I soaped my arm and pushed a hand into the vulva alongside the massive head, but as I reached for the shoulder Clover gave another heave and my arm was trapped agonisingly for a few seconds.

'That's no good,' I gasped, 'there's not an inch of room in there. I'll try my luck with the head.'

I put my hand against the muzzle and pushed steadily, leaning hard as the head went back a few inches. That was as far as I got. Another mighty expulsive effort from the heifer sent me back where I started.

I began to wash my hands and arms again. 'It's impossible, Ted. That calf won't come out till we bring the feet round and there's simply no way of reaching those feet. She's a big, powerful heifer and we can't win pushing against her.'

'Oh 'ell!' He looked at me wide-eyed. 'What do we do, then? Caesarean? That's a big job!'

'Maybe not,' I said. 'I've got another trick up my sleeve.'

I was out to the car and back again in a few moments with a syringe and local anaesthetic. 'Grab the tail, Ted,' I said, 'and move it up and down like a pump handle. That's the way.' I felt for the epidural space between the vertebrae and injected 10 ccs, then I stood back and watched.

I hadn't long to wait. In less than a minute Clover began to relax as though her troubles were over. Ted pointed at her. 'Look at that, she's stopped strainin'!'

'She can't strain, now,' I said. 'She's had a spinal anaesthetic and she can't feel a thing back there. In fact, she really doesn't know what's going on.'

'So if she can't push against us we can maybe get the head back inside?'

'That's the idea.' Another soaping of my arm and I pressed my palm against the broad muzzle, and oh, it was lovely to feel the head and neck and the whole calf moving away from me with no sign of resistance. There was room then to pass a noose inside and snare a foot and then another till I had two cloven hooves showing at the vulva. I grasped one in each hand and as I leaned back the calf's muzzle reappeared and, to my great relief, I saw a twitching of the nostrils.

I laughed. 'This calf's alive, Ted.'

'Oh, thank God for that,' the farmer said, blowing out his cheeks. 'We can get on wi' the job now, can't we?'

'Yes, but there's just one snag. Because she's unable to strain she can't help us. We'll have to do everything ourselves.'

It was still a very tight squeeze and we had half an hour of careful pulling on the legs and head and frequent application of lubricating jelly. We soon began to sweat but Clover was totally unconcerned and paid no attention as she picked away happily at the hay in the rack. My big fear was that the calf might stick at the hips but, with a final heave from us, the little creature slid out into the world and I caught the slippery body as it fell.

Ted lifted a hind leg. 'It's a bull. Reckon it had to be when it was as big as that.' He smiled happily. 'Most times I want heifers, but thus 'un will sell well for breedin'. He's got a fine pedigree on both sides.'

He began to rub ribs and head with straw and the calf responded by raising his head and snuffling. Clover looked round quickly at the sound and gave a soft moo of delight and, it seemed to me, surprise, because she had known nothing of the operation and clearly was a little mystified as to how this enchanting newcomer had arrived. We pulled him up to her head and she commenced an enthusiastic end to end licking of the little body.

I smiled. I never got tired of this – the most rewarding thing in my veterinary life. 'Nice to see, isn't it, Ted. I wish all calvings finished up like this.'

'By gaw, you're right, Mr Herriot, and I can't thank ye enough. I really thought I had a dead 'un on me hands this time.' As I bent over the bucket he gave me a friendly thump on the back.

As I dried my arms, I looked round the byre with its row of well-kept cows. Over some months Ted had gutted the place completely, hacking out the ancient wooden partitions and replacing them with tubular metal, plastering the walls, digging up the cobbled floor and laying down concrete. He had done all the work himself.

He followed my gaze. 'What d'you think of me little place now?'

'It's great, you've done wonders, Ted. And you've built a nice little dairy, too.'

'Aye, ah've got to get that TT licence somehow.' He rubbed his chin. 'But there's a few things that don't come up to standard. Like not enough space between the channel and the back wall. There's nowt I can do about that and one or two other points. But if the Ministry'll grant me a licence, I'll get another fourpence on every gallon of milk and it'll make all the difference in the world to me.'

He laughed, as though reading my thoughts. 'Maybe you don't think fourpence is much but, you know, we don't need a lot o' money. We never go out at night – we're quite happy playin' cards and Ludo and dominoes with the kids, and with these cows to milk and feed and muck out twice a day, three hundred and sixty-five days a year, I'm tied to the spot.' He laughed again. 'Ah can't remember when I even went into Darrowby. No, we don't want much money, but right now I'm just hanging on – only keepin' my head above water. Any road, I'll know after next Thursday. They're having a meeting to decide.'

I didn't say anything. I couldn't tell him that I was the one who had to make a confidential report to the Milk Committee on that day about him and his farm and it all rested on whether I could convince them. Ted's fourpence a gallon was in my hands and it frightened me a bit, because if the TT licence didn't go through I dared not think how much longer he could carry on his struggle to make a go of this wind-blown farm with its sparse pastures.

I packed up my gear and we went outside. Breathing in the cold, clean air I looked at the cloud shadows chasing across the tumbled miles of green hills, and at the few acres that were Ted's world. They made a little wall-girt island lapped around by the tufted grass of the moorland which was always trying to flow over and swamp it. Those fields had to be fed and fertilised to keep them from returning to their wild state, and the walls, twisted and bent by the centuries, kept shedding their stones – another job to be done by that one man. I recalled a time when Ted told me that one of his luxuries was to wake up in the middle of the night so that he could turn over and go to sleep again.

As I started the engine, he waved, raising a huge, work-calloused hand. Bumping down the hillside I looked back at the thin, slightly stooping figure standing by the house with its fringe of stunted trees, and an awareness of his situation welled in me as it had done so often before. Compared to his, my life was a picnic.

6

The following Thursday I awoke with the words of my appeal for Ted spinning around in my head and I kept mouthing a few phrases in the car as I did a couple of early calls. I was due in the Ministry Office at 11 a.m. and by ten o'clock I was back home ready to change.

I was about to go upstairs when Helen came in.

'You'll never believe this,' she said breathlessly, 'but Mr Bendelow saw me as I passed his window and gave me the suit.'

'Mr Pumphrey's suit?'

'Yes, it's all altered and ready for you to wear.' She stared at me, wide eyed.

I looked at the parcel in amazement. 'Well, that's never happened before. We asked for a miracle and got one.'

'That's right,' Helen said. 'And another thing, I feel sure it's a happy omen.'

'What do you mean?'

'You can wear it when you speak to the Milk Committee. You'll really impress them in a suit like that.'

Her words struck home. As an orator I was no Winston Churchill and I needed any help that was going. In the bedroom I tore off my clothes and climbed into the refurbished trousers. They were now exactly the right length but there was something else, something I hadn't noticed when I had tried them on before. The waistband came right up over my chest until it was almost tucked under my arms. Those were the days of high waistbands which rested comfortably well above the hips, but Mr Pumphrey's stature had vastly accentuated this. I was beaten again. I turned and faced Helen and her mouth began to twitch. Then she lowered her head and her body shook with repressed giggles.

'Don't start that again!' I cried. 'They're nearly as funny as last time. You don't have to tell me. Anyway, I can't wear these damned things, that's all there is to it. I'm just a walking pair of trousers with a head and shoulders poking out at the top.'

I was about to pull off the maddening garment when Helen held up a hand. 'Wait . . . wait . . .' she said. 'Put on the jacket.'

'What good will that do?'

'The lapels are very high, just put it on.'

With a feeling of hopelessness I shrugged myself into the jacket and turned towards her.

Helen was looking at me with something like awe. 'It's wonderful,' she whispered. 'Incredible.'

'What is?'

'Look at yourself.'

I looked into the mirror and Lord Herriot of Darrowby looked out at me. The waistband was quite hidden and the suit was there in all its glory of rich material and superb tailoring, draped on me elegantly as if it had been made for me.

'My God,' I breathed, 'I never knew clothes could make all that difference. I'm like another person.'

'Yes, you are,' agreed Helen eagerly. 'You're like an important, prestigious person. You must wear it for the committee – you'll knock them cold!'

While I washed and combed my hair, I had the warm sense of everything slotting into place when all had seemed lost and as I left after a final admiring glance at myself in the mirror I was filled with an airy confidence.

Outside, a bitter wind swept over the fields but I couldn't feel it. Nothing could penetrate my apparel; in fact, I felt sure that, dressed like this, I could walk in comfort to the North Pole without changing.

In the car, my body heat rose rapidly and I had to open the windows. I was glad when I reached my destination and was able to take a few breaths of the cold air. My relief, however, was short lived because as soon as the swing doors of the Ministry Office closed behind me a stifling heat hit me. On my previous visits I had wondered how people could work in this atmosphere with the central heating going full blast and as I walked along the corridor looking through the glass partitions at the typists and technicians and Ministry officials apparently going about their business quite happily, I marvelled anew. Only this time it was worse. Much, much worse. This time I was cocooned almost up to my chin in two layers of carpet-like material.

It was the waistband, of course, that was the trouble, clamped round my entire rib-cage like a great constricting hand, and I had the silly feeling that the suit itself was carrying me along to the double doors of the Conference Room at the end of the corridor. In the big room it was hotter than ever and I had a moment of panic when I thought I wouldn't be able to breathe, but I settled down as the Committee members welcomed me in their usual friendly way and the chairman ushered me to my seat at the long table.

There were about twenty people on the Milk Committee – big farmers, technical officers of the Ministry, two of the great landowners of the district in Lord Darbrough and Sir Henry Brookly, a physician and one practising veterinary surgeon – me. I had felt honoured when I was invited to join and had tried to fulfil my duties to the best of my ability, but this morning was something special.

Sir Henry was chairman and as he started the proceedings I prayed that it would be a short session. I knew I couldn't stand it for long, tightly muffled in this heat, but as the minutes ticked away with agonising slowness I realised that there was a tremendous amount of business to get through. Long discussions about sterilisation, farm buildings and husbandry, cattle diseases, points of law – it went on and on and I sat there getting hotter and hotter. Quite often I was asked for my opinion and I answered in a breathless way which I hoped went unnoticed, but it seemed that my most important contribution was being kept until the end.

My condition deteriorated steadily until, after an hour, I was sure I was suffocating and it was only a matter of time before I fainted away and had to be carried from the room. I was breathing only with difficulty, I could feel the sweat running down my neck onto my collar and had to fight the impulse to tear open my jacket and let out some of the pent up heat, but the thought of this decorous group of men dissolving into laughter at the sight of my chin-high trousers stayed my hand.

It was after almost two hours that Sir Henry looked around the table and introduced my subject. 'Well, gentlemen,' he said, 'to conclude our business this morning we have to decide on the borderline case of hill-farmer Edward Newcombe's application for a Tuberculin Tested licence and I understand that our young friend, Mr Herriot, has been looking into the matter for us. Mr Herriot . . . ?' He smiled across the table at me.

Somebody began to talk about Ted Newcombe and for a few moments I didn't realise it was myself. The words were familiar but they seemed to be coming from somewhere outside me, panting and hoarse. Through the blur of sweat trickling into my eyes I could see them all looking at me kindly. They had always been kind, these men, maybe because I was the youngest member, but as my utterances tumbled out – 'outstanding stocksman' . . . 'cattle in immaculate condition' . . . 'hard worker' . . . 'meticulous attention to hygiene' . . . 'man of the highest integrity' . . . they kept smiling and nodding encouragingly and as the last phrase emerged – 'Edward Newcombe's buildings may not be perfect but he really is a trier and if he is granted his licence he will never let anybody down,' I seemed to be surrounded by cheerful, friendly faces.

Sir Henry beamed at me, 'Ah, thank you so much, Mr Herriot, that is most helpful and we are grateful to you. I think we can take it, gentlemen, that there will be no difficulty in granting the licence?' Hands went up in agreement all round the table.

I have very little recollection of how I left the room, only of rushing downstairs into the men's lavatory, locking myself into one of the cubicles, throwing off my jacket and collapsing, open-mouthed, onto the seat. As I opened the front of the vast trousers, unbuttoned my shirt and lay back, gasping, waves of heat mingled with relief and triumph rolled from me. I had got it over. Ted had his licence and I was still alive – just.

As I slowly recovered I heard two men come in. From my semi-supine position I could see their feet under the door and I recognised the voices of Sir Henry and Lord Darbrough. The feet disappeared as the men retreated to the opposite wall.

There was a silence, then. 'Tell you what, Henry,' boomed His Lordship, 'it did me good to see that young fella fighting his corner for the hill-farmer.'

'Couldn't agree more, George. Damn good show, I thought.'

'Threw everything into it, by gad. Didn't spare himself. Never seen anything like it – sweat was rolling down his face.'

'Mm, I saw. Dedication, I'd call it.'

'That's it, dedication. Good to see in somebody his age.' There was another pause, then, 'Y'know, Henry, there was something else about that young fella.'

'What was that, George?'

'Knows his clothes. Splendid suit. Rather envy him his tailor.'

7

'Look at that little lad!'

Farmer Dugdale was amused as he watched Jimmy directing his torch beam as I calved the cow. My son, ten years old, was taking his duty very seriously. It was quite dark in the loose box and he solemnly followed my every movement with his beam, shining on the cow's rear end as I worked, then on the bucket of hot water each time I resoaped my arms or dipped the ropes in the disinfectant.

'Yes,' I said, 'he loves night work.'

Jimmy, in fact, loved all veterinary work, but if I was called out in the evening before his bedtime it was his particular delight to come with me, sitting by me, quite absorbed, as the headlights picked out the twists and turns of the country lanes.

And tonight, when we arrived, he had been into the boot

before me, picking out the different coloured ropes to go on the calf's head and feet, busily tipping the right amount of disinfectant into the bucket.

'You've got the red rope on the head, Dad?' he asked.

'Yes.'

'Well behind the ears?'

'That's right.'

He nodded. Partly he was seeking information but he was also keeping me right, making sure I didn't make any silly mistakes.

It was a source of wonder to me that both my children were fascinated by my job. I often thought that the sight of their father rushing around all hours of the day and night, missing meals, working on Saturdays and Sundays while my non-veterinary friends played golf, would be enough to turn them away from my profession for life, but instead of that their greatest pleasure was to come with me on my rounds, taking in every detail of my diagnostic efforts and treatments.

I suppose the simple explanation was that, like me, like Helen, they were besotted with animals. To be able to work with these appealing creatures made everything worthwhile, and there was no doubt in the minds of both my children – they wanted to be vets.

It struck me now, that Jimmy, at the age of ten was half way there already. As the calf slipped out on to the loose box floor he quickly wiped away the mucus from the little animal's nostrils and mouth, seized a handful of hay and began to administer a brisk rubdown.

'It's a heifer, Dad,' he said, after an expert glance between the hind legs. 'That's good, Mr Dugdale, isn't it?'

The farmer laughed. 'Aye, it is. We want plenty of heifers. That 'un you're rubbing maybe will be a good milk cow one day.'

The following day was a Saturday with no school, and after breakfast, both children were lined up, ready for action. In fact they had already started. They had the lid of the car boot up and were clearing out the empty bottles and cartons, checking up to see that I had everything I might need.

'You're getting a bit short of calcium, Dad,' Rosie said. She was six now and had been doing the rounds since she was two, so she was very familiar with the contents of the big slotted box which a friend had made for me to hold my drugs and instruments.

'Right, my pet,' I replied, 'you'd better go and get some. Calcium is one thing we can't do without.'

Flushed with importance, she ran inside to the stock room, and I wondered, as often before, why it was that, at home and on the farms, she always ran to get things for me while Jimmy invariably walked.

Often, in the middle of a case, I'd say, 'Fetch me another syringe, Jimmy,' and my son would stroll out to the car, often whistling, perfectly relaxed. No matter how interested he was in what was happening he never hurried. And I have often noticed that now, when he is a highly experienced veterinary surgeon, he still doesn't hurry. This is probably a good thing, because ours can be a stressful occupation and going about things calmly must be the best way.

When all was ready we drove out into the hills. It was a bright morning with the bleak outlines of fell and moorland softened by the sunshine. There had been rain in the night and all the scents of the countryside drifted through the open windows.

The first farm was approached by a lane with several gates and Rosie was delighted because this was her job.

As we drew up at the first one she was out of the car in a flash. Red faced and serious, she opened the gate and I drove through.

'Lucky I was with you this morning, Dad,' she said. 'There's two more up ahead. I can see them.'

I nodded. 'It is indeed, sweetheart. If there's one thing I hate, it's gates.'

My little daughter sat back, well pleased. In the days before she started school she used to be really worried. 'What are you going to do without me?' she would say. 'I've got to go to school soon, and Jimmy's there already. You'll be all alone.'

Jimmy always seemed to be reasonably confident that I'd manage to struggle round on my own, but Rosie had grave doubts. Weekends for her were not just a time to play, but a blessed opportunity to look after her father. And for me it was a wonderful time and I marvelled at my luck. So many men with high pressure jobs see very little of their families but I had it both ways with my little son and daughter so often at my side as I worked.

And there was no doubt about it, it was an absolute boon to have the gates opened for me. Rosie stood stiffly to attention as I drove through the last one. Her hand was on the latch and her face registered the satisfaction of a job well done.

A few minutes later I was in the cow byre, scratching my head in puzzlement. My patient had a temperature of 106 but my first confident diagnosis of mastitis was eliminated when I found that the milk was white and clear.

'This is a funny one,' I said to the farmer. 'Her lungs are okay, stomach working well, yet she's got this high fever, and you say she's not eating?'

'Aye, that's right. She hasn't touched her hay or cake this morning. And look how she's shakin'.'

I pulled the cow's head round and was looking for possible symptoms when my son's voice piped up from behind me.

'I think it *is* mastitis, Dad.'

He was squatting by the udder pulling streams of milk on to the palm of his hand. 'The milk's really hot in this quarter.'

I went round the teats again and sure enough, Jimmy was right. The milk in one quarter looked perfect, but it was decidedly warmer than the others and when I pulled a few more jets on to my hand I could feel flakes, still invisible, striking my palm.

I looked up ruefully at the farmer and he burst into a roar of laughter. 'It looks like t'apprentice knows more than the boss. Who taught you that, son?'

'Dad did. He said you could often be caught out that way.'

'And he was, wasn't he!' The farmer slapped his thigh.

'Okay, okay,' I said, and as I went out to the car for the penicillin tubes I wondered how many other little wrinkles my son had absorbed in his journeys with me.

Later, as we drove back along the gated roads, I congratulated him.

'Well done, old lad. You know a lot more than I think!'

Jimmy grinned. 'Yes, and remember when I couldn't even milk a cow?'

I nodded. Milking machines were universal among the bigger farms but many of the smallholders still milked by hand and it fascinated my son to watch them. I remembered the time he stood by the side of old Tim Suggett as he milked one of his six cows. Crouched on the stool, head against the cow's flank, the farmer effortlessly sent the white jets hissing and frothing into the bucket held between his knees.

He looked up and caught the boy's eager gaze.

'Does tha want to 'ave a go, young man?' he asked.

'Oh, yes please!'

'Awright, here's a fresh bucket. See if ye can fill it?'

Jimmy squatted, grasped a teat in each hand and began to pull away lustily. Nothing happened. He tried two other teats with the same result.

'There's nothing coming,' he cried plaintively. 'Not a drop.'

Tim Suggett laughed. 'Aye, it's not as easy as it looks, is it? I reckon it 'ud take you a long time to milk ma six cows.'

My son looked crestfallen, and the old man put a hand on his head. 'Come round sometime and I'll teach ye. I'll soon make a milker out of ye.'

A few weeks later, I returned from my round one afternoon to find Helen standing on the doorstep of Skeldale House, looking very worried.

'Jimmy hasn't come back from school,' she said. 'Did he tell you he was going to any of his friends?'

I thought for a moment. 'No, not that I can remember. But maybe he's just playing somewhere.'

Helen looked out at the gathering dusk. 'It's strange, though. He usually comes home to tell us first.'

We telephoned round his school friends without result, then I began a tour of Darrowby exploring the little winding 'yards', calling in at people we knew and getting the same reply. 'No, I'm sorry, we haven't seen him', and my attempt at a cheerful rejoinder, 'Oh, thanks very much, sorry to trouble you,' as a cold hand began to grip at my heart.

When I got back to Skeldale House, Helen was on the verge

of tears. 'He hasn't come back, Jim. Where on earth can he have got to? It's pitch black out there. He can't be playing.'

'Oh, he'll turn up. There'll be some simple explanation, don't worry.' I hoped I sounded airy but I didn't tell Helen that I had been dredging the water trough at the bottom of the garden.

I was beginning to feel the unmistakable symptoms of panic when I had a thought. 'Wait a minute, didn't he say he'd go round to Tim Suggett's one day after school to learn to milk?'

The smallholding was actually in Darrowby itself and I was there in minutes. A soft light shone above the half door of the little cow house and as I looked inside there was my son, crouched on a stool, bucket between his knees, head against a patient cow.

'Hello, Dad,' he said cheerfully. 'Look in here!' He displayed his bucket which contained a few pints of milk. 'I can do it now! Mr Suggett's been showing me. You don't pull the teats at all. You just make your fingers go like this.'

Glorious relief flooded through me. I wanted to grab Jimmy and kiss him, kiss Mr Suggett, kiss the cow, but I took a couple of deep breaths and restrained myself.

'It's very good of you to have him, Tim. I hope he hasn't been any bother.'

The old man chuckled. 'Nay, lad, nay. We've had a bit o' fun, and t'young man's cottoned on right sharp. I've been tellin' him if he's goin' to be a vitnery he'll have to know how to get the milk out of a cow.'

It is one of my vivid memories, that night when Jimmy learned how to get the milk out of a cow, so that he could diagnose mastitis and put one over on his old man.

To this day I often wonder if I did the right thing in talking Rosie out of her ambition. Maybe I was wrong, but back in the forties and fifties, life in veterinary practice was quite different from now. Our practice was ninety per cent large animal work and although I loved the work I was always being kicked, knocked about and splashed with various kinds of filth. With all its charms and rewards it was a dirty and often dangerous job. On several occasions, I was called to help out in neighbouring practices where the vet had sustained a broken limb, and I had myself been lame for weeks when a huge carthorse whacked my thigh with his iron-shod hoof.

Quite often I didn't smell so good because no amount of bathing in antiseptics could wholly banish the redolence of delivering decomposing calves and the removal of afterbirths. I was used to people wrinkling their noses when I came too near.

Sometimes after prolonged calvings and foalings, often lasting for hours, every muscle in my body ached for days as though I had been beaten with a heavy stick.

It is all so different now. We have long plastic gloves to protect us when we are doing the smelly jobs, there are metal crushes to hold the big beasts instead of having to plunge among them as they were driven into a passage on the farm, and the Caesarean operation has eliminated the rough side of obstetrics. Also, the gentler small animal work has expanded beyond all expectations until it now makes up more than half our work.

When I entered the veterinary college there was only one girl in our class – a tremendous novelty – but now girls make up at least fifty per cent of the students at the veterinary schools and, in fact, excellent girl veterinary surgeons have worked in our practice.

I didn't know all this forty years ago and although I could imagine tough little Jimmy living my life, I couldn't bear the thought of Rosie doing it. Unfairly at times, I used every wile I could think of to put her off veterinary work and to persuade her to become a doctor of humans instead of animals.

She is a happy doctor, too, but, as I say, I still wonder . . .

8

'Not to put too fine a point on it, Herriot, I think you are dishonest.'

'What!' I had been called a few things in my time, but never that and it hit me hard, especially coming from a tall, patrician veterinary surgeon, looking down his nose at me. 'What the devil do you mean? How can you possibly say that?'

Hugo Mottram's imperious blue eyes regarded me with distaste. 'I say it only because I am forced to no other conclusion. I consider unethical behaviour to be a type of dishonesty and you have certainly been guilty of that. Also, your attempts to justify your actions seem to me to be sheer prevarication.'

This was really nice, I thought, particularly here in Brawton where I was trying to enjoy my precious half-day. I had been browsing happily in Smith's bookshop, and had spotted Mottram walking along by the shelves and, in fact, had been regarding him with some envy, wishing that I looked a bit like him. He was the perfect picture of my idea of a country vet; check cap, immaculate hacking jacket, knee breeches, stockings and brogues together with a commanding presence and hawk-like, handsome features. He was in his fifties, but as he paced among the books, head high, chin jutting, he had the look of a fit young man.

I took a deep breath and tried to speak calmly. 'Mr Mottram, what you have just said is insulting, and I think you should apologise. Surely you realise that neither my partner nor I have any designs on your clients – it was just an unfortunate combination of events. There was nothing else we could have done in the circumstances and if only you would just think about it . . .'

The tall man stuck out his chin even more. 'I *have* thought about it and I mean what I say. I have no desire to waste any more time in discussing this matter, and my hope is that I shall have no further contact with you in the future.'

He turned quickly and strode from the shop leaving me fuming. I stood there, staring at my boots. Helen would be joining me any minute now – she had been having her hair done – and then our happy programme would start; shopping, tea, then the cinema and a late meal with a lot of good conversation, all with my pal, Gordon Rae, the vet from Boroughbridge and his wife, Jean. It was a simple sequence, but a blessed escape from the hard work and we looked forward to it all week. And now it was in ruins, shattered.

This thing with Mottram had started a few weeks previously. I was examining a spaniel with a skin eruption in our surgery when the lady owner suddenly said, 'Mr Mottram of Scanton has been treating this dog for some time. Says it's eczema, but it's not improving and I think it must be something else. I want a second opinion.'

I looked at the lady. 'I wish you'd mentioned that at the beginning. Really, I should have asked Mr Mottram's permission before I looked at your dog.'

'Oh, I didn't know that.'

'Well, yes, that's how it is, and I'm afraid I'll have to speak to him before I do any more.'

I excused myself and went through to the telephone in the office.

'Mottram here.' The voice was as I remembered. Deep, assured, cool. As a neighbouring veterinary surgeon, I had met him a few times and found I couldn't get very near him. His aristocratic haughtiness was, to me, decidedly off-putting. But I had to try to be friendly.

'Oh, hello, this is Herriot, Darrowby. How are you?'

'I am quite well, Herriot. I trust you are the same.' Damn, he still sounded patronising.

'Well now, I have one of your clients, a Mrs Hickson, here with her dog – I see it has a skin condition. She's asking for a second opinion.'

The voice became suddenly glacial. 'You've seen the animal? I think you might have consulted me first.'

'I'm sorry. I didn't get the chance. Mrs Hickson didn't tell me till I had the dog on the table. I do apologise, and I wonder if I might have your permission to carry on.'

There was a long pause, then again the icy tones. 'Well, I suppose if you must, you must.' The phone went down with a bonk.

My face was hot with embarrassment. What was the matter with the chap? This sort of thing happened all the time in veterinary practice. I'd had to approach other neighbouring practitioners and sometimes they'd had to approach me. The response on both sides had always been 'Oh yes, of course, carry on by all means. I'd be glad to know what you think.' And followed by a description of the treatment to date.

None of that with Mottram, and I wasn't going to phone him again. I'd have to find out the past treatment from the owner if I could.

I told Siegfried later.

'Snooty bugger,' he grunted. 'Remember when I asked him to dinner a long time ago? He said that he felt that vets should have an honourable association with their neighbours in opposition, but he didn't believe in their socialising with each other.'

'Yes, I do remember.'

'Okay, I respect his views, but there's no need for this stupid touchiness.'

A couple of weeks later I had a feeling of impending doom when I was feeling my way over the hind leg of a lame dog and the owner, a nice old man, chirped up. 'Oh, by the way, I should have told you. Mr Mottram over at Scanton has been treating him, but I can see no improvement at all and I'd like your opinion.'

My toes began to curl, but there was nothing else for it. I rang up our neighbour again.

'Mottram here.' That same discouraging voice.

I told him what had happened, and asked his permission.

Again that long pause, then a disdainful 'So you're at it again?'

'At it . . . ? What do you mean? I'm not at anything, I'm merely asking your permission to do as your client has requested.'

'Oh, do what you damn well like.' And I heard the familiar thud of the phone at the other end.

I began to sense the eerie workings of fate when Siegfried came in a few days later, looking thoughtful.

'You won't believe this, James. I was called to one of Mottram's clients this morning. Bollands by name, and he was in a state. He had a horse with a broken leg and couldn't get hold of Mottram. Phoned me in desperation. I rang the Scanton practice but he was on his rounds and I had to dash out to Bollands' place. It was a ghastly thing – a horrible compound fracture with the poor creature in agony. No possibility of treatment. There was simply nothing for it but to shoot the poor thing immediately. I couldn't let him suffer. But it would be Mottram – I've tried to contact him again now, but he's still not around.'

I had been helping Siegfried to clean out a dog's cankered ears and we were clearing up when, to our complete astonishment, Mottram appeared in the doorway of the operating room. He was immaculate as usual, clearly in a rage, but in cold control of himself.

'Ah, you're both here.' That superior voice again. 'It's just as well, because what I have to say applies to both of you. This latest escapade at Bollands' is really too much, Farnon. I can only conclude that you are conducting a campaign to steal my clients.'

Siegfried flushed. 'Now look here, Mottram, that is ridiculous.

We have absolutely no desire to poach your clients. As to Bollands' horse, I tried in vain to get in touch with you, but . . .'

Mottram held up a hand. 'I don't want to hear any more. You can say what you like, but I believe in *honourable* relations. Now that this has happened I am glad I stuck to my principles about that "out to dinner together" nonsense.' He nodded down to each of us from his great height and left.

Siegfried turned to me ruefully. 'Well, that's finally torn it. I want to be friends with all my neighbours but we're finished there.'

Now in the bookshop in Brawton, recalling the sequence of events, I felt that I hadn't needed this final onslaught from Mottram. Standing there among the wreckage of my half-day, looking at his retreating back, I knew that he had washed his hands of me.

Like my partner, I was unhappy about the situation, but I put it out of my mind until my bedside phone rang at 1 a.m. about a month later. I reached out a sleepy arm.

The voice at the other end was agitated. 'This is Lumsden, Scanton. Mr Mottram's assistant. I'm treating his horse with a bad colic, but I'm beat with it. I need help.'

Suddenly I was wide awake. 'Where's Mottram?'

'He's on holiday in the north of Scotland.' The young man's voice began to quaver. 'Oh, this would happen when he's away. He adores this horse – it's his favourite, he rides it every day. But I've tried everything and it looks like dying. I don't know how I'm going to face him when he gets back.' There was a pause. 'Actually, I was hoping to speak to Mr Farnon. He's good with horses, isn't he?'

'Yes, he is,' I said. In the darkness, I rested the receiver on my chest and looked at the ceiling as Helen stirred uneasily at my side, then I spoke again. 'Look, Lumsden, I'll have a word with my partner. It's his night off, but I'll see what he says. Anyway, I promise you one of us at least will be out to give you a hand.'

I cut short his thanks and dialled Siegfried's home number. I told him the story and could sense him snapping awake at the other end. 'Oh my God! Mottram!'

'Yes. What d'you think?'

I listened to a long sigh, then, 'I've got to go, James.'

'I'll come with you.'

'Really? Are you sure?'

'Of course. It's my night on, anyway, and I might be able to help.'

On the way to Scanton we didn't say much, but Siegfried voiced our thoughts. 'You know, this is uncanny. It sounds as though we're on a hiding to nothing here and Mottram is going to love us even more when he finds we've been in at the death of his beloved horse. Colics are nasty things at any time, always dangerous, even the straightforward ones, and I'd like to bet that this one will have some complications.'

Mottram's house was just outside Scanton and our headlights picked out an avenue of chestnut trees leading to an impressive bulk with a fine pillared doorway. We drove round the back and found Lumsden waving us with his torch into a cobbled courtyard. As we drew up, he turned and ran quickly into a lighted loose box in the corner of the yard. When we followed him, we could see the reason for his haste. And it was a frightening sight. My stomach lurched and I heard a soft 'Oh, dear God!' from Siegfried. A big chestnut horse, head hanging, staring-eyed and lathered in sweat, was stumbling round the box, buckling at the knees, doing his best to throw himself down and roll which, as any vet knows, can cause torsion of the bowel and inevitable death. The young man was hanging on desperately to the halter shank and urging the animal to keep walking round the box.

Lumsden looked about sixteen, but as a qualified veterinarian he had to be nearly ten years older than that. He was slightly built and his naturally boyish face was pale and exhausted.

'Very good of you to come,' he gasped. 'I hate to get you out of bed, but I've been fighting this colic all day yesterday and all day today, and I'm getting nowhere. The horse is worse if anything and I'm about knackered.'

'That's quite all right, old chap,' Siegfried said soothingly. 'James will hold the horse for a minute while you tell me what you've done.'

'Well, I've been giving Istin as a laxative, chloral hydrate to relieve the pain. Largactil, and a few small shots of arecoline, but I'm frightened to give any more arecoline because there's a hell of an impaction in there and I don't want to rupture the bowel. If only he'd pass a bit of muck, but there's been nothing through him for over forty-eight hours.'

'Never mind, my boy, you've done nothing wrong, so don't worry about that.' Siegfried slipped a hand behind the animal's elbow and felt the pulse. Then as the horse staggered around, he reflected the eyelid and examined the conjunctiva. He looked at it thoughtfully before taking the temperature.

'Yes . . . yes . . .' he murmured without changing expression, then he turned to the young man. 'Would you slip into the house now and get us a bucket of hot water, soap and a towel. I want to do a rectal.'

As Lumsden hurried out, Siegfried swung round. 'By God, I don't like this, James. Lousy weak pulse – can hardly detect it – brick red conjunctiva and temperature 103. I don't want to put the wind up this young chap, but I think we're on a loser here.' His eyes widened. 'And Mottram again! Is there such a thing as a jinx?'

I didn't say anything as I hung on to the struggling animal. A weak pulse is a particularly ominous finding in a horse and the other things pointed to a complicating bowel inflammation.

When the young man came back, Siegfried rolled up a sleeve and pushed his arm deep into the rectum. 'Yes . . . yes . . . bad impaction, as you say.' He whistled softly for a few moments. 'Well, first, we've got to relieve his pain.'

He injected the sedative into the jugular vein, speaking gently to the horse all the time. 'That'll make you feel better, old lad. Poor old chap,' and followed this with a long saline infusion intravenously to combat the shock, and antibiotic for the enteritis. 'Now we'll get a gallon of liquid paraffin into him to try to lubricate that lot in there.' Quickly he pushed a stomach tube up the nostril and into the stomach and held it there as I pumped in the oil.

'Next, a muscular relaxant.' Again he gave an intravenous injection.

By the time he had cleaned and rolled up the stomach tube,

the horse looked a lot happier. Colic is a frightful agony and I've always felt that horses seem to suffer pain more deeply than any other animal, a suffering at times almost unbearable to watch. It was a relief to see the big animal calming down, stopping his repeated attempts to collapse, clearly finding a blessed release.

'Well,' said Siegfried quietly, 'now we wait.'

Lumsden looked at him questioningly. 'Are you sure? I feel very guilty about you losing your sleep. It's after two o'clock – maybe I could manage now.'

My partner gave him a wan smile. 'With respect, laddie, it's going to need a combined operation. That horse is only doped for now, and I don't have to tell you that he is in a very serious condition. If we can't get his bowels moving, I'm afraid he'll die. He's going to need more of everything, including the stomach tube. We'll all see it through, one way or another.'

The young man sat down on a pile of hay and gazed dully at his boots. 'Oh God, I hope it's not the other. Mr Mottram's last words to me were, "Now you'll look after Match."'

'Match?'

'Match Box. That's the horse's name. My boss is devoted to him.'

'I'm sorry,' Siegfried said, 'you're in an awkward position. I shouldn't think Mottram would be the easiest man to explain things to.'

Lumsden ran his hands through his hair. 'No . . . no . . .' then he looked up at us. 'Mind you, he's not a bad bloke. He's always treated me right. It's just his personality. When he gives me one of his looks I feel about six inches high.'

'I know the feeling,' I said.

Siegfried gazed at the young man for a moment. 'What's your name? What does your mother call you?'

'Harry.'

'Well, Harry, you're probably right. And I like your loyalty. Maybe it's just his way, but James and I both seem to have caught him at the wrong time. Anyway, can you fetch us a pot of coffee? It could be a long night.'

It was indeed a long night. We took turns at walking the horse when he showed signs of going down. Siegfried repeated his injections, ringing the changes between sedatives and muscular relaxants with another cautious shot of arecoline and at five o'clock used the stomach tube again to give magnesium sulphate. And all the time as we dosed and yawned, slumped on the hay, we looked for a genuine easing of the pain, a raising of the animal's depression and most of all for a movement of the bowels.

For my part, as I watched Match Box's lolling head and trailing steps, my dominating worry was the knowledge that horses die very easily. Cattle and most other species could survive things so much better and the old saying among the farmers that ''Osses don't stand much' was so true. As the night wore on and my metabolism slowed down, my spirits drooped with it. At any moment, I expected the horse to halt in his painful circling of the box, pitch forward on to his side and groan his last few breaths away. Then we would drive miserably back to Darrowby.

Over the half-door of the box I could see the gradual disappearance of the stars and a lightening of the eastern sky. At around six o'clock, as the birds began to sing in the chestnut trees and the grey light of dawn crept into the box, Siegfried stood up and stretched.

'The big world has started to turn again out there, chaps, so what are we going to do? We've got to see to both our practices so who's going to stay with Match Box? We can't leave him.'

We were looking at each other, bleary-eyed, when the horse suddenly cocked his tail and deposited a small heap of steaming faeces on the floor.

'Oh, what a lovely sight!' cried Siegfried as our weary faces broke into smiles of relief. 'That makes me feel a lot better, but we mustn't get too cocky yet. He's still got a touch of enteritis, so I'll give him another shot of antibiotic before we go. Harry, I think it's safe to leave him now, so we'll be on our way, but don't hesitate to ring us if he doesn't go on right.'

Out in the yard we shook hands. The young man was blinking with tiredness but he looked happy. 'I don't know what to say,' he mumbled. 'I'm so grateful to both of you. You've got me out of a terrible fix and I can't thank you enough.'

'Not at all, my boy,' Siegfried sang out, 'only too glad to be able to help. Get in touch with us any time – but not about colicky horses for the next day or two, if you don't mind.'

We all laughed and waved goodbye as Siegfried started the engine and drove out of the yard.

There was no word from Lumsden until the following day when I answered the phone. 'Match Box is absolutely fine. Bowels normal, nibbling hay, just great,' he said. 'Thanks – thanks again!'

Three weeks passed and, in the rush of work, the Scanton episode began to recede into all the other memories, but one morning Siegfried looked up from his perusal of the appointments book.

'You know, James, I do think Mottram might have made some acknowledgement of our bit of assistance with his horse. I'm not looking for fulsome thanks, but I think he might have said something.'

With an irritable gesture, he scribbled something in the book. 'I expect the toffee-nosed bugger can't unbend even as far as that.'

'Oh, I don't know, Siegfried. Maybe he's still on holiday. We don't know that.'

'Hmm!' My partner looked at me doubtfully. 'Possibly. Could be I'm doing him an injustice, but anyway, we've got the satisfaction of helping to pull that grand horse round.' His face softened. 'Lovely sort.'

Next day I came in from my morning round and found my partner bending over an open crate from whose depths a row of gold-topped bottles protruded.

'What's that?' I asked.

'Champagne. A dozen.' He pulled out a bottle and looked at the label. 'Bollinger, no less!'

'Gosh, where's that come from?'

'No idea. Delivered this morning while we were out, and there's no message inside. But don't worry, it's for us all right. Look. Messrs Farnon and Herriot, Skeldale House.'

'Wonderful. I wonder . . .'

As I spoke, there was a knock on the office door and Hugo Mottram walked in.

We didn't say anything – just stared at him.

He glanced at the crate. 'Ah, I see you got the champagne.'

We spoke in unison. 'You sent it?'

'Yes . . . yes . . . a small gesture of thanks. I returned from holiday only last night and . . . er . . . Lumsden told me what you did for Match.'

'Oh really there's no need . . . only too pleased . . .' Siegfried for once was almost stammering.

Mottram, too, was finding things difficult. Tall and dignified as always, he was nevertheless acutely uncomfortable; unsmiling, searching desperately for words. 'There is indeed a need . . . a need to express my gratitude which . . . which is deeper than I can . . . can truly say. And there is a need, also . . . to apologise to you gentlemen for my stupid and unforgivable remarks when last we met . . .'

'My dear chap, not another word,' Siegfried burst out. 'We never really –'

Mottram raised a hand. 'Please let me say . . . I am profoundly sorry and ashamed. Why I said such things I do not know . . . I've done it before . . . I just seem to be much too . . . prickly. I'm afraid I can't help it.'

As he spoke, he still pushed his chin out, looking down his nose at us. Maybe he couldn't help that either. But it was obvious that his confession was costing the man dear and I could feel the tension in the room rising.

Siegfried, it was clear, felt the situation needed defusing. He threw his arms wide in an all-embracing bonhomie.

'Mottram, Mottram, my dear fellow. What is all this? Just a simple misunderstanding immediately forgotten. Say no more, I beg of you. I assure you that the only concern of James and myself is that your beautiful horse has fully recovered.'

The big man's face softened. 'He is beautiful, isn't he?'

'I tell you this,' Siegfried said softly, 'I wish I had one like him. I do envy you.'

I could see the flash of rapport as the two horse lovers faced each other.

Mottram nodded. 'Ah well, so glad, so glad,' he murmured.

'And by the way, I have something for you from Lumsden.

He, too, is immensely grateful.' He handed Siegfried a small parcel.

My partner unwrapped it quickly and gave a shout of pleasure. 'A bottle of malt whisky! Good old Harry! This is our lucky day. And I think we ought to celebrate Match Box's recovery – among other things. We have all the ingredients right here.' He lifted a bottle of champagne from the crate. 'What do you say, Mottram, old chap? We have a little time to spare before lunch.'

'You're very kind, Farnon. I'd like that.'

'Splendid, splendid, do sit down and make yourself comfortable. Get the glasses, James!'

Within minutes the champagne had popped and we were seated round the table. Siegfried raised his glass and looked appreciatively at the sparkling contents. 'Here's to Match Box, may he never have belly-ache again!'

We drank, and Mottram cleared his throat. 'There is just one more thing I want to say. I wish we had got to know each other socially long ago. I wonder if both of you would come to dinner next Friday?'

9

I was always apprehensive and ill at ease when I had Mrs Featherstone's problem dog on the table, but this time I felt relaxed and full of confidence. But then I was always like that when I was delirious.

Delirium was only one of the countless peculiar manifestations of Brucellosis. This disease, which causes contagious abortion in cattle, ruined thousands of good farmers of my generation and was also a constant menace to the veterinary surgeons who had to deliver the premature calves and remove the afterbirths.

Thank heaven, the Brucellosis scheme has now just about eradicated the disease but in the fifties such a thing hadn't been dreamed of and I and my contemporaries wallowed almost daily in the horrible infection.

I remember standing stripped to the waist in cow byres –

parturition gowns were still uncommon and the long plastic protective gloves unknown in those days – working away inside infected cows for hours and looking with wry recognition at the leathery placenta and the light-coloured, necrotic cotyledons which told me that I was in contact with millions of the bacteria. And as I swilled myself with disinfectant afterwards, the place was filled with the distinctive acrid odour of abortion.

The effects on many of my fellow vets were wide and varied. One big fat chap faded away to a skeleton with undulant fever and was ill for years, others developed crippling arthritis and some went down with psychiatric conditions. One man wrote in the *Veterinary Record* that as part of his own syndrome he came home one night and decided it would be a good idea to murder his wife. He never got round actually to doing it, but recorded the impulse as an interesting example of what *Brucella abortus* could do to a man.

I used to pat myself on the back and thank God that I was immune. I had been bathing in the infection for years and had never experienced the slightest reaction and as I looked around at some of my suffering friends I was so thankful that I had been spared their ordeal. And after all this time I just knew that such a thing would never happen to me.

That was before I started my funny turns.

This was my family's term for a series of mysterious attacks which came unheralded and then passed off just as quickly. At first I diagnosed them as repeated chills – I was always stripping off in open fields, often in the middle of the night – then I thought I must have a type of flu of short duration. The symptoms were always the same – a feeling of depression, then an ice-cold shiveriness which drove me to my bed where within an hour I shot up a temperature of 105 or 106. Once I had developed this massive fever I felt great: warm and happy, laughing heartily, chattering to myself and finally breaking into song. I couldn't help the singing – I felt so good.

This was a source of great amusement to my children. When I was at the singing stage I could always hear them giggling outside the bedroom door, but I didn't mind – I didn't mind anything.

However, I finally had to find out what was happening to me and a blood test by Dr Allinson dispelled all doubts by showing a nice positive titre to *Brucella abortus*. Reluctantly I had to admit that I had joined the club.

The particular attack when Mrs Featherstone brought her dog to the surgery was on a Saturday. I was driving back from a football match in Sunderland with some of my pals. Our team had won and we were all in high spirits, laughing and joking, and I hardly noticed just when I stopped being the life of the party and went quiet. I did know that when I got to Skeldale House and huddled miserably over the fire, shaking like a man with malaria that another funny turn was on the way.

Helen took one look, chased me upstairs and began to fill the hot water bottles. Feeling like death I crawled between the sheets and lay, cuddling one bottle, feet on another, while the bed vibrated with my terrific rigor. Helen piled another eiderdown on top of me, turned out the light and left me to it. We both knew what was going to happen.

It wasn't long before the familiar pattern started to set in. Quite soon I began to feel a bit better – warmer, more cheerful – then the warmth mounted and increased and spread through every corner of my being until I was floating along in a delicious languor, utterly at peace, all my troubles dissolved and gone. This, I felt, was heaven. I could stay like this forever, but the warmth developed into a fiery heat when I felt even better; no longer languorous, but powerful, dominant, foolishly and riotously happy.

This was the time when I usually extended a burning arm to pick up my bedside thermometer and stick it under my arm. Ah, yes, there it was, 106, exactly as I thought. I chuckled with satisfaction. Everything was just fine.

Lying there, I was so full of the joys of life that I began to talk aloud, discussing interesting matters with myself, and then my bursting high spirits had to find some further outlet and singing was the natural thing. 'Maxwelltown braes are bonny, where early fa's the dew, and t'was there that Annie Laurie gie'd me her promise true.' I let rip at full volume and never had my voice sounded as rich and rounded.

A few hee-hees sounded from behind the door followed by Jimmy's whisper, 'There he goes' and a muffled laugh from Rosie. The little beggars were there again, but what the hell? 'Gie'd me her promise true, which ne'er forgot will be!' I hit the high notes without a trace of self-consciousness, ignoring the further outburst from beyond the door.

I had a further chat with myself, agreeing wholeheartedly with everything I said, then I thought I'd try my John McCormack impression of 'The Rose of Tralee'. I took a long breath. 'The pale moon was shining above the green mountain.'

'Ha-ha-ha-haaa!' My children were having a great time out there. Then I heard the ringing of the front door bell, moments later feet on the stairs, then a knock on the bedroom door.

Jimmy's head poked into the room. 'Hello, Dad.' His face worked in his effort to stifle his laughter. 'Mrs Featherstone's downstairs with her dog. She says it's urgent and Mum's had to go out for a few minutes.'

'Right-oh, old lad.' I swung my legs from the bed. 'I'll be down immediately.'

My son's eyes widened. 'Are you sure?'

'Absolutely. I'll be down in two ticks. Put her in the consulting room.'

With a final startled glance, Jimmy closed the door and left.

As I pulled on shirt and trousers, the blood thundered in my ears and my face was afire. Normally, the very mention of Mrs Featherstone made me shrink. Rich, middle-aged, imperious, she had plagued me for years with the imaginary ailments of her little poodle, Rollo.

Rollo was an outstandingly healthy little dog. In fact, like many poodles, he was a tough little animal with the characteristic of being able to leap six feet in the air from a standing position as though he were operated by springs, but where he was concerned Mrs Featherstone was a raving hypochondriac. From a commercial point of view, it may seem ideal to have a rich client willing to pay for regular visits with her dog which has nothing the matter with it, but I found it increasingly wearing. Endless sessions of 'Really, Mrs Featherstone, the thing you are pointing out is quite normal' or 'I assure you, Mrs Featherstone, you are worrying needlessly' with the lady drawing herself up and sticking out her chin. 'Are you suggesting, Mr Herriot, that I am dreaming these things? That I cannot believe the evidence of my own eyes? My poor Rollo is suffering and I expect you to do something about it.'

Weak-mindedly I invariably submitted and fobbed her off with some form of placebo which would do the little animal no harm, but the sense of shame was deep. I had to admit that I was overawed by the woman, a jellyfish and a wimp in her presence, allowing her to dismiss my wafflings with a wave of her hand. Why couldn't I assert myself?

However, at this moment, knotting my tie, humming a happy tune as the glittering eyes in the vermilion face glared back at me from the mirror, my past diffidence seemed totally incomprehensible. I was really looking forward to seeing the lady again.

I ran downstairs, snatched a white coat from its hook, trotted along the passage and found Mrs Featherstone standing by the consulting-room table.

Damn, she wasn't a bad-looking woman! Very very nice, in fact. Funny I had never noticed that before. Anyway, there was not the slightest doubt in my mind as to what I had to do. I would grab her, give her a big, smacking kiss and a good long squeeze and all our past misunderstandings would melt away like the morning mist in the sun.

I was advancing on her when I noticed something strange. She had vanished. I was quite sure she had been standing there a second ago. I was blinking around me in bewilderment when I saw that she had ducked behind the table. How wonderful that she, too, was feeling skittish and ready for a game of peek-a-boo.

In a moment her head bobbed up and I greeted it with a merry cry. 'Yoo-hoo, I see you!' I trilled, but it seemed she had merely been stooping to lift her dog which she deposited on the table.

She gave me an odd look. 'Have you been on holiday, Mr Herriot? You have such a high colour.'

'No, no, no, no. I just feel extraordinarily well. In fact. I –'

The lady pursed her lips and brushed off the rest of my sentence impatiently. 'I really am most frightfully worried about poor Rollo.'

At the sound of his name, the poodle, aggressively fit, began to caper around on the table and jump up at my face.

'You are? Oh, what a shame. Tell me all about it.' I suppressed a chuckle.

'Well, we had just started on our evening walk when he coughed quite suddenly.'

'Just one cough?'

'No, two, like this. Hock-hock.'

'Hock, hock, eh?' I was having terrible trouble keeping a serious face. 'And then what happened?'

'Nothing else happened! Isn't that enough? A nasty cough?'

'Well, tell me, do you mean two hocks or one hock-hock?' I could not suppress a giggle, captivated as I was by my wit.

'I mean, Mr Herriot, one very unpleasant and alarming cough.' A dangerous light glinted in the lady's eye.

'Ah yes.' I took out stethoscope and thermometer and began a thorough examination of the patient. Everything, of course, was normal, and I could swear I detected an apologetic glance from Rollo.

And all the time the giggle was struggling steadily to the surface and finally it burst out into a loud 'Ha-ha!'

Mrs Featherstone's eyebrows shot up and she stared at me. 'Why are you laughing?' she enquired in glacial tones. She made the word seem more portentous by drawing it out into a long 'laawfing'.

'Well, really, you see, it's so funny.' I leaned on the table and laughed some more.

'Funny?' Mrs Featherstone's expression was a mixture of horror and disbelief. Her mouth opened soundlessly a few times. 'I fail to see anything *funny* in an animal's suffering.'

Wrapped in my cloak of heat and euphoria, I wagged a finger at her. 'But he's not suffering, that's what's so funny. He never *is* suffering when you bring him in to me.'

'I beg your pardon!'

'It's true, Mrs Featherstone. All Rollo's ailments are imagined by you.' The table shook as another paroxysm seized me.

'How dare you say such a thing!' The lady glared at me down her nose. 'You are being insulting and I really cannot –'

'Hey, just wait a minute. Let me explain.' I wiped a few tears away and took a few gasping breaths. 'Do you remember being worried to death by that habit of Rollo's where he lifts up a hind leg for a few steps, then puts it down again? I told you it was nothing, just a mannerism, but you insisted on my treating him for arthritis?'

'Well, yes, but I was worried.'

'I know, but you wouldn't believe me and he's still doing it. There's nothing wrong with him. Lots of little dogs do it.'

'Well, possibly, but . . .'

'And another thing,' I said between my chuckles, 'there was the time you made me give him sleeping pills because of his terrible nightmares.'

'Yes, and rightly so. He made the most pathetic whimpering sound while he was sleeping and his paws kept working as though he was running away from something terrible.'

'He was dreaming, Mrs Featherstone! Probably a nice dream about chasing his ball. All dogs have these dreams.'

I took hold of Rollo's head. 'And look here, ha-ha! You must recall your insistence that there were things growing over his eyes. You would never believe me that they were his normal third eyelids, ha-ha-ha! And see, they're still there, aren't they? You can see them now and he's quite happy with them, ha-ha-ha-ha!' I abandoned myself completely and bent over to dig her in the ribs, but she drew back and evaded my finger.

She put her hand over her mouth and continued to stare at me. Her eyebrows had taken up permanent residence high on her forehead. 'You . . . you cannot really mean all this!'

'Oh, but I do, I do. I could go on and on.'

'Well, I don't know what to say. And about his cough tonight?'

'You can take him away,' I said, 'And if there are any more hock-hocks, bring him back tomorrow, but there won't be.' I wiped my streaming face and lifted Rollo from the table.

The lady seemed in a daze as I steered her along the passage to the front door. She kept putting a hand over her mouth and giving me an incredulous sidelong glance, but she remained silent as though stunned.

After I had shown her out I retired to bed and drifted to sleep with the satisfied feeling of having cleared up a problem happily and effortlessly. I had handled the whole thing beautifully.

I didn't feel like that next morning. My latest funny turn was following its usual course. After the elation of the night before, a devastating deflation, lethargy, gloom, despondency and, in this case, the horrid spectre of remorse. As I lay in bed, pulling the sheets round my chin, my recollection of the previous evening was a frightening jumble. I couldn't get any of it sorted out in my mind.

I had been awake only a few moments before the memory hit me. Mrs Featherstone! Oh, my God! What had I said to her? What had I done? Desperately I tried to bring back the details without success, but the main indisputable fact was that I had laughed, even jeered at her, possibly even pawed at her person. Had I really attempted to embrace her? Had I given her a little cuddle as I walked her down the passage? My mouth opened in a series of soft moans.

Of one thing I could be sure – I had been guilty of the most ghastly impropriety and I had a searing conviction that I would have to pay dearly for it. Certainly she would never set foot in my surgery again. The whole shameful story would get around. She might even report me to the Royal College. I could see the headlines in the *Darrowby and Houlton Times*. VETERINARY SURGEON ON SERIOUS CHARGE, HERRIOT TO APPEAR BEFORE DISCIPLINARY BODY.

Groaning, I huddled deeper, gazing sightlessly at the cup of tea which Helen had placed by my bedside. After my funny turns I always had a day's rest and after that I made a remarkably quick recovery. But this time the mental scars would take a long time to heal. And how about the dire consequences?

I couldn't stand the self-torture any longer. I swallowed my tea, pulled on my clothes and trailed downstairs.

'Feeling better, Jim?' my wife asked brightly as she washed the dishes. 'You'll soon be okay again, you always are. What a strange business it is, but anyway, the kids enjoyed it. I understand you were in excellent voice last night.' She giggled as she reached for the towel.

I thought a gentle stroll in the fresh air would make me feel better, so I set off to walk around the town. I could hardly believe it when I saw Mrs Featherstone approaching a mere hundred yards away. Panic-stricken I scuttled over to the other side of the street, but the lady had spotted me and she crossed over too. And as the expensively tweeded figure bore down on me with purposeful strides I knew there was no escape.

Ah well, I told myself, here it comes. 'Mr Herriot, I thought you might be interested to know that I have placed the matter of Saturday night in the hands of my solicitors. Your behaviour was quite outrageous and I feel it my duty to ensure that defenceless women are protected from you in future. I can scarcely believe that a professional man would act as you did – taking advantage of your situation, betraying the trust placed in you. And as for your incredible callousness in the face of my poor dog's suffering – well, I cannot bear to think of it.'

But it wasn't like that at all. When Mrs Featherstone came up to me she put a hand on my arm. 'Now, Mr Herriot, you did me a service last night.'

'Eh?'

'Yes, you were so understanding. I realise now that I have been foolish about Rollo. I must have been such a nuisance to you.'

'Oh, no, no, no . . .'

'You are kind, but I know I have been unreasonable, troubling you over nothing at inconvenient times and here again I was at your door on a Saturday night.'

'I assure you . . .'

'But instead of being upset, you laughed, and it was so wonderful how you made me see the funny side of my silliness. I feel so ashamed that I always refused to listen to you when you so rightly tried to explain that I was worrying needlessly, and I do hope you can forgive me. From now on, I intend to be a sensible dog owner. And Rollo really is quite healthy, isn't he?'

Waves of relief rolled over me as I looked at the little dog, bright eyed, laughing-faced, leaping almost head high at the sound of his name. 'Well, I'm not too sure. He doesn't look very lively to me.'

'Oh, now you are trying to make me laugh again.' She put her hand over her mouth with the same embarrassed gesture I remembered, then gave me a quizzical look. 'I feel I'm going to laugh a lot more in future.'

I haven't had a funny turn for thirty years. They just gradually disappeared from my life. But when I think of that Saturday night with Mrs Featherstone, I still get an attack of the shivers.

10

I couldn't believe I was going to launch this boy on his own into the jungle of veterinary practice. Young John Crooks, so familiar a face after the months he had spent seeing practice with us during his university vacations, watching us work, picking up the practical hints and knowledge, doing the odd job himself, but always under our wings, was standing there by my desk, cheerful and smiling as always, but oh, so youthful. He looked about seventeen. It didn't seem fair to send him out there unprotected.

However, there was no doubt that it was J. L. Crooks Esq., MRCVS standing there, suitcase by his side, bright eyed and eager to go, and I had to adjust to the fact.

I cleared my throat. 'Well, John,' I said, smiling up at him, 'congratulations on qualifying. You're a fully fledged veterinary surgeon now, all your examinations behind you, and it's good to see you here. And, you know, this is quite an occasion. You are the very first assistant to be employed in the practice of Farnon and Herriot.'

He laughed. 'Really? That makes me sound very important. But when I was here as a student you had people working for you?'

'Yes, that's right. Tristan, of course, but he's one of the family and we never thought of him as an assistant. And there were one or two temporary people, but you are the first *official* man.'

'Well, that's nice. And now I'm here I'd better start earning my keep.'

'Okay, we'll get your car kitted out and then you'd better report to your digs. You're lodging with Mrs Barrie, aren't you?'

As the young man filled the car boot with the drugs and instruments he was going to need I could see that he was keen to pitch into the unpredictable world of practice, but I wondered just how nervous he was at the prospect of confronting the tough Yorkshire farmers on his own. Would he make the grade? Some new graduates just couldn't do it, and as he drove away in his Ford 8 with his bag of tricks rattling behind him I found myself crossing my fingers.

I have a big streak of old hen in me as my family will testify and throughout the day I was almost wringing my hands. How was the poor lad getting on? We were so busy that I didn't see him to talk to, and I kept hoping he hadn't come up against any awkward situations. Although our farmers were nearly all no-nonsense but kindly men, there was the odd very difficult client.

I recalled my session with Major Sykes a few days ago. That fierce little man barking at me as I treated his horse. 'Herriot, good God, man! Can't you do better than this? You don't seem to have much idea how to treat this blasted animal!' Then shouting at his groom, 'No, don't put the bucket down there, you bloody fool!' He was impossible to please and verbally steam-rollered people into the ground, treating everybody, especially it seemed, vets, like the more dim-witted private soldiers of his army days. In fact, despite myself, I often found my thumbs edging into line with the seams of my trousers, taking me back to my days in the RAF.

It was late afternoon when I came into the surgery and looked at the appointments book, and the words jumped out at me. 'Major Sykes, Hunting horse, laminitis.' John had ticked it – he'd be there now.

My eyes popped. One of those adored and valuable hunters – and laminitis, a condition with so many nasty possibilities. No job for a newly qualified young chap. The Major would eat him alive. I had to check up and I hurried out to Roova Grange.

As I got out of the car I could hear the Major's aggressive tones coming from a loose box and I feared John was already going through it.

I peeped over the half door of the box. A fine bay mare was standing there in the painful, crouching position of laminitis, her hind feet drawn under her body. A foal, obviously only a few days old, was close by her side. The Major, hands on hips, was almost shouting up into John's face.

'Now look here, er . . . er . . . what d'ye say your name is? Crooks, yes, now look here dammit, Crooks, you say this mare has a bad laminitis. Bloody great temperature, all crippled up, and you're trying to tell me that she'll be all right. Well, I bought her in foal and I bought her in good faith, is she always going to be subject to this, eh, eh? I've heard about horses which are always getting it. Have I been sold a pup, d'ye think? D'you know enough about the job to tell me that, eh, eh?'

The young man, however, did not seem at all put out. He spoke soothingly. 'Now, Major Sykes, I've told you the cause of the trouble. Your mare retained her afterbirth when she foaled and she developed metritis. Laminitis is a common complication of this, and what you have here is an isolated case. I've given her a shot of antibiotic and I'll repeat it over the next day or two. That will clear the metritis.'

Still bristling, the little man stuck out his chin. 'And how about the bloody laminitis, what're you going to do about that, eh, eh?'

'Well, as you saw, she's had an injection for that, too.' John gave him a serene smile. 'And if you'll keep her on bran for a few days and stand her in your pond to cool the feet as I directed I'm sure she'll soon be back to normal.'

'And d'you think she's had it before?'

'No, no, no.'

'How the hell d'ye know that?'

'Well, now, she's got no lines round her hooves, and look here,' he lifted one of the mare's fore feet, 'a lovely concave sole. She's never had laminitis before.'

'And it won't come back, eh?'

'No likelihood of a recurrence.'

'Just hope you're right,' the Major grunted.

'I'm sure I am. You'll see. You worry too much, you know.'

I shuddered and closed my eyes as John reached out and gave the little man a comforting pat on the shoulder. For a moment I thought the Major would erupt, then, to my amazement his face broke into something like a shy smile. 'You think so, eh?'

'I do indeed. You really oughtn't let things upset you so much.'

This was something new in the little man's experience and for a few seconds he looked up into John's face, then he took off his cap and scratched his head. 'Well, maybe you're right. Maybe you're right, young man. Heh-heh-heh!'

I couldn't believe it. He was laughing. John threw back his head and laughed too. It was like a reunion between two old college chums. And suddenly I realised that that wasn't little John Crooks, our student, in there; it was a tall, good-looking, self-assured veterinary surgeon with a fine big voice which lent authority to everything he said. I slunk away to my car and drove off with a resolution already formed in my mind. I wasn't going to worry about John any more.

He had been with us for a few weeks when I answered the phone one morning. 'Hello, is that Mr Herriot?' a cheerful voice enquired. I recognised one of our farmer clients.

'Yes, Mr Gates,' I replied. 'What can I do for you?'

'Nay, it's awright. Ah want to speak to t'yoong man.'

A pang, unexpectedly deep and piercing, shot through me. What was this? I was the 'yoong man', always had been. That was how the clients had invariably referred to me even though I was only six years younger than Siegfried. There was some mistake here.

'Who did you say you wanted?' I asked.

'T'yoong man – Mr Crooks.'

Ah well, there it was. I hadn't realised that I had become so attached to my title and, walking along the passage to fetch John, I felt strangely wistful as I faced the fact that, although I was still in my early thirties I wasn't the 'yoong man' any more.

From then on, I had to live with an ever-increasing flood of requests for the services of a yoong man who wasn't me. However, it was only depressing for a short time, because the compensations were enormous. As John settled in to the practice, I found a miraculous easing of my life. It was rather wonderful to have an assistant, especially a good one like him. I had always liked him, but when I got a call to a calving heifer at three o'clock in the morning and was able to pass it on to him and turn over and go back to sleep, I could feel the liking deepening into a warm affection.

John had his own ideas about treatment and wasn't afraid to express them. One day Siegfried found the two of us in the operating room.

'I've been reading about this Inductotherm. Revolutionary new treatment for strained tendons in horses. You just wrap this electric cable round the leg for a certain time every day and the heat clears up the strain.'

I gave a non-committal grunt. I seldom had any ideas and, in fact, was constitutionally opposed to any change, any innovation. This trait, I knew, irritated my partner intensely so I remained silent.

John, however, spoke up. 'I've read about it, too, but I don't fancy it.'

'Why not?' Siegfried's eyebrows went up.

'Smacks of witchcraft to me,' John said.

'Oh, rubbish!' Siegfried frowned at him. 'I think it sounds perfectly rational. Anyway, I've ordered one of the things and I'd like to bet it'll be a big help to us.'

Siegfried was the horse specialist so I didn't argue, but I was very interested to see how the thing worked and we soon had the opportunity to find out. The Lord of the Manor of Darrowby, usually called the Squire, kept his horses in some stables at the foot of our street, a mere hundred yards away, and it seemed like fate when he reported a case of strained tendons.

Siegfried rubbed his hands. 'Just what we wanted. I've got to go over to Whitby to inspect a stallion, so I'll leave it to you to handle this case, John. I've got a feeling you'll think the treatment is a great advance.'

I know my partner was looking forward to saying 'I told you so' to the young man, but after a week of the treatment, John still wasn't impressed.

'I've been winding this thing round the horse's leg every day and hanging about for the required time, but I can't see any difference. I'm having another session this afternoon, but if it still isn't any better I'm going to suggest a return to the old treatment.'

Around five o'clock that afternoon, with heavy rain sweeping along on the wind, I was drawing up outside the surgery when I froze in my seat. I was looking out at something terrible. Several of the Squire's men were carrying a body down the street. It was John. As I got out of the car they bore him into the house and deposited him at the foot of the stairs. He seemed to be unconscious.

'What on earth's happened?' I gasped, looking down in horror at the form of my colleague draped over the lower steps.

'T'yoong man's electrocuted 'isself,' one of the men said.

'What!'

'Aye, it's right. He were soaked wi' rain and when 'e went to connect up the machine to the plug, 'e must have got his fingers on the live metal. He started to yell, but 'e couldn't let go. He went on yellin', but I were hangin' on to the horse's head and I couldn't help 'im. He sort of staggered about, like, and at t'finish he fell over the horse's hind leg and that broke 'is grip on the thing or I think he'd have been a goner!'

'My God! What can we do?' I turned to Helen who had appeared from the kitchen. 'Could you phone the doctor,' I cried. 'But wait a minute, I think he's coming round.'

John, stretched out on the stairs, had begun to stir, and as he peered up at us through half-closed eyes, an amazing flow of colourful language began to pour from him. He went on and on and on.

Helen stared at me, open-mouthed. 'Just listen to that! And he's such a nice young man, too!'

I could understand her astonishment, because John was an upright, very correct lad who, unlike most vets, did not swear. However, he had a wonderful store within him because some of the words were new even to me, which was surprising considering that I grew up in Glasgow.

After a while the torrent slowed down to an unintelligible mumble, and Siegfried, who had just come in from his round, began to ply him with neat gin which, I believe, is contra-indicated in these cases.

There is no doubt that John could have lost his life but, mercifully, as the minutes passed he recovered steadily until he was able to sit up on the stairs. At last, as we adjured him to take it easy and stay where he was, he shook himself, got up, drew himself up to his considerable height and faced Siegfried.

'Mr Farnon,' he said with great dignity, 'if you ask me to operate that bloody apparatus again I shall tender my resignation.'

And so that was the end of the short career of the Inductotherm.

It was a few days later and as always, I felt a little wary when I saw the formidable figure of Sep Craggs bearing down on me in the passage at Skeldale House.

'Hey, 'erriot,' he barked, 'I want a word wi' you!'

He was a rude man but I was used to his mode of address and put up with it because he was a valuable client with a large farm which he ran with four grown sons whom he bullied and terrorised.

'Well, Mr Craggs, what's the trouble?' I asked peaceably.

He glared down at me from his six foot four bulk and pushed his face close to mine. 'Ah'll tell ye what the trouble is! You've been wastin' ma time!'

'Oh, really? In what way?'

'Remember them mastitis powders you were goin' to put out for me?'

Oh God, those sulphanilamide powders. I'd forgotten about them. 'I'm terribly sorry, I . . .'

'You forgot 'em, didn't you! "Come down this afternoon," you said. "They'll be in the box at the door for you." Well, I came down at three o'clock, but there was nowt in the box and nobody knew a thing about it. Ah'm bloody cross, I tell ye!'

'Well, as I say, Mr Craggs, I'm very sorry . . .'

'Aye, it's awright bein' sorry, but that doesn't help *me*. It's a bloody long way to Darrowby from ma place and I had to leave ma haymakin'. And all for nowt. I'm a busy feller tha knows, and I can't afford to have ma time wasted like this!'

Oh hell, he was rubbing it in, but he had me cold. I picked up the powders from the dispensary and handed them to him.

He was still grumbling. 'I don't want any more of this in the future, so think on. If ye ask me to come here for anything, just think on and 'ave it ready for me.'

I nodded dumbly, but he wasn't finished yet.

'It's you that needs powders,' he grunted. 'Thinkin' on powders!' He gave me a final glare and left.

I took a few deep breaths and hoped fervently that I would never transgress again in that quarter.

The incident was still fresh in my mind the following week when I again found Sep Craggs waiting for me at the surgery when I returned from a round.

His face was inscrutable but I felt a twinge of apprehension as he again towered over me.

'Ah came this mornin' to pick up a bottle of liniment, but it wasn't in the box,' he muttered.

Oh no! Please not again! Was I losing my mind? I dug my nails into my palms. 'I'm so sorry . . . I . . . I really can't remember arranging this.'

But there was no outburst this time. The man was strangely subdued. 'It wasn't you, it was t'yoong man.'

So it was poor John's turn to fall under the lash. How could I divert the wrath from him? I gave a light laugh. 'Oh . . . I see . . . well, Mr Crooks is a splendid chap but he hasn't the best of memories.'

'Nay, nay – don't criticise t'yoong man! He's got enough on 'is mind without botherin' about a little thing like a bottle of liniment.'

'Eh?'

'Aye, don't start blamin' him! I'm not havin' that!' He gave me a disapproving scowl. 'With all he's got to think about, you can't expect 'im to remember everything.'

I opened my mouth, but no words came.

I had never seen Mr Craggs smile, but his granite features relaxed a little and an almost dreamy look came into his eyes. 'By gaw, he does know a lot, does that lad – ah've never met anybody with such learnin'. Ah'll tell tha' summat, 'erriot. He came to a bullock wi' foul in the foot and 'e didn't mess about wi' tar and salt for a week like you do. Never touched the flippin' foot. All 'e did was inject into the *shoulder*, and t'beast was better in two days. What d'ye make of that, eh?' He tapped me on the chest.

I knew he wouldn't believe me if I told him that I, too, was using the new sulphadimidine injection now, so I didn't say anything.

'And ah'll tell tha summat else,' he went on. 'It was the *right* leg that was lame, but 'e injected into the *left* shoulder.' His eyes widened. 'It was like magic!'

'Good . . . good . . .' I croaked. 'Well, I'll get you that liniment.'

I brought the bottle from the dispensary and handed it to him. 'Well, here it is, Mr Craggs. I'm sorry you've had an extra journey.'

The big man shook his head. 'Nay, that makes no matter. It only takes a few minutes to get 'ere.'

As in a dream, I saw him out of the door and as I watched him walk down the street one thought was uppermost. If John could touch the heart of Sep Craggs his future was assured.

In fact, I think it was then that I realised that John was destined for something big. I had from the start begun to detect the seeds of greatness in him because of his uncanny ability to get through to people of all stations in life. It wasn't just his appearance, his confident approach, his rich voice, there was something else and I couldn't quite identify it, but whatever it was, everything about him stamped him as the 'young man most likely to succeed'.

II

John's home town was Beverley with its glorious Minster; this was fifty miles from Darrowby, and on his half days he usually went home for a few hours. Over the next year as he talked to me about these visits, a girl's name began to crop up more and more frequently. She was called Heather and whenever he mentioned her his eyes were inclined to take on a faraway look and his features to fall into an ethereal smile. These symptoms became more and more marked over the months until one day he confided to me that he was engaged and that he and Heather hoped to marry soon.

One wintry day I was kicking the snow off my boots in the porch at Skeldale House when John appeared in the doorway.

'Heather's inside,' he said a little breathlessly. 'She's in the office – I'd like you to meet her.'

I wanted to meet her, too. In fact I was agog after all I had heard about her. I straightened my tie, tried to flatten down my hair and strode briskly into the room. Unfortunately I had a ball of snow stuck on my heel and as I came through the door I took off on the smooth linoleum, soared through the air and landed with a sickening crash on my back on the other side of the room. When I opened my eyes I found I was looking up at a very attractive dark-haired girl who was making valiant efforts to keep a straight face.

That was how I met Heather – looking up at her – and I have looked up to her and admired her ever since. There are all sorts of words to describe her in her future marriage to John – cherished partner through life, staunch helpmeet, happy companion – she was all those things and the mother of three splendid children to boot.

After that first meeting, John's courting proceeded apace and I could see that his impending marriage was more and more on his mind. The previous symptoms became more and more acute and he confessed to short bouts of amnesia when he had to stop his car in the middle of the country on his rounds and try to remember where he was going and what he had to do. Occasionally I caught him smiling to himself and it was clear that his thoughts were on something rather wonderful ahead.

Just how much his future was preoccupying him became clear one wet afternoon. One of our farmers phoned me.

'I've had a message passed on to say that Mr Crooks's fiancée has been taken ill. He'd just left my place and I thought I'd missed 'im, but then I saw that his car had got stuck in the ford just beyond our gate.'

'Oh dear, I'd better come and get him.'

'Nay, there's no need. I slipped down in my car and gave him the message and he jumped out and asked me to run 'im to Darrowby station. He caught a train and he was off.'

'Gosh, that was quick.'

'Aye, by gaw, he didn't mess about!'

'And where's the car now?'

'Still stuck in t'water.'

'Right. Thanks for letting me know. I'll come out with Mr Farnon and we'll fetch it back.'

The scene which met Siegfried and me when we got to the ford is one of the vivid memories of John's time with us. There was a dip in the narrow, hill-girt road where the beck flowed over the tarmac and John's little Ford 8 was standing there, axle deep in the water. There were signs of a hasty exit – the driver's door was hanging open and the windscreen wipers were still in motion, flip-flopping lazily across the glass. John hadn't delayed his departure for a second.

Happily, Heather's illness was not serious and life in our busy practice went on with John doing his share of the routine calvings, foalings, lambings, castrations of colts and proving himself daily as the right man in the right job.

The young couple were married on a fine day in May and they settled in part of Siegfried's house. Heather was a teacher and she taught Siegfried's two children throughout her stay in our practice.

It was a jolt when the inevitable day came when John decided to branch out on his own. He left to set up a practice in Beverley and I felt the loss not only of a great assistant but a friend. I was only about ten years older than John – close enough to have interests and pursuits in common. I suppose as the years passed and other 'yoong men' came and went in our practice, I progressed through the status of ageing colleague, elder statesman and, finally, quaint old fossil, but with the first few assistants I was still in their world, and John and I had a lot of fun together.

Skeldale House had always been a place of laughter and, thank heaven, John brought a vivid brand of humour of his own to the practice. He had his failures and disasters like all of us and used a wonderful gift of mimicry to describe them. He was sensitive and totally lacking in vanity despite his forceful personality.

Above all, I still think of him as a typical Englishman of an almost old-fashioned sort with a passion for cricket, an unshakable belief in the old values and a reverence for the beautiful county in which we worked.

After he had left to set up his own practice in Beverley, we were absorbed in our own busy lives and inevitably saw less and less of each other. There were special occasions, of course. Helen and I were honoured to become Godparents to Annette, the first born of the Crooks family, then we had happy notice of the arrival of James and then Elizabeth. We managed to meet Heather and John occasionally in Scarborough and I saw John at veterinary meetings but the old chapter was closed.

However, with my conviction that he would rise high in the profession, I followed his progress over the years, and noted the rapid growth of his practice until he was employing several assistants. He was being increasingly recognised for his drive and organising ability and was involved in the growth and administration of the profession. I was right in my prognostication; the only thing that at last stopped John's rising was that he couldn't go any higher. In 1983, thirty years after he left Darrowby, he was elected President of the British Veterinary Association.

It touched me then that after all that time he reached back to his first boss and asked me to make the induction speech at his inauguration.

'Those years in Darrowby were the happiest time of our lives for Heather and me,' he said. 'I want you to do it.'

So there it was. The great day came with me sitting in the conference hall of Lancaster University among hundreds of vets from all over the world. All the notables were there – distinguished names everywhere – but as I looked up at the august company on the platform after I had said my piece, it gave me a tremendous kick to realise that right in the middle and the most important of them all was t'yoong man from Darrowby.

My speech over, the ceremony proceeded and John stood tall as he was arrayed in the regalia of President. The Association Secretary helped him into the handsome black gown with green watered silk facings, then the President of the previous year placed the chain of office around his neck. As I saw this chain being fastened from behind, the whole thing suddenly reminded me of dressing up in an obstetric gown before a calving with the farmer tying the tapes from the rear. It seemed that John felt exactly the same because at that very solemn moment he said, 'Could I have a bucket of hot water, soap and a towel please.' A roar of laughter went up from the audience – so many of us had uttered those words a thousand times.

Finally, in full raiment, he turned and faced the assembly. He was bulkier than in his Darrowby days and his hair was a silver thatch, but he was profoundly imposing. I looked towards the front row of the auditorium where Heather and all the family sat, gazing up proudly. Among them I saw baby Emily, first of the grandchildren, perched on James's knee and the years rolled away. Ah well, John wasn't t'yoong man any more, but he was a famous and happy one.

In my speech, I had tried to bring out John's unique ability to influence people and when I had still been stuck for the right words, I had paraphrased a lager advertisement by saying he could reach the parts other veterinary surgeons couldn't reach.

As I sat there watching the ceremony on the platform, the memory of that lonely road among the hills and the stranded car in the water with the door hanging open and the windscreen wipers going flip-flop, flip-flop swam up into my mind. It occurred to me that there could be a clue there. Maybe that epitomised two of the aspects of John's character which had taken him to the top of the profession – devotion to his wife and the power of instant decision.

12

'This house is a woman killer, Mr Herriot.'

I was seeing a farmer out and he was looking down at Helen scrubbing the front door steps. His words went through me like a knife. He was stating baldly something which had been eating away at my mind for a long time.

'Aye,' he said again, 'it's a grand old house, but it's a woman killer.'

That was the moment when I decided that somehow, some way, I had to get Helen out of Skeldale House. We loved the old place but it had vast disadvantages for a young couple of moderate means. It was charming, graceful and undoubtedly a happy house in its atmosphere, but it was far too big and a veritable ice box in cold weather.

I looked up over the ivy covered frontage at the big bedroom windows, then further to the next storey where there was a suite of rooms where, in the early days, we had had our bed-sitter. There was another storey if you counted the tiny rooms under the tiles; here there was a big bell mounted on the end of a spring which used to summon a little housemaid down to the ground floor in the early days of the century.

The old doctor who lived in Skeldale House before we took over had had six servants including a full-time housekeeper, but Helen looked after the whole place with the aid of a series of transient maids, most of whom soon grew tired of the hard work and the impossible inconvenience of the house.

Before going back inside I looked down again at my wife scrubbing away. This was crazy, and the words 'Please stop it!' bubbled up in my mind. But I didn't speak them. It was no good. I had tried to stop her again and again but it was a waste of time. That was the way she was made. She was domestically minded and she just couldn't sit back and admit defeat. She was absolutely determined to keep inside and outside clean and tidy.

This was something which worried and exasperated me. I was married to a beautiful, intelligent, warm-hearted girl, but I wished with all my heart that she would be kinder to herself and take more time to rest. When we were first married, I tried by pleading, and at times by making angry scenes which I wasn't much good at, to make her alter her ways but it was like talking to a wall – she slogged on regardless. Cooking, too. I had never met anybody who could work such magic with food, and as a dedicated eater I realised my good luck, but I wished fervently that she would spend less time over the oven. However, when all my entreaties were in vain and she went her own way, I consoled myself that I could hear her singing as she went round the house with her Hoover and duster. At this moment, she was actually humming softly to herself as she scrubbed that accursed step.

Even now, fifty years later and when we are coming up to the supreme accolade of getting our Golden Wedding pictures in the *Darrowby and Houlton Times*, she still sings as she potters busily around in another, mercifully much smaller house. It dawned on me long ago that she's happy that way.

From the front door, I went along the tiled passage which

would have been full of sunlight and character in the summer but on this cold spring day was just as cold and shivery as the street outside; on and on past dining room and sitting room, then turned left down to the dispensary, then right and left again and to another stretch of passage past consulting room, breakfast room and finally to the kitchen and scullery at the end of the long offshoot at the back of the house. I seemed to have travelled about fifty yards and who could blame Tristan in the old days for riding his bicycle to get to the front door?

On the way, I passed little Rosie, clattering over the tiles in her strong shoes, her legs muffled in thick pantaloons as Jimmy's used to be. I sometimes wondered how we had brought the children up in this relentless cold and I was grateful that they didn't seem to suffer from more coughs and sneezes than other children. The main casualty was Helen who was plagued with terrible chilblains round her ankles.

Next morning as soon as I awoke, my decision welled strongly in my mind. We had to get out. Skeldale would be fine as the practice quarters but we had to find something smaller to live in.

It was the beginning of a kind of obsession and I could think of nothing else that morning as I jumped out of bed, tried in vain to see out of the frosted windows and then dressed quickly in the icy atmosphere. I threw open the bedroom door and, at full gallop, began my morning routine. Down the stairs two at a time, full tilt along the freezing passage – the secret was to keep running – to the kitchen where I put the kettle on. Back along to the dining room at top speed where the bloody-minded anthracite stove was out again. It was the only source of warmth in the whole house but I hadn't time to relight it now.

Back over the long stretch to the kitchen where I made the tea and took up a cup to Helen. Then, blowing on my hands and jumping around to stop the blood freezing, I started a fire in the kitchen. I was never much of a boy scout at fire-lighting – unlike Helen who could have a fine blaze going in no time – and by the time the family came downstairs I had my usual fitful flame peeping out among the coals.

Breakfast was a cheerless affair with a little one-bar electric fire fighting an unequal battle and all of us trying to stop our teeth from chattering. I was silent over the meal, my mind wholly occupied with my fierce resolve, and I kept thinking back over previous festive seasons, remembering how we huddled round the fire in the big sitting room while our backs froze and the Christmas decorations swayed in the assorted draughts.

It was still uppermost in my mind when I called at Mrs Dryden's little semi-detached house on the outskirts of Darrowby. I had been treating her cat for a very bad attack of otodectic mange in the ears.

'Come on, Sooty,' I said, as I lifted him on to the table. 'You look a lot better today.'

His mistress smiled. 'Oh, he is. He's stopped shaking his head and scratching. He was goin' nearly mad before you cleaned his ears out.'

I did some more swabbing then trickled some lotion into the ears as the black cat purred happily. 'Yes. He won't need any more attention from me. Just keep putting the drops in the ears night and morning for another few days and I'm sure he'll be fine.'

I went over to the kitchen sink to wash my hands and looked out of the window at the neat garden. 'This is a nice little house, Mrs Dryden.'

'Aye, it is, Mr Herriot, but I'm leaving it soon.'

'Really, why is that?'

'Well, I need the money. That's the top and bottom of it. When Robert died, he didn't leave much.'

I could believe her. She was a retired farmer's widow, and I knew what a struggle they had had to scrape a living on their smallholding. Bob Dryden and I had shared some hard experiences up there on the hills. Tough calvings and lambings, and I could remember a disastrous spring when many of their calves had died of scour. He was a fine man and I remembered him as a friend.

'But where will you live?' I asked.

'Oh, I'm going to live with me sister in Houlton. I'll be all right there, but I'll be sorry to part with this nice little house. Robert and I were that pleased to be able to buy it when he retired. Still, I'm hopin' to get two thousand pounds for it and that'll be a godsend to me in my old age.'

I had one of my blinding flashes then. This was just the place for us. It was perfect, and I felt sure I'd be able to get a mortgage to buy it.

'Would you sell it to me?' I asked eagerly.

She smiled. 'I would if I could, Mr Herriot, but the arrangements are all made. It goes up for auction at the Drovers' Arms on Wednesday.'

My heart started to thump. 'Well, I'll be there bidding, Mrs Dryden.'

I was positive I would get the house, and as I looked round the kitchen all my worries seemed to dissolve. What a piece of luck! I could just see Helen at that window, looking out on the little garden which gave on to green fields, with the church tower rising from the trees on the other side of the river. And everything was so compact. There was a hatch into the living room – no hiking fifty yards with the food. A little hall with the stairs leading to three bedrooms, almost at arm's length away. You could reach out and touch everything, and I loved the thought. In my frame of mind at that time, small was beautiful. Nothing else mattered.

I saw the man at the Building Society and there was no problem. They would grant me a mortgage. It was a house which would probably fetch around fifty to sixty thousand pounds at the present day but, in the early fifties, two thousand was about right.

I was walking on air until the Wednesday when I rolled up with Helen to the Drovers for the auction. The room was full and as Helen and I took our seats a farmer client nudged me. 'There's old Seth Bootland,' he murmured. 'He wants this house for his son who's just got married. Reckon he'll get it, too. He's rollin' in brass, but he's a hard businessman.'

I looked over at the rich grain merchant. He was impressive with his high-coloured, beaky face and camel coat, and his face wore an expression of grim confidence. I felt a qualm, then came a return of my steely resolve. I was going to buy that house.

The bidding started at fifteen hundred and went rapidly – more rapidly than I had expected – up to my top figure of two thousand. Bootland made it two thousand one hundred. He clearly was used to this sort of thing and just twitched a bored forefinger. I stabbed the air eagerly to put on another hundred – I was quite sure my mortgage could be stretched another little bit – but Bootland flicked the finger again and it was up to me.

Soon there was just the two of us. All other bidders had fallen out and I felt cruelly exposed. The bids were down to fifty now and as the price crept up and up toward three thousand my heart began to pound and I could feel my palms sweating.

Helen was clutching my knee and with each new bid, she whispered desperately, 'No, Jim, no! We haven't any money!' But I was seized by a kind of madness. The money meant nothing. All I could see was Helen in that trim little house looking out on her garden from the pretty kitchen. That was the vision which wouldn't go away and I ploughed on doggedly.

When the price got above three thousand, the audience in the packed room had begun to emit an excited 'Ahh!' at each new bid. It had got down to raises of twenty-five pounds.

'Mr Bootland bids three thousand two hundred and twenty-five.' My mouth was dry as the auctioneer gazed at me enquiringly.

Helen's grip on my knee was like a vice. She was shaking it with her entreaties. 'No, Jim, *no*!'

I raised my hand.

'And fifty. Thank you,' and then the glance at Bootland. 'And seventy-five.' The auctioneer's and everybody's eyes were on me. As in a dream, I raised my hand.

'We have three thousand three hundred pounds.'

Bootland waggled his finger.

'And twenty-five.'

Once again, in the vibrating silence, all the eyes were on me. I felt utterly drained, parched, exhausted. I was trembling and only slightly aware of Helen punching my leg and almost sobbing. 'Stop it! Please stop it!' I thought she was going to cry. I shook my head at the auctioneer and the thing was over.

There was an excited hum of conversation in the room, but I stayed slumped in my seat, only dimly aware of Bootland going up and talking to the auctioneer and of Helen sitting very still beside me. Finally, I rose and looked at her.

'Good heavens, Jim, you're as white as a sheet!' she gasped.

I nodded wordlessly. I did feel extremely white. On the way out I received a savage glance from Mr Bootland. Thanks to me, he had had to pay one thousand three hundred and twenty-five pounds – around thirty thousand at present day prices – more than the house was probably worth. I certainly wasn't his favourite man.

But I didn't care. All I felt was the sense of abject failure. My happy vision of Helen looking out of that window onto the fields beyond was shattered and I was right back where I started. I had accomplished nothing.

Outside in the market place I stood for a moment, drawing in the cool air. I took Helen's arm and was about to move on when I felt a hand on my shoulder. I looked down at the sweet face of Mrs Dryden. She was smiling at me.

'Eee, Mr Herriot, I'm right sorry you didn't get the house, but you've done a lot for me – you'll never know how much. I've got all that extra money to put by me, thanks to you. Believe me, it'll make all the difference in the world. I really cannot thank you enough.'

As she walked away, I looked at her thin, bent figure and her white hair. There was the wife of good old Bob Dryden and he would have been pleased. I had done something after all.

13

I unwound the spiral Hudson's instrument from the cow's teat and drew forth a strong jet of milk.

'Eee, that's wonderful, marvellous,' breathed Mr Dowson reverently. 'I don't know 'ow you do it – you've saved me again. You're a great man, Mr Herriot.'

We were still doing a lot of these teat operations, because milking machines had not come into general use and the farmers' horny-handed pulling at the cows' teats often resulted in damage to the lining and blockage. It wasn't a particularly popular procedure with the vets because there was an excellent chance of having your head kicked off as you crouched down there by the udder, but it was undeniably satisfying to bring a useless teat back to life. A lot of a cow's value was lost when she became a 'three-titted 'un'.

However, valuable though the operation was to a farmer, it was most unusual to receive profuse gratitude like Mr Dowson's. But it was always like that with him. He poured praise on me and though, over the years, I was sure that all my cases on his farm hadn't been triumphs, that was how he pictured it. If anything had gone wrong in the past he would never admit it.

This was in direct contrast to most of our farmer clients. No matter how brilliant a feat of healing we pulled off, we very rarely heard anything about it. Siegfried's theory was that they didn't like to mention our cures in case we put a bit extra on the bill and he may have had a point because they never failed to inform us about our failures. Comments such as 'Hey, that beast you treated never did any good,' were often embarrassingly shouted across a crowded market place.

Be that as it may, Mr Dowson's attitude was always balm to my soul. He was gazing at me now as I put the instrument back in its bottle of spirit, his little brown face crinkled in a benevolent smile. He pulled off his cap and smoothed back the straggling white hair from his brow.

'Ah don't know. There's no end to your cleverness. I was just thinking of that cow of mine with magnesium deficiency. She was laid there like a dead thing – ah was sure she'd stopped breathin' – but you put a bottle into 'er vein, then you looked at your watch. "Mr Dowson," you said, "this beast will get up on her legs in exactly twelve and a half minutes."'

'I did?'

'Ah'm not jokin' nor jestin', that's what you said, and you can believe me or believe me not, just the very second the hands on your watch got round to twelve and a half minutes that cow jumped up and walked away.'

'Good heavens! Did she really?'

'She did that, and I'll tell you summat else, she's never looked back since.'

'Well, that's great.' I had the same feeling of bewilderment as I always felt at Mr Dowson's panegyrics. I could never remember the magical things I had done, but it was very pleasant all the same. Was I really that brilliant or did he make it all up? His habitual phrase of 'believe me or believe me not' suggested that he may have had doubts about it himself, but that didn't alter the fact that his eulogies were always delivered with the greatest certainty and emphasis.

Even the surroundings of his farm were idyllic, and as I walked to my car with a gentle breeze, full of the scents of summer, eddying around me, I looked back at the little farmhouse tucked into the green hillside which dipped down over rig and furrow to the river, sparkling in the sunshine.

As always, I drove away in a rosy glow with Mr Dowson waving until I was out of sight.

I was back there again within a week to deal with a calving heifer. Mr Dowson was worried because she was overdue, but the delivery was uneventful and I soon had a large bull calf snuffling and snorting among the straw in the byre.

'Well, that's fine,' I said. 'Sometimes these big calves are a bit late. It was a tight squeeze, but all's well.'

'Aye, aye,' said the farmer. 'There was no need to worry. I should've known. You told me more than a month ago that that heifer would be exactly five days late, and you were right as usual.'

'Did I really say that? I don't see how I would know . . .'

He shrugged his shoulders. 'Well, Mr Herriot, them was your words. I ought to remember them.'

As we left the byre, Mr Dowson stopped to pat a little Dales pony which was happily cropping the grass by the side of the house. 'Remember this little feller? Remember that bad stoppage he had?'

'Ah yes, of course I do. He looks fine now.'

'He does that, and by gaw 'e was ill! Thought ah was going to lose 'im. Right bunged up and groanin' in pain he was. I'd given him all sorts o' medicines to try to move 'is bowels but they did no good – nothing came through 'im for two whole days. Then I got you in and I'll never forget what you did.'

'What did I do?'

'Ah tell ye, it were like a miracle. You came in the morning and you gave him two injections and you said to me, "Mr Dowson, his bowels will move at two o'clock this afternoon."'

'I said that?'

'You did an' all, and then you said, "At first he'll pass exactly a handful, just like this."' He cupped his hands to illustrate. 'And right on two o'clock, that's what 'e did. No more, no less.'

'Gosh!'

'Aye, and then you said, "At half past two he'll pass just enough to fill that small shovel."' Mr Dowson hurried busily over to the house and picked up a little shovel which stood by the coal bunker. He held it out to me. 'There's the very thing. And right on the dot by my watch he passed just the amount you said. I measured it.'

'Never! Are you sure?'

'You can believe me or believe me not. Then you said, "At three o'clock he'll have a good clear out," and that's just what happened. I was lookin' at my watch when he cocked his tail and got rid of everything that was troubling 'im. And he's been right as ninepence ever since.'

'Well, that's wonderful, Mr Dowson. I'm so pleased to hear it.' I shook my head to dispel the mists of fantasy which had begun to billow around me. I am a run of the mill veterinary surgeon, hard working and conscientious, but that's all, and it knocks me out of my stride to be hailed as a genius, but as always, listening to Mr Dowson was like soothing oil being poured on my oft-bruised ego. I had to admit I enjoyed it, and I didn't demur when he went on.

'And while you're 'ere, just have a look at this pig.' He took my arm and led me into an outbuilding. 'There she is,' he said, leaning over a pen and pointing to a fine big sow stretched on the straw with a litter of piglets sucking busily at her teats. 'That's the one that had that nasty great swelling on her foot. Dead lame she was, and I was right worried about 'er. You gave her a jab and left me some salve to rub on the lump and next morning it was gone!'

'You mean . . . it vanished overnight? All of it?'

'Aye, that's right, ah'm not jokin' nor jestin'. It was gone!'

'Well . . . that's quite amazing.'

'Not to me, it isn't, Mr Herriot. Everything you do for me turns out right. Ah don't know what I'd do without you.'

Even through my confusion I found his faith touching. I hoped it would never be shattered.

I thought that moment had arrived when Mr Dowson called me to his farm a few weeks later.

'What's the trouble this time?' I asked.

The old man rubbed his chin. 'Well, it's a funny one, I tell you. It's this calf.' He pointed to a sturdy young animal about a month old. 'He won't drink 'is milk properly. Look. I'll show ye.' He tipped some milk into a big bucket and set it down in front of the little creature, but the calf, instead of drinking, put his head down and with a fierce butt, sent the bucket flying, spilling the milk in all directions.

'Does he do this every time?'

'Aye, knocks it over every time. It's a dang nuisance. Wastes me good milk, too.'

I examined the calf, then turned to the farmer. 'He seems perfectly healthy to me.'

'Oh aye, he is. Fit as a flea and full o' life. It's just this one thing wi' the bucket. I thought you'd maybe be able to give 'im one of your magic injections to stop him doin' it.'

'Well, really, Mr Dowson,' I said, laughing, 'this isn't a medical problem, it's psychological. He just doesn't like buckets. I'm afraid I can't do anything for you this time. Can't you hold the bucket while he drinks?'

'Yes, that's what I have to do, but even then 'e keeps bashin' at it with his head.' He dug his hands into his pockets and gave me a crestfallen look. 'Ah'm sure you could do something. You say it's not a medical problem, but it's an animal problem and everythin' you've done for me wi' animals has been successful. I wish you'd have a try. Go on, give 'im an injection.'

I looked at the old man's doleful face. I had a feeling that if I walked off the farm without doing something, he would be truly upset. How could I please him without being an absolute charlatan? If I didn't inject something it was going to break his heart, but what . . . what . . . ? Mentally I searched the contents of my car boot and was beginning to despair when in my mind's eye I saw the bottle of Thiamin – Vitamin B injection. We used it for a brain disease called cerebrocortical necrosis and while, of course, the calf wasn't suffering from that or anything like it, at least it had to do with the head. Anyway, I stilled my conscience with the thought that I wouldn't charge the old man anything.

I hurried to the car. 'I'll give him a shot of this,' I said and was rewarded by a radiant smile lighting up Mr Dowson's face. I injected a few ccs with the knowledge that I wasn't doing any harm. The injection would be useless, but it was serving its purpose. The old man was happy and, really, when I thought about it, it would be no bad thing if, for once, my treatment was ineffective. My mantle of infallibility would be stripped from me and I wouldn't be expected to do the impossible any more.

It was more than a month before I saw Mr Dowson again. He was leaning over a rail at the cattle market and he waved and came over to me. I was intrigued at the prospect that for the first time ever he would have to report a failure. What words would he employ? He had never had to do it before. And I was pretty sure that he would hate telling me.

He looked up at me with wide eyes. 'Well, you've done it again, Mr Herriot!'

'Done it again?' I looked at him blankly.

'Aye, that calf. Your injection worked.'

'What!'

'It did an' all.' The familiar happy smile flooded over his face. 'He's never butted a bucket since that day!'

14

Sometimes, when our dog and cat patients died, the owners brought them in for us to dispose of them. It was always a sad occasion and I had a sense of foreboding when I saw old Dick Fawcett's face.

He put the improvised cat box on the surgery table and looked at me with unhappy eyes.

'It's Frisk,' he said. His lips trembled as though he was unable to say more.

I didn't ask any questions, but began to undo the strings on the cardboard container. Dick couldn't afford a proper cat box, but he had used this one before, a home-made affair with holes punched in the sides.

I untied the last knot and looked inside at the motionless body. Frisk. The glossy black, playful little creature I knew so well, always purring and affectionate and Dick's companion and friend.

'When did he die, Dick?' I asked gently.

He passed a hand over his haggard face and through the straggling grey hairs. 'Well, I just found 'im stretched out by my bed this morning. But . . . I don't rightly know if he's dead yet, Mr Herriot.'

I looked again inside the box. There was no sign of breathing. I lifted the limp form on to the table and touched the cornea of the unseeing eye. No reflex. I reached for my stethoscope and placed it over the chest.

'The heart's still going, Dick, but it's a very faint beat.'

'Might stop any time, you mean?'

I hesitated. 'Well, that's the way it sounds, I'm afraid.'

As I spoke, the little cat's rib cage lifted slightly then subsided.

'He's still breathing,' I said, 'but only just.' I examined the cat thoroughly and found nothing unusual. The conjunctiva of the eye was a good colour. In fact, there was no abnormality.

I passed a hand over the sleek little body. 'This is a puzzler, Dick. He's always been so lively – lived up to his name, in fact, yet here he is, flat out, and I can't find any reason for it.'

'Could he have 'ad a stroke or summat?'

'I suppose it's just possible, but I wouldn't expect him to be totally unconscious. I'm wondering if he might have had a blow on the head.'

'I don't think so. He was as right as rain when I went to bed, and he was never out during t'night.' The old man shrugged his shoulders. 'Any road, it's a poor look out for 'im?'

'Afraid so, Dick. He's only just alive. But I'll give him a stimulant injection and then you must take him home and keep him warm. If he's still around tomorrow morning, bring him in and I'll see how he's going on.'

I was trying to strike an optimistic note, but I was pretty sure that I would never see Frisk again and I knew the old man felt the same.

His hands shook as he tied up the box and he didn't speak until we reached the front door. He turned briefly to me and nodded. 'Thank ye, Mr Herriot.'

I watched him as he walked with shuffling steps down the

street. He was going back to an empty little house with his dying pet. He had lost his wife many years ago – I had never known a Mrs Fawcett – and he lived alone on his old age pension. It wasn't much of a life. He was a quiet, kindly man who didn't go out much and seemed to have few friends, but he had Frisk. The little cat had walked in on him six years ago and had transformed his life, bringing a boisterous, happy presence into the silent house making the old man laugh with his tricks and playfulness, following him around, rubbing against his legs. Dick wasn't lonely any more, and I had watched a warm bond of friendship growing stronger over the years. In fact, it was something more – the old man seemed to depend on Frisk. And now this.

Well, I thought, as I walked back down the passage, it was the sort of thing that happened in veterinary practice. Pets didn't live long enough. But I felt worse this time because I had no idea what ailed my patient. I was in a total fog.

On the following morning I was surprised to see Dick Fawcett sitting in the waiting room, the cardboard box on his knee.

I stared at him. 'What's happened?'

He didn't answer and his face was inscrutable as we went through to the consulting room and he undid the knots. When he opened the box I prepared for the worst, but to my astonishment the little cat leaped out onto the table and rubbed his face against my hand, purring like a motor cycle.

The old man laughed, his thin face transfigured. 'Well, what d'ye think of that?'

'I don't know what to think, Dick.' I examined the little animal carefully. He was completely normal. 'All I know is that I'm delighted. It's like a miracle.'

'No, it isn't,' he said. 'It was that injection you gave 'im. It's worked wonders. I'm right grateful.'

Well, it was kind of him, but it wasn't as simple as that. There was something here I didn't understand, but never mind. Thank heaven it had ended happily.

The incident had receded into a comfortable memory when, three days later, Dick Fawcett reappeared at the surgery with his box. Inside was Frisk, motionless, unconscious, just as before.

Totally bewildered, I repeated the examination and then the injection and on the following day the cat was normal. From then on, I was in the situation which every veterinary surgeon knows so well – being involved in a baffling case and waiting with a feeling of impending doom for something tragic to happen.

Nothing did happen for nearly a week, then Mrs Duggan, Dick's neighbour, telephoned.

'I'm ringin' on behalf of Mr Fawcett. His cat's ill.'

'In what way?'

'Oh, just lyin' stretched out, unconscious, like.'

I suppressed a scream. 'When did this happen?'

'Just found 'im this morning. And Mr Fawcett can't bring him to you – he's poorly himself. He's in bed.'

'I'm sorry to hear that. I'll come round straight away.'

And it was just the same as before. An almost lifeless little creature lying prone on Dick's bed. Dick himself looked terrible – ghastly white and thinner than ever – but he still managed a smile.

'Looks like 'e needs another of your magic injections, Mr Herriot.'

As I filled my syringe, my mind seethed with the thought that there was indeed some kind of magic at work here, but it wasn't my injection.

'I'll drop in tomorrow, Dick,' I said. 'And I hope you'll be feeling better yourself.'

'Oh, I'll be awright as long as t'little feller's better.' The old man stretched out a hand and stroked the cat's shining fur. The arm was emaciated and the eyes in the skull-like face were desperately worried.

I looked around the comfortless little room and hoped for another miracle.

I wasn't really surprised when I came back next morning and saw Frisk darting about on the bed, pawing at a piece of string which the old man was holding up for him. The relief was great but I felt enveloped more suffocatingly than ever in my fog of ignorance. What the hell was it? The whole thing just didn't make sense. There was no known disease with symptoms like these. I had a strong conviction that reading a whole library of veterinary books wouldn't help me.

Anyway, the sight of the little cat arching and purring round my hand was reward enough, and for Dick it was everything. He was relaxed and smiling.

'You keep gettin' him right, Mr Herriot. I can't thank you enough.' Then the worry flickered again in his eyes. 'But is he goin' to keep doin' it? I'm frightened he won't come round one of these times.'

Well, that was the question. I was frightened too, but I had to try to be cheerful. 'Maybe it's just a passing phase, Dick. I hope we'll have no more trouble now.' But I couldn't promise anything and the frail man in the bed knew it.

Mrs Duggan was showing me out when I saw the district nurse getting out of her car at the front door.

'Hello, Nurse,' I said, 'you've come to have a look at Mr Fawcett? I'm sorry he's ill.'

She nodded. 'Yes, poor old chap. It's a great shame.'

'What do you mean? Is it something serious?'

'Afraid so.' Her mouth tightened and she looked away from me. 'He's dying. It's cancer. Getting rapidly worse.'

'My God! Poor Dick. And a few days ago he was bringing his cat to my surgery. He never said a word. Does he know?'

'Oh yes, he knows, but that's him all over, Mr Herriot. He's as game as a pebble. He shouldn't have been out, really.'

'Is he . . . is he . . . suffering?'

She shrugged. 'Getting a bit of pain now, but we're keeping him as comfortable as we can with medication. I give him a shot when necessary and he has some stuff he can take himself if I'm not around. He's very shaky and can't pour from the bottle into the spoon. Mrs Duggan would gladly do it for him, but he's so independent.' She smiled for a moment. 'He pours the mixture into a saucer and spoons it up that way.'

'A saucer . . .?' Somewhere in the fog a little light glimmered. 'What's in the mixture?'

'Oh, heroin and pethidene. It's the usual thing Dr Allinson prescribes.'

I seized her arm. 'I'm coming back in with you, Nurse.'

The old man was surprised when I reappeared. 'What's matter, Mr Herriot? Have you left summat?'

'No, Dick, I want to ask you something. Is your medicine pleasant tasting?'

'Aye, it's nice and sweet. It isn't bad to take at all.'

'And you put it in a saucer?'

'That's right. Me hand's a bit dothery.'

'And when you take it last thing at night there's sometimes a bit left in the saucer?'

'Aye, there is, why?'

'Because you leave that saucer by your bedside, don't you, and Frisk sleeps on your bed . . .'

The old man lay very still as he stared at me. 'You mean the little beggar licks it out?'

'I'll bet my boots he does.'

Dick threw back his head and laughed. A long, joyous laugh. 'And that sends 'im to sleep! No wonder! It makes me right dozy, too!'

I laughed with him. 'Anyway, we know now, Dick. You'll put that saucer in the cupboard when you've taken your dose, won't you?'

'I will that, Mr Herriot. And Frisk will never pass out like that again?'

'No, never again.'

'Eee, that's grand!' He sat up in bed, lifted the little cat and held him against his face. He gave a sigh of utter content and smiled at me.

'Mr Herriot,' he said, 'I've got nowt to worry about now.'

Out in the street, as I bade Mrs Duggan goodbye for the second time, I looked back at the little house. '"Nowt to worry about," eh? That's rather wonderful, coming from him.'

'Oh aye, and he means it, too. He's not bothered about himself.'

I didn't see Dick again for two weeks. I was visiting a friend in Darrowby's little cottage hospital when I saw the old man in a bed in a corner of the ward.

I went over and sat down by his side. His face was desperately thin, but serene.

'Hello, Dick,' I said.

He looked at me sleepily and spoke in a whisper. 'Now then, Mr Herriot.' He closed his eyes for a few moments, then he looked up again with the ghost of a smile. 'I'm glad we found out what was wrong with t'little cat.'

'So am I, Dick.'

Again a pause. 'Mrs Duggan's got 'im.'

'Yes. I know. He has a good home there.'

'Aye . . . aye . . .' The voice was fainter. 'But oftens I wish I had 'im here.' The bony hand stroked the counterpane and his lips moved again. I bent closer to hear.

'Frisk . . .' he was saying, 'Frisk . . .' Then his eyes closed and I saw that he was sleeping.

I heard next day that Dick Fawcett had died, and it was possible that I was the last person to hear him speak. And it was strange, yet fitting, that those last words were about his cat.

'Frisk . . . Frisk . . .'

15

I have to go back now to those early days when John Crooks departed from the practice and it was difficult to adjust my mind to the fact that he had gone for good. I couldn't believe that I would never hear that booming voice on the other end of the phone saying, okay, I could stay in my bed and he'd go out into the cold darkness to calve that heifer. And it wasn't just that. As I have said, I was young enough then to be a friend to an assistant and I was losing a friend now – two, in fact, when John and Heather set off to build their own life in Beverley – and it left me with an empty feeling.

However, it was no use brooding. We had to have another assistant and since our advertisement in *The Veterinary Record* had been successful, there was one on his way to us at this moment. I looked at my watch. It was nearly two thirty. Calum Buchanan's train would be pulling in to Darrowby in a few minutes. I ran out to the car and drove to the station.

When the train drew in, only one passenger alighted. He was a tall young man with a huge lurcher dog trotting by his side, and as he came along the platform towards me I took in the battered suitcase, flowing black moustache and very dark eyes, but the most striking feature was a large hairy animal draped over his left shoulder.

He put out his hand and grinned. 'Mr Herriot?'

'Yes ... yes ...' I shook his hand. 'You'll be Calum Buchanan.'

'That's right.'

'Good . . . good . . . but what's that on your shoulder?'

'That's Marilyn.'

'*Marilyn?*'

'Yes, my badger.'

'Badger!'

He laughed – a carefree laugh. 'Sorry, maybe I should have warned you in my letter. She's my pet. Goes everywhere with me.'

'Everywhere?'

'Absolutely.'

All kinds of apprehensions boiled up in my mind. How did a veterinary assistant carry out his duties with a wild animal hanging from his shoulder at all times? And what sort of man would roll up to a new job not only with a badger but with a giant dog?

Anyway, I knew I would soon find out, so I pushed my misgivings to one side and led him out to the car, running a gauntlet of pop-eyed stares from a booking-clerk, two ladies sitting on the platform seat and from a porter who nearly wheeled a load of packing cases into a wall.

'I see you've got a dog, too,' I said.

'Yes, that's Storm. Lovely, good-natured animal.'

The lurcher waved his tail and gazed up at me with kind eyes. I patted the shaggy head. 'He looks it.'

'Incidentally,' I said, 'with a name like yours, I was expecting a Scottish accent and you haven't got one.'

He smiled. 'No, I grew up in Yorkshire, but my ancestry is Scottish.' His eyes gleamed and his chin went up.

'You're proud of that, eh?'

He nodded gravely. 'I am indeed. Very proud.'

At Skeldale House, I showed him his car and helped to kit him out with the essential equipment we all carried – the drugs, instruments, obstetric gown and protective clothing – then I took him up to the flat where his main interest seemed to be directed not at the interior but at the birds and flowers he could see through the window overlooking the long garden.

'By the way,' I said, 'I should have asked you earlier. Have you had lunch?'

'Lunch?'

'Yes, have you had something to eat?'

'Eat . . . eat . . . ?' The black button eyes took on a thoughtful expression. 'Yes, I'm sure I had something yesterday.'

'Yesterday! My God, it's nearly four o'clock in the afternoon. You must be starved!'

'Oh no, not at all, not in the least.'

'You mean you're not hungry?'

He seemed to find the question unusual, even irrelevant, and replied with a non-committal shrug of the shoulders.

'Anyway,' I said, 'I'll slip downstairs and see what I can find for you.'

In the office cupboard was a large uncut fruit cake which Helen had just baked to go with the cups of coffee we snatched between visits. I put it on a plate with a knife and took it up to the flat.

'Here you are,' I said, placing the cake on the table. 'Help yourself and then you can get a proper meal later.'

As I spoke I heard footsteps on the stairs and Siegfried burst into the room.

'Calum Buchanan, Siegfried Farnon,' I said.

They shook hands then Siegfried pointed a trembling finger at the young man's shoulder. 'What the devil is that?'

Calum smiled his engaging smile. 'Marilyn, my badger.'

'And you're going to keep that animal here?'

'That's right.'

Siegfried took a long breath and let it out slowly through his nose, but he didn't say anything. Instead, he continued to look fixedly at our new assistant.

The young man was talking easily about his experience in practice, his pleasure at coming to a charming town like Darrowby, and about the things he could see in the garden.

He had started on the cake, but didn't bother to use the knife. Instead, he crumbled pieces off absently as he spoke. 'What a beautiful wisteria! Finest I've ever seen. There's a pretty little bullfinch, and surely that's a tree creeper on your apple tree – not many of them about.' And, popping a large chunk of sultana-laden comestible into his mouth, 'My word, I can see an albino blackbird over there – what a beauty!'

Siegfried was a keen naturalist and ornithologist and normally this conversation would have been right up his street, but he remained silent, his eyes straying unbelievingly from the badger to the dog and to the steadily disappearing cake.

Finally, Calum swept up the last few crumbs with his fingers – I had the impression that he had no interest in what he had eaten – and turned away from the window.

'Well, thank you very much. I'll get unpacked now, if I may.'

I swallowed. 'Right, see you later.'

We went downstairs and Siegfried led me rapidly into the empty office. 'What the hell have we got here, James? An assistant with a blasted badger round his neck! And a dog as big as a donkey!'

'Well, yes . . . but he seems to be a nice bloke.'

'Maybe so, but *very* strange. Did you see – he ate that whole bloody cake!'

'Yes, I saw. But he was very hungry – he hadn't eaten since yesterday.'

Siegfried stared at me. 'Not since yesterday! Are you sure?'

'Sure as I can be. He didn't seem to know himself.'

My partner groaned and slapped a hand against his forehead. 'Oh, God, we should have had an interview before we took this chap on. But he had such glowing references from the university. They said he was outstanding. I thought we couldn't go wrong.'

'You never know. He may be good at the job, that's what really counts.'

'Well, we'll have to hope so, but he's a bloody odd ball and I sense trouble.'

I didn't say anything, but I had my own misgivings. John Crooks with all his great qualities was, at bottom, just an ordinary nice guy, but there was nothing ordinary about that dark-eyed young man upstairs.

The telephone interrupted my musings. I took the call and turned to Siegfried. 'That's Miles Horsley. He's got a heifer calving.'

My partner nodded, then pursed his lips thoughtfully. After a few moments he raised a decisive finger. 'Right, we'll send the new man. We've been wondering if he can do the job. This is our chance to find out.'

'Wait a minute, Siegfried,' I said. 'The young chap's newly qualified and this is Miles Horsley. He's an expert – you never get an easy calving there, and it's a heifer, too. It could be very tough. Maybe I'd better go.'

Siegfried shook his head vigorously. 'No, I want to find out what this fellow's made of and the sooner the better. Shout him down will you.'

Calum received the instructions calmly, whistling softly as we pointed out the farm on the map. As he turned to go, Siegfried fired a parting shot. 'This could be a difficult job, but don't come back till you have calved that heifer. Do you understand?'

My blood froze but Calum didn't seem in the least put out. He nodded, gave us a casual wave of the hand and went out to his car.

After he had left, Siegfried turned to me with a grim smile. 'You may think I'm hard, James, but I don't want him coming back here in half an hour with the story that it's an unusual presentation and would we take over. No, in at the deep end, I say. It's the best way.'

I shrugged. I just hoped the new young man could swim.

That was around five thirty and by half past seven I was suffering from almost unbearable tension. Pictures of the hapless rookie rolling around on a byre floor, covered in blood and muck, passed through my mind and I found myself looking at my watch every five minutes. I had almost reached the stage of pacing the floor when Siegfried came in, carrying a little dog which had torn its flank and needed stitching. 'How did Buchanan get on?' he asked.

'I don't know. He's not back yet.'

'Not back!' My partner gave me a level stare. 'Something's wrong, then. Let's get this dog stitched, then one of us had better get out there and see what's going on.'

We were both silent as I anaesthetised the little animal and Siegfried began to clean out the wound. I knew we were thinking the same thing – it had been a mistake to send the new man to the Horsley farm. As Siegfried inserted the sutures I noticed that he, too, kept glancing at his watch.

It was just after eight o'clock when the operating room door opened and Calum Buchanan walked in.

My partner, needle poised, looked at him. 'Well . . . ?'

'I'm afraid it was an impossible presentation,' Calum replied. 'Small heifer, huge calf with lateral deviation of the head. Right away back, out of reach. No way I could possibly calve her.'

Siegfried flushed and a dangerous light glinted in his eyes.

'So . . . ?'

'So I did a Caesarean.'

'You did *what*?'

Calum smiled calmly. 'A Caesarean. It was the only thing to do. The calf was alive, so embryotomy was out of the question.'

Siegfried looked at him open-mouthed. 'And tell me . . . what . . . what happened?'

'Oh, pretty straightforward, really. The heifer was up and looking fine when I left, and we got a lovely live calf.'

'Well . . . well . . .' My partner seemed lost for words – the Caesarean operation on cows was a rare undertaking in the fifties – but finally his natural sense of justice reasserted itself. 'Well, my boy, you've obviously done a splendid job and I do congratulate you. It was your very first call as a qualified man, too. Well done indeed.'

The young man flashed his dark-eyed smile. 'Thank you very much.' He looked down at his hands, 'I could do with a bath now if you don't mind.'

'My dear chap, by all means. And get something to eat, too.'

As the door closed behind our new assistant, my partner gave me a wide-eyed look. 'Well, what do you make of that?'

'Absolutely great!' I said. 'Anybody who can tackle a job like that when he's only just arrived must be good. My God, he's hardly had time to get his instruments sorted out in his car!'

'Yes . . . yes . . .' Siegfried's expression was preoccupied as he finished his stitching and he didn't say anything as he put down his needle and went over to the basin against the wall to wash his hands. Then he turned to me suddenly. 'You know, I still can't quite believe it, James! Do you think he's having us on?'

I laughed. 'Oh no, of course not. He wouldn't dare.'

'I don't know,' grunted Siegfried. 'There's something very odd about that chap. I don't know where I am with him somehow.' He finished drying his hands and then his face broke into a slow smile. 'Tell you what. When we've cleared up here, we'll slip out to Miles Horsley's place. It's only ten minutes' drive and we can have a beer in the village pub. It's nearly opposite the farm. I won't be satisfied till I've had a look for myself.'

Miles Horsley was a rangy, six foot Dalesman – a decent man but not one to cross. An advanced dairy farmer, a perfectionist. His granite features relaxed as he answered the door.

'Now then, gentlemen, we're seeing a lot o' vets this evening. What's up?'

'Ah yes, Miles,' Siegfried said airily. 'James and I were having a drink over at the Blacksmith's Arms and we thought we'd just check on your heifer.'

The farmer nodded. 'Aye, right. Come and see.' He led the way over the dark yard, opened a loose box at the far end and switched on the light.

A fine roan heifer was nibbling casually at a rackful of hay while a strapping calf sucked at her udder. On the heifer's left flank an almost perfect rectangle of hair had been shaved away and running down the middle of it was as neat a row of stitches as I had ever seen.

'That's a good young feller you've got,' said the farmer. 'But, mind you, I wondered who was comin' when I saw that badger on his shoulder!'

Siegfried was still staring bemusedly at the operation site. 'Yes . . . yes, indeed.'

'Aye, very confident was t'lad,' continued the farmer. 'And I liked the way he went about the job. Careful and very clean. Brought all 'is instruments into the house and boiled them up thoroughly before he started work. There'll be no infection after this job, I'll warrant. And I've got a real smashin' calf into the bargain.'

Siegfried ran his hand over the heifer's back and rubbed the calf's head. 'I'm so pleased things have turned out well. Many thanks, Miles, for letting us have a look.'

In the Blacksmith's Arms my partner took a thoughtful pull at his glass. 'Beautifully tidy work, James, but it's a funny thing – I can't help feeling there's a catch somewhere.'

'Why, whatever do you mean? We've got a first class vet in the practice, that's obvious.'

'Oh yes, so it seems. But he's very peculiar – and I keep thinking about that damn badger. And that funny big walrus moustache. And that cake! I've never seen anybody demolish an enormous bloody fruit cake at one go – and he didn't seem to notice what he was doing.'

I laughed. 'Oh yes, I know. There's no doubt he's a very unusual young man. But he looks to me like a nice fellow – there's something very likable about him – and he's good at the job. That's the main thing.'

'I agree, I agree.' Siegfried ran his hand through his hair and churned it about a bit. 'I'm probably worrying needlessly, but . . . time will tell . . .'

16

'Nice dog,' I said, as I evacuated the anal glands of the big animal on the table. He was making a grumbling sound up front, but it was good to see the waving, friendly tail even though he couldn't have been enjoying my squeezing at his bottom. 'I'm glad his tail is wagging.'

'Aye, but –' old Mrs Coates began, but she was too late. As I moved forward to take a look at his eyes, the dog, to my astonishment, turned on me, all teeth and snarling lips, and made a ferocious grab at my face. My evasive technique has become polished over the years, but I only just avoided a nasty wound.

'Stop it, Wolfie! You naughty bad dog!' screamed the old lady. 'Just behave, or I'll give you such a smackin', that I will!'

The big animal subsided under his mistress's scolding and I took a step back out of harm's way. 'You know, Wolfie is remarkable,' I said, looking at him, wide-eyed. 'His tail is still wagging like mad and yet he's growling and showing his teeth as if he'd like to tear me to bits.'

'Aye, that's t'trouble, Mr Herriot. He's allus givin' people the wrong impression. They think he's that good-natured when they see 'im waggin', then they get a shock.'

'Well, he certainly had me fooled, Mrs Coates. He's the only dog I've ever seen that wags and growls at the same time. Depends which end you look at, doesn't it?'

Mrs Coates lived in a row of council bungalows for old people. Some time after my visit I called on an elderly couple, Mr and Mrs Hart, further along the same row.

Their cat which was, like themselves, quite old was losing its hair and going bald in places. As I parted the hair and examined the skin I could see the obvious signs of miliary eczema.

'This is a condition which often affects neutered toms like your Peter. I'll be able to clear it up with a hormone injection and a course of tablets.'

Peter didn't stop purring as I inserted the needle under his skin – he was a cat who appreciated any kind of attention – but I noticed that his owners looked a little uneasy. They seemed even more unhappy when I tipped some tablets into a box and began to write the instructions.

'We're a bit worried, Mr Herriot,' the old man said suddenly. 'This treatment will cost a bit and we can't pay you. Not today, any road.'

'That's right,' his wife broke in. 'We allus like to pay on the dot, but we 'aven't any money right now. We've been robbed.'

'Robbed?'

'Aye, unfortunately. My husband hasn't been well lately and the garden's got a bit untidy. Two men came in and said they'd do the garden up for us, but when we were talkin' to one of them here in the parlour, the other 'un was in the kitchen stealin' our pension money and a bit o' ready cash we kept on the mantelpiece.'

'Well, what a dirty trick!' I said. 'But please don't worry about paying me. Any time will do. I'm really very sorry – this must have upset you terribly.'

As I left the house it was difficult to believe that there were such people – who would come into the homes of decent old folks and rob them of their precious few pounds. But sadly I had heard this story before. These two men had been going around Darrowby lately, getting into houses on any pretext and carrying out their despicable actions. They specialised in robbing elderly people. They weren't very brave.

A few days later I happened to be passing Mrs Coates's bungalow so I thought I might as well check on Wolfie. The old lady let me in and I looked at the big dog lashing his tail vigorously and snarling at the same time.

'He's champion,' Mrs Coates said. 'Never shuffles round on 'is bottom now.'

'Oh, that's good,' I said. 'It's an unpleasant thing for a dog.'

She caught my arm. 'Ah've got summat else to tell you. Ah've had the thieves in!'

'Oh no, those two men? Not you, too! I'm so sorry.'

'Aye, but listen!' she said excitedly. 'One of them fellers was talkin' to me and t'other was in the kitchen with Wolfie. I heard 'im sayin' "Nice doggie, nice doggie," then there was a terrible yell and a scuffle and the feller went past the parlour door screamin', with Wolfie hangin' on to 'is backside. The other 'un ran off, too, but Wolfie caught 'im just as he was goin' through the door and he didn't half holler out! Last thing I saw was the two of them runnin' for their lives down t'street with Wolfie after them.'

She reached into the corner of the fireplace and handed me a jagged piece of blood-stained cloth, obviously from the seat of a man's trousers. 'Wolfie brought that back with 'im.'

I laughed so much that I had to lean against the mantelpiece. 'Oh, what a lovely story. I bet we'll never see those two around here again.'

'Nay, nay, that we won't.' The old lady put her head in her hands and giggled. 'Eee, I can't help laughin' when I think of that feller saying, "Nice doggie, nice doggie."'

'Yes, it's very funny,' I said. 'He must have been looking at the wrong end.'

17

Ninety per cent of horses' lamenesses are in the feet. So the old saying goes and I could see it was true here.

The big Clydesdale was lifting his near hind leg, holding the foot, quivering, a few inches from the ground, then putting it down carefully. I had seen this sort of thing a hundred times before and it was diagnostic.

'He's got gravel,' I said to the farmer. This was the local term for an infection of the foot. It happened when the horse bruised or cracked its sole, allowing the entrance of bacteria. An abscess formed and the only cure was to pare down the horn and evacuate the pus.

This involved lifting the hoof and either resting it on your knee in the case of a hind foot or between your legs in a fore and cutting through the sole with a hoof knife. Sometimes the horn could be as hard as marble and the exact spot difficult to find and I had spent many back-breaking sessions hacking away with the horse resting his full weight on me as the sweat ran down my nose and dripped on to the hoof.

'Right,' I said, 'let's have a look at it.' I ran my hand down the leg and was reaching for the foot when the horse whickered with anger, turned quickly and lashed out at me, catching me a glancing blow on the thigh.

'He can still kick with that bad foot, anyway,' I murmured.

The farmer took a firmer grip on the halter and braced his feet. 'Aye, he's a cheeky sod. Watch yourself. He's given me a clout or two.'

I tried again with the same result and, at the third attempt, after the flailing foot had narrowly missed me, the horse swung round and sent me crashing against the side of the box. As I got up and, grimly determined, had another go at reaching the foot, he reared round at me, brought a fore foot crashing on my shoulder, then tried to bite me.

The farmer was an elderly man, slightly built and he didn't look happy as he was dragged around by the plunging animal.

'Look,' I said, panting and rubbing my shoulder, 'we've got a bit of a problem. I have to bring Denny Boynton out to another gravelled horse near here this afternoon. We'll call in about two o'clock and treat this chap. He's got a shoe on, anyway, and it's a lot easier to do the job with a blacksmith.'

Farmer Hickson looked relieved. 'Aye, that'll be best. I could see we were goin' to have a bit of a rodeo!'

As I drove away, I mused on my relationship with Denny. He and I were old friends. He was a bit younger than I and accompanied me regularly on horse visits. In the fifties, the tractor had more or less taken over on the farms but some farmers still liked to keep a cart horse and took a pride in them. Most of them were big, docile animals and I had always had a strong empathy with them as they plodded patiently through their daily tasks, but that one back there was an exception.

Normally I would have taken the shoe off without much trouble before exploring the foot. All vets did courses in shoeing early in their education and I carried the tools with me, but I would have had some fun trying to do that with Hickson's animal. It was a job for Denny.

The Boynton smithy stood right at the end of Rolford village and as I drove up to the squat building with its clustering trees and backdrop of green hillside I felt, as I often did, that I was looking at one of the last relics of the past. When I first came to Yorkshire, every village had its blacksmith's shop and Darrowby itself had several. But with the disappearance of the draught horse they had just melted away. The men who had spent their lives in them for generations had gone and their work places which had echoed to the clatter of horses' feet and the clang of iron were deserted and silent.

Denny's shop was one of the few which had survived, mainly because he was an expert farrier, skilled in the often specialised shoeing which riding horses required. As I walked in, he was bent over the foot of a strapping hunter, laughing and joking with the attractive young owner who stood nearby.

'Now then, Mr Herriot,' he cried as he saw me. 'Be with you in a few minutes.' He was holding the hot shoe against the foot and the smell of the smoke rising from the seared horn, the glow of the forge and the ringing bang-bang as his still sprightly father hammered the glowing metal on the anvil evoked a hundred memories of a richer past.

Denny wasn't very big but he was lean and hard, the muscles on his forearms bulging and tensing as he worked. He had the broad strong back essential to his trade but, apart from that, he projected the same image of stringy durability as the Dales farmers who worked alongside me every day.

Now he was tapping the nails into the shoe and after a couple of minutes he straightened up and slapped the horse's rump. 'Right, Angela, you can take this awd screw away, now,' he said, flashing the girl a white-toothed grin.

She giggled and it struck me that it was a typical scene. Denny with his impish eyes and the hint of recklessness in his craggy features was undoubtedly attractive to the many county young ladies who brought their horses to him and I had never seen him working without a running badinage. A visit to the Boynton smith was in some ways a social event.

As horse and rider left, he reached for his bag of tools. 'Right, Mr Herriot. At your service!'

'Will you have time to do another gravel job on the way, Denny?' I asked.

He laughed. 'We'll mek time. Anything to oblige a gentleman!'

As we drove away I felt I ought to put him in the picture about Hickson's horse. I knew he had been dealing with skittish, often dangerous horses since childhood, and I had seen him again and again pushing big, explosive animals around effortlessly as though they were kittens, but it was only right to warn him.

'Denny,' I said, 'this horse at Hickson's could be difficult. He's a wild beggar and I could hardly get near him.'

'Oh aye?' Tool bag on knee, cigarette dangling from his lips, the young man was lazily observing the passing countryside. He didn't seem to be listening.

I tried again. 'He had a few goes at me with his hind foot, then started to wave his fore feet about . . .'

He dragged his eyes unwillingly from the window. 'It'll be right, Mr Herriot, it'll be right,' he murmured absently, stifling a yawn.

'He's a biter, too. Damn nearly got me on the shoulder just as I was trying to get away from –'

'Hey, wait a minute!' Denny shouted as we passed a roadside farmhouse. 'That's George Harrison in the yard. Just slow down a second, will you, Mr Herriot?' He wound down the window quickly. 'Nah then, George, how ista?' he yelled at the young farmer who was shouldering a straw bale. 'Have ye sobered up yet? Ha-ha-ha-ha!'

The two men exchanged a few shouted pleasantries before we took off. Denny turned to me. 'By gaw, George had a skinful last night at the Licensed Victuallers' Ball. Still looks a bit green – heh-heh!'

I decided to give up my attempts at warning him. He clearly wasn't interested.

He chatted away, filling me in with some uproarious details of the previous evening, but as we drew up in Hickson's yard he fell silent. His face was suddenly drawn and serious as he peered this way and that through the car windows. I knew what was coming next.

'Any savage dogs here, Mr Herriot?'

I suppressed a smile. Through all the years I had known him, he had always said this.

'No, none at all, Denny,' I replied.

He stared suspiciously at an elderly sheep dog enjoying a drink of milk at the kitchen door. 'How about that 'un?'

'That's old Zak. He's twelve! Quiet as a sheep.'

'Aye, mebbe, but that doesn't mean you can trust 'im. Get 'im inside, any road.'

I walked across the yard, waited until the old dog had licked out his bowl then ushered him, white muzzle upturned and tail waving at the attention, into the house. I had done this so many times, but still Denny wasn't keen to leave the car. After a final inspection in all directions he got out and stood warily on the cobbles for a few moments, then he hurried to the loose box where Farmer Hickson and horse were waiting.

The farmer gripped the halter tightly and smiled uncertainly at Denny as he came in. 'Watch 'im, lad. He's a funny sod.'

'Funny, is he?' The young man, hammer dangling from his hand, grinned and stepped close to the horse, and the animal, as though determined to prove the words, laid back his ears and lashed out.

Denny avoided the flying foot with practised ease and gave a demon king's laugh, throwing back his head. 'Aha! You're like that, are ye? Right, ya bugger, we'll see!' Then he moved in again. I don't know how he kept clear of the horse's repeated attempts to injure him, but within a minute he caught the claw of his hammer in the iron shoe in full flight and pulled it toward him. 'Okay, ya big bugger, I've got ye now, haven't I, eh?'

The horse, on three legs, made a few half-hearted attempts to pull his foot away as Denny hung on and chattered at him but it was clear that he realised that this new man was an entirely different proposition. Denny, with the foot on his knee, reached for his tools, muttering threats all the time and as I watched unbelievingly, he knocked up the clenches, drew out the nails with his pincers and removed the shoe. The horse, motionless except for a quivering of the flanks, was totally subjugated.

Denny displayed the sole for my inspection. 'Now, where d'you want me, Mr Herriot?' he asked.

I tapped along the sole until I found a place which seemed tender. To make sure, I squeezed at the place with the pincers and the animal flinched.

'That's the spot, Denny,' I said. 'There's a crack there.'

The young farrier began to cut away the horn with expert sweeps of his sharp knife. This was a job I had done so often by myself, but it was a joy to see an expert doing it. In no time at all he had followed the crack down and there was a hiss then a trickle of pus as he reached the site of the infection. It was one of the most satisfactory things in veterinary practice because, if the abscess is not evacuated, it causes the most acute agony for the animal. Sometimes the pus can work up under the wall of the hoof until it bursts out at the coronet after a long period of pain, and in other cases I have seen horses having to be put down when all attempts to relieve the infection have failed and the poor animal was laid groaning with a hugely swollen foot. Such memories from the old carthorse days always haunted me.

Nothing of that was going to happen this time and my relief was as strong as always. 'Thanks, Denny, that's great.' I administered antibiotic and antitetanus injections and said to the farmer, 'He'll soon be sound now, Mr Hickson.'

Then Denny and I set off for our next appointment. As we drove out of the yard I looked at the young blacksmith. 'Well, you certainly dealt with that wild horse. It was amazing how you quietened him.'

He leaned back in his seat, lit another cigarette and spoke lazily. 'Nobbut a bit daft, 'e was. It was nowt. There's lots like 'im – silly big bugger.'

He resumed his account of the previous evening, chuckling softly at times, and as I glanced round at him, totally relaxed, cap on the back of his head, smiling his carefree smile, he looked as though nothing could ever upset him. However, as I stopped the car at the farm where we had to see the other horse, his insouciant air fell away from him as though snatched by an unseen hand. Clutching his tool bag, he anxiously scanned every corner of the farmyard. I waited confidently for his next words.

'Any savage dogs here, Mr Herriot?'

18

'What is it?' 'What the devil is that?' 'A badger? Never!'

Pandemonium broke out in the Drovers' Arms. Calum and I had just returned from a communal visit and when I suggested a beer he got out of the car, slung Marilyn over his shoulder and strode into the bar.

The eyes of the regulars popped, they spluttered into their glasses and in a few seconds we were the centre of an excited crowd. I detached myself and sat quietly with my beer as the young man held court, answering the volleys of questions calmly and with a quiet satisfaction. It was clear that he loved to display his adored pet to anybody who was interested, and with most people it wasn't just a case of interest, he created a sensation wherever he went.

It was the same when I introduced him to my family in the

sitting room at Skeldale House. My children were making music, Rosie at the piano and Jimmy with his harmonica, when the tall, walrus-moustached figure came in with his wild animal. I had become a connoisseur of soaring eyebrows and open mouths, and Helen was typical, but the reaction of Jimmy and Rosie was wide-eyed delight.

'Oh, how lovely!' 'Can I stroke her?' 'Where did you get her?' 'What is she called?' Their questions were endless and Calum, laughing and teasing, was just about as big a hit with the children as his hairy companion.

Everything was going with a bang when Dinah, our second beagle and successor to Sam, ran in from the garden.

'This is Dinah,' I said.

'Oh-ho, oh-ho, little fat Dinah,' said Calum in a rumbling bass. It was not a complimentary remark, because my little dog was undoubtedly too fat, and an embarrassment to a vet who was constantly adjuring people to keep their dogs slim, but Dinah didn't seem to mind. She wagged her whole back end until I thought she would tie herself in a knot. Her response was remarkable and she clearly found this new voice immensely attractive. Calum bent down and she rolled on her back in ecstasy as he rubbed her tummy.

Helen laughed. 'Gosh, she really likes you!'

We didn't know it then, but her words were setting a scene which would be a familiar and intriguing one in the future. I was to find that all animals were attracted to Calum and that he had a rapport with them which was unique. They loved the very sound, sight and scent of him – a heaven-sent asset for a veterinary surgeon.

When the civilities were over with Marilyn scuttling merrily round the floor, happily accepting the petting of the children, Calum sat down on the piano stool and began to play. He was no Rubinstein, but he could knock out a rollicking tune with no trouble at all and the children clapped their hands and stamped their feet in delight.

Jimmy held out his harmonica. 'Can you play this, too?'

Calum took the instrument and held it to his mouth with his hands in a Larry Adler-like attitude, and after the first few notes you could see that he was in a different league from my son whose concert piece was 'God save the Queen'. After a couple of minutes of Mozart my new assistant handed back the harmonica and roared with laughter.

The young people were enchanted. 'I'm going for the concertina,' cried Jimmy.

He ran from the room and came back with one of the relics from my visits to house sales when Helen and I were first married. In those days I was often despatched to house sales to bring back essentials like tables and chairs and usually returned with quite impractical objects, ornamental ink stands and such like. In this case it was the concertina. It was an ancient little instrument, six-sided, with carved wooden ends and leather straps worn and frayed with age. It raised images of a mariner playing sea shanties on the deck of an old-time sailing ship and I had found it irresistible, but unfortunately nobody had been able to extract a tune from it and it had rested for years in the attic with many of my other useless purchases.

Calum lifted it from its wooden box and turned it over tenderly. 'Oh nice, very nice.' He slipped his hands through the straps, his fingers felt their way over the little ivory buttons and in a moment the room was filled with melody of a piercing sweetness. It was 'Shenandoah' and as we listened, suddenly hushed, to the totally unexpected richness which came from the instrument I was back on the deck of the sailing ship which I had dreamed of all those years ago.

I have many memories of Calum, but the one which lingers most hauntingly in my mind is that one of him sitting among my family, his dark eyes, unfathomable as they often were, fixed somewhere high on the wall, while his fingers coaxed that plaintive music from our little squeeze-box.

When he finished there was a spontaneous burst of applause and the children jumped about, clapping their hands. Calum was fixed in their minds for ever as a wonder man. He had a badger, he could play anything, he could do anything.

Just then, we began to wonder about Marilyn. She had been wandering quietly around the room but now there was no sign of her. We peered under the sofa and tipped up the arm chairs without success and were looking at each other in bewilderment when there was a rattling from the fireplace and the badger, abundantly clothed in soot, shot out from the chimney. She didn't want to be caught and raced a few times round the room before Calum grabbed her and carried her outside.

Jimmy and Rosie were almost hysterical. They hadn't had such fun for a long time, but Helen and I, looking at the devastation to our carpet and furniture, were not so amused.

It was a sudden comedown from inspirational heights to chaos, and in an intuitive moment a thought came to me. Was this the way it was always going to be with Calum?

19

I have heard it said that all tailors used to sit cross-legged on a table to ply their trade, but the only one I ever saw in this position was Mr Bendelow.

The cottage door opened straight from the street into the kitchen and the scene was so familiar. The cluttered little room with a thousand cloth clippings littering the floor, the sewing machine in the corner; Blanco, his enormous white dog, giving me a welcoming wag as he lay by the fire and Mr Bendelow, cross-legged on the table, talking to a customer, his needle poised above some garment or other.

It struck me, not for the first time, that Mr Bendelow's needle always seemed to be poised. I don't think I had ever seen it actually dig into any fabric, because he was always too busy talking. He was at it now, chattering into the slightly bemused face of a farmer's wife.

'You'd hardly believe what I've been tellin' you, would you, Mrs Haw?'

'No, right enough, I wouldn't, Mr Bendelow, but I wonder if you've managed to do that waistcoat for me husband. You said –'

'But it all really happened all them years ago, sure as I'm sittin' here. You wouldn't credit the things –'

'I'd like to tek it with me if you've finished it. He wants it for a –'

Mr Bendelow cackled. 'Ah'm not an old man, nobbut fifty, but the things that went on in them days . . . I remember . . .'

'You've had that waistcoat for three months, you know, you promised it for –'

'Oh aye, ah knaw, ah knaw. I've that much on. Don't know where to turn. But come back in a fortnight, love, you shall 'ave it then.'

'But 'e wants it for –'

'Best ah can do, love. Ta-ra.'

Mrs Haw, empty-handed and doleful, passed me on the way out and I put on my best smile as I took her place.

'Now then, young man.' Mr Bendelow's thin, gypsy-like face did not change expression but his eyes shot a sidelong glance of sheer hatred at the trousers I carried on my arm.

'Now what's this you've got for me?' he grunted.

'Well, it's these trouser bottoms, Mr Bendelow. They've got a bit frayed and I thought . . .'

'Aye, ye thought I'd just mek 'em like new for you. No trouble at all. You'll kill me, you know, you'll kill me. I'm goin' like 'ell with Christmas comin' on. At it night and day – never a minute.'

'Well, it's just the bottoms, Mr Bendelow . . .'

'And then there's me bad leg. How long have I had it? Oh, years. I went to Dr Allinson. He said, "Have you had this before?" I said, "Yes." He said, "Well, you've got it again." He gave me sixty tablets and when I'd had 'alf I was a lot better and when I'd 'ad the lot I was nearly cured. But the doctor 'ad planned that. "Mr Bendelow," he said, "when you've had half of these tablets you'll be much better and when you've had the other half you'll think you're cured. But you won't be, you know, you won't be. I know what you're like and you won't want to come back to me. But when you've had your sixty tablets I want to see you. On that very day."

'So I goes back to 'im on the very day he said, and he says, "Now then, Mr Bendelow, you're here then." And I said, "Yes, Doctor, right on the day you said." "And you've finished your sixty tablets?" he says. And I says, "Yes, I've 'ad the lot." And 'e gives me another 'undred.'

'Well, that's fine, Mr Bendelow. My wife says if you would just take a look at these frayed bottoms –'

'And he says, "You've got to stop runnin' up and down them stairs." And I says, "I can't, Doctor. I can't stop. I'm always workin'. I never cease." But listen to this, Mr Herriot. I'm goin' to tell you something now. I've never made a penny. And I'll tell you something else. If you've never made a fortune before you're forty you'll never make one.'

'These bottoms are just a little bit frayed as you can see . . .'

'Ah yes, you can talk about makin' a fortune on the football pools if you like, Mr Herriot. I can tell you about Littlewoods. Just listen to this, now.'

As he leaned forward from the table, his face intent, the street door opened and a big man came in. I recognised Jeremy Boothby, son of one of the big landowners and a person of considerable presence.

'You'll excuse me,' he boomed as he brushed past me. 'I've called for my suit, Bendelow. I was in last week.'

The tailor didn't even look at him. 'Do you know that I used to win regular on Littlewoods? But allus on the four aways and the most I won was six bob. So I says to myself if you go for the big money then you'll win the big money.'

'Do you hear me, Bendelow?' The great voice filled the room. 'I've been in every week since October and –'

'So I fills up a perm on the treble chance and I had twenty-four points straight away. I was waitin' for the big cheque for seventy-five thousand comin', but it never came. Oh no, I got a letter from one of the head men at Littlewoods.'

'Now look here, Bendelow!' Mr Boothby's shout made the windows rattle. 'You've had that suit for a year now and –'

He stopped in mid flow. Blanco had strolled round from the fireside and was standing by the table, looking up at him. He didn't have all that far to look, because he must have been just about the biggest dog I had ever seen. Mr Bendelow had described him to me as a Swedish Mountain Dog and I could remember his smug smile of superiority when I told him I had never heard of that breed. I was pretty sure Blanco was a cross but whatever he was he was magnificent – snow-white and vast. And now as he stood close to Mr Boothby, quite motionless, the lion head poised, there was a menacing fixity in his gaze and a faint growl rolled from deep in his rib cage.

As man and dog eyed each other the growl became louder and for a second Blanco's lips fluttered upwards giving a glimpse of a row of crocodilian teeth.

Boothby stepped back, then spoke in a softer tone. 'Will you let me have my suit . . . ? I . . .'

Mr Bendelow, clearly irritated by the interruption, gestured with his needle. 'Not ready yet – call next week.'

With a final glance at Blanco, the big man turned and left.

'A lovely letter of apology, it was,' continued the tailor. 'He told me I had got the twenty-four points all right but he couldn't give me the seventy-five thousand because of one little detail. Yes, I'm tellin' you, one little detail. I'd put down sixteen matches instead of eight. It was a lovely letter and 'e sounded real sorry, but there was nothing he could do about it.'

'Well, well, what a shame. Could you possibly do these trousers for some time next week. I would be very –'

'But all that money would be no good to me. I could tell you something about moneyed people . . .'

I dropped the garment on the table, gave him a hurried farewell wave and fled.

As I walked slowly down the street, my head spinning with the barmy torrent of words which, thanks to contemporary note-taking, I have reproduced here verbatim, I ruminated on the phenomenon of Mr Bendelow. In time, he did disgorge the work brought to him, so presumably he did most of his sewing and cutting at night. He was, in fact, a fine tailor and I had seen suits of such perfect fit and neat hand-stitching that I realised why people like Boothby continued to patronise him. It was all a question of luck – occasionally he had surprised me by coming up with a repair or an alteration in reasonable time.

He had supreme confidence in his own ability and intellectual gifts. In fact, convinced as he was that he knew everything about everything, particularly in the realm of domestic finance, he considered it his bounden duty to impart his knowledge to anybody who crossed his path, and since he had never married, he had no other outlet than his customers.

I had only once seen him at a loss. It was some years earlier when he measured Helen for a skirt and didn't give her a fitting until several months later. When that day finally came, the skirt waist didn't meet by a couple of inches. He stared in disbelief and tugged and pulled at the cloth a few times but it made no difference. Quickly he passed a tape measure round her middle, then consulted his notebook and measured again. From his kneeling position he looked up at us, totally baffled.

Helen smiled and relieved his agony. 'I should have told you,' she said, 'I'm pregnant.'

He looked at her narrowly, but since he was responsible for the long delay he was in no position to complain. However, the unheard of loss of face might have put a strain on our relations but for my long-standing rapport with Blanco, to whom he was devoted.

Blanco was around five years old and although he had been mainly healthy he had required my attention a few times, usually to extract pins embedded in his pads. He was the only tailor's dog I knew and I had often thought that it was an occupational hazard, lying daily as he did among the debris of his master's trade. There was no doubt that those pins often got right in and had to be extracted by digging deep with forceps. Blanco always appeared to be grateful; in fact, he was one of those dogs who actually enjoyed coming to my surgery. Some dogs crossed to the other side of the road when they entered Trengate and slunk past the surgery with their tails down, but Blanco nearly tugged Mr Bendelow off his feet as he fought to drag him through our door.

He had been in for his annual distemper booster the previous week and he had come prancing along the passage, wagging his tail furiously and poking his head sociably round the office door on his way to the consulting room. So different from a big yellow labrador bitch who followed him and had to be sledged along on her bottom the entire length of the passage tiles, her face a mask of misery even though she was only going to have her paw bandaged.

Blanco was the soul of good nature and the only time he showed a gleam of anger was if he thought Mr Bendelow was being threatened. This protectiveness was invaluable to the tailor because the set-up in that house was conducive to exasperation and I had heard a few blustering men and screeching women driven to distraction by the interminable delays. But the great white head and cold eyes appearing round the corner of the table had a wonderfully calming effect. Sometimes a little growl or a pointed sniffing round the customer's ankles was required but I had never seen a failure.

In my musings, I had often thought that Blanco was a vindication of my long-held theory that big dogs came from little houses and little dogs from big ones. In fact, it seemed to me to be the ultimate corroboration because in the greatest of battlemented, multi-acred mansions you got down to Border Terriers and Jack Russells while in tiny, one-up, one-down dwellings you found something like Blanco.

A week later, ever optimistic, I returned to Mr Bendelow's establishment. He was in his usual place, cross-legged like a little gnome on his table.

Another customer, a disgruntled-looking farmer, was just about to leave, but he was giving the tailor a few parting words.

'Ah'm about fed up comin' here every week after you've promised.' His voice took on an angry tone. 'You don't seem bothered, but it's not good enough, you know.'

Mr Bendelow gave the familiar gesture with his needle. 'Next week . . . next week.'

'Aye, that's what you always say,' barked the farmer, and I looked over the table at Blanco, stretched by the fire. This was the sort of thing that always brought him to his feet, but he showed no interest and didn't move as the farmer, with a final snort, turned and left, banging the door behind him.

'Good morning, Mr Bendelow,' I said briskly. 'I've just dropped in for –'

'Now then, Mr Herriot!' The little man stabbed his needle at me. 'I was just goin' to tell you summat about moneyed people when you left. Old Crowther, down Applegate. Left eighty thousand and when I patched his trousers for 'im he had to stay in bed. I'm not jokin' nor jestin', he had to stay in bed.'

'Talking about trousers, Mr Bendelow –'

'He 'ad a housekeeper – Maud something was her name – she did everything for 'im. Got 'im in and out of bed, cooked for 'im, slaved for 'im for thirty years. But, do you know, he never left her a penny. She contested the will, you know, but she only got five hundred pounds. Money all went to some distant relatives.'

'Are my trousers ready? I do need them for –'

'And I could tell you a worse case than that, Mr Herriot. When I was a lad, I worked for a farmer. That man was worth thousands, but he never went into a pub, never went to the pictures, never went anywhere. Saved every penny. Don't know what 'e did with it all. Maybe kept it about the house. Oh, that reminds me of a story.'

I was about to utter another plea when a stout lady behind me burst out. 'Now look 'ere, I don't want to butt in, but I'm in a hurry. I want my dress now – you promised it for today.'

The tailor waved his needle. 'Not ready. Been too busy. Come next week.'

'Too busy! Too busy chatterin' is more like it.' She had a high, piercing delivery and she gave the tailor the full blast. I looked at Blanco, still motionless by the fire. His lack of interest was unusual.

Mr Bendelow, too, seemed to miss his dog's support because he was untypically abashed by the lady's attack.

'Aye, well,' he mumbled, 'you shall 'ave it next week, definite.' He gave me a sidelong glance. 'You, too, Mr Herriot.'

When I called the following week, I stopped in the doorway, transfixed by the amazing sight. Mr Bendelow was actually stitching. Up on his table, his head bent low over a jacket, his hand flashing over a lapel with wonderful deftness. And he wasn't talking.

The talking was being done by a man and his wife who were submitting him to an aggressive barrage of complaints. The tailor, silent and unhappy, made no reply. And Blanco was still asleep by the fire.

In the quest for my trousers, I called in a few times during my rounds but there was always a queue and I didn't have time to wait. I did notice, however, that on each occasion Mr Bendelow on his table was working, silent and subdued, while his dog was motionless by the fire. The picture saddened me. Talking was the little man's life, his hobby and solace in his bachelor existence. Something was very wrong.

I called round one evening and found Mr Bendelow alone, still stitching.

I didn't mention my trousers. 'What's wrong with Blanco?' I said.

He looked at me in surprise. 'Nowt, as far as I know.'

'Is he eating all right?'

'Aye, he is.'

'Getting plenty of exercise?'

'Yes, a good walk night and mornin'. You know I look after me dog, Mr Herriot.'

'Yes, of course you do. But . . . he's not up round your table like he used to be. Not . . . er . . . interested in the customers.'

He nodded miserably. 'Aye, that's t'only thing. But he isn't ill.'

'Let's have a look at him,' I said. I went over to the fire and bent over the dog. 'Come on, Blanco, old lad, let's see you on your feet.'

I tapped him on the rump and he got up slowly. I looked at the tailor. 'He seems a bit stiff.'

'Aye, maybe, but 'e soon works it off when I take him out.'

'Not really lame, though? No pins?'

'Nay, nay, ah can allus tell when he's picked one up.'

'Hmm. Still, I'd better check on his paws.'

Whenever I lifted one of Blanco's feet I had the same feeling as when I examined a horse's hoof and, indeed, had to stop myself from saying 'Whoa, there, boy' and tucking the paw between my knees.

I carefully inspected each foot, squeezing the pads which were the usual sites for the dangerous pins, but all seemed normal. I took his temperature, auscultated his chest and palpated his abdomen without finding any clues. But as I looked down at the big animal I could not rid myself of the nagging certainty that there was something amiss.

Blanco, tiring of my attention, sat down, and he did so gingerly, lowering himself carefully on to the fireside rug.

That wasn't right at all. 'Get up, lad,' I said quickly.

There had to be some trouble at his rear end. Impacted anal glands, perhaps? No, they were all right. I passed my hands down the massive thighs and on the left side, as I felt my way down the musculature, the dog winced suddenly. There was a painful swelling there and as I clipped away the hair all became clear. Deeply embedded in the flesh was one of his old enemies, a pin.

It was a moment's work to extract it with my forceps and I turned to Mr Bendelow. 'Well, there it is. He must have sat on this when it got onto the rug. It's a wonder he hasn't been lame, but there's a little abscess which has been upsetting him. An abscess is a depressing thing.'

'Aye . . . aye . . . but what can you do?' He looked at me with worried eyes.

'I'll have to get him round to the surgery and drain the pus away. Then he'll be fine.'

Blanco's visit to Skeldale House passed off smoothly. I evacuated the abscess and filled up the cavity by squeezing a few of the ever-useful penicillin intramammary tubes into it.

I didn't visit Mr Bendelow for another week. I clung to the hope that he might have repaired my working trousers. My wardrobe was very limited and I sorely needed them.

The scene was as always. The tailor on his table and Blanco stretched by the fire. And strangely, Mrs Haw, the farmer's wife I had seen at my first visit was there.

She was having a kind of tug-of-war with her husband's waistcoat which Mr Bendelow had apparently mended at last but was reluctant to release. His lips were moving rapidly with his quick-fire delivery. 'And that's what the feller said to me. You wouldn't believe it would you, and that's not all . . .'

With a quick tug, the lady managed to win possession of the waistcoat. 'Thank ye very much, Mr Bendelow. I'll 'ave to go now.' She nodded, waved and scurried past me, looking exhausted but triumphant.

The tailor turned to me. 'Ah, it's you, Mr Herriot.'

'Yes, Mr Bendelow, I was wondering . . .'

'You'll remember I was just goin' to tell you that story about the rich man.'

'About my trousers . . .'

'He was an old farmer, he kept his brass in the house in buckets. His missus brought up a bucket and she said, "There's fifteen hundred pounds in this bucket," and the old chap said, "There's summat wrong somewhere. There should be two thousand in that 'un." And do you know, that man and his wife used to pay separately for their own food. It's true what I'm tellin' you – she went out and bought hers and 'e did the same. And I'll tell you summat else, Mr Herriot . . .'

'Have you, by any chance managed to –'

'Just listen to this, Mr Herriot –'

'Hey, Bendy!' A big man had just come in and was roaring at the tailor over my shoulder. 'I can 'ear you and ah'm not listenin'! I want my bloody jacket!'

It was Gobber Newhouse, hugely fat, notorious drunk and a bully. Stale beer fumes billowed around him as he bellowed again. 'Don't give me any of your bloody excuses, Bendy, ah know you!'

Like a surfacing white whale, Blanco rose from the fireside and surged to the table. He seemed to know the kind of man he was dealing with and didn't waste any frills on him. Stretching up his mighty head, he opened his mouth wide and bayed with tremendous force into the red sweating face. 'Whaaa! Whaaa!'

Gobber backed away. 'Bloody dog . . . siddown . . . gerrim away, Bendy.'

'Whaaa! Whaaa! Whaaa!' went Blanco.

The big man was half out of the door when Mr Bendelow signalled with his needle. 'Come next week.' Then he turned his full attention to me. 'As I was sayin', Mr Herriot . . .' he continued.

'I really do need –'

'Next week, definite, but let me tell you . . .'

'Must go, I'm afraid,' I muttered, and escaped into the street.

Out there my feelings were mixed but, on the whole, happy. I still hadn't got my trousers, but Blanco was right back on form.

20

Five o'clock in the morning and the telephone jangling in my ear. Ewe lambing at Walton's, a lonely farm on the high moorland, and as I crawled from the haven of bed into the icy air of the bedroom and began to pull on my clothes, I tried not to think of the comfortless hour or two ahead.

Pushing my arms through my shirt sleeves I gritted my teeth as the cloth chafed the flesh. In the pale dawn light, I could see the little red fissures which covered my hands and ran up to my elbows. In lambing time I hardly ever seemed to have my jacket on and the constant washing in the open pens or in windy fields had turned my skin to raw meat. I could detect the faint scent of Helen's glycerine and rose water which she applied to my arms every night and made them bearable.

Helen stirred under the blankets and I went over and kissed her cheek. 'Off to Walton's,' I whispered.

Eyes closed, she nodded against the pillow, and I could just hear her sleepy murmur. 'Yes . . . I heard.'

Going out of the door I looked back at my wife's huddled bulk. When this happened, she, too, was jerked into the world of work and duty. That phone could blast off again at any time and she would have to get in touch with me. And on top of this, she would have to get the fires lit, the tea made and the children started with their breakfast – the little tasks I tried to help her with and which weren't easy in our big, beautiful ice box of a house.

Through the tight-shut, sleeping little town, then on to the narrow road winding between its walls until the trees dwindled and disappeared, leaving the wide windswept fells bare and unwelcoming at this hour.

I wondered if there was any chance of the ewe being under cover. In the early fifties, it didn't seem to occur to many of the farmers to bring their lambing ewes into the buildings and I attended to the great majority out in the open fields. There were happy times when I almost chuckled in relief at the sight of a row of hurdles in a warm fold yard or sometimes the farmers would build pens from stacked-up straw bales, but on this occasion my spirits plummeted when I drew up at the farm and met Mr Walton who came out of the house carrying a bucket of water and headed for the gate.

'Outside, is she?' I asked, trying to sound airy.

'Aye, just ower there.' He pointed over the long, bracken-splashed pasture to a prone woolly form in the distance which looked a hell of a long way 'ower there'. As I trailed across the frosty grass, my medical bag and obstetric overall dangling, a merciless wind tore at me, picking up an extra Siberian cold from the long drifts of snow which still lay behind the walls in this late Yorkshire spring.

As I stripped off and knelt behind the ewe I looked around. We were right on top of the world and the panorama of hills and valleys with grey farmhouses and pebbled rivers in their depths was beautiful but would have been more inviting if it had been a warm summer afternoon and me preparing for a picnic with my family.

I held out my hand and the farmer deposited a tiny sliver of soap on my palm. I always felt that farmers kept special pieces of soap for the vet – minute portions of scrubbing soap which were too small and hard to be of any use. I rubbed this piece frantically with my hands, dipping frequently into the water, but I could work up only the most meagre film of lather. Not enough to protect my tender arm as I inserted it into the ewe, and the farmer looked at me enquiringly as I softly ooh'd and aah'd my way towards the cervix.

I found just what I didn't want to find. A big single lamb, jammed tight. Two lambs are the norm and three quite common, but a big single lamb often spells trouble. It was one of my joys in practice to sort out the tangles of twins and triplets but with the singles it was a case of not enough room and the big lamb had to be eased and pulled out as gently as possible – a long and tedious business. Also, often the single lamb was dead through pressure and had to be removed by embryotomy or a Caesarean operation.

Resigning myself to the fact that I was going to spend a long time crouched on that windy hilltop, I reached as far as possible and poked a finger into the lamb's mouth, feeling a surge of relief as the little tongue stirred against my hand. He was alive, anyway, and with a lifting of my spirits I began the familiar ritual of introducing lubricating jelly, locating the tiny legs and fastening them with snares and, finally, as I sat back on my heels for a breather I knew that all I had to do now was to bring the head through the pelvis. That was the tricky bit. If it came through I was home and dry; if it didn't I was in trouble. Mr Walton, holding back the wool from the vulva, watched me in silence. Despite his lifetime experience with sheep he was helpless in a case like this because, like most farmers, he had huge, work-roughened hands with fingers like bananas and could not possibly have got inside a ewe. My small 'lady's hand' as they called it was a blessing.

I hooked my forefinger into the eye socket – my favourite trick, there was nothing else to get hold of except the lower jaw which was dangerously fragile – and began to pull with infinite care. The ewe strained, crushing my hand against the pelvic bones – not as bad as in a cow but painful, and my mouth opened wide as I eased and twisted and pulled until, with a blessed surge, the head slipped through the bony pelvic opening.

It wasn't long, then, until feet, legs and nose appeared at the vulva and I brought the little creature out onto the grass. He lay still for a moment, snuffling at the cold world he had entered, then he shook his head vigorously. I smiled. That was the best sign of all.

I had another wrestle with the morsel of soap, then the farmer wordlessly handed me a piece of sacking to dry my arms. This was quite common in those days. Towels were scarce commodities on the farms and I couldn't blame the farmers' wives for hesitating to send out a clean towel to a man who had just had his arms up the back end of an animal. An old soiled one was the usual and, if not, the hessian sack was always at hand. I couldn't rub my painful arms with the coarse material and contented myself with a careful patting, before pushing them, still damp, into the sleeves of my jacket.

The ewe, hearing a high-pitched call from her lamb began to talk back with the soft deep baa I knew so well, and as she got up and began an intensive licking of the little creature I stood there, forgetful of the cold, listening to their conversation, enthralled as ever by the miracle of birth. When the lamb, apparently feeling he was wasting time, struggled to his feet and tottered unsteadily round to the milk bar I grinned in satisfaction and made my way back to the car.

After breakfast, my next call was to a 'cleansing', the removal of the afterbirth from a cow and again, after a struggle with a rock-hard marble of soap, I was offered a sack to dry myself, only this time it had recently contained potatoes and I found I was powdering my chapped arms with soil. Later that morning, after a rectal examination for pregnancy diagnosis, I had the choice of a truly filthy 'cow house towel' which must have had an astronomical bacterial count and declined it in favour of yet another piece of hessian.

My arms were red hot inside my sleeves when I drove into the Birrell farmyard, but I knew better things awaited me here. Wonderful things, in fact.

I never knew what George Birrell's attitude to towels might be or that of his wife, but his mother, old Grandma Birrell, had very clear views on the matter. When I had finished stitching a tear on the cow's udder I stood on the cobbles, blood-spattered and expectant, waiting for the old lady. Right on cue, she came into the byre, hand in hand with four-year-old Lucy, the youngest of her grandchildren. She set down a milking stool and laid out in a perfectly folded oblong a newly laundered towel of snowy whiteness and on top of this she placed a tablet of expensive lavender toilet soap in its wrappings, virgin and unopened. A brightly scoured aluminium bucket of steaming water completed the picture, as pretty a one as ever I had seen.

Reverently I peeled the paper from the soap – it was always a new tablet – and as I dipped into the water and spread the rich lather on my burning arms, inhaling the fragrance of the lavender, I almost crooned with ecstasy. The farmer stood by impassively with perhaps the faintest twitch of amusement round his mouth, but Grandma Birrell and Lucy watched my ablutions with rapt enjoyment.

It was always like this at the Birrells and I loved it but I could never quite understand why it happened. Maybe Siegfried had a point when he said that old ladies liked me, and he was always pulling my leg about my 'harem' of over-seventies who insisted on my services for their dogs. Anyway, whatever the cause, I revelled in the patronage of Grandma Birrell. In her eyes, everything had to be right for me. Nothing was too good for Mr Herriot.

It was a Saturday morning when Siegfried pushed the *Darrowby and Houlton Times* across the office desk to me.

'Bit of sad news for you, I'm afraid, James,' he murmured, pointing to an entry.

It was in the deaths column. 'Mrs Marjorie Birrell, aged 78, dearly beloved wife of the late Herbert Birrell . . .' I read it through with a growing sense of loss, a rising wistfulness at the feeling of something good coming to an end.

Siegfried gave me a lop-sided smile. 'Your old clean-towel friend, eh?'

'That's right.' Her clean towels were her expression of friendship and it was as a friend I would always remember her. In my mind's eye, I could see her plainly in her flowered apron standing by the milking stool with Lucy. She was of the farming generation which had come through the tough times before the war and her gaunt, slightly bowed frame and lined face bore testimony to the hard years. It was the kind of face I had seen on so many of the old Yorkshire folk – grim, but kindly. I knew I was going to miss her.

Just how much I would miss her came to me forcibly on my next visit to the Birrell farm. As I finished my job I looked at my soiled hands with the renewed pang of realisation that the old lady wouldn't be coming through that door. I knew George Birrell wouldn't offer me a sack, but what was going to happen?

As I pondered, the half-door was pushed open and little Lucy came into the byre, staggering slightly as she carried the familiar shining bucket of hot water. Then from under her arm she produced a towel and soap and laid them on a milking stool. And it was the same spotless, geometrically folded towel and the same pristine toilet soap as before.

Slightly flushed, the little girl looked up at me. 'Gran said I had to look after you,' she said breathlessly. 'She told me what to do.'

I swallowed a big lump. 'Well, Lucy . . . that's wonderful. And you've done everything just right.'

She nodded, well pleased, and I stole a look at her father, standing there, leaning on a cow. But George's face was inscrutable.

I peeled the wrapper from the soap and began to wash and as the scent of the lavender rose around me I was carried back to all the other days.

I lathered my hands in silence, then the little girl spoke again. 'Mr Herriot, the only thing is, I'm five now and I'll soon be goin' to school. I don't know how you're goin' to manage.'

An overwhelming flood of déjà vu washed over me. My own daughter, Rosie, at that same age, had been consumed with worry at how I was going to carry on my life without her and had consoled me with the reassurance that she'd still be available at weekends.

I didn't know what to say, but her father broke in.

'Don't worry, luv,' he said, 'I'll do me best if you'll teach me how, and anyway, from now on I'm goin' to try to call Mr Herriot out only on Saturdays.'

21

I felt a little breathless as I lifted the phone.

'I'm sorry, Lord Hulton,' I said, 'I'm afraid I'll be a little late in visiting your horse this morning. My house blew down last night.'

There was a silence at the other end and I could sense the amiable peer having some difficulty in absorbing my announcement. I felt I should explain further.

'As you know, there was a gale during the night – ninety miles per hour, I understand – and the house I am having built had just got to roof height. I've been along to have a look as I usually do each morning and, as I say, it's blown down. Piles of bricks everywhere and masses of twisted scaffolding. I have a few arrangements I must make.'

There was another silence, quite a long one, then just two words.

'Oh, crumbs.'

It was a traumatic moment in my life and I have never forgotten that brief riposte from the eccentric but endearing Marquis of Hulton. Those two words in his habitual exquisitely modulated tones conveyed all the shock and compassion which the little man so clearly felt.

This event marked one more step in my efforts to move my family to a more suitable dwelling, and they had started quite soon after my abortive attempt to buy Mrs Dryden's house.

It took me quite a while to recover from that bidding battle in the Drovers' Arms. I had built my hopes so high and the sense of failure hung heavily on me as I had to watch my wife still slogging away in the wide reaches of Skeldale House. Helen herself, undoubtedly a better adjusted character than I, just laughed the whole thing off.

'Something else will turn up,' she said as she scrubbed and polished happily. That was the maddening thing about it – she didn't mind. But I did and my obsession remained. Somehow I would get her out of Skeldale.

There was a sudden gleam of light when I spotted the notice in the *Darrowby and Houlton Times*.

'Look at this, Helen!' I said eagerly, pointing to a picture among the estate agents' advertisements on the front page. 'I know that house. It's a very nice place.'

She peered over my shoulder. 'Oh yes, along the Dennaby road. I've seen it – very attractive.' Then she gave me a questioning glance. 'But it's a detached house, not too big, I know, but not like Mrs Dryden's little semi. It will make a lot of money.'

'No, old Bootland and I between us pushed up the price of Mrs Dryden's. That little place was only worth about two thousand pounds. This one will go for its right price – around three thousand. I think the building society would lend me that much.'

I came in for lunch that day, flushed with success. The man at the society had been very accommodating – the mortgage would be possible.

'Things are looking up, Helen,' I said. 'Really it's a good job we didn't get the other house. This one is just right. A bit bigger, but compact and a nice sized garden with an orchard and a lovely view down the dale. The auction is next Friday so we haven't long to wait. This is it, Helen – I know it is!'

My wife gazed at me thoughtfully. 'Jim, I'll only agree to this if you promise to keep calm at the sale.'

'Calm? What do you mean?'

'Well, you know very well that you got all worked up and bid way past the price we could afford. All I'm asking is for you to keep calm and not get yourself into a state like last time.'

'Calm . . . ? State . . . ? I don't understand you,' I said haughtily.

Her smile was patient. 'Oh, you must remember. You were white, like a ghost, and shaking all over at the end of it. I wondered if you'd ever be able to get up and walk out.'

'You're exaggerating,' I replied with dignity. 'I was under a certain amount of pressure, that's all.'

Helen's smile suddenly turned to a grin. 'Oh, I know, but I'm not going with you unless you promise to go as far as that three thousand and not a penny more. I mean it, Jim.'

'Right . . . right . . . I promise, of course. I wouldn't do anything so silly, anyway.'

This little contretemps vanished quickly from my mind and I was soon back in my old fantasy – imagining Helen floating around effortlessly in the new house, the children climbing the trees and picking the fruit in the orchard. On my rounds I kept changing my route so that I could go along the Dennaby road and feast my eyes on the place. Helen and I had had a look round and it was perfect. And soon, very soon, it would be mine.

I didn't come off my cloud until the Friday afternoon when we walked across the market place to the Drovers. When we went into the crowded room where the auction was to be held I felt a sudden lurch at my stomach. It was all horribly reminiscent of last time. Same room, same rows of heads, same auctioneer on the platform drumming his fingers on the table in front of him and looking over the throng with a pleased smile. By the time we had squeezed into a place and sat down, my heart was thumping.

Soon the auctioneer started his preamble, telling us all the nice things I already knew about the house. As he went on, Helen, squashed tightly against me and possibly sensing some slight quivering in my limbs, gripped my hand, interlacing her fingers with mine.

'Just relax, Jim,' she whispered.

I sniffed. 'I'm perfectly relaxed, I assure you,' I mumbled, trying to ignore the thudding in my ears as the bidding started. I did feel, however, that a few deep breaths would help in a situation like this.

It was at about the third deep breath that I heard the words 'And now I have two thousand nine hundred' from the auctioneer. He seemed to have arrived at the figure unexpectedly quickly and I shot up my hand. Other hands rose all around me and I heard 'I have three thousand.'

At that moment Helen's grip on my hand tightened fiercely. She was a big strong girl and it came to me with certainty that if I pursued this matter further she would reduce my fingers to a pulp.

It would have made no difference anyway because the whole business was raging away out of my control. 'Three thousand one hundred, two hundred, three hundred, three thousand four hundred . . .' Then, in no time at all, as I sat mute, he was over four thousand with forests of bids going in. There was a slight slowing down in the late four thousands but before I had finished my deep breathing exercise I heard the hammer going down on the table – sold to Mr Somebody-or-other for five thousand pounds. It was all over – and I hadn't even had a look in.

As we rose and began to shuffle out with the crowd, I saw a grey-haired man shaking hands with the auctioneer and laughing in what I thought was an insufferably smug manner, then we were outside, walking over the cobbles of the market place.

The deflated feeling was the same as before. Helen was still holding my hand and I managed to work up a smile.

'Well, it's happened again,' I murmured. 'But maybe I'm not as white this time?'

My wife studied my face for a moment. 'No . . . a bit pale perhaps, but nothing like last time.' Then she laughed. 'Poor old lad, you never had the chance to go really white. It was over in a flash. Anyway, never mind – I often think that so many things happen for the best.'

'Still, it's another disappointment,' I said. 'Last time we had Mrs Dryden to console us a bit, but there's nobody today.'

As I spoke, I felt a tug at my sleeve. I turned and saw Bert Rawlings, whose smallholding's fields bordered the house which had just been sold.

'Hullo, Bert,' I said. 'Been to the sale?'

'Aye, I 'ave, Mr Herriot, and I'm right glad you didn't get that 'ouse.'

'Eh?'

'I say it was a lucky thing you didn't get it, because I've been in that place many a time and I can tell ye it's not all it appears.'

'Really?'

'Aye, it's a good-lookin' house, but the roof leaks like 'ell.'

'Never!'

'I'm not jokin'. I've been up in the attic and seen rows of buckets and pots and pans set out to try to catch the watter. They've been tryin' to mend that roof for years but they've never managed it.'

'Heavens!'

'And the timbers up there are rotten with all the damp.'

'My God!'

He patted my arm and laughed 'So you see, you 'ad a lucky escape. Just thought I'd tell ye.'

'Well, thanks, Bert. That does make us feel better.' I waved to him as he hurried away across the market place, then I turned to Helen.

'Well, isn't that strange. We have had somebody to cheer us up after all. Maybe next time will be third time lucky.'

Despite our latest defeat our determination was as strong as ever, or rather mine was, because, as I say, Helen didn't seem all that worried. But my mind was set in a groove. I scanned all the advertisements in the local newspapers, stopped eagerly at every For Sale board in the gardens of the district, but nothing really got moving until we were introduced at a party to Bob and Elizabeth Mollison. They were young architects, about our own age, who had opened an office in a nearby market town.

'You know', said Elizabeth, 'you're going through the mill

trying to find a suitable house, but we could build you a really nice house for £3,000 – planned by yourselves with all the features you want. It would be a far better prospect for you, and in fact, probably cheaper in the long run.'

Helen and I looked at each other. We had never thought of that.

'If you can find a plot of land, Bob and I could have a place built for you in a few months,' Elizabeth went on. 'Think it over, anyway.'

I really didn't need to think it over. The whole horizon seemed filled with blinding light. 'This is the right idea,' I said eagerly, and Helen nodded, too. 'Why didn't we think of this before? We'll do it!'

The Mollisons regarded us uncertainly. 'Are you quite sure? Why don't you think about it for a few days.'

I shook my head decisively. 'No, no, we'll go right ahead. You draw up some plans and I'll find a plot somewhere as I go round the country.'

Bob smiled. 'Fine, but hold on – we'd have to have a proper conference to know just what you want. We'd need a lot of details.'

'We want a hatch,' I said.

'A hatch? That's all . . . ? How about you, Helen?'

'A hatch,' replied my wife firmly. In both our minds there floated the heavenly image of our meals being handed through that little hole in the wall from kitchen to dining room. After the years of tramping the long passage at Skeldale House that had to be number one on the list.

The Mollisons had a good laugh at this, but then they hadn't seen the Skeldale passages.

'Right,' Elizabeth said between giggles, 'so we design this house round the hatch, eh?'

'Absolutely.' More laughter, but for Helen and me there was a very serious core to our jollity.

Later, we did have our conference and worked out the less important aspects like bedrooms and bathrooms and it wasn't long before the young couple produced a most attractive plan.

'It's a lovely house,' Helen murmured as she studied it. 'Such a nice little hall and staircase and all those useful cupboards and wardrobes built in. You've thought of everything.'

'Especially the hatch!' said the Mollisons together, and the laughter started again.

Meanwhile I was scouring the countryside for a plot and this was proving very difficult. Something called Town and Country Planning had come into being so it was no good asking one of my farmer friends to sell me a bit of land in one of their fields where there was a nice view.

Nice chaps as they were, they wanted to help, but couldn't.

'I'd be delighted, Jim,' one of them said, 'but it's not allowed. I can't even build a house in my fields for me own son!'

That was the story everywhere and finally I realised that I had to find a bit of ground somewhere inside the tight building line which had been drawn around Darrowby. My search became more and more desperate until, one day, I ended up with a plot between two houses on the edge of the town. It was a pleasant situation but very narrow.

'There's only one thing for it,' Bob Mollison said. 'If you buy this plot we'll have to put the house in long ways on.'

This worried us. 'But what a shame,' Helen said. 'It's such a pretty house – I just love that frontage.'

Bob shrugged. 'I'm afraid it's that or nothing. Lots of people are trying to find land to build on. You might have to wait ages for anything else to turn up. And we can make modifications. We can make it look very attractive the other way round.'

Elizabeth came to us with a modified design and indeed it was an acceptable compromise. We bought the land and prepared for action.

Almost immediately we came up against other unexpected snags. In the early fifties, Britain was still recovering from the austerities of the war. Many things were still in short supply – including builders. We tried everywhere but couldn't find anybody to take on the contract. Finally we decided that the only way to get started was to employ the various tradesmen – joiners, bricklayers, plumbers etc. – ourselves. This was done and before long we had the foundations laid.

It was exciting from then on, but frustrating, too, because time after time I would call at the site to find the bricklayers sitting about smoking and drinking tea. The explanation was always the same: 'We can't get on. The joiners haven't turned up.' Or it was the joiners drinking tea because the bricklayers hadn't arrived. 'We can't get on' was a phrase I grew to dread.

Because of this, progress was slow. After several weeks, the walls were only knee high. We went off for a fortnight's summer holiday and as we drove past the site on our return, expecting to see a big advance, our hopes were dashed when we found that the house had not grown at all.

However, the troubles began to sort themselves out at last and there was a rush of activity over several weeks when the place began to rise at magical speed. The big day arrived when the bricklayers, honest lads and keen to please me, had the gable end nearly up to roof height.

'We'll have t'roof on tomorrow, Mr Herriot,' one of them said cheerfully. 'Only thing is the joiners should've been here to put the ridge and last spars in, but we'll build up the gable to full height and the joiners will be here this afternoon to support it. Then we'll all be happy – we'll put up the flag. You'll be glad to see that!'

He spoke the truth. I would be more than glad, in fact ecstatic and fulfilled, to see the roof on our new house with the traditional flag flying. I couldn't wait to get along first thing next morning to see it.

It had been a windy night with a ninety mile an hour gale according to the radio, but I didn't think anything about it until I drew up my car and looked out at the devastation. The joiners had not arrived when expected and the unsupported gable which fronted the road lay in a tumbled heap of bricks in the front garden. Twisted scaffolding hung around everywhere. I cannot quite describe my emotions.

Yes, on that one fateful night, the gale came and blew the whole thing down. It was just bad luck, nobody's fault, and that was how I came to be apologising to Lord Hulton for my delayed visit to his horse.

Like most of the little disasters of life, this was overcome. The gable was rebuilt and the house triumphantly completed within weeks. And a fine house it was; a brilliant success and a lasting testimony to the skills of Bob and Elizabeth with its many innovative features and modern ideas.

The whole concept of building for ourselves was vindicated and in the end we had what we wanted – a happy home for our family for many years. But at times my mind goes back to that morning when I drove along the Brawton road and looked from my car as the wind still howled over the heap of bricks and mangled scaffolding.

That was a really bad moment. Oh crumbs, it was.

22

There was one time during Calum's reign when I was sure I was hallucinating. I came in through the front door of Skeldale House one morning and there, in the passage, I saw Calum's badger, Marilyn, waddling unhurriedly towards me. She had the run of the house now and I had grown fond of the amiable little animal.

'Hello, old girl,' I said, patting the attractive striped head. 'You really are friendly, aren't you? I'm beginning to understand your master's passion for your breed.'

I turned into the office and stood in shock for a moment. Calum was sitting at the desk with Marilyn on his shoulder.

'What . . . what . . .' I stammered.

Calum looked up and was about to reply when Siegfried strode into the room. For a few seconds he stared unbelievingly at the young man. 'What the hell's this? I nearly tripped over your bloody badger out there and now she's in here.'

Calum smiled. 'Ah yes,' he said airily. 'That's not Marilyn in the passage, it's Kelly.'

'Kelly?'

'Yes, my other badger.'

Siegfried flushed. '*Other* badger . . . I didn't know you had *another* one.'

'Oh well, I just had to get him. I could see Marilyn was lonely – I know the signs. You see,' he said earnestly, 'I know she has me for company, but really, when an animal's lonely, there's no substitute for another of the same species.'

'Yes, that's all very fine,' said Siegfried, his voice rising, 'but I wasn't keen on having one of those things around and now there's two. What d'you think this place is – a lonely-heart home for badgers?'

'Oh no, no. But you must admit that they're nice, friendly little things – they're no trouble at all.'

'That's not the point – I . . .' My partner was stopped in mid flow by the phone ringing. He lifted the receiver and, as he listened, Kelly shuffled into the room. After a few moments Siegfried put down the phone and jumped to his feet. 'Damn! That good horse at Lord Hulton's isn't any better, in fact, it's worse. I've got to go.' With a final incredulous glance at the two badgers, playing now on the office floor, he hurried from the room.

'He isn't upset, is he?' Calum enquired.

'Well, just a bit, but he'll forget about it. I'd leave Kelly in your flat for a few days if I were you.'

He nodded, then pointed out of the window. 'There's Rod Milburn's van just arrived. He's brought a ewe. Thinks it's ringwomb.'

We were in the thick of lambing, and this was the year when the Caesarean operation on sheep, previously uncommon, soared into popularity. The reasons were several. Farmers and vets were unanimous that in many protracted lambing cases it was better to operate on the ewe and 'tek 'em out of t'side' as the saying went. It was absolutely fatal to be the slightest bit rough with a ewe –

forcing open a cervix to pull out an oversized lamb could easily tear the tissues – and for some reason the condition of ringwomb had become very common.

Ringwomb was when the cervix didn't present its usual corrugated feel but was simply a smooth band of tissue which just would not yield, even after the usual injections for undilated cervix. In these cases it was best to operate without delay to avoid suffering for the ewe and to obtain one or more live lambs.

Vets were also doing the Caesarean for bad cases of pregnancy toxaemia because, once delivered of her lambs, the ewe had a better chance of recovery. The upshot was that we were doing the operation so frequently that often the farmers would bring their ewes into the surgery to save us a journey.

We ushered Rod Milburn round to the yard where Calum scrubbed up an arm and explored inside the ewe.

'Typical ringwomb, Rod,' he said, 'so we'd better not mess about. We'll boil up while you do your clipping.'

The farmer produced his clippers from the van, tipped up the ewe and expertly cut away the thick fleece from the flank. I shaved, disinfected and infiltrated the site with local anaesthetic before Calum reappeared with the sterilised instruments on a tray. I have never known a vet more meticulous about asepsis – wherever he went on his rounds, he carried a metal container with freshly boiled knives, forceps and needles and he hadn't been with us very long before his high rate of success became apparent. When Calum operated, his patients lived.

I was letting him have a go now and it was impressive to see his big, strong-fingered hands at work, quickly incising skin, muscles and peritoneum before opening the uterus and drawing out two wriggling black-faced lambs. In no time at all, he was stitching up, grinning at the two tiny creatures determinedly tottering towards the udder.

Rod was delighted. 'That's great! A good job I came down right away. We've got live twins and a healthy mother.' He lifted the lambs into the straw in the back of his van and the ewe hopped in after them as though nothing had happened to her.

I had done a lot of these operations, but I never ceased to be amazed at how little the ewe seemed to be affected. On one occasion I had just finished stitching after a Caesarean in a loose box on the farm when the ewe jerked her head from the farmer's grasp, jumped from the straw-bale operating table where she had been lying and, with a mighty leap, cleared the half-door and galloped off across the field.

When I saw the farmer a few days later and enquired about her, he said, 'Aye, she came back for 'er lambs, otherwise God knows when I'd 'ave seen her again!'

After Rod Milburn had driven away with the new family, we started on our work in the surgery. I did a laparotomy on a labrador which had swallowed his favourite ball and Calum removed a mammary tumour from a springer spaniel with his customary aplomb.

We were cleaning up when he pointed to three cat cages standing by the door. 'What's happening to those cats?'

'Oh, they're spays. I'm taking them through to Granville Bennett.'

'Don't you ever do those jobs yourself?'

'No. All cat and bitch spays go to Granville.'

Calum stared at me. 'Why on earth do you do that?'

'Oh, he's a top man – brilliant. Makes a great job and they all come back in good shape.'

'I'll bet they do. I've heard all about Granville Bennett, but Jim, you're perfectly capable of doing these yourself.'

'Oh, I know, but we've always done it this way. We're a large animal practice. This is only a side line.'

He laughed. 'Since I came here I've seen you do laparotomies, enterotomies, pyometras. What's the difference?'

'Well, I really don't know, Calum. These other things are emergencies. Maybe it's because when you're doing a spay you're starting on a healthy animal. Silly, I suppose.'

'I know what you mean. You can't bear the thought of a client bringing in his fit little animal and then the operation goes wrong.'

'Something like that. Maybe it all stems from a lack of confidence. I can't help thinking of myself as a farm animal doctor who shouldn't be doing such things.'

Calum raised a finger. 'Well, with respect, Jim, you've got to change your ideas. Small animal work is the thing of the future and the day has gone when country vets can turn their backs on routine things like spays just because they think they haven't the time.'

'Maybe you're right. I suppose we ought to start some time.'

'Why not now?'

'Eh?'

'Let's have a crack at these three. Spays are easy – I did quite a few at the college clinic.'

I was beginning to raise objections, but Calum hoisted a cage onto the table and lifted out a pretty twelve-week-old kitten. 'Here we go,' he cried, 'spay number one – the beginning of a new era in Skeldale House.'

I was carried along by his enthusiasm and we soon had the little creature anaesthetised and the site prepared. Calum poised his knife and made a tiny incision in the flank. 'Key-hole surgery is the order here. It's so easy that you don't need a lot of room to work. You just fish out the uterus like this.' He probed through the incision with forceps. 'It's no trouble at all.'

He fished out a slender strand of tissue on the end of the forceps. 'There it is, you see. Child's play.' Then he paused. 'No, that's not it.' He pushed the thing back and searched further within. But when he withdrew the forceps it still wasn't the uterus he had hold of but the same mysterious pink-white thread.

'Damn! I've never had this trouble,' he grunted, and began another exploration in the small abdomen. He had just pulled the wrong thing out again when the phone rang.

'Milk fever, flat out. Urgent. Afraid I've got to go, Calum. Can you manage?'

'Of course, I'm okay. But where the hell is this uterus?'

I left him staring down at the little cat in exasperation.

When we met later in the day, he gave me a rueful grin. 'I'm sorry I made a hash of my demonstration, Jim. You'd hardly got through the door before I found the uterus and finished the job in a few minutes. I did the other two cats after that on my own – no problem.'

I believed him. If ever there was a naturally gifted surgeon it was Calum. But that wasn't the end of the story. A few days later, we admitted four more spays and since Calum was the only man around he anaesthetised them with nembutal instead of using our oxygen and ether apparatus and then did them himself. When I walked along to the operating room he was starting on the last one.

'I'm glad to see you, Jim,' he said. 'I've just done those three,' pointing at the sleeping cats. 'Did 'em in double quick time. Piece of cake. Anyway, I can show you what I mean now you're here.'

He inserted his forceps in the incision and pulled out, not the uterus, but the same string-like filament as before. He stared at it for a moment and then he tried again and then a third time but with the same result.

'I don't believe it!' he exploded. 'It's like black magic!'

I laughed and patted him on the shoulder. 'I'm sorry I can't wait, Calum. I just dashed along between jobs to see how you were getting on.'

'I was getting on fine till you came in,' he shouted as I went out.

When I think back, I realise this was one of the strange and unaccountable little episodes in my life, because on the third occasion, around a week later when I walked into the operating room I found my colleague bent over a sleeping cat.

He looked up and gave me an eager smile. 'Ah, here you are again, Jim. I've done a couple of spays like hot cakes and I'm just starting on this one. Now watch, and I'll show you how to do it.'

Quickly and confidently he reached inside with his forceps and instead of the expected uterus there appeared the same fine cord of baffling origin. He pushed it back and tried again, and again and again without success.

'Bugger it!' he yelled. 'What's going on? When it happened before I thought it was because I was too cocky, but now I know. It's you!' He stared at me, wild-eyed. 'You're a hoodoo! You put the evil eye on me every time!'

'Oh dear, I'm sorry, Calum,' I said, fighting the giggles. 'It's just unfortunate – but anyway, what *is* that thing you keep pulling out? Has it got a name?'

'It has now,' my colleague growled. 'It's called Herriot's duct.'

That passed into the language of the practice and, long after spaying had lost its novelty in the practice and become a regular, trouble-free routine, whenever that errant piece of tissue showed itself the cry went up.

'Hello, there goes Herriot's duct again!'

23

When I awoke on the first morning after our move to Rowan Garth, I found myself in the usual mental state of acute readiness, like a sprinter on his blocks, ready to hurl on my clothes and take off on my daily gallop round the icy acres of Skeldale House. I was so much in the groove that when my alarm went my legs started twitching, ready for the off. It took me a minute or two to realise that such things as the sessions of firelighting, wrestling with the anthracite stove and running to keep warm were all in the past.

Everything was to hand. Almost effortlessly, I donned a dressing gown and meandered down the few stairs to the little hall and then into the kitchen where a blissful warmth from the Aga cooker enveloped me. Dinah the beagle came wagging from her basket and as I patted her and exchanged the usual morning pleasantries I could discern an 'isn't this wonderful' expression in her eyes.

It was heaven. As in a trance, I slid the kettle onto the hot plate and dropped the tea into the teapot, and I hardly noticed the ascent as I sailed up with Helen's morning cup.

Back in the kitchen I poured tea for myself and stood for a few moments, imbibing the fragrant fluid, nestling up to the Aga as I looked out at the green fields and the hills and feeling like a sultan. Life, I thought, didn't have much more to offer.

It was all so clear now. My failures to buy those other houses had seemed at the time a black demolition of all my hopes, but in fact they had been blessed strokes of luck. I had a far better house now than either of them – modern, reasonably small, convenient . . . and warm. I gazed for a moment at the long-desired hatch: oh yes, it was the realisation of a dream.

Lulled by these thoughts I sank gratefully into my chair, but rocketed up again instantly as a rasping sound exploded beneath me. My peace shattered, I lifted the cushion and found a whoopie device underneath. Shrill laughter came down from the top of the stairs as I threw open the door and saw Jimmy and Rosie hanging gleefully over the banisters.

'You young blighters!' I yelled as I stormed upwards. 'The very first morning! I'm coming to get you!' But they had locked themselves in their bedrooms by the time I arrived and I hadn't time to go further into the matter.

Sitting down for the second time I ruminated on the fact that I'd have to take extra care from now on. Playing jokes on dad was a hobby of my children – imitation ink blots, buns which squeaked when bitten, envelopes which emitted a terrifying buzz when opened – particularly in the mornings when my defences were down. Every time we visited my parents in Glasgow they made a bee-line for Tam Shepherd's joke shop in Queen Street to lay in further supplies and in this small house I was infinitely more accessible.

However it took only a few soothing draughts of tea before I slid back into my previous euphoria. I couldn't believe the warmth and comfort and the feeling that you could reach out and touch everything. Life was going to be so much easier for Helen.

The peace didn't last long. Within minutes of the children coming downstairs the kitchen was reverberating with deafening noise. Jimmy had rigged up an extension speaker on a shelf to play records from our beloved Murphy radiogram which was now stationed in the dining room next door and within minutes Elvis Presley was blasting his message into my ears.

I escaped for a few moments by taking up Helen's second cup. For a long time at Skeldale House it had been her only concession to my pleas to take things easier in the mornings and I was determined that this routine would continue in our new home. When I came downstairs I lifted the morning paper from the door, picked up my teacup and settled down again at the table.

Rosie, sitting next to me, was rocking back and forth in time with the music and she got so carried away that, on one of the ways down, she swivelled and the bottom of the chair leg crunched on to my slippered toe. She was a fat little girl at that time and very heavy, and I yelped in pain and my tea flew into the air and descended in a warm shower on my newspaper. As I leaped to my feet and hopped around in agony my son and daughter shrieked with laughter and Dinah set up a joyous barking to join in the fun.

Through my anguish I reflected that this was the second time within a few minutes that those two had had a good laugh at dad's expense. A memorable day for them.

Music was to be a regular pre-school routine every morning and at first it was torture because as a lifelong devotee of classical music, I found the pop scene bewildering. To me it was just a loud, unpleasant noise. But as the months passed at Rowan Garth and each day I was subjected to 'Blue Suede Shoes', 'Don't Be Cruel', 'Jailhouse Rock' and others, I developed something approaching affection for old Elvis, and now, forty years later, any of his songs coming over the radio can transport me back to those mornings in the kitchen at Rowan Garth with the children at their cornflakes, my dog at my side and the whole world young and carefree.

And yet . . . there was at that time another pull on my emotions. Leaving Skeldale had been a far greater wrench than I had ever imagined. After the van had taken the last of our things away I roamed through the empty rooms which had echoed to my children's laughter. The big sitting room where I had read the bedtime stories and where, before all that, Siegfried, Tristan and I had sprawled in bachelor contentment, seemed to reproach me with its ageless charm and grace. The handsome fireplace with its glass cupboard above, and the old pewter tankard which used to hold our cash still resting there, the french window opening onto the long, high-walled garden with its lawns, fruit trees, asparagus and strawberry beds – these things were part of a great surging ocean of memories.

Upstairs, I stood in the large alcoved room where Helen and I had slept and to where we had brought our children as babies to sleep in the cot which once stood in that corner. I clumped over the bare boards to the dressing room which Jimmy and Rosie had shared, almost hearing their giggles and teasings which were the beginning of each new day.

I climbed another flight to the little rooms under the eaves where Helen and I had started our married life, where a bench against the wall and a gas ring once served as our only cooking arrangements; then I walked to the window and looked over the tumbled roofs of the little town to the green fells and swallowed a huge lump in my throat. Dear old Skeldale. I was so glad it was going to be kept on as the practice house and I would walk through its doors every day, but my family was leaving and I wondered if we could ever be as happy again as we had been here.

24

'Can I speak to the vet wi' t'badger?'

As I handed the phone to our new assistant, it struck me that this request was becoming common and it did me good to hear it. It meant that Calum was being accepted by the farmers. I didn't mind at all if some of them wanted him instead of me. What I dreaded hearing was 'Don't send that young bugger!' which I had heard about from some of my neighbouring vets when they employed new assistants.

We had been so lucky with John Crooks who had been an outstanding asset to our practice and it seemed to be asking too much of fate for a second top class man to come along. All the new graduates were better educated than I had been but there were other reasons why a few didn't make the grade. Some of them just couldn't face the long rough and tumble of general practice with its antisocial hours, others lacked the ability to get on with the clients, and one or two were academically bright but unpractical.

Calum, to my vast relief, seemed to be slotting into the job effortlessly but, just as John and Tristan had been different from each other, so was he from them. Very different. His ever-present badger fascinated people, his tall, walrus-moustached appearance, eager friendliness and unusual outlook on life made him interesting to both farm and small animal clients but, most important of all, he knew his stuff. He was a fine vet.

Phin Calvert, one of the characters in our practice who always addressed me as 'Happy Harry' on my visits to his farm, gave me his opinion of Calum in his usual forthright way.

'That feller,' he said, 'is a VITNERY!'

On this particular day, my colleague put down the phone and turned to me. 'That was Eddie Coates. Said he had a beast "a bit dowly". I'm getting to be an expert with dowly beasts.'

I laughed. 'Good, Calum. You'd better get along, then.'

He looked thoughtful for a moment, then, 'Something I wanted to ask you, Jim. Could I change my hours a bit?'

'In what way? Different half-day?'

'No, I'd like to start at six o'clock every morning and finish at two in the afternoon.'

I stared at him in amazement. 'What's the idea of that?'

'It would give me more opportunity to get about the country-side – find out more about the wild life and flora around here.'

'Well, I'm sorry, Calum. I know you're dead keen on that sort of thing, but those hours are just not practical. We can't do that – it wouldn't work.'

He shrugged philosophically. 'Okay,' and turned to go.

'Just a minute, Calum,' I said. 'While we're talking, I'd like to mention something else to you. You are a bit elusive.'

'Eh?'

'Yes. Difficult to find when we want you. As you know, quite a few of the small farms aren't on the phone and sometimes the only time I am able to get hold of an assistant is to catch him at mealtimes. But your eating habits are irregular and often you're in and out again without my knowing, and there might be something urgent waiting. So please, give me a ring whenever you do come in.'

Calum gave me a mock salute. 'Very good, sir, I will unfailingly report.'

We went out together to the dispensary and in the passage I was assailed by a dreadful stench. Sickly, horrible, it seemed to be coming from upstairs and I could see wisps of steam issuing from Calum's flat.

'Hell, Calum, that bloody awful stink! What's going on up there?'

He looked at me in mild surprise. 'Oh, I'm just boiling up some tripe for my animals.'

'Tripe! What sort of tripe?'

'Just ordinary cow's stomachs. Left overs at the butcher's. He says he'll let me have any tripe that's gone off a bit whenever I want it.'

I put my handkerchief over my face and shouted through the folds. 'Off-colour tripe! You're not kidding! For God's sake, get up there quickly and take that pan off. And cancel your order at the butcher's!'

I reeled into the back garden and took a few deep breaths and, as I leaned against the wall, a little thought swam in my mind. I was sure I was going to have a happy relationship with Calum, but nothing in the world was ever quite perfect.

Later that day, when I came in to lunch, it was confirmed that he had heeded my words of the morning. The phone rang and it was Calum's voice at the other end. 'Permission to eat, sir!'

'Granted, young man,' I replied, falling in gladly with his sally. I didn't know it then but throughout the time he stayed with the practice I would hear those words every day. He never ever came in at mealtimes without checking, and now when I look back over the years and think of him I seem to hear those words.

'Permission to eat, sir!'

25

When we first set up house in Skeldale I often went to house sales to look for the many essential things we needed, but for some reason I repeatedly brought home useless objects. There was a long list of them – a fully-rigged sailing ship in a bottle, brass candlesticks, the little concertina of course and, on one memorable occasion, *The Geography of the World in Twenty-four Volumes*.

When we started in Rowan Garth, I was again eager to help. One big idea I had was to make a grass tennis court in the back garden, mainly for the children but also for Helen and myself since we were keen players – when we could find the time.

After mapping out the court, I realised that the big problem was to stop the balls from being knocked out of the garden and far away. Obviously a lot of high netting was required and I thought my problem was solved when a fisherman came to the door selling off yards of fishing nets. He had just gone out of business, he said, and he was selling off these superb nets at a giveaway price. I bought an enormous bundle of the things, tightly tied up with tarry rope, for £12 and proudly showed my purchase to Helen.

She was not impressed. 'Are you sure you haven't done something silly again, Jim? You know you are very easily taken in.'

I was indignant. 'Taken in? Impossible! You could see that this fisherman was as honest as the day. He was from Fraserburgh and was wearing a navy blue jersey. Cheerful, red, open face, I could smell the tar and salt off him. He said these were the last of the nets and he was selling them off extra cheap to get rid of them so that he can get back home.'

'Hmm. I don't like the sound of that, either,' Helen murmured. 'Did you look in his van to see if he had any more?'

'Well, no . . . that was quite unnecessary. I assure you I've made a good buy this time. Come on, I'll prove it to you.'

We went out to the lawn and I began to untie the vast bundles of nets. As I opened them up, my spirits began to sink. They were a mass of enormous holes, some of them several feet in diameter. Helen began to giggle, and as I unrolled one holey net after another she staggered around, laughing helplessly.

'Oh dear,' she said, wiping away the tears, 'it's a good thing there's one practical person in this family. Thank heaven I never do silly things like this.'

Badly discomfited, I looked glumly at the useless things. 'Maybe I could patch up those holes with string,' I said.

'Oh stop it,' Helen said, beginning to fall about again. 'Don't start me off again. I feel weak.'

Those nets were a sore point and I kept away from the subject over the next few weeks, but I did, on several occasions, surreptitiously retire to the lawn when nobody was watching and have a go, unsuccessfully, at doing a bit of patching.

After this disaster I tried to win back a little credibility by thinking of some new ideas for the improvement of the garden. I noticed an advert in one of the Sunday papers for cloches to protect tender plants and it struck me that they would be an excellent thing in the harsh Yorkshire climate. The pictures showed the cloches standing in long trim rows, neat and functional, and they seemed extraordinarily cheap, too.

Without mentioning it to Helen I sent away for a substantial supply. I expected them to arrive in some enormous crate and was very surprised when the postman delivered a modest flat parcel. How could they possibly be the things I had seen in the picture?

The mystery was quickly solved because it turned out that what I had thought was rigid plastic was in fact ordinary floppy polythene sheeting. Not only that, but the rest of the outfit consisted of a mass of flimsy wires with ominous instructions to slide rod A into notch B and engage with flange C. I have never been any good with such things and spent maddening hours wrestling with the wires as Helen watched me curiously.

I was forced to confess my scheme to her and was irritated by the immediately sceptical reaction. She looked doubtfully at my tangled purchases and the corner of her mouth twitched as though she were fighting back a big grin. I fought on doggedly and at last had a row of the wires assembled and began to drape the polythene sheets over them.

The result was pathetic. Helen came out to have another peep just as I was surveying what looked like a long, low-slung line of washing with the polythene half attached to the wires and flapping disconsolately in the wind.

It was too much for my wife. She collapsed against the wall of the house and after a minute or two of unrestrained laughter had to go inside and sit down. I was left in the garden trying to muster a bit of dignity, but I couldn't bear to look at the cloches any more. I bundled them as quickly as I could into their original parcel and hid them away in the garage. It was another catastrophe and my stock plummeted even lower.

A week later I came in from my round and found Helen in an unusual mood. She was wide-eyed and excited, slightly breathless.

'Come in and look at this, Jim,' she said, leading me into the sitting room. The furniture had been pushed back to accommodate an extraordinary carpet, a huge, garish thing, thick and knobbly.

'What the devil's this?' I asked.

'Well,' she was more breathless than ever, 'a man came to the door this afternoon with this lovely carpet. It's a genuine Kasbah.'

'A what?'

'A Kasbah. It's a very rare oriental type of carpet.'

'Oriental?'

'Yes, this man's just come from India. He got it from a tribesman on the frontier.'

'A tribesman? The frontier?' My head was beginning to swim. 'What *are* you talking about?'

Helen drew herself up. 'It's surely quite simple. We have the opportunity to buy this beautiful carpet. It's something we need, and it's a bargain.'

'How much?'

'Twenty pounds'

'*What!*'

'It's very cheap,' said Helen, colouring. 'It's a genuine Kasbah. The man said it would cost hundreds of pounds, only he was lucky enough to meet this tribesman on the . . .'

'Don't start that again,' I said. 'I can't believe what I'm hearing. Where is this man?'

'He's coming back any minute now. I told him you'd want to see him.'

'I certainly do.' I bent down and felt the Kasbah. It seemed to be made of some spiky material and prickly strands came away and pierced my fingers painfully as I examined it. The violent colorations built up every few inches into mounds high enough for anybody to trip over. I had never seen anything remotely like it. Hot words were on my lips but I held my peace. I had a long record of this kind of boob and I wasn't on firm ground. I couldn't say it was a horrible carpet. Care had to be my watchword.

'Helen,' I said gently, 'are you really sure we want this? Look, it's so lumpy you can't close the door over it.' I demonstrated. 'And don't you think the colours are a bit bright?'

My wife began to look doubtful. 'Well . . . maybe I have been rather hasty . . . but I think that's the man at the door now.'

She led in the carpet specialist, a pleasant faced chap in his forties, radiating a powerful selling technique. Smiling warmly, he wrung my hand and presented a card to prove he was a seafaring man. Then, words pouring from him, teeth flashing, he extolled the Kasbah. His eyes never left mine and the effect was hypnotic. But when he started on about the tribesman on the frontier I managed to marshal my wits and stopped him.

'Many thanks, but we really don't want the carpet.'

He was astounded and indeed incredulous that we should throw away this heaven-sent opportunity, but I stuck grimly to my gentle refusals. He was fluent and persuasive, but as he lowered the price again and again, familiar ominous phrases began to creep in. 'Now, I'll tell you what I'll do for you,' and 'To be perfectly honest', 'I'll be very frank' until, finally, I managed to stop the torrent.

'I'll help you carry it out,' I said.

Clearly deeply disappointed in me, he inclined his head gravely. The thing was unbelievably heavy and we staggered out in a glum silence, shedding thousands of multi-coloured spicules on the way.

After he had gone I didn't say much about the incident and, in fact, I have kept pretty quiet about it ever since. With my record I cannot afford to be uppity. Helen is undoubtedly the sensible and practical member of our partnership and that carpet was her only aberration, but over the years whenever I landed in deeper than usual trouble it has been nice to have something up my sleeve. I have always been able as a last resort to bring up the subject of the genuine Kasbah.

26

Bouncer was the only all-round canine games player I had ever met.

'Come on, lad,' cried his master, Arnold Braithwaite, 'let's see Lew Hoad's big serve.'

Eagerly, the dog, a handsome border collie, stood up on his hind legs, waved his right fore paw above his head and brought it down in an authentic sweep.

I laughed in delight. 'That's wonderful, Arnie. I didn't know he was a tennis player too.'

'Oh aye.' The big man bent and gazed at his pet with intense gratification, then bent over and fondled the shaggy head. 'There's nowt 'e can't do in that line. He's like his master – an expert at all sports. And I've been able to teach him that serve knowin' Lew Hoad like I do.'

'You've met him, have you?'

'Met 'im? He's an old friend. Me and 'im's big pals. Thinks a lot about me, does Lew.'

I looked at Arnie, feeling the wonderment welling in me as it always did when I was with him. He was a retired builder, or that was how he described himself, but nobody could remember him doing much building. A bulky, fit-looking bachelor in his late sixties, he had a fanatical devotion to all forms of sport. His knowledge was encyclopaedic and he appeared to know everybody. How he managed this was not clear because he rarely left Darrowby, but there seemed to be few among the world's top sportsmen who were not his friends.

'Now then, lad,' he said, addressing his dog, 'let's have a bit o' cricket.' We went out to the little lawn behind the house. 'You're fieldin' in the slips, right?' He lifted a bat and a soft ball and as Bouncer crouched in anticipation he struck the ball swiftly to one side of him. The dog leaped, caught the ball in his mouth and brought it back before taking up his position again. Arnie repeated the action, first to one side, then the other, and every time the dog brought off a clean catch.

'Never drops a catch,' chuckled Arnie with deep satisfaction. He held up the bat. 'That's the bat ah was tellin' you about. Len Hutton borrowed it a time or two for some of his big innings. I remember 'is very words. "A fine bit o' wood, Arnie, 'e said."'

I'd heard that one before. The legendary Len Hutton, later Sir Leonard, was at that time captain of England, holder of the record test match score, a household name throughout the world, and quite simply a god in cricket-mad Yorkshire.

'And these boots.' He held up a pair of well-blanco'd cricket boots. 'Them's the ones Len borrows, too. Borrows 'em a lot. Says they bring 'im luck.'

'Yes, I remember you saying so, Arnie.'

'Aye, ah've had some times in cricket.' His eyes took on a dreamy look and I knew he was going into one of his sporting reminiscences from the First World War. I had only dropped in as I was passing to clip Bouncer's nails, but I knew that would have to wait.

'Aye, it was when our battalion was playing the Gunners out

in France. Our bowlin' was getting knocked all over t'place and the score was mountin' fast. The colonel threw me the ball. "I'll have to call on you, Braithwaite," he said. "Things are looking bad." Well I did the hat-trick straight away.'

'You did?'

'Aye, three wickets, just like that. Then the colonel came over to me. "I'd better take you off, Braithwaite," he said. "That's kept the score down, but we don't want to push it too far the other way." Well, the same thing happened. Their batsmen started to clout our bowlers for sixes and fours, so the colonel came over to me again. "I'm sorry, Braithwaite," he said, "I'm going to have to call on you once more."'

Arnie paused and looked at me seriously. 'Well, I did it again.'

'You mean . . . another hat-trick?'

'That's right.'

'Extraordinary. Quite amazing.' I held up the nail clippers and clicked them a few times, but Arnie didn't seem to notice.

'Let's do your Tom Finney,' he cried, producing a football and rolling it along the grass. This was one of Bouncer's party tricks and I'd seen it before, but I still shared the big man's enjoyment as the dog dribbled the ball round the lawn, controlling it between his paws, weaving this way and that. 'Now score a goal!' shouted Arnie, and Bouncer made straight for two miniature posts at the edge of the lawn and knocked the ball between them with his nose.

We both laughed and clapped our hands and the big dog leaped up at us, wagging his tail furiously. It did me good to see Bouncer so sprightly because he was quite elderly; over nine years old.

'He loves that, doesn't he, Arnie?' I said.

'He does, there's nothin' he likes better than a bit of sport. He's never happier than when he's playin' one of his games.' He blew out his cheeks thoughtfully. 'It's a bit since I've seen Tom.'

Tom Finney was then at the peak of his glorious career. English international in three different positions and arguably the greatest English footballer of all time.

'You know him?' I said.

'Oh, I do, I do, we're great pals. Must get together with him soon. Hey, Bouncer,' he waved at his dog again, 'how about a bit o' golf. Let's see your Bobby Locke.'

I held up a hand. 'Some other time, Arnie. I must get this job done.'

'Okay, Jim, I don't want to keep you.' He smiled ruminatively. 'Just thinkin' about golf reminds me of the good times I've had with Bobby.'

'Another friend, eh?'

'Not half!'

As I snipped at Bouncer's nails I wondered if there were any of the world's famous sportsmen Arnie didn't know. At that time Locke was a giant in world golf, but just another chum for all that.

Like most dogs, Bouncer wasn't keen on having his nails done and as I grasped each paw he panted apprehensively, mouth wide, tongue lolling, but he was a good-natured animal and he resigned himself to his fate without any growling or snarling.

'These black claws are tricky,' I said. 'One can't see how far the quick comes down like one can on white claws and I'm having to go very carefully. You'd never forgive me if I got into the painful bit, would you, Bouncer?'

Despite his fear, the big dog lashed his tail briefly at the sound of his name, and as I patted his head at the end of the little operation, he leaped away and cantered around the lawn in relief.

'Come in and have a cup o' tea before ye go, Jim,' Arnie said.

I hesitated. I didn't have time for all this, but I knew he loved to talk and I always found he had interesting things to say. 'Well thanks, Arnie,' I said, 'but it'll have to be a quickie.'

It was a bachelor's kitchen, functional but comfortless, and when I saw Bouncer following his master around as he put on the kettle and fetched the cups I realised what a blessing his companionship must be. That kitchen would have been even more cold and bare without his shaggy presence, and Arnie chatted away to him as he pottered about. But there was no sign of poverty because Arnie always seemed to have enough money.

He sipped appreciatively at the steaming cup. 'There's nowt like a good cup o' tea, is there, Jim?'

'It's very refreshing, Arnie. But you've always loved your tea more than most, haven't you? You must have suffered during the war when you couldn't get it.'

He shook his head vigorously. 'Nay, not me. I 'ad no trouble. One or two Indian rajahs kept sendin' me supplies all the way through.'

'Rajahs, eh?'

'That's right. Durin' the first war ah was stationed in India for a bit and I got well in with a lot o' them rajahs. Nice fellers they were, too. And, by gum, they remembered me when t'second war broke out. I allus had plenty of tea.'

'Well, that's wonderful.' Arnie's army service had taken him to an amazing variety of countries. I'd heard about France, Belgium, Italy, Mesopotamia, Africa, Egypt and now India.

I finished my tea and left to continue my rounds. As I left, Arnie was starting a game of golf with his dog.

Apart from my professional duties I saw quite a bit of Arnie, as he was to be found every night in the same chair at the end of the bar at the Drovers. I was returning one evening from a calving during which I had lost a bit of sweat and dropped in for a thirst quencher. The big man was there in his usual place, Bouncer, as always, under his chair, and I sat down next to him.

'I've had a lovely day at Headingley,' he said. 'Saw some good cricket, too.'

'Lucky you. I wish I'd been there.' I had been listening to the Test Match on my car radio as I drove round the farms, and had been nourishing the thought that I might be able to go across to Leeds with Helen on the Saturday.

'Aye, it were right excitin', and you know, I was sittin' there on the front row when Denis Compton walked up to me. "Well Arnie, how nice to find you," he said. "I was hoping I'd see you. One of the lads said you would be here today and I've come to take you to lunch. I've been looking everywhere for you."'

'Oh, great,' I said, 'so you had lunch with the teams?'

'Oh aye, it was smashin'. There was Bill Edrich and Cyril Washbrook and all them great Australians. Keith Miller, Neil Harvey, Ray Lindwall and all the rest. They were right glad to see me again – I'd met them all before, of course.'

'Of course.'

Just then, Kenny Ditchburn, a beefy, red-faced young man, plumped himself down on the other side of my friend.

'Now then, Arnie,' he said, grinning, 'talkin' cricket, eh? Have you been lendin' Len Hutton your boots lately?'

Arnie turned an unsmiling face toward him and his eyes narrowed. 'Now then, Kenny,' he replied gruffly, then turned back to me.

His reminiscences had given him something of a reputation in the town and the younger element were at all times trying to take the mickey out of him, but he had become hyper-sensitive to the blunt approach and would clam up immediately. Throughout my many meetings with him, I had never ever initiated a conversation about his sporting experiences, never showed any particular interest in them, and it was then, when he was relaxed, with his guard down, that the fascinating tales came pouring out.

The poor man was a victim not only of teasing, but of a whole series of apocryphal anecdotes which were falsely attributed to him and bandied around among the locals. According to some, Arnie had described how, when serving in France in that first war, he had gained such a reputation as a football goalkeeper that finally a lot of famous dead shot players were lined up to take penalty kicks against him. For ages they booted that ball at him but they couldn't score. Arnie was impregnable. At last, in desperation, they loaded a football into a cannon and fired it at him. Apparently, Arnie's laconic ending to the tale was, 'Well, I saved it all right, but I broke a couple of ribs.'

It was also put about that he had told a story that, while on winter manoeuvres in Russia, the soldiers had organised a kicking contest. Arnie had won, and in fact he had sent the ball so high that it had snow on it when it descended. These and many other far-out yarns were put in Arnie's mouth by the local lads, but I personally had never heard them from him and so discounted them, as I did Arnie's reputed description of how, during a crisis in the Egyptian campaign, he had carried General Allenby across the Nile.

However, they all passed into local folk-lore, and I expect they will always be talked about. I remember one occasion at a charity concert in Darrowby's town hall when a comic violinist got up on the stage and declaimed, to loud laughter, 'I shall now play the second movement from a fantasy by Arnie Braithwaite.'

Never mind, I liked the old boy. I, too, was a sports buff and Arnie, when he wasn't reminiscing, talked with great knowledge of all aspects of the sporting scene. I always enjoyed his conversation. Also, he was an animal lover and devoted to his dog and that made another bond.

One sunny afternoon, a few weeks after the nail-clipping, I was walking my little beagle in the riverside fields when I saw Arnie with Bouncer. As usual, he was playing one of his games and the big dog was leaping around, chasing a ball under the great willows which overhung the water.

'He's lost a bit of weight, Arnie,' I said, looking at the hollows in Bouncer's flanks and his prominent ribs. 'Is he all right?'

'Oh aye, full of beans and eatin' like a horse. He's fit, that's all. In full training for the football season. Come on, lad, do your Stanley Matthews.'

Bouncer capered around with the ball, pushing it this way and that in a mazy dribble which did indeed make me think of the great man.

'Haven't seen Stan for a bit,' Arnie said ruminatively. 'He must be wondering where I'm hidin' myself.'

A month passed before I heard from the old man again. His voice on the telephone was strained. 'Wish you'd come and see my dog, Jim, he's right poorly.'

'What's he doing, Arnie?'

'Nowt, really. Got no life in 'im.'

The inseparable pair were in the garden when I called. I was shocked at Bouncer's appearance. He was emaciated, sitting motionless on the lawn, and he made no attempt to give me his usual greeting.

'My God, Arnie,' I said, 'why have you let him get to this state? He looks awful!'

'Well, I could see he was gettin' thinner, but he was eating so well, eatin' like a horse. I thought maybe he was just runnin' around too much. He's got suddenly worse over the last few days. I'm not one to neglect me dog, am I?'

'No, no, of course you're not. And he's still eating well, you say?'

'Aye, never better, that's what puzzles me.'

'And is he drinking a lot?'

'He is – allus at it.'

I began to examine Bouncer, but even before I started there wasn't much doubt in my mind. Loss of weight, voracious appetite, abnormal thirst, extreme lethargy. It could mean only one thing.

'Arnie,' I said, 'I think he has diabetes.'

'Oh 'ell, is that bad?'

'Yes, I'm afraid it is when it has got as far as this. It can be fatal.'

The big man stared at me, totally shocked. 'Oh, don't tell me that! Is he goin' to die?'

'I hope not. There's a lot we can do.'

'Can you start right away, Jim?' He ruffled his hair distractedly. 'I mustn't lose 'im.'

'I will, Arnie, but first I've got to make sure. I must eliminate one or two other things like kidney trouble. First thing tomorrow morning, I want you to get a urine sample from him. Stick a nice clean soup plate under him when he cocks his leg and put it in this bottle, and bring it straight round with Bouncer to the surgery.'

He nodded. 'Right . . . I will . . . but maybe he's not as bad as all that.' He picked up a football and rolled it up to the dog. 'Now, lad,' he cried eagerly, 'let's see you do your Tom Finney.'

Bouncer did not move. He touched the ball listlessly with his nose, then looked up at us with lack-lustre eyes. His master went over to him and stroked his head. 'Oh Bouncer, Bouncer,' he whispered.

Next morning I tested the sample. Positive for glucose.

'Now we know for sure, Arnie. It is diabetes, so this is what we do. I'm now giving him this injection of a small amount of insulin and you must come in every morning bringing Bouncer with a fresh sample which I will test. If still positive, I will slightly increase the dose of insulin until he is stabilised, that is when the urine is negative for glucose.'

'Aye, ah'll come in every day, for as long as it takes . . . that is, if he . . . if he stays alive.' The old man's face was a doleful mask.

I nodded. 'If he stays alive, Arnie.'

Sometimes in diabetes, the first shot of insulin brings a spectacular improvement, but it wasn't so with Bouncer. He was too far gone for that. For several mornings Arnie brought him round to the surgery and I looked in vain for even a hint of better things. The big dog was a woebegone, lifeless creature, so different from the all-round athlete of former days. Arnie, grim and resolute, was there on the dot of nine o'clock, and after ten days I commiserated with him.

'Arnie, it's tough on you having to do this day after day.'

He stuck out his chin, 'I'll come round here on me hands and knees till kingdom come if it'll save me dog.'

It was just around then that I sensed a difference in Bouncer. He was still as skinny as ever, still as apathetic, but there was the suggestion of a gleam in his eyes – they were losing something of their dead look. From then on my hopes grew as the big dog slowly began to show signs of his old vitality and after three weeks of the treatment the daily sample was negative and I had a happy, tail-wagging animal looking at me as though he was almost ready for a game.

'Arnie,' I said, 'he's stabilised at last. He's going to be all right. But it's over to you, now. You'll have to give your dog a shot of insulin every morning for the rest of his life.'

'Eh? Me inject him?' He didn't look very happy about that.

'Yes, you can do that, can't you? After his morning meal. It'll soon be part of your daily programme.'

He gave me a doubtful look, but didn't say anything and I supplied him with all he would require.

Once Bouncer had turned the corner his recovery proceeded at a galloping pace and Arnie after a few days brushed aside my doubts about his ability to carry out the injections. In fact it transpired that for a period he had been a sort of personal assistant to an army surgeon during the Balkans campaign and was very familiar with hypodermics.

My final happy memory of the diabetes episode was when I looked over the hedge into Arnie's garden and saw him wrestling with Bouncer on the grass.

'What *are* you up to, Arnie?' I cried.

'Doing a low tackle on Bouncer – teachin' him rugby,' came the reply.

As autumn stretched into winter, there was considerable excitement in Darrowby when it was announced that the important men's hockey match between the rival counties of Yorkshire and Lancashire was to be played on the local ground. They were two of the top teams and contained several international players. Everybody was looking forward to seeing these famous men in action and on the Saturday afternoon I got to the ground in what I had hoped would be good time. However, people were already standing several deep round the touchlines – I'd never seen such a crowd there – and I was wondering where I could find a vantage spot when I heard a voice calling.

'Hey, Jim, there's a spare seat over here.'

It was Arnie, comfortably settled in one of the seats in front of the club-house.

'Are you sure, Arnie?'

'Aye, ah've been keeping it for you. Sit down.'

Well, this was very nice. The game was just about to start and I had a perfect view. I felt something stirring against my trouser leg and saw that it was Bouncer's nose pushing at me. He was in his usual place under his master's seat and he seemed to be telling me that he was in top form again.

I tickled his ears while I watched the match. As expected, the standard of play was very high with the four internationals shining above the rest.

Arnie kept up a running commentary. 'That's Pip Chapman, Yorkshire captain and England centre forward – old pal of mine. And Greg Holroyd, captain of Lancashire and England winger – another good old mate, and those two other internationals, Tim Mowbray and Johnnie Hart, I know 'em all well, known 'em for years.'

At half time as the players gathered in the middle of the pitch, Arnie was in expansive mood. 'It's nice to see the winter games startin' again, but I keep thinkin' about that last cricket match of the season at the Scarborough cricket festival. I was just sittin' there enjoying the sunshine when Fred Trueman spotted me. "Arnie," he said, "I've been looking for you everywhere."'

This last remark attributed to another of cricket's immortals seemed to amuse a group of young men sitting behind us. After a few half-stifled giggles, one of them spoke up.

'Fred Trueman, Arnie? The *real* Fred Trueman? Looking for you everywhere?' Arnie, grim-faced, nodded slightly with the dignity born of long practice, and this evoked another outburst of sniggers with sotto voce repetitions of 'Looking for you everywhere,' a phrase which seemed to tickle them.

My friend ignored them, rigid in his seat, eyes gazing fixedly ahead, until another of the youths returned to the attack. 'I hear you've got some old pals out there on the field, too, Arnie? Those four top men – known 'em for years, eh?' Again Arnie nodded briefly and I felt a sharp twinge of apprehension. We were heading into deep water this time with the tangible evidence of his claims running around in front of us. Arnie was sitting on the end seat, right next to the aisle up which the teams would have to pass to get to the club-house; those men would be within touching distance of him. They couldn't fail to see him.

When the final whistle blew and the players began to make their way towards us, my throat tightened. Something awful was surely going to happen and I wished with all my heart that I was somewhere else.

Holroyd, the big, black-moustachioed Lancastrian, was the first to come clumping up the steps, face sweating, knees mud-spattered. He glanced at Arnie and brushed past him, then, as my stomach began to lurch, he stopped and took a step back. There was a pause as he looked down, then, 'It's Arnie Braithwaite!' he burst out. 'Hello! How are you old chap?' He began to pump my friend's hand and called out to his team mates. 'Hey, Pip, Johnnie, Tim, look who's here. It's our old chum!' There was a jam of players in the aisle as the four men gathered round Arnie, thumping his back, laughing and shouting. Bouncer jumped from under the seat and, as dogs like to do, began to add a joyful barking to the general merriment.

Pip Chapman gazed down at Arnie with warm affection. 'Do

you know, Arnie, we thought you might be here and we've been scanning the touchline all through the match. We've been looking for you everywhere.'

27

My clients' opinion of me varied widely, and although there were the odd one or two who thought I was brilliant, a large majority looked on me as a steady, reliable vet, while a few regarded me as of strictly limited ability. But I really think that only one family nourished the private conviction that I was not quite right in the head.

They were the Hardwicks, and it was a pity because they were some of my favourite people.

The situation was due to a few unfortunate little accidents and on this sharp and sunny January morning I had no inkling that I was going to sow the seeds of my image disintegration that very day. There had been just enough snow overnight to turn the world white and I could see the road to the Hardwick farm threading its way through a glittering frostiness under a sky of cloudless blue.

It was a long, long road too, not much more than a rough track, trailing ever upwards for nearly a mile, disappearing from time to time behind bluffs or rocky outcrops until it reached the farm whose faded red roofs were just visible as I drove up to the first gate.

These farms of many gates were places of dread on busy days, eating up the precious minutes with nothing to show for all the effort. But this particular morning, as I got out of the car, the sun struck warm on my face and the crisp air tingled in my nostrils and, pushing back gate one, I looked around at the wide landscape, silent and peaceful under its white mantle, and blessed my good fortune. There were six of these gates, and I hopped out happily at each one, the snow crackling under my feet.

Seb and Josh Hardwick were attacking a mountain of turnips in the yard, forking them up onto a cart which stood in the farmyard. Despite the cold, their faces gleamed with sweat as they turned smilingly to me.

'Now then, Mr Herriot, grand mornin'.' They were typical Dales farmers – quiet, polite, even-natured – and I had always got on well with them.

'How are the calves today?' I asked.

'Lot better,' Seb said. 'And thank 'eavens. We were a bit worried.'

I was relieved, too. Salmonella is a nasty thing – highly fatal to young animals and dangerous to humans – and when I had seen the calves a couple of days previously the whole picture had looked ominous.

I went into the fold yard with the brothers and over to the big pen at one end where my patients, twenty in all, were standing, and I felt a glow of satisfaction. Everything was different. Two days ago, there was an air of doom over that pen, with the little creatures, listless and dejected, hanging their heads as the diarrhoea trickled down their tails, but now they were brighter and livelier, looking at me with interest as I leaned over the rails.

Actually I was mentally patting myself on the back because I felt I had done rather well. I could easily have treated this as an ordinary case of scour, but the high temperatures and a tell-tale soft cough had alerted me. The rectal swabs I had taken had confirmed my diagnosis. I had given them the usual combination of chloromphenicol injections and furazolidone by the mouth and it was clearly doing the job.

'Well, that's fine,' I said, climbing into the pen. 'So far, so good. I'll repeat the injections and you must carry on with the powders for another five days and I think all is going to be well. And don't forget to wash your hands well after each time.'

Josh took off his cap and wiped his streaming face. 'That's what we like to hear, Mr Herriot. It's a good job we got you in right away or we'd have 'ad some dead 'uns lyin' about.'

After the injections, Seb waved me towards the house. 'We'll all want a wash, and it's time for our ten o'clock, anyroad.'

Later, in the kitchen, as I sipped my tea and bit into a home-made scone, the two attractive young wives, one dark, the other a blazing redhead, chatted away to me. As I sat in the warmth of the fire with a baby crawling round my feet and two toddlers wrestling happily on the stone flags, I felt that life was pretty good. I could have stayed there all day, but my other work was pressing. The brothers, too, who had joined me for the tea, had begun to fidget, no doubt thinking of all those turnips outside. It was no good – I had to go.

In the yard, we made our farewells, the two men lifted their forks and I put my hand on the car door, but nothing happened. I tried to turn the handle but it wouldn't move. I went round, trying the other doors, but the result was the same. I was locked out.

My little beagle, Dinah, was the culprit. While I was treating the calves I had heard her barking at the farm dogs, which was one of her hobbies, and in the process, as she had thrown herself at each window, her paws must have pushed down the knobs which locked the doors.

I called to the brothers. 'Look, I'm very sorry, but I can't get into my car.'

'Oh aye, what's happened?' They came over and looked inside and Dinah, tongue lolling, tail lashing delightedly, looked out at them. Behind her, my keys hung in the ignition switch, just an arm's length away but maddeningly inaccessible.

I explained the situation and Josh looked at me in surprise. 'You allus carry that little dog with you, don't you?'

'Oh, yes.'

'But you don't take your keys out when ye leave the car?'

'No . . . no . . . I'm afraid not.'

'Funny thing it's never 'appened before, then.'

'Well, yes, suppose it is, when you think about it. And it's a great pity it's happened away out here.'

'How's that?'

'Well, I'm afraid I'm going to have to ask you to give me a lift home to get my spare key.'

Seb's mouth fell open. 'Back to Darrowby?'

'Afraid so. Nothing else I can do.' I tried not to think of the ten miles.

The Hardwicks looked at each other in alarm, then at the vast heap of turnips and finally back at me. I knew what they were thinking. It wasn't only the turnips; there were always a thousand jobs to be done on a farm and I was about to wreck their chances of getting some of them done that morning.

But, nice fellows that they were, they didn't tell me what a daft bugger I was. Seb blew his cheeks out. 'Aye, well, we'd better get started then.' He turned to his brother. 'I'll 'ave to leave ye to it, Josh. When you've shifted them turnips you'd better get on with the muckin' out. We can move that lot o' sheep down to t'low garth this afternoon.'

Josh nodded and wordlessly seized his fork again while his brother got out the family car. Like a lot of the hill farmers' vehicles, it was very large and very old. We rattled down the track and as I opened each gate I was enveloped in a cloud of acrid fumes from the exhaust.

The road to Darrowby seemed very long, and longer still on the way back. I tried to pass the time with comments on sport, the weather and farming conditions but for the last half-hour the conversation languished. At the farm Seb opened the car door, gave me a hasty wave and trotted away to find his brother.

Dinah was in transports at my return, jumping all over me, licking at my face but, driving away, I had the strong feeling that I wasn't as popular with the humans I had left behind.

However, when I made my final check on the calves a week later, all seemed to be forgiven. I had no doubt been a damn nuisance, but the Hardwick brothers greeted me smilingly – although there was a bad moment when I got out of the car and both men shouted, 'Hey, get your keys out! Don't forget that!' as I was about to close the door.

Sheepishly, I complied, feeling foolish because ever since the previous incident I had made a point of doing just that.

I felt a lot better when I saw that the calves were completely recovered and after washing my hands and drinking the ritual cup of tea in the kitchen I felt that I could consign the whole silly episode to the past.

A few days afterward, Helen met me with a strange message on my return home. 'I've had a funny phone call from a Mrs Hardwick.'

'How do you mean, funny?'

'She says you've pinched her husband's spectacles.'

'What?'

'That's what she said.'

'How . . . how? I don't know what you're talking about.'

'Well, they've searched high and low for those spectacles and they're definitely not in the house and the only visitor they've had was you. She's convinced you've got them.'

'I've never heard anything so daft in my life. What the devil would *I* want with them?'

Helen spread her hands. 'I've no idea, but Mr Hardwick wants them badly. They're his reading glasses and he can't read *The Farmer and Stockbreeder*. He's quite upset. You'd better have a search.'

'This is crazy,' I said, but I went over to my working coat and began to go through the pockets. And there, among the little bottles and scissors and other veterinary odds and ends, was the spectacle case, lying next to the wallet in which I kept my thermometer and which it closely resembled.

I looked at it in disbelief. 'My God, it's here, right enough. I must have picked it up by mistake after I'd rinsed my thermometer in the kitchen.'

I rang the farm and apologised to Seb. 'Another silly thing I've done,' I said laughingly. He didn't disagree, but was still polite and declined my offer to bring the spectacles to him.

'No, it's awright, I'll come down for 'em now.' Clearly, *The Farmer and Stockbreeder* was waiting.

I was embarrassed at the thought of his long and needless journey on my account, and the feeling hadn't left me three days later when I looked in the appointments book and saw that I had another call to the Hardwicks' farm.

When I arrived I found the brothers in the cow byre, forking hay into the racks. They didn't give me the usual greeting. In fact, they seemed surprised to see me.

'I've come to see your lame cow,' I announced cheerfully.

They looked at each other expressionlessly, then back at me.

'We haven't no lame cow,' Josh said.

'But . . . there was a call from you this morning.'

Again the blank look between them.

'Well . . . there must be some mistake.' I tried a light laugh which wasn't reciprocated, and I couldn't help looking along the line of cows.

Seb raised a hand. 'Honest, Mr Herriot. There's none of 'em lame. You can examine them if you like.'

'No, no, no, of course not. I . . . somebody in the practice has got a message wrong. Do you mind if I use your phone?'

Seb led me into the kitchen and as I dialled the surgery it didn't make me feel any better when I saw him lift his spectacle case from the table and slip it unobtrusively into his pocket. When I got to Skeldale House, I found that I should have gone to the Borthwicks' farm, only half a mile away. But what was happening? Why did I have to keep making a fool of myself here?

I lifted the ballpoint by the side of the phone and wrote the name down so that I could not make any more mistakes, and turned to the two young wives. 'I'm terribly sorry, I'm always being such a nuisance to you.' I was about to leave when one of them held out her hand. 'Could we have our pen back, Mr Herriot?'

Hot-faced, I took it from my pocket and fled.

My embarrassment was acute when I was called back to the farm within a few days.

When I arrived, Seb was pointing gloomily at a young heifer lying on the cowhouse floor. 'She just can't get up,' he said, 'and that hind leg's stuck out, funny like.'

I bent over the animal and flicked her ear. 'Come on, lass, let's see you try.'

She replied by struggling briefly, then subsided on to the cobbles, and there was no doubt that her right hind leg was the cause of the trouble. It seemed to be useless.

I ran my hand up the shaggy limb and when I reached the pelvic region diagnosis was easy.

'She's got a dislocated hip, Seb,' I said. 'There's nothing broken, but the head of the femur is right out of its socket.'

'Are ye sure?' The farmer looked at me doubtfully.

'Absolutely positive. Here, feel this prominence. In fact, you can just about see it sticking up there.'

Seb didn't bother to take his hands out of his pockets. 'Well, ah don't know. I thought she'd maybe just strained 'erself. Maybe you could give me summat to rub on 'er – that might put her right.'

'No, I assure you. There's no doubt in my mind.'

'Awright, then, what do we do?'

'Well, we'll have to try to pull the joint back into place. It's not easy, but since it has only just happened I'd say there was a good chance of success.'

The farmer sniffed. 'Very well, then. On ye go.'

'I'm sorry,' I said, smiling, 'but it's quite a big job and I can't do it by myself. In fact, you and I can't do it. We'll need some help.'

'Help? I haven't got no 'elp. Josh is right over on the far field.'

'Well, I'm really sorry about that, but you'll have to get him back. And I hate to say it, but we'll also need one of your neighbours to lend a hand. And he'd better be a big strong chap, too.'

'Bloody 'ell!' Seb stared at me. 'What's all this for?'

'I know it seems a big fuss to you, but although she's only a young beast, she's big and strong and in order to get the joint back in place we have to overcome the muscular resistance. It needs a right good pull, I can tell you. I've done a lot of these jobs and I know.'

He nodded. 'Ah well, I'll go and see if Charlie Lawson can come over. You'll wait 'ere, then?'

'No, I'll have to go back to the surgery for the chloroform muzzle.'

'Chloroform! What the 'ell next?'

'I told you about the muscular resistance. We need to put her to sleep to overcome that.'

'Now, look 'ere, Mr Herriot.' The farmer lifted a portentous forefinger. 'Are ye sure we have to go through all this carry on? Don't ye think we could just rub summat on? A bit of embrocation, maybe?'

'I'm sorry, Seb, it's all necessary.'

He turned and strode out of the cowhouse, muttering, while I hurried across to my car.

On the journey to Darrowby and back, two thoughts were uppermost in my mind. This was one of the tricky jobs in veterinary practice but, when successful, it was spectacular. A hopelessly lame animal would rise and walk away, good as new. And I did feel I badly needed something to resuscitate my reputation on this farm.

When I returned with the muzzle, Josh and Charlie Lawson were waiting in the yard with Seb. 'Now, Mr Herriot,' 'Now then, Mr Herriot,' but they looked at me sceptically, and I could tell that the other brother had been voicing his doubts.

'It's good of you gentlemen to rally round,' I said cheerfully. 'I hope you're all feeling strong. It's a tough job, this.'

Charlie Lawson grinned and rubbed his hands. 'Aye, we'll do our best.'

'Okay, now.' I looked down at the heifer. 'We'd better move her nearer the door. You'll get a stronger pull that way. Then we'll get the chloroform muzzle on and rope the leg. You'll haul away while I put pressure on the joint. But first let's roll her over.'

As the farmers pushed against the animal's side, I tried to tuck the lame leg underneath her. As she rolled over there was a loud click, and after a rapid look around her she rose to her feet and walked out through the door.

The four of us watched her as she ambled across the yard and through a gate into the field. She was perfectly sound. Not the slightest trace of lameness.

'Well, I've never seen that happen before,' I gasped. 'The rolling movement and the pressure on the joint must have clicked it back. Would you believe it!'

The three farmers gave me a level stare. It was clear that they didn't believe it.

Retreating to my car, I heard Seb confiding to the other two. 'Might as well have rubbed summat on it.' And as I drove away past the heifer grazing contentedly on the green hillside, Siegfried's words at the beginning of our partnership came back to me. 'Our profession offers unparalleled opportunities for making a chump of yourself.'

How true that was. How true it would always be. But why, why, *why* did it have to happen this time at the Hardwicks'?

I couldn't believe it when I saw the Hardwick name on the book for another visit less than a week afterwards.

'Siegfried,' I said, 'I wish you'd go there. There's a jinx on me at that place.'

He looked at me in surprise. 'But it's one of your favourite spots. And they always ask for you personally.'

'Oh, I know, but I've got a feeling of doom at the moment.' I told him about my recent experiences.

'Nonsense, James!' He made a dismissive gesture. 'You're imagining things. These are tiny happenings.' He sat back in his chair and laughed. 'Amusing, I grant you, but of no importance. The Hardwicks are a grand family – they won't have given a thought to such details.'

'I'm not so sure. I know they're good people, but I'm convinced they think I've got a screw loose. A touch of kleptomania for a start.'

He laughed again. 'Oh, what rubbish! Off you go. It's only a sick pig. Nothing can go wrong this time.'

It was possibly my imagination, but I thought the brothers looked a little apprehensive as I got out of the car at the farm. The pig in question was a sow with a family of a dozen piglets squealing around her. She was lying in a dark corner of the fold yard, and the gloom was such that I could hardly see the animal, but I was used to this and had always done a lot of my work by touch and feel.

I climbed into the pen where the sow could only be seen as a dim bulk. I got out my thermometer and groped my way toward her rear end.

'Hasn't eaten today, you say?'

'Nay, not a thing,' replied Josh. 'And she hasn't moved from that spot. The little pigs look hungry, too – they don't seem to be gettin' much milk.'

'Yes . . . yes . . . yes . . . I see . . .' I was fumbling desperately to find the anus to insert my thermometer, but I just couldn't locate it. It was as black as pitch down there, but I had found many a pig's anus in the dark. I couldn't make it out. I could feel the tail and if I slid my hand down there, the thermometer would pop into the anus, but it didn't and when I found something lower down it was the vagina. The solution burst on me like a great light.

'This pig's got no backside!' I cried. For a moment it seemed like a triumphant scientific discovery to be shared with the world, but I realised suddenly that I was in the wrong place for such things.

The brothers were looking down at me in tight-lipped silence. Seb spoke with a touch of weariness in his voice. 'No what?'

I looked up at him from my crouched position. 'No backside, no anus. A very rare condition. Quite fascinating. Common enough in little pigs, but I've never seen it in an adult animal.'

'Oh aye,' said Josh, 'and if she 'asn't got no backside, where does all that muck come from? I 'ave to shovel a hell of a lot out of 'ere every morning.'

I replied eagerly, 'The faeces are coming through the vagina! That's what happens in this condition.'

'And she's been doin' that for all them years?'

'Yes, really she has. Look, bring me a torch and I'll show you.'

The brothers exchanged another look. 'It's awright, we believe you.' It was very obvious that they didn't.

I launched into further explanation, but I realised I was beginning to gabble and so desisted. In any case, when I rested my hand on the sow's belly I could feel her udder, inflamed and lumpy.

'Anyway, I don't need to take her temperature, she's got mastitis. Her udder's very hot and swollen. I'll give her a shot of antibiotic and I'm sure she'll be okay.' I was trying to be brisk and businesslike, but I wasn't impressing anybody.

Josh spoke again. 'So you don't 'ave to take the temperature?'

'That's right, there's no need.'

'Of course, there's no need,' he said, and they both nodded. 'Don't you worry, Mr Herriot. It doesn't matter.'

I felt my toes curling. They were trying to humour me. That was the worst part.

Mechanically, I gave the sow her antibiotic injection, hurried through my hand-washing and declined a cup of tea.

As I drove away, Seb and Josh, side by side on the cobbles of the yard, raised their hands gravely in farewell and I saw the young women watching from the kitchen window. I could read their thoughts.

Poor old Herriot. Not a bad chap, really. It was so sad to see him losing his mind like this.

28

As I passed my stethoscope over the old dog's ribs, I wondered how much longer he could last.

'Don's heart isn't any better,' I said to old Mr Chandler, who sat hunched in the armchair by the kitchen fire.

I was doing my best to avoid being gloomy. The heart was definitely worse; in fact, I couldn't remember when I had listened to such a heart. It wasn't just the ordinary murmur of valvular incompetence, it was a swishing, squirting cacophony, filling me with amazement that the life-giving blood could possibly be driven round the organs of the old dog's body.

Don was fourteen, a shaggy collie cross, and with the heart weakness there was the inevitable chronic bronchitis adding its own bubblings and gurglings to the symphony within the chest.

'Aye, maybe so,' Mr Chandler leaned forward in his chair, 'but he's not so bad in other ways. Eats right well, 'e does.'

I nodded. 'Oh yes, he's happy enough, there's no doubt about that.' I patted the old dog's head as he lay on the fireside rug and the tail thumped vigorously as though to prove my words. 'He's not in any pain and still enjoying life.'

'If only it wasn't for that danged cough,' his master grunted. 'He's allus got it and it was worse than ever today. That's why I called ye out.'

'Ah well, he'll never get rid of that now, but I can help him when it gets really bad. I'll give him a shot now and leave some tablets for him.'

After the injection I counted out a supply of the faithful occytets.

'Thank ye, Mr Herriot.' The old man took the packet and placed it on the mantelpiece. 'What do you think his chances are?'

'It's very difficult to say, Mr Chandler.' I hesitated. 'I've seen dogs with bad hearts go on for years, but then – you never know. Anything could happen any time.'

'Aye . . . aye . . . I understand. I'll hope for the best. But it's a bit depressin' when you're an awd widower like me.' He scratched his head and smiled ruefully. 'I've 'ad a rotten night. The television's good company but even that's not workin'.' He pointed to the blank screen in the corner of the room. 'It started goin' funny at teatime. I've twiddled all the flippin' knobs, but it's no good. Do you know anythin' about these things?'

'Afraid not, Mr Chandler, I've only just bought a set myself.' Television was a new wonder in the early fifties and an impenetrable miracle to a non-mechanical mind like mine. However I went over and switched on the set. I began to play with the various dials and knobs, pushing in wires, flicking switches off and on.

I heard a sudden cry from the old man. 'Hey, it's back! The picture's back again!'

I stared unbelievingly at the screen. Sure enough, there was a posse thundering over the Texan plain. Somehow, I had done the trick.

'Eee, that's champion, Mr Herriot!' The old man's face was transfigured. 'That's really cheered me up.'

I felt an unaccustomed flush of triumph. 'Well, I'm glad I was able to help.' But I didn't feel so cheerful as I looked at the dog stretched out on the rug.

'You'll let me know if he gets any worse,' I said, and as I left the cottage I had a nasty feeling that I'd soon be hearing bad news from Mr Chandler. It would be the end of something, because I had become attached to old Don, one of my good-natured patients, a friendly tail-wagger I had treated for years.

I didn't have long to wait. It was seven o'clock in the evening, three days later, when the phone rang.

'It's Chandler 'ere, Mr Herriot.'

The voice was strained and anxious, and I steeled myself for what was coming next.

'I don't what to bother ye, Mr Herriot, but I wonder if ye'd slip out to my place?'

'Yes, of course, Mr Chandler, I'll come straightaway. I can hear how distressed you are.'

'Aye, it's a terrible thing but I know you can fix it.'

I remembered the sounds that had come through my stethoscope, and felt I had to be honest. 'Mr Chandler, fourteen years is a long time. The old valves do wear out, you know.'

'Fourteen? Damned thing is nobbut two!'

'*Two?*' Was the old man going soft? 'Don? Two?'

'Don? Ah didn't say Don. T'awd dog's fine since the tablets. It's that flippin' TV, gone off again. Do ye think ye could come and put it right for me?'

29

Farmer Whitehead rubbed his chin doubtfully.

'I don't really know what to make of this feller,' he said. 'He doesn't seem like a farm man, in fact he says he used to be a school teacher, but you can tell he knows something about stock keeping. Anyway, I'm givin' him a trial. It's a heck of a business finding men who'll work up here in this isolated spot, and I can't be too choosy. Let me know what you think about him.'

I nodded. 'Right, I will. Married man, is he?'

'Not half!' the farmer laughed. 'Seven kids, too.'

'Seven! That's quite a family.'

'Aye, it is. And I suppose it's one reason why I took him on. He seemed desperate for a place to live and we've got a good big cottage here. I felt a bit sorry for the chap.' He paused and looked thoughtfully across the yard. 'As I said, he's out of the ordinary.'

I was walking away when he called after me. 'By the way, his name's Basil Courtenay. That's a bit different, too, isn't it?'

In the cow house, I studied Basil with interest. Somewhere in the mid thirties, I thought. Very slim, dark, almost Spanish looking. He greeted me with a wide grin. 'Now then, vitnery, it's nobbut cold today. It 'ud freeze your lugs off out in them fields.'

'You're right,' I replied, 'it's really nippy.' I scrutinised him afresh. He didn't sound like a school teacher. But there was a jaunty cheerfulness about him, a friendliness in the dark eyes. I liked him.

The cow I had been called to see was lame in the off hind foot, and as I bent down and put a finger between the cleats she aimed a warning kick at me.

'Just hold her head, will you please,' I said.

Basil inclined his head graciously, gave a slight bow and moved into the stall. But he didn't grab a horn and put his fingers in the nose as was usual. He wound his arms round the neck and hugged the head tightly to his chest. I had never seen it done that way, but it seemed to have the desired effect and the cow stood quietly as I lifted the foot.

By tapping the sole with the handle of my hoof knife I found a tender area.

'There's a little abscess in there,' I said. 'I'll have to pare it out. It would be best to pull her leg up over that beam to do it. Can you fetch me a piece of rope, please?'

Again the little inclination of the head, the bow, and he went down the byre with long, graceful steps. When he returned he proffered the rope graciously, bending from the hips rather like a high-class tailor displaying his wares.

I tied the rope round the foot, threw the other end over the beam, and with Basil pulling cheerfully I began to pare the sole.

'I hear you've done a bit of teaching,' I said, as I scraped away at the hard tissue.

'Oh aye, I 'ave. Ah've done a good bit o' that in me time, ah can tell ye.'

'Really. What subjects did you teach?'

'Well now, a bit o' this and a bit o' that. There's nowt ah couldn't turn me 'and to, tha knows.'

'I see. And where did you teach? Which schools?'

'Oh, 'ere and there, 'ere and there. Ah got around a bit, like.' Basil shook his head and smiled as though the words raised happy memories.

As I worked on the foot he chattered away and, without being at all specific, he suggested that he had also taught in universities.

'You actually lectured?'

'Oh aye, ah did, ah did.'

A feeling of unreality was beginning to envelop me, but I had to ask.

'Which universities?'

'Well . . . 'ere and there, 'ere and there.'

The conversation was brought to a close by a trickle of pus appearing under my knife, a happy outcome to my paring.

'There it goes.' I said. 'She'll be fine now. I'll give her a shot and she ought to be sound in a day or two. But I'll want some hot water to wash my hands.'

Basil made an expansive gesture. 'Ye can come into t'house and 'ave a proper wash.'

I followed him to the cottage next to the farm buildings and he threw open the door before ushering me ceremoniously inside.

A table ran down one side of the big kitchen and the entire family were at their Saturday dinner. Mrs Courtenay, very fat, blonde and smiling, presided over an array of healthy-looking children who were attacking the heaped plates with relish. In the centre of the floor a sturdy infant was seated on a chamber pot from whose interior a series of explosive poppings and splutterings accompanied the child's expulsive efforts.

Basil waved a hand over the domestic scene. 'This is ma wife and family, Mr 'erriot, and we're all right glad to meet ye.'

He did not exaggerate. There was an outburst of eager smiles and nods from the children as their father looked on proudly. A happy family indeed.

Basil led me to the kitchen sink which was filled to overflowing with the unwashed debris of several meals. In fact, it was difficult to get my hands under the tap until Basil cleared a small space for me, pushing greasy pans and dishes to one side, daintily picking pieces of congealed bacon and sausage from around the soap dish.

As I washed, the toddler on the floor decided to vacate his seat on the chamber pot. Basil went over, lifted the vessel and surveyed the interior with satisfaction. Then he strode to the coke-burning cooker against the wall, lifted the lid and hurled the contents of the pot into the depths. And even this movement was performed with a graceful sweep of the arm.

Mrs Courtenay half rose from her seat. 'You'll 'ave a cup o' tea, Mr 'erriot?'

'No . . . er . . . no, thank you. I have a couple of visits waiting and I must get on. But thank you again, and it's been nice meeting you.'

I had to visit the farm several times over the next few months and Basil seemed to be coping reasonably well with his job. But I couldn't help noticing that he did things differently from all other stockmen I had known; his way of handling the animals was unusual, in fact, his whole approach had something strange about it. On one occasion, in order to get a halter on a loose heifer he hung upside down from a beam – it was as though he had a smattering of the farming business but not a lot of experience.

During my visits, Basil was always full of chat and his conversation was interspersed with shadowy references to his amazingly varied past. Little snippets emerged of his involvement in the acting world, in architecture and many other professions. It seemed, too, that at one time he had taught ballroom dancing. But all attempts to pin him down never got beyond the usual response of ''ere and there.'

I also saw Basil a few times in Darrowby. He wasn't a big drinker but he liked to visit one of the local pubs on a Saturday evening, and when I first saw him there I was struck again by his distinctive behaviour. He was at a big table with a bunch of grinning farm men sitting behind tall pint glasses, but Basil wasn't drinking beer. He was lying back in his chair, legs outstretched, and he was holding a glass of red wine, cupped in his palm, the stem protruding beneath his fingers. I had seen people in films – foreign noblemen and the like – holding wine glasses in this way, but never anybody in a Yorkshire pub.

As always, he presented a picture of elegance and grace. Almost reclining in his seat, he was holding forth to his audience, waving a debonair hand to emphasise his points, sipping occasionally at his wine. And it was clear that the farm men were lapping it all up. The outbursts of laughter, the delighted nods, the expressions of amazement all testified to their enthralment in Basil's recital.

He soon became a celebrity among these men and I gathered that, although he was an object of mystery to them, the facet which had most intrigued them was his vague allusions to his university experiences. They christened him 'Professor Baz' and as such he was known throughout the agricultural community. The usual ''ere and there' was all anybody could elicit but, though various theories about him were bandied around, one thing was universal – everybody seemed to like him.

During the month of March I began to see quite a lot of Basil. It is the time of year when the health of livestock is at its lowest ebb. The animals have been confined to the buildings through the long winter and their resistance to disease has worn very thin. Calves especially are vulnerable at this time and the ones under Basil's care had been struck down by the dreaded scour – the highly fatal diarrhoea which has been one of the curses of calf rearing for generations, always lurking, always ready to strike. Any fault in feeding or environment brings trouble.

Fortunately, modern advances have put vastly improved weapons in the hands of the vets and at that time I was having good results with a granular mixture of antibiotics and sulphonamides, but I wasn't doing very well with these calves.

There were sixteen of them in a long row of pens and I looked at them with growing apprehension. They were miserable and depressed, many with whitish liquid faeces trickling down their tails, some prostrate in the straw.

'Basil,' I said, 'are you sure you're getting the right dose into them?'

'Oh aye, Mr 'erriot, just exactly wot you said.'

'And you're giving it to them last thing at night and first thing in the morning? That's important.'

'Definitely. You don't 'ave to worry about that.'

I dug my hands deeper into my pockets. 'Well, I don't understand it. They're not responding. And the next thing's going to be pneumonia. I don't like the look of them at all.'

I administered vitamin injections to back up the medication and left, but I had a nasty feeling that something very unpleasant was just round the corner.

It had been bitterly cold all day and the wind had that piercing quality which usually precedes snow. I wasn't surprised when, around eight o'clock that evening, the big white flakes began to drift down and within an hour the countryside was blanketed in white. The snow stopped then and I was grateful, because a heavy fall made it almost impossible to reach some of the high farms. A shovel was essential equipment.

When I had a call at 7 a.m. next morning to a calving at a remote smallholding at the top of the dale, I was relieved that no more snow had fallen during the night. I had finished the job by nine o'clock and as I drove home, warm with the satisfaction which the delivery of a live calf always gives me, I marvelled at the new world around me. It was always beautiful up there, but the snow had made a magical change, adding a white stillness and peace.

I was looking at the delicate roadside drifts which the wind had shaped so exquisitely in the night when I saw the gate to Mr Whitehead's farm. It was a good chance to check on those calves and I turned my car along the lane.

All was quiet when I reached the buildings and the first thing I noticed was that between Basil's cottage and the calf house stretched a long expanse of unbroken snow.

I knocked at the door and Basil answered, as cheerful and full of bounce as ever.

'Come in, Mr 'erriot! How ista this mornin'? Missus is upstairs makin' the beds. Ah'll shout 'er down and she'll get ye a cup o' tea.'

'No thanks,' I replied, 'I just dropped in to see those calves. How are they this morning?'

'Oh, about t'same, ah reckon.'

'And you've given them the granules?'

'Oh aye, I 'ave. Gave 'em before breakfast.'

I beckoned him to the kitchen window. 'Come over here, Basil.'

Together we looked out and he stood very still as he gazed at the carpet of virgin snow.

'You've never been out there at all, have you?' I said. 'And you weren't out last night, either. That snow stopped at nine o'clock and you were to dose them just before bedtime.'

He didn't say anything, but his head turned slowly towards me, and it was as though a mask had been stripped from his face. The jaunty smile had gone, leaving a terrible defencelessness. He looked at me with hunted eyes.

The transformation was so dramatic that my first anger dissolved. We stared at each other in silence for a few moments then I spoke slowly.

'Now look, Basil, I'm not going to tell your boss about this, but you've let me down badly. Will you promise me you'll do your job properly in future?'

He nodded dumbly.

'Right,' I said. 'Let's get over to the calves now.'

He sat down and began to pull on his wellingtons, then he looked up at me with a haggard expression.

'Ah tell ye, Mr 'erriot, ah don't mean no harm. Ah don't want to neglect them calves, but it's like me heart's not in the job. Ah'm not a proper farm man – never will be.'

I didn't say anything and he went on.

'Ah've spoken to t'boss about it and ah'll be leavin' soon.'

'Have you got another job to go to?'

'Aye . . . aye . . . ah've got summat in mind. But till ah go, you don't 'ave to worry. Ah'll look after them calves.'

He did, too. From that day the little creatures began to improve and, on my final visit, there was the warming sight of all sixteen of them, frisky and upright in their pens, poking their heads out into the passage as they looked for their food.

Shortly after this, Basil left the district, but the reputation of 'Professor Baz' lingered on, and his departure was bemoaned among the farming community. One cowman expressed the general sentiment to me.

'By gaw, he was a rum feller,' he said, 'but we 'ad some fun with 'im. You couldn't help liking 'im.'

I nodded. 'Yes, that's how I feel. I wonder where he's gone.'

The man laughed. 'Nobody knows, but I expect it'll be "'ere and there".'

I thought I had seen the last of Basil, but I was wrong. One night, Helen and I drove into Brawton to celebrate her birthday. We had booked for dinner at one of the fine hotels in the town and the festive feeling was strong in us as we sat in the pillared splendour of the dining room, lapped around by the Victorian opulence which is one of Brawton's lasting charms.

It was a special treat for us and we enjoyed every bite of the meal, but as we sat over our coffee I noticed Helen staring intently across the vast room.

'That waiter, Jim, working right at the far end. You've had your back to him, but . . .'

I turned and looked. 'My God!' I said, 'it's Basil!'

I shifted my seat so that I could observe properly and there was no doubt. Basil it was. He was unbelievably elegant in white tie and tails and as he bent to serve an elderly couple it struck me forcibly that with his dark good looks, his courtly manner and his natural grace he was everything that a waiter should be.

I watched, spellbound. He was turning to the lady now, proffering vegetables with that inclination of the head I knew so well, smiling and bowing as she made her choice. He was talking, too, and I could imagine the same effortless flow which had entertained me so often in the cow house. The old couple were nodding and laughing, clearly captivated by him. I wondered what he was telling them. Was it about his colourful past? It looked very like it.

The coffee in my cup turned cold as I sat there. The more I watched him the more convinced I was that Basil had found his niche at last. The graceful way in which he glided among the tables, balancing plates along his arm as though he had been doing it all his life, his happy relaxed attitude, his obvious delight in dealing with his guests. This was really him. I found myself hoping, quite fervently, that there would be no further convolutions in the career of Professor Baz.

'Are you going to speak to him?' Helen asked.

I hesitated. 'No . . . no . . . better not.'

As we left the dining room, we passed within a few feet of the table where he was again attending the white-haired couple. They were all laughing, and the old gentleman raised a hand.

'By the way,' he asked, 'where was it that you were doing this?'

'Oh, 'ere and there,' Basil replied. ''ere and there.'

30

Calum gave me a friendly dig in the ribs. 'I wish you'd come with me to watch the deer one morning, Jim. I keep asking you, but I can never pin you down.'

We were sitting over a couple of pints in a cosy corner of the Drovers, and it was comparatively peaceful now that the regulars had become accustomed to the badger. At first, going for a beer with Calum almost caused a riot because he always brought Marilyn slung over his shoulder and the entire population of the bar would converge on us, but the situation had settled down to amused glances and cheerful greetings. The 'vet wi' t'badger' as the farmers called him was part of the local scenery now.

I took a pull at my glass. 'Oh, I will; Calum, I will. I promise you.'

'That's what you always say. Why not tomorrow?' He trained his dark-eyed stare on me and I felt trapped.

'Oh, I don't know. There's a lot doing tomorrow.'

'No, there isn't really. Doug Heseltine cancelled his tuberculin test, and it's left a big gap in the morning. It's an ideal chance.'

I didn't know what to say. Part of me wanted a glimpse of Calum's world of nature – he spent all his spare time roaming the countryside, studying the plants and flowers, observing the habits of the wild creatures – but I felt woefully ignorant by comparison. I had grown up in the big city of Glasgow and though I had fallen in love with the Yorkshire countryside I knew that a deep knowledge of flora and fauna was something best acquired in childhood. Siegfried had it, both my children had it and were always trying to educate me, but I knew I'd never be an expert. Certainly not like Calum. He was steeped in the things of the wild. It was his consuming passion.

'Tomorrow, eh?' As the level of my glass went down, my doubts began to evaporate. 'Well, maybe I could make it.'

'Great, great.' My colleague ordered two more pints. 'We'll go up to Steadforth Woods. I've built a hide there.'

'Steadforth Woods? Surely there aren't any deer in there.'

Calum gave me a secret smile. 'Oh yes, there are – lots of them.'

'Well, I'm amazed. I've passed those woods a thousand times. I've walked my dogs through them, but I've never seen a trace of a deer.'

'You'll see some tomorrow. Just you wait.'

'Okay. When do we start?'

He rubbed his hands. 'I'll pick you up at three o'clock.'

'*Three o'clock!* As early as that?'

'Oh yes, we've got to be up there before daybreak.'

As I finished my second pint the whole thing seemed pleasantly attractive. Up and away before the dawn to plumb the secrets of the woods. I couldn't understand my previous misgivings.

I felt different the next morning when the alarm blasted in my ear at 2.45 a.m. Years of being jerked from slumber in the small hours had bred in me a fierce love of my bed, and here I was deliberately quitting the warm nest to drive out into the cold darkness and sit in a wood – just for fun. I must be mad.

When I met Calum, it was clear he didn't share my feelings.

He was bubbling with enthusiasm and he laughed as he thumped me on the shoulder. 'You're going to love this, Jim. I've really been looking forward to doing this with you.'

I shivered as I got into his car. It was bitterly cold and the street was like a pitch black well. I huddled in the seat and Calum drove away, whistling.

He kept up a bright chatter on the way and it was easy to see that this was Calum in his natural element, roaming the countryside while the world was asleep, but after we had covered a few miles I knew something was wrong.

'Hey,' I said, 'this isn't the way to Steadforth Woods. We should have taken a left turn back there.'

He turned to me with a smile. 'We're going a different way. My hide is at the far end of the woods, a long way from the main road. We get to it from Fred Welburn's farm.'

'Fred Welburn's! My God, we'll have to walk about two miles!'

'Don't worry. I've arranged transport.'

'Transport . . . ? What *are* you talking about?'

Calum giggled. 'You'll see.'

We left the car near Fred Welburn's farm which was perched on high ground from which the field stretched away down a steep slope to a stream before rising again towards the edge of the distant woods. It was still dark and I knew this only from memory. In total bewilderment, I wondered about the transport.

Calum reached in to the back of the car and produced a bucket of corn.

I stared at him. 'What's that for?'

'It's for the horses.'

'Horses?'

'Yes. I'm going to tempt those two horses over to us so that we can ride them down into the woods.'

'What! You never said anything about that!' I burst out.

He smiled reassuringly. 'Oh, it's all right. It'll make everything much easier.' He rattled his bucket and my mouth fell open as two enormous Shires came trotting out of the gloom, their great hooves thudding on the grass.

'This is crazy!' I stared in disbelief at the animals. I was no equestrian, especially when it came to riding cart horses bare-backed.

'We can't ride those bloody great things! And what about Fred Welburn? What's he going to say?'

'All taken care of. I've got permission from Fred to use them whenever I want them. Come on, now, I'll give you a leg up.'

I was still protesting when he hoisted me on to the nearest animal and scrambled on to the other. He dug in his heels, gave a joyous whoop, and before I knew what was happening we were thundering down the grassy slope.

'Hang on,' cried Calum. 'There's a beck at the foot of the hill.'

He didn't have to tell me. I was hanging on as never before, gripping the mane tightly, eyes popping, absolutely certain that, within seconds, I would be cast from the great smooth back into the outer darkness. But somehow I kept my seat as our mounts leaped the stream like steeplechasers, then we were off again, galloping up the hill on the other side.

We were going at a terrifying pace, but it didn't seem to be fast enough for Calum who kept yelling encouragement at his steed. Dimly ahead, I saw him hurtling through a narrow gateway and I suffered a moment's panic at the certain thought that my fat animal would never get through that opening. I was partly right because the gatepost caught my knee such a fearful whack that I thought my leg had been torn off.

We made a hectic traverse of another long field, then my colleague pulled up and dismounted.

'My, that was great!' he breathed as I slithered groaning on to the grass. 'But you're lame! What's wrong?'

'Cracked my knee on the gate back there,' I grunted as I hobbled around, rubbing the painful joint.

'Oh, sorry about that, but it saved us a long walk. We're right up to the woods now.'

We climbed a fence and he led me for a long way among the dark trunks into the very heart of the wood, to his hide which he had built near a clearing. In the first pale light I could see that it was a well-hidden place, carefully constructed of branches of larch and spruce and tufts of grass.

'Sit here,' whispered my colleague. He was clearly in a state of high excitement, his eyes wide, a half smile on his face.

We hadn't long to wait. As the dawn light filtered through the branches, there was a rustling and a sound of movement among the trees, then, one by one, the deer began to appear in the clearing. Through all the years I had never seen a deer in these woods but here they were there in profusion; gentle does and majestic, antlered stags moving around, cropping the grass. It was a scene of indescribable peace and beauty, and with the feeling that I was a privileged observer I sat there enthralled, all my discomforts forgotten. There was a badger sett nearby and Calum pointed in delight as his favourite animals came out to play with their young.

Afterwards we walked through the scented silence of the woods, the pine needles soft under our feet, and he talked, not only about the deer, but about the other wild creatures of the forest and about the plants and flowers which flourished in those secret places. He seemed to know it all and I began to understand the depths of the interest which coloured his entire life. He held the key to a magic world.

As we reached the field the sun came out and, looking back, I could see long drifts of bluebells among the dark boles of the trees, and in the glades, where the first rays struck through the branches, primroses and anemones shone like scattered jewels.

By the time we had ridden back up the hill – slowly and gently at my request – and I had limped to the car, my knee had stiffened up and I groaned as I dragged my leg inside.

'Oh, bad luck about your knee.' Calum gave me a sympathetic smile, then his expression changed. 'But never mind, I've got a surprise for you.'

I could feel my eyes narrowing to slits as I looked at him. 'What kind of surprise?'

He grinned widely. 'I want you to come to dinner with me.'

'Dinner? Where?'

'In my flat. I know Helen's going to a meeting tonight and she was to leave you something to eat. Well, I've arranged it with her. I'm going to give you a meal. We're having roast duck.'

'Duck! Who's cooking it?'

'I am. It will be plucked and roasted by my own fair hand.'

My head began to swim a little. I knew he kept ducks at the bottom of the garden – an activity which Siegfried regarded with a jaundiced eye as being part of a 'menagerie' – but all this, coming from a man who had no interest in food and, in fact, seemed to eat only on rare occasions, was difficult to take in. But I was sure he was trying to be kind.

'Well, Calum . . . it's very good of you . . . what time do you want me?'

'Eight o'clock on the dot.'

At the appointed time I climbed the stairs to the flat and received an effusive welcome. Calum sat me down with a drink and as he went through to the kitchen I looked round the little sitting room. It was exactly as when he walked in that first day. Previous occupants had added or altered things according to their taste but Calum had not the slightest interest in carpets, curtains or furniture. The table was bare except for two sets of knives and forks and salt and pepper.

He was soon back again, banging down a plate for each of us, then a delicious aroma drifted in from the kitchen as he opened the oven door.

'Here we are, Jim!' he cried triumphantly as he carried in a roasting tin containing two ducks. He speared one bird with a fork and clumped it on my plate, then took the other for himself.

I was waiting for the vegetables and other trimmings, but Calum dropped into his chair and waved a fork at me. 'Wade in, Jim, I do hope you'll enjoy it.'

I looked down at my plate. Well, so this was dinner with Calum. A duck apiece with no adornment. He was eating busily and I started on my bird, but I was slowed down by the fact that my colleague had left quite a number of feathers on and I had to pick my way gingerly among the quills and crisped up plumage.

Nothing seemed to deter Calum, however, and he ate rapidly, then sat back with a sigh of deep contentment. I was surprised at his speed until it occurred to me that he probably hadn't bothered to have any food for the last twenty-four hours or so.

We didn't have dessert or coffee or anything like that and it wasn't long before he was ushering me out.

Around ten o'clock Helen came back from her meeting. 'Well, how was your day with Calum?' she asked as she took off her coat.

I rubbed my knee. Somehow it wasn't an easy question to answer. 'I enjoyed it. It was fun . . . exciting . . . quite fascinating . . .' I was casting around for the word. 'It was different!'

She laughed. 'You've just about described Calum.'

'That's it,' I said, laughing too, 'it was a Calum day.'

31

'That was old William Hawley,' Siegfried said as he put down the phone. 'Sounded a bit agitated. One of his calves is laid out unconscious, thinks it may be dying, and he hasn't many of them, poor old lad. We'll have to get there quick.'

I looked up from the appointments book. 'But we've got to take those tumours off Colonel Foulter's horse at ten this morning.'

'Yes, I know, but we can drop in at Hawley's place on the way. It's in the same direction.'

It was a familiar situation as we drove off together. Siegfried eagerly anticipating one of his equine operations; myself, his anaesthetist, by his side and our enamel tray with all the freshly sterilised instruments rattling behind us in the back. It was a fine morning which was good, because the open fields were our operating table.

After three miles we struck off down a narrow side road and soon we could see the Hawley farmhouse, not much bigger than the grey stone barns which dotted the wide green miles of the fell above. To me, those barns, squat and sturdy, and that pattern which the endless stone walls traced on the high pastures were at the very heart of the Dales scene. As I looked from the car I thought, as I always did, that there was nowhere else in the world quite like this.

The farmer, white hair straggling from under a tattered cap, watched anxiously as Siegfried bent over the prostrate calf in a pen in the corner of the cow house.

'What do ye make of it, Mr Farnon?' he asked. 'I've never seen owt like it.'

The appeal in his eyes was mingled with a deep faith. Siegfried was his hero, a wonder worker, the man who had brought off miracle cures for years, even before I had come to Darrowby. William Hawley was one of a breed of simple, unsophisticated farmers who still survived in the fifties but who have long since melted away under the glare of science and education.

Siegfried spoke gravely. 'Very strange indeed. No scour, no pneumonia, yet the little thing's flat out like this.'

Carefully and methodically he went over the little body with his stethoscope, auscultating heart, lungs and abdomen. He took the temperature, opened the mouth and peered at the tongue and throat, examined the eyes and ran his hand over the roan hairs of the coat. Then slowly he straightened up. His face was expressionless as he looked down at the motionless form.

Suddenly he turned to the old man. 'William,' he said, 'would you be so kind as to fetch me a piece of string.'

'Eh?'

'A piece of string, please.'

'String?'

'Yes, about this length.' Siegfried spread his arms wide. 'And quickly, please.'

'Right, right . . . I'll get ye some. Now where can I lay me hands on a bit that length?' Flustered, he turned to me. 'Can ye come and give me a hand, Mr Herriot?'

'Certainly.' I followed him as he hurried from the cow house and outside he clutched at my arm. It was clear he had only asked me to come with him to enlighten him.

'What does 'e want a piece of string for?' he asked in bewilderment.

I shrugged. 'I really have no idea, Mr Hawley.'

He nodded gleefully as though that was only what he expected. An ordinary vet couldn't possibly know what was in the mind of Mr Farnon, a man of legendary skill who was known to employ many strange things in the practice of his art – puffs of purple smoke to cure lame horses, making holes in jugular veins and drawing off buckets of blood to cure laminitis. Old William had heard all the stories and he was in no doubt that if anybody could restore his animal to health by means of a piece of string, it would be Mr Farnon.

But the maddening thing was that as we trotted round the buildings he couldn't find such a thing.

'Dang it,' he said. 'There's allus a coil of binder twine hangin' there, but it isn't there now! And I'm allus trippin' over bits o' string all over t'place, but not today. What'll he think of a farmer wi' no string?'

In a growing panic he rushed around and he was almost in tears when he saw a piece lying across a heap of sacks. 'How about this, Mr Herriot? Is it t'right length?'

'Just about right, I'd say.'

He grabbed it and ran as fast as his elderly limbs would carry him back to Siegfried.

'Here y'are, Mr Farnon,' he panted. 'Ah'm not too late, am I? He's still alive?'

'Oh yes, yes.' Siegfried took the string and held it dangling for a moment as he measured the length with his eye. Then, as we watched, wide-eyed, he quickly tied it round his waist.

'Thank you so much, William,' he murmured, 'that's much better. I couldn't work with that damned coat flapping open as I bent over. I lost a couple of buttons yesterday. Cow got her horn underneath them and tore them off – it's always happening to me.'

'But . . . but . . . the string . . .' The old man's face was a picture of woe. 'Ye can't do anything for my calf, then?'

'Of course I can. Whatever makes you think I can't?'

'Well . . . do ye know what ails him?'

'Yes, I do. He's got CCN.'

'What's that?'

'Cerebrocortical necrosis. It's a brain disease.'

'It's a terrible big name. And his brain? It'll be a hopeless case?'

'Not a bit. I'm going to inject vitamin B into his vein. It usually works like a charm. Just hold his head for a moment. You see how it's bent over his back? That's called opisthotonos – typical of this condition.'

Siegfried quickly carried out the injection and got to his feet. 'One of us will be passing your door tomorrow, so we'll look in. I'd like to bet he'll be a lot better.'

It was I who called next day and indeed the calf was up and eating. William Hawley was pleased.

'Must have been wonderful stuff Mr Farnon gave 'im,' he said.

To him it was another miracle, but in his manner I sensed something of the deflation I had seen the day before when Siegfried tied up his coat. His favourite vet had done the trick again, but I knew that in his heart there was still the wistful regret that he hadn't done it with that piece of string.

32

Siegfried, lounging by the fireside, was at his most expansive. 'Nice of you to drop in, James. Good to see you at any time – we don't get much chance to talk during the day, eh?'

I had called in at his home after an evening call nearby. He had pressed a drink on me and then flopped down in the armchair, exuding bonhomie. 'Any problems?'

'No, no. I've just been to a milk fever at John Lancaster's. The cow was up when I left.'

'Ah, splendid, splendid. He's a nice chap, is John.'

'Yes, a good bloke. He was really pleased when I slapped that beast on the rump and she staggered to her feet.'

'Excellent. The little triumphs of veterinary practice. I've had that sort of day, too – everything going well and, my word, isn't it grand to settle down by the fire on a cold night and relax with a quiet mind. What time is it?' He glanced up at the clock on the mantelpiece. 'Half past seven. Nice feeling to be off duty and looking forward to a few hours of peace.'

'That's right, Siegfried. I'm on. You're in the clear till tomorrow.' I sipped my drink and regarded him with affection.

He reached a long leg towards the fire and poked a log into place with a slippered toe. 'And there's another thing – it adds to the pleasure to have that television to look at.' He pointed to the new TV set flickering about at the other side of the hearth, its sound turned down. 'There's a lot of inverted snobbery going around – people talking about the goggle box and the idiot's lantern but I enjoy a lot of the programmes. I know it's a new fangled thing in the Dales but, I tell you, I've just been sitting here, watching an interesting programme and I find it very soothing.'

He sank lower in his chair and stretched his legs to the blaze. 'I was at Derek Mattock's place this afternoon. They'd had a pig killing and they gave me a great pile of cuttings – spare rib, liver, fillet – they are the most generous people.'

'Yes, you could say that about the Dales farmers in general. I'm always getting presents. Butter, eggs, vegetables from their gardens.'

Siegfried nodded. 'How true. I had a long talk with Derek and he mentioned something I'd better tell you about. You promised to do some de-hornings for him about a fortnight ago and he hasn't heard from you.' He gave me a quizzical look.

'Oh, damn, yes! I'll get on to him tomorrow. The beasts aren't taking any harm, anyway.'

He smiled again from down among the cushions. 'No, my boy – but you forgot, didn't you?'

'Yes, I suppose I did. But I'll put it right.'

'I'm sure you will, James.' He nodded gravely and was silent for a few moments. 'Strangely enough, there was something else in the same vein. Bob Hardy told me his tuberculin test was overdue. You said you'd do it last month.'

I shrugged. 'Oh, hell, that's right. But it's only a week or two overdue. Not serious. I'll see to it.'

Siegfried gave me the smile again and wagged a finger. 'But you forgot, didn't you?'

'Okay, okay, but as I say –'

'If you'll excuse me, James, for just a moment.' He held up a hand. 'You are inclined to forget things quite frequently. It is a tiny flaw in an otherwise excellent character. There is no more conscientious and capable veterinary surgeon than yourself and yet being forgetful can project quite a different image. People can think you're not concerned about their animals, that you don't care.'

'Wait a minute –'

'Let me finish, James. This is for your own good.' He put his fingertips together. 'Forgetfulness is a trait which can be easily cured if you know how to go about it. These unfortunate incidents can be prevented if you simply impress on your mind right at the beginning what it is you want to remember.'

'My God, this is really rich . . . what about . . . ?'

'One moment more, my dear chap. As I say, whenever you make an appointment, make a definite conscious effort to imprint that promise strongly on your mind. It's perfectly easy – I use this method regularly myself. You'll always remember that way.'

I was about to raise my strong objections to being lectured on forgetfulness by the most forgetful man in Yorkshire when the phone rang.

Siegfried extended a languid arm and picked up the receiver. 'Ah, how are you, Wilf, my old friend?' His eyes were half closed as he burrowed deeper in the cushions.

'I'm awright, Mr Farnon,' came the full-throated reply. It was Wilf Bramley, president of the local farmers' discussion group. He was one of the old school who considered it helped the voice to carry across the miles if they shouted and I could hear him clearly from where I sat. 'But I just 'ope you're awright, too.'

'I'm absolutely grand, Wilf,' Siegfried murmured, holding the receiver well away from his ear.

'Ah well, that's good. We just thowt something had happened to you.'

'Happened . . . ? Why is that?'

'Well, the hall's full – packed to t'doors and we were expectin' you half an hour ago. We worried you might have had an accident on your rounds.'

Siegfried snapped suddenly upright and his mouth fell open. 'Hall . . .?'

'Aye, there must be two hundred of us 'ere. You gave us such a grand talk last year I knew there'd be a lot wantin' to hear you again and they're all waitin' patiently. We can't start without t'speaker, tha knows! Heh-heh-heh!'

Siegfried's expression was haggard. He seemed to have aged several years in those few moments. 'I really am frightfully sorry, Wilf, I . . .'

'Nay, nay, Mr Farnon, there's no need for you to apologise. A busy feller like you. You'll never know what's goin' to happen from one minute to the next. Rushed off your feet all the time. You can't help bein' a bit late now and again.' Wilf's voice swelled even more in volume. 'After all, we know you're not just sittin' there watchin' television! Heh-heh, heh-heh!'

Siegfried's eyes bulged. 'Yes, Wilf, yes, that's right . . . of course. Ha-ha-ha! What an idea. Ha-ha-ha!' The strangled laughter emerged with difficulty from the distraught face. 'I'm nearly ready – I'll be with you in a few minutes.'

My partner crashed the receiver down and catapulted from his chair. 'Got to go, James. See you in the morning.'

As he galloped towards the door, an unworthy impulse welled in me.

'Siegfried!' I called.

He stopped at the door and glared at me, wild-eyed.

I wagged a finger at him, feeling my features creasing into a leer. 'You forgot, didn't you?'

33

Siegfried caught my arm as I passed him coming out of the dispensary. He looked harassed.

'James,' he burst out, 'Calum wants another dog now! Has he mentioned it to you?'

'He did say something. Said he was going to speak to you about it. Apparently it's a dog he's had for some time. It's with his mother and he just wants to bring it to Darrowby. It's okay for him to do that, isn't it?'

My colleague stuck out his chin. 'I don't think it is. He started with a badger and a dog, now he's got two badgers and a dog, and on top of that he wants two badgers and two dogs up in that little flat. Anyway, I've told him it's not on.'

'Oh, I think you're being a bit hard, Siegfried. He's probably lonely, living on his own. He just wants his animals for company.'

Siegfried took a sharp breath. 'That's what he says, of course, but as I see it, it's only the thin edge of the wedge. I feel it in my bones – if we give in now he's going to have a bloody menagerie up there!'

'Oh, come on,' I said, laughing 'you're exaggerating. There's absolutely no fear of that. He's a good lad, as you know, and an asset to the practice. I think we should help him to feel settled and happy and it's only natural that he should want to be reunited with his other dog.'

My partner did some more rapid breathing as he stared at me. 'I thought you'd say that. You're too easily swayed. But I know I'm right – I'm not going to have it, and that's final.' He stuffed a couple of bottles of calcium into his pockets and strode away.

Over the next few days, Calum made several appeals to me and his request seemed perfectly reasonable, but Siegfried had dug his toes in. He refused to be moved.

When I raised the question yet again over a beer at the Drovers he flushed, but he heard me out.

'I wish you'd change your mind,' I said. 'I can't see what possible harm there is in his having his dog. Two dogs aren't much more trouble than one. And as I said, he's doing well and I think he should be encouraged. You've just got a thing about him – your worries are absolutely groundless.'

'Groundless, eh?' He choked a little in mid swallow, then put down his glass. 'I don't think so. I've got this feeling and it won't go away.' He paused and looked round the bar for a few moments. 'But you're beginning to wear me down and I'm tired tonight. I see you are both going to go on and on about this, so you can tell him to go ahead and do as he likes.'

I clapped him on the shoulder and laughed. 'Oh, thanks, Siegfried. I know it's the right thing. You'll never regret it.'

He gave me a weary smile. 'You may laugh, but I tell you, we'll be making a big mistake.' He waved a finger in my face. 'I'll regret it, all right. Mark my words!'

Next morning, Calum was delighted when I gave him the news and I felt a glow of satisfaction when, a few days later, I heard the sound of fresh barking from the top flat.

Siegfried was opening some letters in the office and I turned to him with a smile. 'Nice to hear that,' I said. 'Calum will be happy now.'

He gave me a cold look in return and just then our assistant walked into the office. By his side were two enormous Dobermann Pinschers.

'What the hell's this?' Siegfried enquired, rising to his feet.

'Oh, just my other dogs,' Calum replied with a light laugh. 'Meet Maggie and Anna.'

'*Dogs!*' Siegfried exploded. 'You said *dog* before!'

'Oh, I know. That was my intention. I was just going to bring Maggie, but poor Anna looked so pathetic, I hadn't the heart to leave her behind. They're such friends, and really, they're as gentle as old sheep.'

'They don't look so bloody gentle to me!' My partner's voice rose to a shout. 'You get round me to bring an extra dog here, then you walk in with these two killers!'

There was something in what he said. An air of quiet menace surrounded the Dobermanns, something unnerving in the way they stood motionless, tall and lean, looking thoughtfully from one strange man to the other. They gave me the impression that they could go into unpleasant action at any moment.

'This just isn't good enough!' Siegfried was working up into full cry, waving a hand in Calum's face, when the dogs, resenting the display of aggression, began to growl, softly but chillingly, their eyes fixed on my partner's face, their lips quivering, showing a lot of white teeth.

'Quiet!' rapped Calum. 'Sit!' Both dogs dropped immediately onto their haunches and looked up at him adoringly. Clearly, they, like all animals, were in his thrall.

'Well, there's a cow down at Jack Skinner's.' The young man consulted his list. 'I'd better get on.' He turned and left with the two big creatures trotting at his heels.

Siegfried looked at me wearily. 'Remember what I said? It's started.'

The following week I was coming down the garden path to the back of the house when I heard the sounds – a loud barking and snarling accompanied by a man's voice calling for help. There was a smaller yard immediately outside the operating room and the noise seemed to be coming from there. We didn't use this little yard very much – it held the surgery's dustbins, an outhouse and an ancient outside privy which had been there since the early days of the house.

There was a side door which led from the garden to the yard and I peered through. It was Siegfried's voice raised in frantic appeal that was coming from the old toilet whose door hung crazily on one hinge and to my horror I saw the two Dobermanns hurling themselves repeatedly at this flimsy bastion and baying for blood. My blood froze. My partner was in there and if that old door gave way something terrible was going to happen. There was nothing I could do. I am not afraid of dogs but I had a sure conviction that if I exposed myself to those two I wouldn't last very long.

I rushed from the garden and into the house. 'Calum! Calum!' I yelled.

He came running down the stairs and when he heard the uproar he galloped through with me to the back of the house. 'Maggie! Anna! You bad dogs! Come here at once!'

The noise was switched off immediately and the Dobermanns came slinking round Calum's feet, looking up at him furtively, their faces fixed in ingratiating grins. 'Get upstairs!' he shouted, and the dogs shot off into the house.

Wisely, Calum decided to follow them, leaving Siegfried to me. I dragged the broken door open to release one very cross veterinary surgeon. 'By God, James,' he said, wild-eyed, 'that was a near go! I was picking plums last night and I ate a few too many. Got caught short and had to make a dash for the nearest loo. I was just lowering myself on to the seat when those two man-eaters came roaring into the yard and I only just managed to jam the door with one foot against it. I'm bloody sure if I had moved that foot an inch they'd have had me! I've been stuck in there for ages!'

'Gosh. I'm sorry, Siegfried,' I said. I wasn't just sorry. I was riddled with guilt. This was my fault. I was the one who had persuaded my partner against his better judgment and he had been so right. The menagerie was on its way.

34

Eight o'clock on a Saturday evening and as I prepared to visit a sick calf the phone rang.

'This is Mr Birse, number 10 Ivy Street. I 'ave a dog bad, will you come?'

'What's the trouble, Mr Birse?'

'Doan't know. Won't eat. Will you come?' The voice was surly and impatient. It sounded as though the man had other, more pressing affairs to attend to.

'All right. I'll be along very soon.'

Bonk went the phone at the other end and I pondered, not for the first time, on the fact that vets weren't regarded as people. They had no interest in staying at home with their families on a Saturday night like others.

Number 10 was one of a long row of mean, brick-built

dwellings and I rang the bell and waited. Nothing happened and I tried again. Still no result, yet I could tell by the light in the window that there was somebody at home. I must have rung and hammered on the door for several minutes before a man aged about fifty, in shirt and braces, opened the door. He seemed in a big hurry and, after beckoning peremptorily, he turned and almost trotted along the passage and into the front room. He stabbed a finger at a dog basket in the corner before dropping into a chair to join the family who were grouped around a blaring television set.

Not one of the intent faces, staring at the screen, showed the slightest interest in me and when it was clear that I wasn't going to get a case history from any of them, I went over to the basket to inspect my patient. He was a big black labrador dog, chin resting on the rim of the basket looking at me with the kind eyes of his breed. As I knelt down his tail thrashed against the bedding and he licked at my hand, but then he turned away immediately and began a frantic scratching and worrying at his coat. I could see now that there were bald patches and sores all over his body. I lifted up his fore leg and then his hind and saw that the skin inflammation was most intense under elbow and thigh. Typical sarcoptic mange, but in this case neglected until the sheer misery of the irritation had put the poor animal off his food.

I was pretty sure of my diagnosis but decided to take the routine skin scraping. Nobody took any notice as I went out to the car for scalpel and slide, leaving the door ajar. Back inside, I scraped a little of the inflamed tissue onto the glass slide and slipped it into an envelope as the dog gazed at me patiently and the television boomed.

When I had finished I went into the kitchen and washed my hands at a sink filled with dirty dishes to which congealed vegetables and Yorkshire pudding adhered. Back in the living room I looked round the unheeding group. Father, mother, and a son and daughter in their twenties all puffing cigarettes, all gaping wide-eyed at the bawling screen. I had to communicate somehow and I chose father.

'Your dog has mange,' I shouted into his ear. For an instant his eyes flickered toward me, then, as the screen belched out a screech of brakes and a volley of shots, they resumed their hypnotic stare.

I held out two packets of my activated sulphur mange wash. More modern treatments for external parasites were coming on to the market, but I had always had great results with my beloved Number Three Wash as we called it and I remained faithful to it.

'Follow the directions on the packet,' I bellowed. 'Give him a really thorough bath tomorrow and be sure to get into every nook and cranny of his body. Repeat with the other pack in a week and then I'll have another look at him.'

Mr Birse nodded, glassy-eyed. It didn't seem as though I could do anything more, so I put the packets on the sideboard and let myself out.

In the dark street I leaned on my car for a moment. Strange things happened in veterinary practice, but this was really very strange. All that time in there without a word spoken and why, after they had let that nice dog get into such a state which must have taken several weeks, had they decided to call assistance on a Saturday night? Ah well, part of the rich tapestry. I got into the car and drove away.

The sick calf was at Mr Farrow's farm, two miles outside Darrowby. I walked into the fold yard where the farmer was forking straw to bed up a group of young heifers. When he saw me he put down his fork and opened his arms wide in delight. 'Well, Mr Herriot, well, well, well.'

He spoke the words slowly, almost reverently and a delighted smile transfigured his face. 'I'm sorry to bother ye on a Saturday night, but it is lovely to see you again. It's been a long time!' His tall son went by with a sack of meal on his shoulder and he, too, grinned and waved.

I was about to turn into the calf house when Mr Farrow held up a hand. 'Nay, nay, you'll 'ave to come and see t'missus first.' He hurried with me to the farm kitchen.

'Edith, Edith!' he called out eagerly. 'Here's Mr Herriot come to see us again!'

Mrs Farrow was a shy lady, but she got up from her chair and gave me a gentle smile. 'Well, Mr Herriot, it's a bit since you were here. You're a sight for sore eyes. I'll put t'kettle on and you'll come in for a cup o' tea when you're done, won't you?'

'Yes, thank you very much, I will.' I went out into the yard, feeling the cold air on my face but warmed inside by the welcome. The Farrows were always like that but it was particularly sweet after my visit to the Birse household.

The difference in their concern for their animal, too, was marked. The calf was suffering from a congestion of the lungs which could easily have progressed into pneumonia and after I had injected it, the farmer and his son, without my telling them, began to thread binder twine through the corners of a thick sack and by the time I was ready to leave, the little creature's chest was warmly wrapped.

'That's good to see,' I said. 'With all these new sulpha drugs and antibiotics it's easy to forget the nursing of animals, but it's still so important.'

Back in the surgery I put my skin scraping under the microscope and the nasty little *Sarcoptes scabei* looked up at me; the unpleasant, bristly-legged mite which was burrowing pitilessly into the skin of that nice dog and making his life a torment. However, it was better than the other horror, the cigar-shaped Demodex which sounded the death knell of so many dogs.

Demodectic mange was often incurable, but my trusty Number Three Wash would clear up this present case, bad as it was. And yet, over the weekend, the thought kept recurring; would those Birses have done the job properly? Would they have done it at all? Somehow, the solicitude of the Farrows with their calf seemed to make the situation almost unbearable.

By Monday morning I could stand it no longer and I rang the doorbell at 10, Ivy Street. 'Good morning, Mrs Birse,' I said breezily. 'I was just passing and thought I'd have another look at your dog.'

'Aye, well . . .' The woman seemed a little nonplussed, but as she hesitated I slipped past her and into the front room.

The big dog was still in his basket and my two white packets were on the sideboard where I had put them.

'We've been a bit busy,' she muttered. 'We'll get 'im done tonight.'

I looked at the dog. I have always thought that there is a special beauty in the lustrous coat of a black labrador but this was a desecration. The ravaged skin looked even worse in the daylight and the hind legs moved convulsively in response to the constant itching.

'What's his name?' I asked.

'Jet.'

I bent down and stroked the dog's head. 'Poor old Jet,' I said. 'You are in a state.' And as the tail thumped and the tongue reached for my hand I made up my mind.

'Give me a bucket of warm water, will you please, Mrs Birse. I'll give him his first treatment. It'll only take a minute or two.'

'Come on, lad,' I said, and Jet trotted obediently after me into the back garden where a few tired-looking Brussels sprouts stood among a jungle of weeds. I tipped the packet into the water and stirred the mixture rapidly, feeling an irrational compulsion to get at those mange mites. I felt a bit awkward, too, because I had never done this on a client's premises before but I decided I didn't care and slapped the thick liquid on to Jet's coat with a kind of savage joy.

As I rubbed the stuff into the dog's skin, working it deeply into the clefts of thigh and elbow, he looked up at me happily, his tail waving. Dogs in my experience hate being bathed, but it seemed as though the big animal was only too pleased to have any sort of attention. He was enjoying the whole thing.

As I worked I became aware of a head watching me over the garden hedge. I looked up and an elderly man nodded cheerfully.

'Mornin'. You'll be t'vitnery.'

'That's right.'

He blew out his cheeks. 'By gaw, you must be a busy feller goin' round washin' all them dogs all the time.'

I smiled at his idea of a veterinary surgeon's life. 'Oh, yes, it's quite a job.'

I was aware of his intent gaze as I completed my shampoo and began a brisk towelling, happy in the knowledge that I had delivered the first blow against those malignant little beasties in the skin.

'Grand dog, that,' said the old man.

'He is indeed.'

The man lowered his voice to a conspiratorial whisper. 'Them folks don't bother with 'im, tha knows. He's in a 'ell of a state.'

I didn't say anything, but the sight of Jet standing bedraggled and half bald like a canine scarecrow bore out his words.

'Can ye cure 'im?'

'I think so, but it's going to take time and regular bathing with this stuff of mine. Every week until he's right.'

'Next week for a start, eh?'

'That's right. I'm going to ask Mrs Birse to do it next Monday.'

'You'll be lucky,' the old man grunted and his head moved away from the hedge.

In the kitchen I passed on my instructions to Mrs Birse and she sniffed. 'Ah see you've been talkin' to awd Howell. He's a nosy awd bugger. Allus watchin' ower that hedge.'

Nosy or not, I thought, he was a lot more concerned about her dog than she was. And as I took my leave with a last look back at Jet wagging his tail cheerfully despite his plight, I knew that I'd be back at No 10 next Monday.

And, feeling daft but determined, I was duly there on the day, ringing that bell. Mrs Birse displayed her usual lack of enthusiasm and beckoned me unsmilingly into the house. She led me into the back garden and jerked her head in the direction of the hedge.

'Them next door's doin' 'im.' She turned and went back into the house.

I looked over the hedge. In the middle of a tidy little garden Jet was standing by a steaming bucket while Mr Howell and his wife busily rubbed the mange wash into his coat.

The old man looked up at me and grinned. 'Now then, vitnery, we're doin' your job. Them Birses would never bath 'im every week like you said so I asked if we could have a go. We like this dog.'

'Well . . . that's fine. You're doing a good job, too.'

Jet looked up at me and although his face was thickly smeared with my concoction his eyes danced with pleasure and his tail lashed. This, he was telling me, is great. As the two old people worked, they were talking to him all the time. 'Now then, a bit more on 'ere, Jet, lad.' 'Let's have hold of that other leg, old feller.' The friendly murmurings went on, and the big dog was lapping up the unaccustomed affection.

I watched until they were finished and as they towelled my patient I spoke again. 'That's absolutely terrific. You've done him properly, you haven't missed an inch.'

The old lady smiled. 'Aye, well, we heard what you said at t'start. We want to get 'im better.'

'Good . . . good . . . you're going the right way about it.' I looked at Jet, still as bare and scruffy as ever. 'You understand that it's going to be a long time before his coat gets back to normal, if it ever does, but the main question is – is he scratching less?'

'Oh aye,' replied Mr Howell. 'He still does a bit, but nothing like before. He's much less itchy now, and he's eatin' well again.'

'Fine, fine. So far, so good, but there's a lot of work still to do. Are you prepared to do this for several weeks? After all, he isn't your dog.'

'Oh, we'll do 'im all right,' said the old lady eagerly. 'We'll stick to 'im – you needn't worry about that.'

I looked at the two Howells in wonder. 'You're real dog lovers, aren't you. And yet you haven't got a dog of your own?'

There was a silence. 'Oh, we did 'ave,' said the old man. 'Had 'im for twelve years, but you never saw him, Mr Herriot, because he never ailed a thing.' He paused and swallowed. 'But he was knocked down and killed just a month ago.'

I gazed for a few moments at the stricken faces. 'I'm so sorry, I know what it's like. It's awful. But . . . you didn't think of getting another dog? It's the only thing to do, you know.'

Mrs Howell shrugged. 'We understand that and we thought about it, but we're both in our seventies and if we got a pup now and anythin' happened to us he'd be left and we'd never know if he was properly looked after.'

I nodded and looked at the old couple with renewed respect. It was the attitude of caring people.

'Anyway,' I said, 'you've got a good friend in Jet for the time being. I can see that he appreciates all you're doing for him. I'll leave you a few more packets of the wash and I know he'll be in good hands.'

My confidence was such that I didn't bother to call at the house and it was three weeks before I saw Jet again. The Howells were shopping in the market place and Jet was by their side. He was cheerful, but his skin was still wrinkled and hairless with many half-healed sores.

'You've got him out, then,' I said.

'Aye, we have.' The old lady clutched my arm. 'He's ours now.'

'Yours?'

'Yes. Mrs Birse said 'e was still bare and scabby and she didn't think he'd ever get better and she didn't want a big vet bill with all them visits and packets of stuff. She said her husband and her wanted Jet put down.'

'Oh dear . . . what then?'

'Well, I said we'd tek 'im and we'd pay the bill.'

'You did?'

'Aye. She wasn't sure at first but I said it would be a whackin' big bill and you'd charge double for comin' out that Saturday night.'

I looked at her for a moment and detected the suggestion of a twinkle in her eye.

'We don't do that. Maybe we should, but we don't. But . . . maybe you wanted to persuade her, eh?'

'Well . . .' It was indisputably a twinkle.

I smiled. 'Anyway, Jet has moved next door and I'm sure it's a good thing for everybody. Even the Birses – they didn't seem to have any interest in him.'

'Aye, that's right, and he's lovely. They never took 'im out for a walk – just let him wander about by himself. I don't know why some people have dogs at all.'

'And how about what you were saying to me before. About your fears about being too old?'

She squared her shoulders. 'Oh well, we talked that over, and we thought that after all, Jet isn't a pup – he's six now, so . . . the three of us will just potter on together.'

'That's great. Grow old along with me! The best is yet to be.'

They both laughed, and Mr Howell held up a finger. 'Yes, that's just it. That poem's got it right. It's so grand havin' Jet – it was awful being without a dog after we lost our Nobby. We've always had one and now we're happy.'

They did indeed look happy as did Jet, laughing up at me and lashing his tail.

It was many weeks before I saw them again. I was walking along one of the many bridle tracks which wound among the fields around Darrowby. The sun was blazing from a cloudless sky and even from a distance it was easy to see the rich black gloss of Jet's coat. When I came abreast of them I bent and stroked the big dog's head.

'Well, what a handsome dog you are!' I said, running my hand over the flawless sheen of the neck and ribs. I turned to the old couple. 'There's not a bare patch anywhere – I can nearly see my face in his coat. You've done wonderfully well with him.'

The Howells smiled modestly and Jet, perfectly aware that we were talking about him, wagged his entire rear end and capered around in panting delight.

'Oh, it's been worth it,' said the old lady. 'We're having a great time with 'im – we can't believe our luck having such a dog.'

I watched them as they went their way along the green path and under the overhanging branches of an oak tree. Jet was chasing a stick and I could hear the cheerful voices of the Howells as they shouted their encouragement to him.

I thought again of Browning's lines, and as I watched the trio until a patch of woodland hid them from view I felt a strong conviction that the best was yet to be for those three.

35

'Right, Mr Busby,' I said, feeling a rising tension in response to the urgency of the voice at the other side of the phone, 'I'll be out very soon.'

'Well, see that you are! Ah don't like the look of this cow at all. She's sunken-eyed and gruntin' and she won't look at 'er hay. She could die. Don't be long!'

As I listened to the aggressive harangue I could almost see the red-haired man shouting, bulging-eyed, into the receiver. He had told me all the symptoms several times over to make sure they penetrated my thick skull. Mr Busby wasn't a bad chap, but he had a temper to go with his hair and always seemed to operate on the edge of panic. I knew I'd better hurry.

I looked at my list, then at my watch. It was 9 a.m. and there weren't any really urgent calls. I could do Mr Busby first and keep him happy.

I grabbed my bag and trotted to the front door. Young Mrs Gardiner was standing on the step with her terrier under her arm. She looked upset.

'Oh, Mr Herriot, I was just going to ring your bell. Something has happened to William. He went out this morning and jumped over the garden gate and now he can't use one of his front legs.'

I managed a strained smile. 'All right, bring him in.'

We went through to the consulting room and I lifted the little dog on to the table. It took only a quick feel to tell me that there was a fracture of radius and ulna.

'He's broken his leg, I'm afraid.'

'Oh dear,' the lady wailed, 'how awful!'

I tried to be cheerful, 'Oh, don't worry. It's a clean break and it's a lot easier on a fore leg. We'll soon put him right.'

William, trembling and anxious with his leg dangling, looked up at me with a mute appeal. He was hoping somebody would do something for him, and soon.

'Has he had any breakfast?' I asked as I fished the plaster of Paris bandages out of the cupboard.

'No, nothing yet today.'

'Good. I can go ahead with the anaesthetic.' As I filled the syringe, the old feeling came back that this was the sort of thing which gave vets ulcers. Mr Busby would have to wait and I could picture him stamping round his farmyard and cursing me.

A few ccs of nembutal sent William into a peaceful sleep and I began to soak the bandages in tepid water. Mrs Gardiner held the shaggy leg straight while I carefully applied the bandages. Normally, this was a job I enjoyed, seeing the plaster hardening until it formed a firm supporting sheath and knowing that the little animal would wake up to find his pain gone and his leg usable, but at this moment I was conscious mainly of the passage of time.

I tapped the plaster. It had set like a rock.

'Right,' I said, lifting the sleeping dog from the table, 'he'll have to keep that on for at least a month, then you must bring him back. If you're worried before that, give me a ring, but I'm sure he'll be fine.'

I deposited William on the back seat of the lady's car and looked at my watch – 9.45 a.m. I picked up my gear again and set off for the second time.

It took me half an hour's hard driving along the narrow, drystone-walled roads to reach the Busby farm and as I approached I could see the farmer standing, hands on hips, legs splayed on the cobbled yard, a menacing picture against the squat buildings and the bracken-clad fells behind. When I got out of the car the farmer looked exactly as I had imagined him. His eyes were glaring and the ginger fringe thrusting from under his cap seemed to bristle with rage.

'Where the bloody hell have you been?' he yelled. 'You said you were coming straight out.'

'Yes, I know, but I had to attend to a dog just as I was leaving.'

I thought Mr Busby would explode. 'A dog! A bloody dog! Ma good cow's a lot more important than any bloody dog!'

'Well, yes, but I had to treat him. He had a broken leg.'

'I don't give a bugger what he had. This cow's my livelihood. If she dies it's a serious loss for me. The other thing's just a flippin' pet, a lapdog.'

'Not a lapdog, Mr Busby, a tough little terrier and he was in pain. The lady owner is very fond of him.'

'Fond, fond! What does that matter. It's not touching her pocket, is it? It isn't costing her anything?'

I was going to say something about her heart being touched and about the importance of pets in the lives of people, but Mr Busby's feet had begun to twitch and then to move up and down on the cobbles. I had never seen a man actually dancing with rage and I didn't want to start now. I made for the cow house.

I was vastly relieved to find that the cow only had a mild stasis of the rumen and it turned out that she had been in the fold yard earlier in the morning and had stolen a few extra turnips. But as I examined and injected her, the farmer kept up a grumbling monologue as he held the tail.

'Ah've got to live on a little spot like this and you don't think one cow is important. Where do you think I'm gettin' the money to buy another? Ah'll tell ye, it's a job makin' ends meet on a little hill farm, but you don't seem to 'ave any idea. Dogs . . . bloody dogs . . . flippin' pets . . . this is my livin' . . . you don't care . . .'

I was fundamentally a cow doctor and I made the greatest part of my own personal living from hill farmers whom I regarded as the salt of the earth, but I held my peace.

When I called again the following day, I found the cow completely recovered, but Mr Busby was still sulky. He hadn't forgiven me.

It was a few weeks later that Helen stopped me as I was leaving to start the morning round.

'Oh, Jim. I've just taken a call. There's a dog coming in. It's crying out in pain. I didn't get the name – the man put the phone down quickly.'

I rubbed my chin. In those days we were almost totally a large animal practice and had no set surgery hours, certainly not in the morning.

'Whoever it is will have to wait,' I said. 'Rod Thwaite has a bullock bleeding badly – knocked a horn off. I'll have to go there first.'

Trying to be in two places at once was a constant problem in our job. I did my best not to think about the dog and sped into the hills at top speed.

It was a typical broken horn with a pretty ornamental fountain of blood climbing several feet into the air and onto anything near. Mr Thwaite and I were soon liberally spattered as we tried to hold the beast still while I packed the stump with sulphonamide, applied a thick pad of cotton wool and bandaged it in a figure of eight to the other horn. It all took quite a time as did the cleaning-up process afterward, and more than an hour had gone by before I declined Mrs Thwaite's offer of a cup of tea and headed back towards Darrowby.

At Skeldale House I hurried down the passage and pushed open the waiting room door. I halted there in surprise. It was Mr Busby. He was sitting in the far corner with a little corgi on his knee and his face bore exactly the same expression as when I paid the first visit to his cow.

'Where the bloody 'ell have you been?' he barked. The words

were the same too. 'I've been sittin' here for a bloody hour! And I made an appointment!'

'I'm very sorry, Mr Busby. I had a bleeding bullock. I just had to go.'

'A flippin' bullock! And how about ma poor dog, waitin' here in agony! That doesn't matter, does it?'

'Of course it does, but you know as well as I do that that beast could have bled to death. It would have been a big loss to the farmer.'

'A big loss? Aye, a big loss o' money, you mean. But what if me good dog dies? He's worth more than any money. You couldn't put a price on him!'

'Oh, I do understand, Mr Busby. He looks a grand little chap to me.' I hesitated. 'I didn't know you had a pet beside your farm dogs.'

'Of course, I 'ave. This is Dandy. Missus and me think the world of 'im. If anything happens to 'im, it 'ud break our hearts! And you neglect 'im for a flippin' bullock!'

'Oh, come on, now, it's not a case of neglecting him. You must appreciate that I couldn't leave that beast to go on bleeding – it's the farmer's livelihood.'

'There ye go again! Money! It's all you can think about!'

I bent down to lift the little dog and almost as soon as I touched him he screamed out.

Mr Busby's eyes popped further. 'Listen to that! I told you he was in a desperate state, didn't I?'

I carried the corgi along the passage, feeling his muscles as tense and rigid as a board. Already I was sure I knew what was wrong with him. On the table I gently squeezed his neck and the dog yelped again, with Mr Busby moaning in response.

The temperature was normal, in fact everything was normal except the rigidity and the pain.

'Is he goin' to die?' The farmer stared into my face.

'No, no, he's got rheumatism. It's a terribly painful thing in a dog, but it does respond well to treatment. I'm sure he'll soon be well again.'

'I hope you're right,' the farmer grunted. 'I just wish you'd seen 'im sooner instead of leaving 'im to suffer while you run off to a bullock. It's all right you harpin' on about money, but love and companionship mean a lot more than that, you know.'

I filled my syringe. 'I quite agree, Mr Busby. Just hold his head, will you.'

'There's more things in life than money, young man. You'll find that out as you grow older.'

'I'm sure you're right. Now give him one of these tablets night and morning and if he's not a lot better by tomorrow, bring him back.'

'I will and I 'ope you'll be here if I do.' Mr Busby's rage had subsided and was replaced by a lofty sanctimoniousness. 'I would ha' thought that a chap like you would know what it means to have a pet. Material things ain't everything.'

He tucked the corgi under his arm and made for the door. With his hand on the knob he turned. 'And I'll tell tha' summat else.'

I sighed. The lecture wasn't over yet.

He waved a finger. 'Man shall not live by bread alone.'

As he walked along the passage, Dandy turned his head and looked back at me. He seemed better already. Mercifully, rheumatism, though terrifying in its onset, is just as dramatically curable.

Yes, Dandy would soon be himself again, but I knew his master would remember only my mercenary outlook and my heartlessness.

36

It was late when the Darrowby police sergeant's voice came on the telephone.

'I think we have a criminal character here, Mr Herriot. Found him skulking down Docker's Alley in the dark, wearing a face mask. Asked him what he was doing there at ten o'clock at night and he said he was on the way to the fish and chip shop. That sounded a bit thin to me – we've had a lot of petty break-ins and thieving lately – so we've brought him in to the station.'

'I see. But where do I come in?'

'Well, he insists he's innocent and says you can vouch for him. Says his name's Bernard Wain and he has a little farm out on the moors near Hollerton.'

All became suddenly clear and I laughed. 'And the face mask is a red-and-white spotted handkerchief?'

'Yeah! How the heck did you know?'

'Because that's the Cisco Kid you have there.'

'What!'

It would have taken a long time to explain to the sergeant but it all fitted in.

Bernard was in his forties and he shared a smallholding with his redoubtable elder sister. It would be wrong to say that he ran the place because he simply did as he was told, Miss Wain's opinion of him being summed up in her favourite word, 'useless'.

For some years now I had become accustomed to her constant refrain on my visits. 'Aye, well, you'll 'ave to manage as best you can, Mr Herriot. Bernard won't be much good to you. He's useless.'

I recounted to the sergeant the events surrounding my visit to the Wains earlier that evening. It had been a ewe lambing. Miss Wain rang from the village kiosk. 'She's been on all afternoon. Bernard's had 'is hand in and he says there's summat far wrong but I don't suppose you'll 'ave much trouble. It doesn't take much to flummox Bernard. He's useless.'

There were three gates on the rough track to the farm and as I drove into the yard, Bernard was standing there in the headlights' beam. Small, dark, perpetually smiling as I had always known him.

He rubbed his hands and, ever anxious to please, bowed slightly as I got out of the car. 'Now then, Mr Herriot.' But he didn't make any sort of move until his sister came strutting from the house, her bandy legs carrying her dumpy little frame rapidly over the cobbles.

She was at least ten years older than her brother, and her jaw jutted as she looked at him. 'Come on, don't just stand there. Take this bucket and show Mr Herriot where t'ewe is. Eee, I don't know.' She turned to me. 'We've got 'er in the stable, but I think he's forgotten!'

As I stripped off in the makeshift pen and soaped my arms I looked at the ewe. She stood knee deep in straw, straining occasionally, but she didn't look unduly distressed. In fact, when Bernard made a clumsy grab at the wool of her neck she skipped away from him.

'Oh, can't you even hold the thing for Mr Herriot?' his sister wailed. 'Go on, get your arms round her neck properly and haul her in the corner. Eee, you're that slow! Aye, that's it, you've got 'er at last. Marvellous! And where's that towel I gave you to bring? You've forgotten that, too!'

As I slipped my hand into the ewe's vagina, Miss Wain folded her arms and blew out her cheeks. 'Ah don't reckon you'll have any problems, Mr Herriot. Bernard can't manage, cos 'e's got no idea about lambin' a ewe. In fact, 'e's got no idea about anything. He's useless.'

Bernard, standing at the animal's head, nodded and his smile widened as though he had received a compliment. He wasn't really feeble-minded, he was just a supremely ineffectual, vague man, a gentle soul, totally unfitted for the rough farming life.

Kneeling on the straw, I reached forward into the ewe and Miss Wain spoke again. 'Ah bet everything's all right in there.'

She was right. Everything was fine. Sometimes this first exploration revealed a single, over-sized lamb, maybe dead, with no room for the hand to move and everything dry and clinging; little wonder that the farmer was unsuccessful, however long he had tried doing the job himself. But on this occasion, there was all the room in the world, with at least two tiny lambs lying clean and clear and moist in the large uterus, beautifully lubricated by the placental fluid. The only thing that was stopping them from popping out was that two little heads and a bunch of legs were trying to enter the cervix at the same time. It was simply a case of repelling a head and relating the legs to the relevant lamb and I'd have them out, wriggling in the straw in one minute flat. In fact, I had corrected the legs with one finger while I was thinking about it, then I realised that if I did a lightning job Bernard was going to be in big trouble.

He could, of course, have done the whole thing easily but anything so earthy as guddling round inside a ewe was anathema to him. I could just imagine his single, shuddering exploration before he capitulated.

I looked up and detected a trace of anxiety in the smiling face. There was no doubt about it; I was going to have to hold these lambs in for a little while.

I gasped and grunted as I rotated my arm and the first lamb moved his tongue against my hand.

'My word, Miss Wain, this is a right mix up. Could be triplets in here and all tangled up together. It's a tricky business, I can tell you. Now let's see . . . which lamb does that leg belong to? . . . no . . . no . . . gosh, it isn't easy.' I gritted my teeth and groaned again as I fought my imaginary battle. 'This is a real vet's job, I can tell you.'

As I spoke, Miss Wain's eyes narrowed. Maybe I was overdoing it. Anyway, Bernard was in the clear now. I hooked a finger round the tiny legs which were first in the queue and drew out lamb number one. I deposited him in the straw and he raised his head and shook it vigorously; always a good sign, but possibly he was puzzled at the delay.

'Now then, what else have we got?' I said worriedly as I reached back into the ewe. The job was as good as over now, but I was still making a meal of it for Bernard's sake and I did a bit more panting and grunting before producing a second and then a third lamb. They made a pretty sight as they lay wriggling and snuffling in the straw. The first one was already making efforts to rise on wobbly legs. It would soon be on its way to the milk bar.

I smiled up at Miss Wain. 'There you are, then. Three grand lambs. I'll put in a couple of pessaries and that's that. It was a complicated business, though, with the legs all jumbled up together. It's a good job you called me or you might have lost these three.'

Arms still folded, her head sunk on her chest, she regarded me unsmilingly. I had the impression that part of her was sorry she had been deprived of another opportunity of castigating her brother. However, she had another line of attack.

'Tell ye what,' she said suddenly, 'there's a cow been hanging her cleansin' for five days. You might as well take it away while you're here.'

This was the kind of routine job which you didn't usually do at nine o'clock at night, but I didn't demur. It would save another visit.

'Okay,' I said. 'Will you bring me some fresh water, please?'

It was then that I noticed the alarm flickering in Bernard's eyes. I remembered that he couldn't stand smells, and in the odoriferous trade of country vetting, removal of the bovine afterbirth is the smelliest. And he would have to hold the tail while I did it.

When he came back with the steaming bucket, he set it down and whipped out a large red-and-white spotted handkerchief from his pocket. Carefully he tied it round his face, knotting it tightly at the back of his neck, then he took up his place by the side of the cow.

As I put my arm into the animal and looked at Bernard's big eyes smiling above the mask, I thought again how fitting was our nickname for him. It was Tristan who had first christened him the Cisco Kid because of his uncanny resemblance to the famous bandit. In all the unpleasant procedures which assailed Bernard's nostrils – stinking calvings, autopsies, releasing the gas from tympanitic cows – the handkerchief came out and, in fact, in every image I had of him he was wearing that mask.

It seemed to give him a feeling of security, because he was able to make cheerful, if muffled, replies to my attempts at conversation, although occasionally he closed his eyes in a pained manner as though some alien whiff had got through to him.

Fortunately this was an easy cleansing and it wasn't long before Bernard was waving me good-bye as I drove away. In the darkness of the yard he still had the handkerchief round his face – the Cisco Kid to the life.

I felt I had managed to put the police sergeant in the picture.

However, he still wasn't quite convinced.

'But he still wouldn't be wearing that mask when he came into Darrowby.'

'Bernard would.'

'You mean he just forgot to take it off?'

'Absolutely.'

'Well, he's a rum sort of feller.'

I could understand his wonderment, but to me Bernard's actions were quite in character. He'd had a traumatic evening with the lambing and the cleansing and it was totally understandable that he would jump on his bike and pedal into the town to seek solace in a parcel of fish and chips. I knew for a fact that they were his greatest pleasure. A little matter like removing the handkerchief would easily slip his mind.

'Aye well,' the sergeant said, 'I suppose I can take your word about him.'

'Sergeant,' I said, 'that man you have there is the most harmless character in North Yorkshire.'

There was a pause. 'Okay, then, we'd better get the handcuffs off him.'

'What! You haven't . . .'

'No, no, heh-heh-heh! Just having a bit o' fun with you, Mr Herriot. You did it to me with your flippin' Cisco Kid, so I'm giving it back to you.'

'All right, fair enough.' I laughed in return. 'Is Bernard very upset?'

'Upset? Not him. Not a care in the world. His only worry is that the fish and chip shop might be closed.'

'Oh dear. And is it?'

'No, I'll be able to reassure him about that. They're stayin' open till eleven o'clock tonight.'

'Good, good, so it's a happy ending for Bernard.'

'Guess so.' The sergeant laughed again as he put down the receiver.

But it could have been so different. If the little farm had been on the phone, Miss Wain would have received that call. My mind reeled at the thought of her reaction when she learned that Bernard couldn't even go out for fish and chips without landing in the hands of the police.

I could imagine her exasperated cry. 'Useless! Quite useless!'

37

There are few sights more depressing than a litter of dying piglets.

'Looks pretty hopeless, Mr Bush,' I said as I leaned over the wall of the pen. 'And what a pity, it's a grand litter. Twelve of them, aren't there?'

The farmer grunted. 'Aye, it allus happens like that.' He wasn't a barrel of laughs at any time but now his long, hollow-cheeked face was set in gloom.

I looked down at the little pink creatures huddled in a heap, liquid yellow faeces trickling down their tails. Neonatal scour, the acute diarrhoea which afflicts new-born piglets and was nearly always fatal unless treated quickly.

'When did they start with this?' I asked.

'Pretty near just after they were born. That were three days ago.'

'Well, I wish I'd seen them a bit sooner. I might have been able to do something for them.'

Mr Bush shrugged. 'I thought it was nowt – maybe t'milk was too rich for 'em.'

I opened the door and went into the pen. As I examined the little pigs, their mother grunted as if in invitation. She was stretched on her side, exposing the long double row of teats, but her family weren't interested. As I lifted and laid the limp little bodies I felt sure they would never suckle again.

However, I just couldn't do nothing. 'We'll give it a go,' I said. 'You never know, we might manage to save one or two.'

The farmer didn't say anything as I went out to the car. I couldn't remember ever having seen him smile and his hunched shoulders and sombre features added to the general atmosphere of doom.

For my part I was disappointed I hadn't been called earlier because I had a new product with me which might have helped. It was a Neomycin mixture contained in a plastic bottle which enabled the antibiotic to be squirted into the mouth. I'd had some good results with it in calves but hadn't had the chance to try it on pigs, but as I handled the unresisting little creatures, giving each one a shot onto its tongue and laying it, apparently lifeless, back on the floor, I felt I was wasting my time.

I supplemented the treatment with a small injection of a sulpha drug, and having satisfied my conscience with the feeling that I had done everything, I prepared to leave.

I handed the Neomycin bottle to the farmer. 'Here, if there's any alive tomorrow, give them a squirt. Let me know if you manage to save any – it isn't worth my paying another visit.'

Mr Bush nodded wordlessly and walked away.

After three days I had heard nothing and presumed that my unhappy prognostications had been correct, but it was on my mind that I ought to have given the farmer some advice for the future. There were some preventive *E.coli* vaccines which could be given to the sow before farrowing and he had a couple of other sows which ought to be protected.

Since I happened to be passing right by Bush's farm on my way home from another visit, I turned in at the gate. As I got out of the car the farmer was sweeping up in a corner of the yard. He didn't look up and my spirits sank. At the same time I felt a little annoyed; it wasn't my fault he had lost his litter. He didn't have to ignore me – I had done my best.

Since he still didn't pay any attention to me, I walked into the piggery and looked into the pen.

At first I thought I was looking in the wrong place, but no, I recognised the sow – she had a small nick out of one ear. What my mind could hardly grasp was the sight of a pink jumble of little creatures fighting to get hold of the best teat. It was difficult to count them in the scramble but finally they settled down to a rapt sucking, each contented with his lot. And there were twelve of them.

I looked out of the doorway. 'Hey, Mr Bush, they're all alive! Every one of them!'

The farmer walked slowly across the yard, trailing his brush and together we looked down into the pen.

I still couldn't believe it. 'Well, that's marvellous. A miracle. I thought they'd all die – and there they are!'

There was no joy in Mr Bush's face. 'Aye,' he muttered, 'but they've lost a bit o'ground.'

With Mr Bush's unimpressed line still groaning in my ear, I drove out to Lord Gresham's farm.

It was only when I was in the RAF with the SP's bawling, 'Hey, you, c'mere!' that I realised that the quiet respect I usually received as a veterinary surgeon on the Yorkshire farms was something I had taken for granted and yet it was very special in my life. It was nothing to do with success or failure in my work – things sometimes went wrong and occasionally I was ticked off by my clients – but behind it all there was the feeling that I was a professional man doing my best for the animals and I was esteemed accordingly.

But I never got any more respect from Lord Gresham's men than I did from Mr Bush. Danny, Bert, Hughie and Joe regarded me with a total detachment which I always found disquieting. It wasn't that they disliked me or were rude in any way, it was the fact that no matter what I did they were totally unimpressed, not, seemingly, even interested.

This was strange because, as every vet knows, there are some places where everything goes right and others where everything goes wrong and Lord Gresham's place was one of the former. I always felt that my good fairy was watching over me there, because every single case had gone like a breeze and in fact I had pulled off a long succession of cures that warmed my heart.

Today, after climbing out of my car and walking into the fold yard, I believed I would do it again. I looked at the cow standing alone and disconsolate in the deep straw. She was a pathetic sight with, it seemed, half her insides hanging out of her. Prolapsed uterus. It was a scene to wipe the smile from any veterinary surgeon's face – a promise of hard labour with the animal's life at stake. But with the passage of years it had lost a lot of its dread and, although I was naturally apprehensive, I had the feeling that with my new knowledge and equipment I could restore this poor cow to normal. But at the same time I knew I would get no credit for it, no respect. Not on this farm anyway.

By bringing up a tractor and, using the recently invented Bagshaw hoist clamped on the cow's pelvis, I raised the cow's back end so that I was working downhill. I administered a spinal anaesthetic and replaced the uterus with none of the labour of past years.

The cow walked away, good as new, and while I felt delighted at the magical return to normal, the men were completely unmoved and strolled off without a word. It was always like this here.

Shortly after this, I attended some sheep going round in circles with listeriosis. An injection of penicillin and they were right within a couple of days – quite a spectacular cure. Same reaction from the men. No interest. Not a scrap of respect.

A week later, I was called to a cow with a twisted uterus. She was unable to calve and was lying straining, distressed, on the point of exhaustion. Without my help she would have had to be slaughtered, but by rolling her over several times I righted the twist and produced a beautiful live calf. As I looked wonderingly and with deep satisfaction at the result of my work, the men offered no comment but went phlegmatically about the business of clearing up after the operation. For the umpteenth time I wondered what I had to do to get through to them.

I was putting on my jacket when an envelope fell out of my pocket. It was from Liverpool, from the football pools firm and, just for the sake of breaking the silence, I said, 'Ah, my winnings for this week.'

The effect was electric and the previous apathy was replaced by acute interest. They studied the enclosed postal order, which was only for two pounds, with total absorption. 'By gaw, look at that!' 'We can't do any good with them things!' 'Fust time I've ever seen a winner!' The remarks flew thick and fast. Then Danny, the foreman, said, 'De ye often win?'

Carried away by the excitement and the unprecedented interest, I replied casually, 'Oh yes, regularly,' which was an exaggeration because I very rarely won but the remark was received with open-mouthed fascination. For the first time ever I was the centre of concentrated attention.

After a few moments, Danny cleared his throat. 'Mr Herriot, the lads and me do the three draws every week – we each put on a shillin' – and we've never 'ad a touch yet. Will you fill up our coupon for us?'

With a wistful feeling that my sudden popularity would be soon exploded I took the coupon and, using the cow's back as a desk, I did as they asked.

It was a winner and, during that week, Danny appeared at my surgery. 'We've got thirty bob apiece, Mr Herriot. It's never happened before and t'lads are over the moon. Will ye do t'same again?'

'Certainly,' I replied airily and put my crosses in the little squares. It won again, and this time all four of the men turned up at the surgery, smiling and triumphant. 'Another thirty bob each, Mr Herriot! It's champion! We're goin' to put a bit more on this week.'

I felt that things were getting out of hand. 'Look, chaps, I'd really rather not do this again. I don't want to lose you a lot of money and you will if you start putting on bigger stakes. Anyway, I'm no expert at this – I was only kidding when I gave you the idea that I won every week.'

A hush fell upon the room and four pairs of eyes narrowed to slits. They didn't believe a word.

Helplessly I looked from one to the other but they stood there as though carved from stone, waiting for me to make my move.

'I tell you what,' I said at length, 'I'll do your coupon this week, but it will be for the last time. All right?'

There were nods all round. 'Aye, that'll do us fine,' Danny said.

'Just this week and never n'more.'

Once more I entered the crosses in the squares and as I handed over the coupon I made my final appeal. 'And you'll never ask me to do this again?'

Danny raised a hand. 'Nay, never n'more, Mr Herriot. That's a promise.'

For the third successive week, their coupon was a winner. Even as I write, I feel I can hardly ask anybody to believe it, but it is a true story. And a growing sensation of the eerie workings of fate was strengthened when I myself had my biggest ever win – seventy-seven pounds four shillings and elevenpence – on the treble chance. The sum is engraven on my memory until the end of time.

That evening I showed the postal order tremblingly to my partner. 'Look at this, Siegfried. All this money! And if I had had just one more draw I'd have won the first prize – sixteen thousand pounds!'

Siegfried whistled as he studied the postal order. 'James, this calls for a celebration. Let's get over to the Drovers.'

In the bar, Siegfried bustled to the counter. 'Two large whiskies, Betty,' he cried. 'Mr Herriot's just won sixteen thousand pounds on the pools!'

'No, no . . .' I protested, trying to restrain my ebullient colleague. 'It wasn't as much as that . . .'

But it was too late. The barmaid's eyes popped, the other occupants nearly choked on their beer and the damage was done. The news swept through Darrowby like a prairie fire. Sixteen thousand pounds was a vast fortune in those days and wherever I went over the next few weeks I was greeted with secret smiles and knowing winks. It happened nearly forty years ago, but to this day there are many people in our little town who are convinced that Herriot became rich on the pools.

The next time I had to visit Lord Gresham's farm was to carry out the tuberculin test on the cattle. I didn't have to do anything clever to the beasts – just clip a couple of inches of hair from the necks and inject into the skin, but there was a different atmosphere altogether from the previous occasions when I was pulling off miracle cures, saving animals' lives with my veterinary skill. The four men seemed to hang on my every word, treating my requests with the greatest deference. 'Yes, Mr Herriot.' 'Right you are, Mr Herriot.' And, whereas before they had always acted as though I weren't there, they now watched my smallest move with the greatest concentration. It became clear to me that I was forever enshrined in their minds as the one man to whom the mysteries of the football pools were an open book, to be manipulated as the fancy took me, and as I looked round the four men I could read something in their eyes which I had never seen before.

It was respect – deep, abiding respect.

38

I was in a familiar position. Lying flat on my face on a hard cobbled floor with my arm up to the shoulder inside a straining heifer. I had been doing this for over an hour and was beginning to despair. There was a huge live calf in there and the only thing stopping the delivery was that there was a leg back – normally a simple malpresentation and easily corrected. That was the cause of my frustration – I couldn't believe that such a thing could beat me, but the trouble was that this was a very small heifer and there was no room to work. Time and again, I had managed to reach the calf's foot but I could only get a couple of fingers round it and as soon as I tried to pull, it slipped away from me. And on top of this, the heifer was giving me hell with her expulsive efforts, trapping my hand painfully between the calf's head and the pelvic bones.

With all my soul, I wished that my arm had been a few inches longer. If only I could get my fingers beyond the smooth wall of the hoof and grasp the hairy leg, the job would be over in minutes, but this was what I had been trying to do for that long hour and my arm was becoming paralysed and useless.

In these situations I would often get a big farm lad to strip off and try to reach inaccessible places for me, but Mr Kilding and his son were stocky, short-armed chaps – they wouldn't get as far as I had.

Suddenly I remembered something. Calum was doing a tuberculin test on a farm less than a mile away. If I could get hold of him my troubles would be over because among his many attributes Calum had very long arms.

'Mr Kilding,' I said, 'could you phone the Ellertons and ask Mr Buchanan to come round and give me a hand. I'm afraid I need a bit of help.'

'Buchanan? Vet wi' t'badger?'

I smiled. Calum was known as such not only in our own practice but for many miles beyond. 'Yes, that's the man.'

The farmer hurried off and returned quickly. 'Aye, he's just finished the test. Says 'e'll be round in a minute or two.' He was a nice man, and wasn't complaining at my long, unproductive rolling about on his byre floor, but he couldn't hide his anxiety. 'I 'ope you'll be able to do summat, Mr Herriot, I've been really lookin' forward to getting this calf.'

A few minutes later Calum strode into the byre. He looked down at the prostrate animal and grinned. 'Having a little trouble, Jim?' His manner, as always, was breezy.

I explained the situation and he quickly whipped off his shirt. We lay down together on those cobbles which had been getting steadily harder. I inserted my left arm until I could feel the calf's muzzle against the palm of my hand and Calum pushed in his right arm alongside mine.

'Right,' I said, 'I'll push the head back while you try to get hold of that foot.'

'Okay,' he replied. 'Fire away.'

I pushed and just as the head moved away, making the vital room we needed, the heifer gave a mighty strain and pushed it back at me. Calum yelped as his fingers were trapped. 'Ouch, that hurt! You'll have to do a bit better than that.'

I gritted my teeth and tried again, bracing my arm desperately against the heifer's expulsive efforts.

'I'm nearly there,' grunted Calum. 'Nearly . . . nearly . . . push, you're not pushing!'

'I *am* pushing, dammit!' I gasped, 'but she's stronger than I am, and I've been doing this for an hour, you know. My arm's like spaghetti.'

We tried again, several times, groaning and panting, then Calum let his head slump onto his shoulder. 'I know. Let's have a rest for a few seconds.'

I was all for that and I relaxed, feeling the calf's rough tongue licking at my palm. He was still alive, anyway.

As we lay there, practically cheek to cheek, arms still inside the heifer, my colleague put on a bright smile. 'Well, now, what shall we talk about while we're resting?'

I didn't feel like light conversation, but I tried to fall in with his sally. 'Oh, I don't know. Have you any interesting news?'

'Well, yes. As a matter of fact I have. I'm going to get married.'

'*What!*'

'I said I'm going to get married.'

'You're joking!'

'No. I assure you, I am.'

'When?'

'Next week.'

'Well . . . well . . . Anybody I know?'

'No, no. Girl who works in the surgery department at the London College. I met her there while I was taking the course.'

I lay there, thunderstruck. I found it difficult to take in. I had never imagined that a chap like Calum would ever entertain dreams of domestic bliss. I was still trying to sort out my thoughts when he brought me back to reality. 'Come on, let's have another go.'

And it seemed as though the shock to my system had brought a surge of adrenalin with it, because this time I gave a great, pop-eyed heave and was able to hold the head back until I heard Calum's triumphant cry. 'I've got it!'

And, having got it, he wasn't going to let go. Eyes closed, teeth bared, he pulled until the elusive foot appeared at the vulva. His sweating face broke into a delighted grin. 'That's a lovely sight!'

It was indeed. We had two legs and a head now, although nearly everything was still inside. I slapped the heifer's rump. 'Come on, old girl. This is when we need you. You can push as much as you like now.'

As if in reply, the heifer gave us enthusiastic help as we pulled on the legs and soon the muzzle appeared, nostrils twitching, the big, wide brow and the eyes – which, I imagined, held a glimmer of disapproval at the delay – then, the rest of the head and body till we had a fine calf wriggling on the straw.

I felt good – I always did – but on this occasion something else was crowding in my mind. Calum's bombshell about his impending nuptials.

I could hardly wait to see what kind of girl Calum would bring back. He was such an unusual chap with ideas so far different from the ordinary man that the new woman could be anything – ugly, eccentric, fat, skinny – my mind played restlessly with the possibilities.

I was put out of my pain quite soon. I opened the sitting room door one afternoon and my young colleague was there with a girl at his side. 'This is Deirdre,' he said.

She was quite tall, and the first words which came to me were 'kind' and 'motherly'. But I would like to banish any thought that being kind and motherly meant that she wasn't attractive. Dierdre was very attractive indeed and now, nearly forty years later, when I think of her wonderful family of six young Buchanans I feel I deserve full marks for intuition.

As we shook hands, her smile was wide and warm, her voice gentle, and it struck me that Calum had done it again – with all his funny ways he seemed to get the fundamental things right, and now, when it came to choosing a wife he had found the kind of girl any young man would be glad to see first thing every morning.

Any notion we might have harboured of celebrating an exciting wedding was soon quashed, and in a way which I realised was typical of them. They slipped away quietly to Keeler church and the ceremony was carried out there without fuss.

I have never in my travels through Britain seen anything quite like Keeler. It is an ancient church of great beauty built by the Normans around 1100, standing quite alone among surrounding fields. There is a farm nearby but the nearest village is two miles away. It is on the borders of our practice area, but it can be clearly seen from the main road and whenever I drive past I always slow down to look yet again at that lovely building, solitary among the fields with the hills rising behind. To me, it is a romantic, thrilling sight.

Throughout the centuries, services have been conducted regularly there with a small congregation drawn from the surrounding farms and nearby villages, so that the church has been preserved in all its glory. Its beauty is a stark beauty of massive stone with nothing like the traceried battlements and buttresses of Darrowby's splendid church which is famed to such an extent that it is often referred to as a little cathedral. Helen and I were married there and have never ceased to be enthralled by its sheer magnificence.

However, Calum and Deirdre went to Keeler in its wild and lonely setting and I could understand its appeal which would reach out to them. There was a brief honeymoon and that was all.

Whenever I pass the old church standing in its solitary dignity looking over the empty fields and the long line of hills as it has done for nine centuries, I think again how fitting it was that those young Buchanans should pledge their future life within its walls.

I had the good feeling that Deirdre would add the woman's touch to Calum's flat – introduce a little more comfort in the way of her own individual furniture and decorations – but it was not to be. Deirdre didn't care any more about that side of life than Calum – her interests were all outside. Like his, in the creatures, the plants and flowers of North Yorkshire.

The flat stayed spartan – no chintz covers on the furniture or anything like that – but she seemed perfectly happy as she padded round up there, very often in slacks and bare feet, her mind completely in tune with her new husband's.

When they had time off together they spent it in rambling and observation in the woods and hills, and if Calum's work prevented him from doing something important in his world of exploration, Deirdre would happily stand in for him. I saw an example of this one balmy summer evening around dusk when I had to send the young man to a call.

'Calum,' I said, 'there's a colic at Steve Holdsworth's – will you get there as soon as you can?'

'Certainly,' he replied. 'Just give me a few minutes to put Deirdre up a tree and then I'll be on my way.'

39

It was around the time when Calum's third badger arrived that an uncanny sense of the inevitable began to settle on me.

The new badger was called Bill and Calum didn't say much about his unheralded advent. He did mention it in an off-hand way to me, but prudently failed to take Siegfried into his confidence. I think he realised that there wasn't much point in upsetting my partner further – it seemed only reasonable to assume that Siegfried was getting a little punch-drunk with the assorted creatures milling around and wouldn't even notice.

I was discussing the day's work with my colleagues in the doorway of the dispensary when Siegfried ducked down. 'What the hell was that?' he exclaimed as a large feathery body whizzed past, just missing our heads.

'Oh, it's Calum's owl,' I said.

Siegfried stared at me. 'That owl? I thought it was supposed to be ill.' He turned to our assistant. 'Calum, what's that owl doing here? You brought it in days ago and it looks fit enough now, so take it back where it came from. I like birds as you know, but not rocketing round in our surgery like bloody eagles – could frighten the life out of the clients.'

The young man nodded. 'Yes . . . yes . . . she's almost recovered. I expect to take her back to the wood very soon.' He pocketed his list of visits and left.

I didn't say anything, but it seemed certain to me that once Calum had got his hands on an owl of his very own he wasn't going to part with it in a hurry. I foresaw some uncomfortable incidents.

'And listen to those fox cubs!' Siegfried went on. 'What a racket they're making!' The yapping, snarling and barking echoed along the passage from the back of the house. There was no doubt they were noisy little things. 'What does Calum want them in here for?'

'I'm not sure . . . He did say something, but I can't quite recall . . .'

'Well,' Siegfried grunted, 'I just hope he'll remove them as soon as the problem is over.'

Later that day, Siegfried and I were setting a dog's fractured radius when Calum walked into the operating room. Marilyn, as usual, was on his shoulder, but today she had company; seated comfortably in the crook of the young man's arms was a little monkey.

Siegfried looked up from his work. He stopped winding the plaster of Paris bandage and his mouth fell open. 'Oh, my God, no! This is too much! Not a bloody monkey now! It's like living in a bloody zoo.'

'Yes,' replied Calum with a pleased smile. 'His name is Mortimer.'

'Never mind his name!' Siegfried growled. 'What the hell is he doing here?'

'Oh, don't worry, this isn't a pet – in a way, he's a patient.'

Siegfried's eyes narrowed. 'What do you mean – in what way? Is he ill?'

'Well, not exactly . . . Diana Thurston has asked me to look after him while she's away on holiday.'

'And you said yes, of course! No hesitation! That's just what we need here – bloody monkeys roaming the place on top of everything else!'

Calum looked at him gravely. 'Well, you know, I was in a difficult position. Colonel Thurston is a very nice man and one of our biggest clients – large farm, hunting horses and umpteen dogs. I couldn't very well refuse.'

My partner recommenced his winding. The plaster was setting and I could see he wanted time to think. 'Well, I see your point,' he said after a few moments. 'It wouldn't have looked so good.' He glanced up at Calum. 'But it's definitely just while Diana's on holiday?'

'Oh, absolutely, I promise you.' The young man nodded vigorously. 'She's devoted to the little chap and she'll pick him up as soon as she returns.'

'Oh, well, I suppose it'll be all right.' Siegfried shot a hunted look at the monkey which, open-mouthed, teeth-bared and chattering, was apparently laughing at him.

We lifted the sleeping dog from the table and carried him to one of the recovery kennels. My partner seemed indisposed to speak and I didn't break the silence. I had no desire to discuss Calum's latest acquisition because I happened to know that Diana Thurston wasn't just going to Scarborough for a fortnight – she was off to Australia for six months.

I was called out that evening and went to the surgery for extra drugs. As I walked along the passage I could hear a babel of animal sounds from the end of the house and, on opening the door to the back room, I found Calum among his friends. The three badgers were nosing around the food bowls, the owl flapped lazily onto a high shelf. Storm, vast and amiable, waved his tail in welcome, while the Dobermanns regarded me contemplatively. Mortimer the monkey, clearly already under Calum's spell, leaped from a table into the young man's arms and grinned at me. In a corner, the fox cubs kept up their strange yapping and growling and I noticed two cages containing a couple of rabbits and a hare – apparently new arrivals.

Looking round the room I realised that Siegfried had been right from the very beginning. The menagerie was now firmly installed. And as I opened the door to leave I wondered just how big it was going to grow.

I had stepped into the passage when Calum turned from the table where he was stirring some nameless comestible in a large bowl.

'Before you go, Jim, I've got some very exciting news!' he cried.

'Oh, what's that?'

He pointed to one of the Dobermanns. 'Anna's having pups next month!'

40

As I got out of my car to open the gate to the farm, I looked with interest at the odd-looking structure on the grass verge; it was standing in the shelter of the dry-stone wall, overlooking the valley. It seemed as though sheets of tarpaulin had been stretched over metal hoops to make some kind of shelter. It was like a big black igloo, but for what?

As I wondered, the sacking at the front parted and a tall, white-bearded man emerged. He straightened up, looked around him, dusted down his ancient frock coat and donned the kind of high-crowned bowler hat which was popular in Victorian times. He seemed oblivious of my presence as he stood, breathing deeply, gazing at the heathery fellside which ran away from the roadside to the beck far below. Then after a few moments he turned to me and raised his hat gravely.

'Good morning to you,' he murmured in the kind of voice which could have belonged to an archbishop.

'Morning,' I replied, fighting with my surprise. 'Lovely day.'

His fine features relaxed in a smile. 'Yes, yes, it is indeed.' Then he bent and pulled the sacking apart. 'Come, Emily.'

As I stared, a little cat tripped out with dainty steps, and as she stretched luxuriously the man attached a leash to the collar round her neck. He turned to me and raised his hat again. 'Good day to you.' Then man and cat set off at a leisurely pace towards the village whose church tower was just visible a couple of miles down the road.

I took my time over opening the gate as I watched the dwindling figures. I felt almost as though I were seeing an apparition. I was out of my usual territory because a faithful client, Eddy Carless, had taken this farm almost twenty miles away from Darrowby and had paid us the compliment of asking our practice if we would still do his work. We had said yes even though it would be inconvenient to travel so far, especially in the middle of the night.

The farm lay two fields back from the road and as I drew up in the yard I saw Eddy coming down the granary steps.

'Eddy,' I said, 'I've just seen something very strange.'

He laughed. 'You don't have to tell me. You've seen Eugene.'

'Eugene?'

'That's right. Eugene Ireson. He lives there.'

'What?'

'It's true – that's 'is house. He built it himself two years ago and took up residence. This used to be me dad's farm, as you know, and he used to tell me about 'im. He came from nowhere and settled in that funny place with 'is cat and he's never moved since.'

'I wouldn't have thought he would be allowed to set up house on the grass verge.'

'No, neither would I, but nobody seems to have bothered 'im. And I'll tell you another funny thing. He's an educated man and the brother of Cornelius Ireson.'

'Cornelius Ireson, the industrialist?'

'The very same. The multi-millionaire. Lives in that estate you pass about five miles along the Brawton road. You'll have seen the big lodge at the gates.'

'Yes . . . I know it . . . but how . . . ?'

'Nobody knows the whole story, but it seems Cornelius inherited everything and his brother got nowt. They say that Eugene has travelled the world, living rough in wild countries and havin' all kinds of adventures, but wherever he's been he's come back to North Yorkshire.'

'But why does he live in that strange erection?'

'It's a mystery. I do know he has nowt to do with 'is brother and vice versa and anyway 'e seems happy and content down there. Me dad was very fond of 'im and the old chap used to come up to the farm for the odd meal and a bath. Still does, but he's very independent. Doesn't sponge on anybody. Goes down to the village regularly for his food and 'is pension.'

'And always with his cat?'

'Aye.' Eddy laughed again. 'Allus with his cat.'

We went into the buildings to start the tuberculin test, but as I clipped and measured and injected over and over again, I couldn't rid my mind of the memory of that odd twosome.

When I drew up at the farm gate three days later to read the tuberculin test Mr Ireson was sitting on a wicker chair in the sunshine, reading, with his cat on his lap.

When I got out of the car, he raised his hat as before. 'Good afternoon. A very pleasant day.'

'Yes, it certainly is.' As I spoke, Emily hopped down and stalked over the grass to greet me, and as I tickled her under the chin she arched and purred round my legs.

'What a lovely little thing!' I said.

The old man's manner moved from courtesy to something more. 'You like cats?'

'Yes, I do. I've always liked them.' As I continued my stroking, then gave her tail a playful tug, the pretty tabby face looked up at me and the purring rose in a crescendo.

'Well, Emily seems to have taken to you remarkably. I've never seen her so demonstrative.'

I laughed. 'She knows how I feel. Cats always know – they are very wise animals.'

Mr Ireson beamed his agreement. 'I saw you the other day, didn't I? You have some business with Mr Carless?'

'Yes, I'm his vet.'

'Aah . . . I see. So you are a veterinary surgeon and you approve of my Emily.'

'I couldn't do anything else. She's beautiful.'

The old man seemed to swell with gratification. 'How very kind of you.' He hesitated. 'I wonder, Mr . . . er . . .'

'Herriot.'

'Ah yes, I wonder, Mr Herriot, if, when you have concluded your business with Mr Carless, you would care to join me in a cup of tea.'

'I'd love to. I'll be finished in less than an hour.'

'Splendid, splendid. I look forward to seeing you then.'

Eddy had a clear test. No reactors, not even a doubtful. I entered the particulars in my testing book and hurried back down the farm road.

Mr Ireson was waiting by the gate. 'It is a little chilly now,' he said, 'I think we'd better go inside.' He led me over to the igloo, drew back the sacks and ushered me through with old world grace.

'Do sit down,' he murmured, waving me to what looked like a one-time automobile seat in tattered leather while he sank down on the wicker chair I had seen outside.

As he arranged two mugs, then took the kettle from a primus stove and began to pour, I took in the contents of the interior. There was a camp bed, a bulging rucksack, a row of books, a Tilly lamp, a low cupboard and a basket in which Emily was ensconced.

'Milk and sugar, Mr Herriot?' The old man inclined his head gracefully. 'Ah, no sugar. I have some buns here, do have one. There is an excellent little bakery down in the village and I am a regular customer.'

As I bit into the bun and sipped the tea, I stole a look at the row of books. Every one was poetry. Blake, Swinburne, Longfellow, Whitman, all worn and frayed with reading.

'You like poetry?' I said.

He smiled. 'Ah, yes. I do read other things – the van comes up here from the public library every week – but I always come back to my old friends, particularly this one.' He held up the dog-eared volume he had been reading earlier. *The Poems of Robert W. Service.*

'You like that one, eh?'

'Yes. I think Service is my favourite. Not classical stuff perhaps, but his verses strike something very deep in me.' He gazed at the book, then his eyes looked beyond me into somewhere only he knew. I wondered then if Alaska and the wild Yukon territory might have been the scene of his wanderings and for a moment I hoped he might be going to tell me something about his past, but it seemed he didn't want to talk about that. He wanted to talk about his cat.

'It is the most extraordinary thing, Mr Herriot. I have lived on my own all my life but I have never felt lonely, but I know now that I would be desperately lonely without Emily. Does that sound foolish to you?'

'Not at all. Possibly it's because you haven't had a pet before. Have you?'

'No, I haven't. Never seemed to have stayed still long enough. I am fond of animals and there have been times when I felt I would like to own a dog, but never a cat. I have heard so often that cats do not dispense affection, that they are self-sufficient and never become really fond of anybody. Do you agree with that?'

'Of course not. It's absolute nonsense. Cats have a character of their own, but I've treated hundreds of friendly, affectionate cats who are faithful friends to their owners.'

'I'm so glad to hear you say that, because I flatter myself that this little creature is really attached to me.' He looked down at Emily who had jumped onto his lap and gently patted her head.

'That's easy to see,' I said and the old man smiled his pleasure.

'You know, Mr Herriot,' he went on, 'when I first settled here,' he waved his hand round his dwelling as though it were the drawing room in a multi-acred mansion, 'I had no reason to think that I wouldn't continue to live the solitary life that I was accustomed to, but one day this little animal walked in from nowhere as though she had been invited and my whole existence has changed.'

I laughed. 'She adopted you. Cats do that. And it was a lucky day for you.'

'Yes . . . yes . . . how very true. You seem to understand these things so well, Mr Herriot. Now, do let me top up your cup.'

It was the first of many visits to Mr Ireson in his strange dwelling. I never went to the Carless farm without looking in through the sacks and if Eugene was in residence we had a cup of tea and a chat. We talked about many things – books, the political situation, natural history of which he had a deep knowledge, but the conversation always got round to cats. He wanted to know everything about their care and feeding, habits and diseases. While I was agog to hear about his world travels which he referred to only in the vaguest terms, he would listen with the wide-eyed interest of a child to my veterinary experiences.

It was during one of these sessions that I raised the question of Emily in particular.

'I notice she is either in here or on the lead with you, but does she ever go wandering outside by herself?'

'Well, yes . . . now that you mention it. Just lately she has done so. She only goes up to the farm – I make sure she does not stray along the road where she may be knocked down.'

'I didn't mean that, Mr Ireson. What I was thinking about was that there are several male cats up there at the farm. She could easily become pregnant.'

He sat bolt upright in his chair. 'Good heavens, yes! I never thought of that – how foolish of me. I'd better try to keep her inside.'

'Very difficult,' I said. 'It would be much better to have her spayed.'

'Eh?'

'To let me do a hysterectomy. Remove the uterus and ovaries. Then she'd be safe – you couldn't do with a lot of kittens in here, could you?'

'No . . no . . . of course not. But an operation . . .' He stared at me with frightened eyes. 'There would be an element of danger . . .?'

'No, no,' I said as briskly as I could. 'It's quite a simple procedure. We do lots of them.'

His normal urbanity fell away from him. From the beginning he had struck me as a man who had seen so many things in life that nothing would disturb his serenity, but now he seemed to shrink within himself. He slowly stroked the little cat, seated, as usual, on his lap. Then he reached down to the black leather volume of *The Works of Shakespeare* with its faded gold lettering which he had been reading when I arrived. He placed a marker in the book and closed it before putting it carefully on the shelf.

'I really don't know what to say, Mr Herriot.'

I gave him an encouraging smile. 'There's nothing to worry about. I strongly advise it. If I could just describe the operation, I'm sure it would put your mind at rest. It's really keyhole surgery – we make only a tiny incision and bring the ovaries and uterus through and ligate the stump . . .'

I dried up hurriedly because the old man closed his eyes and swayed so far to one side that I thought he would fall off the wicker chair. It wasn't the first time that one of my explanatory surgical vignettes had had an undesirable effect and I altered my tactics.

I laughed loudly and patted him on the knee. 'So, you see, it's nothing – nothing at all.'

He opened his eyes and drew a long, quavering breath, 'Yes . . . yes . . . I'm sure you're right. But you must give me a little time to think. This has come on me so suddenly.'

'All right. I'm sure Eddy Carless will give me a ring for you. But don't be too long.'

I wasn't surprised when I didn't hear from the old man. The whole idea obviously terrified him and it was over a month before I saw him again.

I pushed my head through the sacks. He was sitting in his usual chair, peeling potatoes and he looked at me with serious eyes.

'Ah, Mr Herriot. Come and sit down. I've been going to get in touch with you – I'm so glad you've called.' He threw back his head with an air of resolution. 'I have decided to take your advice about Emily. You may carry out the operation when you think fit.' But his voice trembled as he spoke.

'Oh, that's splendid!' I said cheerfully. 'In fact, I've got a cat basket in the car so I can take her straight away.'

I tried not to look at his stricken face as the cat jumped on to my knee. 'Well, Emily, you're coming with me.' Then as I looked at the little animal, I hesitated. Was it my imagination or was there a significant bulge in her abdomen?

'Just a moment,' I murmured as I palpated the little body, then I looked up at the old man.

'I'm sorry, Mr Ireson, but it's a bit late. She's pregnant.'

His mouth opened, but no words came, then he swallowed and spoke in a hoarse whisper. 'But . . . but what are we going to do?'

'Nothing, nothing, don't worry. She'll have the kittens, that's all and I'll find homes for them. Everything will be fine.' I was putting on my breeziest act, but it didn't seem to help.

'But Mr Herriot, I don't know anything about these things. I'm now terribly worried. She could die giving birth – she's so tiny!'

'No, no, not at all. Cats very rarely have any trouble that way. I tell you what, when she starts having the kittens – probably around a month from now – get Eddy to give me a ring. I'll slip out here and see that all is well. How's that?'

'Oh, you are kind. I feel so silly about this. The trouble is . . . she means so much to me.'

'I know, and stop worrying. Everything will be absolutely okay.'

We had a cup of tea together and by the time I left he had calmed down.

The next time I saw him was under unimagined circumstances.

It was about two weeks later and I was attending the annual dinner of the local Agricultural Society. It was a formal affair and the company consisted of an assortment of farmers, big landowners, and Ministry of Agriculture officials. I wouldn't have been there but for my elevation to the Milk Sub-Committee.

I was having a pre-prandial drink with one of my clients when I almost choked in mid swallow. 'Good heavens! Mr Ireson!' I exclaimed, pointing to the tall, white-bearded figure, immaculate in white tie and tails standing among a group at the far end of the room. The usually untidy bush of silver hair was sleeked back and shining over his ears and, glass in hand and with a commanding air, he was rapping out his words to the group who were nodding deferentially.

'I can't believe it!' I burst out again.

'Oh, it's him, all right,' my friend grunted. 'Miserable bugger!'

'What!'

'Aye, he's a right old sod! He'd skin 'is own grandmother.'

'Well, that's funny. I haven't known him long, but I like him. I like him very much.'

The farmer raised his eyebrows. 'I reckon you're about the only one as does,' he muttered sourly. 'He's the hardest bugger I've ever known.'

I shook my head in bewilderment. 'I can't understand this. And those clothes – where the heck did he get them? I've only seen him in his roadside hut and he seems to have no more than the bare essentials.'

'Hey, wait a minute!' The farmer laughed and punched me in the chest. 'Now I get it. You're talkin' about his brother, old Eugene. That's Cornelius over there!'

'My God, how amazing! The likeness is incredible. Are they twins?'

'Nay, there's two years between them but, as you say, you can hardly tell 'em apart.'

As though he knew we were discussing him, the tall man turned towards us. The face was almost Eugene's, but where there was gentleness, there was aggression, where there was softness and serenity there was a fierce arrogance. I had only a chilling glimpse before he turned away and began to harangue his companions again. It was an uncanny experience and I continued to stare at the group until my friend broke in on my thoughts.

'Aye, a lot of people have made that mistake, but they're only alike in appearance. You couldn't find two people more different in character. Eugene's a grand old lad, but as for that bugger – I've never seen 'im smile.'

'Do you know Eugene?'

'As well as most people, I reckon. I'm nearly as old as him and my farm's on the Ireson estate. Cornelius was left everything when the father died, but I don't think Eugene would've been interested in running the textile empire and the estate. He was a dreamer and a wanderer – kind and friendly, but somehow unworldly. Money or social position meant nothing to him. Went to Oxford, you know, but soon after that he took off and nobody knew if he was alive or dead for years.'

'And now he's back in that little place by the roadside.'

'Aye, it's a rum 'un, isn't it?'

It was a rum 'un indeed – one of the strangest stories I'd ever heard, and it was never far from my mind over the following weeks. I kept wondering how the old man and his cat were getting on in that igloo, and if the kittens had arrived yet? But they couldn't have – I was sure he would have let me know.

I did hear from him at last one stormy evening.

'Mr Herriot, I am telephoning from the farm. Emily has not yet produced those kittens, but she is . . . very large and has lain trembling all day and won't eat anything. I hate to trouble you on this horrible night but I know nothing about these things and she does look . . . most unhappy.'

I didn't like the sound of that, but I tried to sound casual. 'I think I'll just pop out and have a look at her, Mr Ireson.'

'Really – are you sure?'

'Absolutely. No bother. I'll see you soon.'

It was a strange, almost unreal scene as I stumbled through the darkness and parted the sacks forty minutes later. The wind and rain buffeted the tarpaulin walls and by the flickering light of the tilly lamp I saw Eugene in his chair, stroking Emily who lay in the basket by his side.

The little cat had swollen enormously – so much as to be almost unrecognisable and as I kneeled and passed my hand over her distended abdomen I could feel the skin stretched tight. She was absolutely bursting full of kittens, but seemed lifeless and exhausted. She was straining, too, and licking at her vulva.

I looked up at the old man. 'Have you some hot water, Mr Ireson?'

'Yes, yes, the kettle has just boiled.'

I soaped my little finger. It would only just go into the tiny vagina. Inside I found the cervix wide open and a mass beyond, only just palpable. Heaven only knew how many kittens were jammed in there, but one thing was certain. There was no way they could ever come out. There was no room for manoeuvre. There was nothing I could do. Emily turned her face to me and gave a faint miaow of distress and it came to me piercingly that this cat could die.

'Mr Ireson,' I said, 'I'll have to take her away immediately.'

'Take her away?' He said in a bewildered whisper.

'Yes. She needs a Caesarean operation. The kittens can't come out in the normal way.'

Upright in his chair, he nodded, shocked and only half comprehending. I grabbed the basket, Emily and all, and rushed out into the darkness. Then, as I thought of the old man looking blankly after me, I realised that my bedside manner had slipped badly. I pushed my head back through the sacks.

'Don't worry, Mr Ireson,' I said, 'everything's going to be fine.'

Don't worry! Brave words. As I parked Emily on the back seat and drove away, I knew I was damn worried, and I cursed the mocking fate which had decreed that after all of my airy remarks about cats effortlessly giving birth I might be headed for a tragedy. How long had Emily been lying like that? Ruptured uterus? Septicaemia? The grim possibilities raced through my mind. And why did it have to happen to that solitary old man of all people?

I stopped at the village kiosk and rang Siegfried.

'I've just left old Eugene Ireson. Will you come in and give me a hand? Cat Caesar and it's urgent. Sorry to bother you on your night off.'

'Perfectly all right, James, I'm not doing a thing. See you soon, eh?'

When I got to the surgery Siegfried had the steriliser bubbling and everything laid out. 'This is your party, James,' he murmured. 'I'll do the anaesthetic.' I had shaved the site of the operation and poised my scalpel over the grossly swollen abdomen when he whistled softly. 'My God,' he said, 'it's like opening an abscess!'

That was exactly what it was like. I felt that if I made an incision the mass of kittens would explode out in my face and, indeed, as I proceeded with the lightest touch through skin and muscle, the laden uterus bulged out alarmingly.

'Hell!' I breathed. 'How many are in here?'

'A fairish number!' said my partner. 'And she's such a tiny cat.'

Gingerly, I opened the peritoneum which, to my relief looked clean and healthy, then, as I went on, I waited for the jumble of little heads and feet to appear. But with increasing wonderment I watched my incision travel along a massive, coal black back and when I finally hooked my finger round the neck, drew forth a kitten and laid it on the table, I found that the uterus was otherwise empty.

'There's only one!' I gasped. 'Would you believe it?'

Siegfried laughed. 'Yes, but what a whopper! And alive, too. He lifted the kitten and took a closer look. 'A whacking great tom – he's nearly as big as his mother!'

As I stitched up and gave the sleeping Emily a shot of penicillin, I felt the tensions flow away from me in happy waves. The little cat was in good shape. My fears had been groundless. It would be best to leave the kitten with her for a few weeks, then I'd be able to find a home for him.

'Thanks a lot for coming in, Siegfried,' I said. 'It looked like a very dodgy situation at first.'

I could hardly wait to get back to the old man who, I knew, would still be in a state of shock at my taking away his beloved cat. In fact, when I passed through the sacking doorway, it looked as though he hadn't moved an inch since I last saw him. He wasn't reading, wasn't doing anything except staring ahead from his chair.

When I put the basket down by his side, he turned slowly and looked down wonderingly at Emily who was coming round from the anaesthetic and beginning to raise her head, and at the black newcomer who was already finding his private array of teats interesting.

'She's going to be fine, Mr Ireson,' I said, and the old man nodded slowly.

'How wonderful. How simply wonderful,' he murmured.

When I went to take out the stitches ten days later, I found a carnival atmosphere in the igloo. Old Eugene was beside himself with delight, while Emily, stretched in the back with her enormous offspring sucking busily, looked up at me with an expression of pride which bordered on the smug.

'I think we ought to have a celebratory cup of tea and one of my favourite buns,' the old man said.

As the kettle boiled, he drew a finger along the kitten's body. 'He's a handsome fellow, isn't he?'

'He certainly is. He'll grow up into a beautiful cat.'

Eugene smiled. 'Yes. I'm sure he will, and it will be so nice to have him with Emily.'

I paused as he handed me a bun. 'But just a minute, Mr Ireson. You really can't do with two cats here.'

'Why not?'

'Well, you take Emily into the village on a lead most days. You'd have difficulty on the road with two cats, and anyway you don't have room in here, do you?'

He didn't say anything, so I pressed on. 'A lady was asking me the other day if I could find her a black kitten. Many people ask us to find a specific pet for them, often to replace an older animal which has just died, and we always seem to have trouble obliging them, but this time I am delighted that I was able to say I knew the very one.'

He nodded slowly, and then after a moment's cogitation, said, 'I'm sure you're right, Mr Herriot. I hadn't really thought about it enough.'

'Anyway,' I said, 'she's a very nice lady and a real cat lover. He'll have a very good home. He'll live like a little sultan with her.'

He laughed. 'Good . . . good . . . and maybe I'll hear about him now and then?'

'Absolutely. I'll keep you posted regularly.' I could see I had got over the hurdle nicely and I thought I'd change the subject. 'By the way, I meant to tell you, I saw your brother for the first time not so long ago.'

'Cornelius?' He looked at me expressionlessly. We had never mentioned the subject of his brother before. 'And what did you think of him?'

'Well . . . he didn't look very happy.'

'He wouldn't. He is not a happy man.'

'That's the impression I got. And yet he's got so much.'

The old man smiled gently. 'Yes, but there are so many things he hasn't got.'

I took a sip at my tea. 'That's right. For instance, he hasn't got Emily!'

'Very true! In fact I was about to say that but I thought you might think me silly.' He threw back his head and laughed. A merry, boyish laugh. 'Yes, I have Emily, the all-important thing! I'm so glad we agree about that. Come now, do have another bun.'

41

'Ooh! Aaah! Oooh! Ya bugger, 'erriot! What the hell 'ave ye done?' Nat Briggs staggered round the calf pen clutching his left buttock, and glaring at me in fury.

'Sorry, Nat,' I said, holding up the syringe loaded with Strain 19 abortion vaccine. 'I'm afraid you fell right on to my needle.'

'Fell on? You stuck the bloody thing right up me arse, that's what you mean!' He was a big man with a habitually glowering expression, but at the moment he looked positively murderous. He had been holding the calf's head as I was about to make the injection and the animal had swung round at the wrong moment.

I tried a placatory smile. 'No really, Nat. It was just a little prick.'

'Don't give me that!' The big man arched his back, kneaded his buttock and groaned. 'Ah felt it go right in!'

His rage was not allayed by the peals of merriment from his comrades, Ray and Phil. The three were long-time workers on Sir Eustace Lamburn's farm and we knew each other well, but Nat was the odd man out. The other two were always cheerful and ready for a joke but Nat was surly and seemed to carry a permanent chip on his shoulder.

A lot of my work consisted of preventive injections and in the many wrestling matches with beasts packed in pens or down passages my needles did occasionally score a bull's-eye in human rather than animal flesh. The most common victim was myself because my patients rarely stood still and with one hand pinching the skin and the other poising the syringe an inch away, it was the easiest thing in the world to pierce my hand. The vet coming to grief either in this way or by getting toes stood on was invariably good for a laugh and there was always an outburst of hilarity as I yelped and hopped around, but having it happen to the dour Nat was nearly as good, especially as I had found my target in his backside.

'Aye, ye can laugh,' snarled the big man, 'but what's goin' to happen now? Ah've had a bloody dose of that abortion stuff, and what's that goin' to do to me?'

'You're not in calf are ye, Nat, lad?' giggled Phil. 'They say that vaccine's only dangerous to pregnant cows, but ah can't see you slippin' your calf.' There was another eruption of mirth from the two.

Briggs stuck out his jaw. 'It's awright you talkin' but that's mucky stuff. It could do summat inside me.'

'Look, Nat,' I said, 'you haven't had a dose of anything.' I held up the syringe showing the full 5 cc dose within. 'You've just had a prick from the needle. You might be a bit sore and I do apologise, but it can't do you any harm.'

'That's what you say, 'erriot, but we'll see. Any road, I'm keepin' clear of you. Somebody else can hold the rest of the buggers.'

Ray clapped him on the shoulder. 'Never mind, Nat. You've just got married, so you'll be well looked after. Your new missus'll get you a cushion whenever you want to sit down.'

There was no doubt that the little accident made the day for

Phil and Ray, but for a long time afterwards I had to suffer complaints from their cantankerous colleague every time I visited the Lamburn farm. It transpired that the buttock had swelled up and remained painful for a long time, causing immense inconvenience, but I was sure the rigmarole was exaggerated and I paid little attention until one day a vastly more serious charge was laid at my door.

Nat Briggs pushed his irascible face close to mine. 'Ah'm goin' to tell tha summat, 'erriot. You've stopped me ever havin' a family.'

'What!'

'Aye, ah'm not jokin'. Missus and me have been trying for a long time but there's no sign of anything happenin'. The doctor doesn't know why, but ah do! It's your bloody injection!'

'Oh, come on, Nat, that's ridiculous. How could that little accident possibly have such an effect?'

'How could it? Ah'll tell you! That bloody stuff you injected into me was to do with abortion and breedin' and all that sort o' thing. It stands to reason that you've stopped me and the missus ever havin' kids!'

I couldn't believe what I was hearing. I pleaded and expostulated, but the man was in deadly earnest. I had ruined his life and he'd never forgive me.

His mates didn't help.

'Don't listen to 'im, Mr Herriot,' cried Ray. 'He can't do it properly – he's only makin' excuses.' More laughter and coarse comments followed.

Despite the jocularity, I found the thing upsetting because it wasn't only on the farm that I had trouble. I never knew when I was going to run into the man. I received dirty looks from Briggs in Darrowby market place, and in the evenings when I was sipping a soothing beer in some country inn it shattered my peace when I found his disapproving gaze trained on me.

Over many months my visits to the Lamburn farm were uncomfortable. The leg-pulling had stopped, but I sensed the hostility from Briggs at all times. He rarely mentioned the matter, but the thing was accepted between us. I was responsible for his permanent sterility and that was that.

*

A long time after the abortion incident I was back on the farm treating a batch of beasts with pneumonia. It was the usual rodeo with about twenty strong young cattle packed in a penned-off corner of the fold yard. I was poising my syringe charged with antibiotic as the men squeezed their way among the crush. Briggs was hanging on to a particularly wild stirk, his back towards me and I'll never know if he was thrown back or if one of the other men nudged my arm because, next moment, he let out an anguished yell.

'Ya rotten bugger, 'erriot, you've done it again!' He staggered about, clutching his behind and staring wide-eyed at me.

I couldn't believe it. Surely history couldn't repeat itself so exactly. But there was no doubt about it, the scene was the same. Briggs bellowing and clutching his buttock, the other two men falling around laughing, myself transfixed in horror.

Still grasping his backside, Briggs turned on me, his fifteen stones hanging over me menacingly. 'What's *this* stuff goin' to do to me, eh?' he barked. 'You've done me enough damage, ya bugger, with that fust lot, but what am I goin' to suffer now?' He glowered at me.

'Nat, I'm truly sorry, but I can only tell you again that it can't possibly do you any harm. There's only antibiotic in the syringe – like penicillin only stronger.'

'Ah don't care a bugger what it is – it's meant to go into the bloody beast, not me. Ah'm bloody fed up with you, 'erriot, doin' the same thing to me again.'

'It's not the same, Nat,' cried Phil. 'You got it in the right cheek this time. Mr Herriot's just levellin' you up – I've allus said he was a tidy worker and it's only natural 'e would want to square the job up.' He and Ray abandoned themselves to helpless mirth.

After that incident, I was grateful that Sir Eustace's livestock had a long spell of good health and I was able to pass the few visits which came up on to Siegfried. It was nearly a year later before the three men and I were together again. As we carried on with our work, I was relieved to find that Briggs was not particularly unfriendly. Whereas the last time I thought he had been going to hit me, now he caught and held the struggling animals without comment.

During a moment's respite, as I refilled my syringe, Ray piped up. 'We've got a bit o' news for you, Mr Herriot.'

'Oh yes?'

'Aye, red 'ot news. Nat's become a dad!'

'Hey, that's great! Congratulations, Nat! What is it – boy or a girl?'

Fatherhood seemed to have mellowed the big man because a sheepish smile spread over his face. 'Twins,' he said proudly. 'Boy and a girl!'

'Well – terrific. You can't do better than that!'

Phil broke in. 'We've been tellin' him, Mr Herriot. He blamed you for stoppin' the job with that first injection you gave 'im. Well, the second jab must have been the antidote!'

42

'Something for you to think about, James,' Siegfried said one day as he closed the appointments book and rose from the desk.

He was unusually serious and I looked at him in surprise. 'What's that?'

'Well, I know you've had many happy years at Rowan Garth but you've always had an ambition to live right out in the country in a village.'

'That's right – some time in the future, anyway.'

'Well, there's a grand little place – High Field House – coming up for sale in Hannerly and I think it's something special. I'm sure it will soon be snapped up – maybe you'd care to have a look.'

It gave me a jolt. I had certainly nourished this idea for a long time, but as one who hated change of any kind I had never got further than regarding it as a distant dream. Now I was suddenly brought right up against it.

I rubbed my chin. 'I don't know – I wasn't thinking about it yet for a while. Maybe some day . . .'

'James, it takes a lot to stir you into action.' My partner wagged a finger at me. 'But I tell you this, that day will come some time and when it does you will start to thrash around and you'll never find anything better than this place I'm talking about. There isn't a prettier village than Hannerly and the house is ideal for you.'

I felt trapped at the suggestion. Siegfried knew me so well. But as the hours passed and my mind went through its usual gradual adjustment I finally came round sufficiently to mention the proposition to Helen.

My wife was much less diffident than me. 'Let's have a look,' she said.

We did have a look, right away, spurred by Helen's better developed sense of urgency. I knew Hannerly well, sitting as it did right in the heart of our practice. It was tiny; a peaceful backwater of a dozen houses, several of them farms, tucked into the sheltering fellside and strung along a quiet little road which led nowhere in particular. It was beautiful, but not with the chocolate box prettiness of the tourist villages. No shop, no pub, no street lights. To me, it was a secret corner of Yorkshire, a little tableau in stone of that stern and lovely county.

The doctor who was leaving showed us round. The house was modest but charming, resting on the face of its own field, a steeply sloping pasture where sheep grazed. An extensive lawn stretched down to a swiftly running beck which widened into a pond where a score of mallard duck floated serenely and great willows bent their branches towards the water.

Afterwards, in the May sunshine, Helen and I climbed with our dog Dinah behind the house, up the grassy bank, past trees heavy with blossom, then over a stile to a lofty green plateau which seemed to overlook the whole world.

We flopped on to the grass and from our eyrie we looked down past the sheep unhurriedly cropping the grass to the house lying below us. Behind us was a great crescent of tree-covered hillside with the rim of the high moorland peeping above the trees. This majestic sweep curved away to a headland where a tall cliff dominated the scene – a huge friendly slab of rock gleaming in the sunshine. Away in the other direction, over the roofs of the hamlet, there was a heart-lifting glimpse of the great wide plain of York and the distant hills beyond.

After a cold spring, the whole countryside had softened and the air had a gentle warmth, rich with the scents of May blossom and the medley of wild flowers which speckled the grass. In a little wood to our right a scented lake of bluebells flooded the shady reaches of the trees.

As we sat there, three squirrels hopped one after another from a tall sycamore and, pursued optimistically by fat Dinah, flitted, quick and light as air, over the greensward and disappeared behind a rise, leaving her effortlessly behind.

Helen voiced my thoughts. 'Living here would be heaven.'

We almost ran down the hill to the house and closed the deal with the doctor. There were none of the traumas of our previous house-buying efforts; a shake of the hand and it was over.

Helen's words were prophetic. It was a sad moment when we had to leave the happy memories of Rowan Garth behind, but once we were installed in High Field we realised that living in Hannerly was heaven indeed. At times I could hardly believe our luck. To be able to sit outside our front door, drinking tea in the sunshine and watching the mallard splashing and diving on our pond; with the hillside before us aflame with gorse and, away above, that changeless cliff face smiling down. And to live always in a quiet world where the silence at night was almost palpable.

Picking my torchlit way with Dinah on our nocturnal strolls I could hear nothing except the faintest whisper of the beck murmuring its eternal way under the stone bridge. Sometimes on these nightly walks, a badger would scuttle across my path, and under the stars I might see a fox carrying out a stealthy exploration of our lawn.

One morning on an early call just after dawn, I surprised two roe deer in the open and watched enthralled as they galloped at incredible speed across the fields and, clearing the fences like steeplechasers, plunged into the woods.

Here in Hannerly, just a few miles from Darrowby, there was the ever present thrill for Helen and me that we were living on the edge of the wild.

43

'By God, ah's sweatin'!' Albert Budd gasped as he collapsed his sixteen stones onto a chair next to me and wiped his face with a bright red-spotted kerchief. Then he gave me an anguished look, 'And ah know ah'm goin' to start fartin' in a minute.'

'What!' I stared at him in alarm. We had just finished a set of quadrilles at Calum's newly formed Highland dancing club in the village hall, and I was puffing, too, as I rested down next to the young farmer. 'Really? Are you sure?'

'Aye, nothin' surer. When Calum roped me in for this dancin', I didn't know there'd be all this jumpin' and jogglin', and I've just had a bloody good feed with three Yorkshire puddin's. This is murder!'

I didn't know what to say but I tried to be reassuring. 'Just sit quietly for a bit – I expect you'll be all right.'

Albert shook his head. 'No chance! I can feel it comin' on.. He's a bugger is Calum. He came in and grabbed me as soon as I'd finished me dinner. Me mother allus gives me a special do on a Wednesday night after I get back from Houlton market – a few good slices o' beef, sprouts and taties and, like I said, three Yorkshire puddin's and a smashin' spotted dick and custard. I'd had a few pints at the Golden Lion, too, and I was just goin' to put me feet up for half an hour when he walked into the house. Said I had to come with him, but I thought the dancin' would be like Victor Sylvester on the television.'

The stab of pity I felt for the poor chap's predicament was sharpened by the fact that everybody else in the hall was having a wonderful time. Calum's persuasive energies had obviously been successful and there was a good turnout of the local people forming up for an eightsome reel as the gramophone poured out Jimmy Shand's foot-twitching beat.

Helen and I had gladly fallen in with the dancing idea and this was our third visit. With my Glasgow upbringing, I had done it all before at school and parties, but I was rusty and had forgotten some of the steps. However, to the majority of the company – farmers, school-teachers, doctors, and a good cross-section of local people – the whole business was strange and new. But they were definitely fun to learn, and at times the loud laughter almost drowned the music.

I could understand that Albert didn't find it funny at all. He was about twenty-five and lived with a doting mother who looked after him far too well. He was one of the many young farmers who had formed a friendship with the ebullient new vet and were eager to join him in his activities, but this Scottish dancing was definitely not his scene.

I had often noted that there weren't many fat chaps among the farmers but Albert was a striking exception. Six feet three, beacon-faced and with an enormous belly which he somehow managed to carry round his milking, hay-making and other farming chores. His appetite was legendary in the district and he was a constant menace to those carvery restaurants where you could pay a set amount and eat as much as you liked.

He looked acutely uncomfortable at this moment, resting his

hands on his vast stomach and gazing at me with intensely worried eyes.

I could sympathise with him. I had seen his streaming face bouncing aimlessly above the crowd in the quadrilles and there was no doubt he must be suffering.

'Ah tell ye this, Jim,' he went on, 'if I have to do any more jumpin' around I've had it. I'm goin' to start fartin', and when ah do ah can't stop!'

'Oh dear, I'm sorry, Albert. It's a bit awkward for you with all these ladies around.'

I hadn't meant to be cruel but he stared at me in horror. 'Oh 'ell!' he groaned, then, 'By God, I'm startin'! I'm gettin' out – I'm off 'ome!'

He was about to heave himself off his chair when the curate's young wife came over.

'Really, Mr Budd,' she said, with mock disapproval, 'we can't have you sitting against the wall when we need a man for this reel.'

Albert gave her a ghastly smile. 'Nay . . . nay . . . thank ye. I was just . . .'

'Oh, come now, you mustn't be shy. Most of us are still learning.' She put out her hand and Albert gave me a last despairing glance before he was led onto the floor.

His eyes registered acute anxiety as he was stationed between the curate's wife and a pretty young teacher from Darrowby Infants' School, but there was no escape. The gramophone sounded the opening chord, they bowed, then they were off, skipping round hand in hand one way and then the other. I watched in morbid fascination as he halted and faced his partner. On my God, they were starting the pas de bas! That was fatal! For a few moments I watched the tortured face bob-bob-bobbing up and down, the great belly quivering like a blancmange as the music reverberated round the hall then I just couldn't look any longer.

I tore my eyes away and as I searched for some distraction among the dancing throng, it struck me that all this jollity was another example of something new which Calum had brought to Darrowby. These people were just a few of the many on whom he had laid his hand. I looked at him now, the tall, black-moustached figure, magnificent as any highland chieftain in his kilt, leaping high, kicking out his feet, toes pointed in the classical manner while Deirdre, tartan-sashed and graceful, glided expertly among the stumbling rookies.

The thought recurred that Calum had an irresistible attraction for a large number of people and he had brought fresh, meaningful angles into their lives, yet there seemed always to be a faint spice of danger for those who followed closely in his beguiling wake – whether it be myself on that bare-backed cart horse, Siegfried with the Dobermanns and now the hapless Albert jogglin' in agony out on that floor.

44

'Look at that, Jim! Surely that's a stray cat. I've never seen it before.' Helen was at the kitchen sink, washing dishes, and she pointed through the window.

Our new house in Hannerly had been built into a sloping field. There was a low retaining wall, chest high, just outside the window and, behind, the grassy bank led from the wall top up to some bushes and an open log shed perched about twenty yards away. A lean little cat was peering warily from the bushes. Two tiny kittens crouched by her side.

'I think you're right,' I said. 'That's a stray with her family and she's looking for food.'

Helen put out a bowl of meat scraps and some milk on the flat top of the wall and retired to the kitchen. The mother cat did not move for a few minutes, then she advanced with the utmost caution, took up some of the food in her mouth and carried it back to her kittens.

Several times she crept down the bank, but when the kittens tried to follow her, she gave them a quick 'get back' tap with her paw.

We watched, fascinated, as the scraggy, half-starved creature made sure that her family had eaten before she herself took anything from the bowl. Then, when the food was finished, we quietly opened the back door. But as soon as they saw us, cat and kittens flitted away into the field.

'I wonder where they came from,' Helen said.

I shrugged. 'Heaven knows. There's a lot of open country round here. They could have come from miles away. And that mother cat doesn't look like an ordinary stray. There's a real wild look about her.'

Helen nodded. 'Yes, she looks as though she's never been in a house, never had anything to do with people. I've heard of wild cats like that who live outside. Maybe she only came looking for food because of her kittens.'

'I think you're right,' I said as we returned to the kitchen. 'Anyway, the poor little things have had a good feed. I don't suppose we'll see them again.'

But I was wrong. Two days later, the trio reappeared. In the same place, peeping from the bushes, looking hungrily towards the kitchen window. Helen fed them again, the mother cat still fiercely forbidding her kittens to leave the bushes, and once more they darted away when we tried to approach them. When they came again next morning, Helen turned to me and smiled.

'I think we've been adopted,' she said.

She was right. The three of them took up residence in the log shed and after a few days the mother allowed the kittens to come down to the food bowls, shepherding them carefully all the way. They were still quite tiny, only a few weeks old. One was black and white, the other tortoiseshell.

Helen fed them for a fortnight, but they remained unapproachable creatures. Then one morning, as I was about to go on my rounds, she called me into the kitchen.

She pointed through the window. 'What do you make of that?'

I looked and saw the two kittens in their usual position under the bushes, but there was no mother cat.

'That's strange,' I said. 'She's never let them out of her sight before.'

The kittens had their feed and I tried to follow them as they ran away, but I lost them in the long grass, and although I searched all over the field there was no sign of them or their mother.

We never saw the mother cat again and Helen was quite upset.

'What on earth can have happened to her?' she murmured a few days later as the kittens ate their morning meal.

'Could be anything,' I replied. 'I'm afraid the mortality rate for wandering cats is very high. She could have been run over by a car or had some other accident. I'm afraid we'll never know.'

Helen looked again at the little creatures crouched side by side, their heads in the bowl. 'Do you think she's just abandoned them?'

'Well, it's possible. She was a maternal and caring little thing and I have a feeling she looked around till she could find a good home for them. She didn't leave till she saw that they could fend for themselves and maybe she's returned to her outside life now. She was a real wild one.'

It remained a mystery, but one thing was sure: the kittens were installed for good. Another thing was sure: they would never be domesticated. Try as we might, we were never able to touch them, and all our attempts to wheedle them into the house were unavailing.

One wet morning, Helen and I looked out of the kitchen window at the two of them sitting on the wall, waiting for their breakfast, their fur sodden, their eyes nearly closed against the driving rain.

'Poor little things,' Helen said, 'I can't bear to see them out there, wet and cold, we *must* get them inside.'

'How? We've tried often enough.'

'Oh, I know, but let's have another go. Maybe they'll be glad to come in out of the rain.'

We mashed up a dish of fresh fish, an irresistible delicacy to cats. I let them have a sniff and they were eager and hungry, then I placed the dish just inside the back door before retreating out of sight. But as we watched through the window the two of them sat motionless in the downpour, their eyes fixed on the fish, but determined not to go through the door. That, clearly, was unthinkable.

'All right, you win,' I said and put the food on the wall where it was immediately devoured.

I was staring at them with a feeling of defeat when Herbert Platt, one of the local dustmen, came round the corner. At the sight of him the kittens scurried away and Herbert laughed.

'Ah see you've taken on them cats. That's some nice stuff they're gettin' to eat.'

'Yes, but they won't come inside to get it.'

He laughed again. 'Aye, and they never will. Ah've know'n that family o' cats for years, and all their ancestors. I saw that mother cat when she first came, and before that she lived at awd Mrs Caley's over the hill and ah remember that 'un's mother before her, down at Billy Tate's farm. Ah can go back donkey's years with them cats.'

'Gosh, is that so?'

'Aye, it is, and I've never seen one o' that strain that would go inside a house. They're wild, real wild.'

'Ah well, thanks, Herbert, that explains a lot.'

He smiled and hoisted a bin. 'Ah'll get off, then, and they can finish their breakfast.'

'Well, that's it, Helen,' I said. 'Now we know. They're always going to be outside, but at least we can try to improve their accommodation.'

The thing we called the log shed, where I had laid some straw for them to sleep, wasn't a shed at all. It had a roof, but was open all down one side, with widely spaced slats on the other three sides. It allowed a constant through-wind which made it a fine place for drying out the logs but horribly draughty as a dwelling.

I went up the grassy slope and put up a sheet of plywood as a wind-break. Then I built up a mound of logs into a protective zariba around the straw bed and stood back, puffing slightly.

'Right,' I said. 'They'll be quite cosy in there now.'

Helen nodded in agreement, but she had gone one better. Behind my wind-break, she put down an open-sided box with cushions inside. 'There now, they needn't sleep on the straw any more. They'll be warm and comfortable in this nice box.'

I rubbed my hands. 'Great. We won't have to worry about them in bad weather. They'll really enjoy coming in here.'

From that moment the kittens boycotted the shed. They still came for their meals every day, but we never saw them anywhere near their old dwelling.

'They're just not used to it,' Helen said.

'Hmm.' I looked again at the cushioned box tucked in the centre of the encircling logs. 'Either that, or they don't like it.'

We stuck it out for a few days, then, as we wondered where on earth the kittens could be sleeping, our resolve began to crack. I went up the slope and dismantled the wall of logs. Immediately the two little creatures returned. They sniffed and nosed round the box and went away again.

'I'm afraid they're not keen on your box either,' I grunted as we watched from our vantage point.

Helen looked stricken. 'Silly little things. It's perfect for them.'

But after another two days during which the shed lay deserted, she went out and I saw her coming sadly down the bank, box in one hand, cushions under her arm.

The kittens were back within hours, looking round the place, vastly relieved. They didn't seem to object to the wind-break and settled happily in the straw. Our attempts to produce a feline Hilton had been a total failure.

It dawned on me that they couldn't bear to be enclosed, to have their escape routes cut off. Lying there on the open bed of straw, they could see all around them and were able to flit away between the slats at the slightest sign of danger.

'Okay, my friends,' I said, 'that's the way you want it, but I'm going to find out something more about you.'

Helen gave them some food and once they were concentrating on the food, I crept up on them and threw a fisherman's landing net over them and after a struggle I was able to divine that the tortoiseshell was a female and the black and white a male.

'Good,' said Helen, 'I'll call them Olly and Ginny.'

'Why Olly?'

'Don't really know. He looks like an Olly. I like the name.'

'Oh, and how about Ginny?'

'Short for Ginger.'

'She's not really ginger, she's tortoiseshell.'

'Well, she's a bit ginger.'

I left it at that.

Over the next few months they grew rapidly and my veterinary mind soon reached a firm decision. I had to neuter them. And it was then that I was confronted for the first time with a problem which was to worry me for years – how to minister to the veterinary needs of animals which I was unable even to touch.

The first time, when they were half grown, it wasn't so bad. Again I slunk up on them with my net when they were feeding and managed to bundle them into a cat cage from which they looked at me with terrified and, I imagined, accusing eyes.

In the surgery, as Siegfried and I lifted them one by one from the cage and administered the intravenous anaesthetic, I was struck by the fact that although they were terror-stricken at being in an enclosed space for the first time in their lives and by being grasped and restrained by humans, they were singularly easy to handle. Many of our domesticated feline patients were fighting furies until we had lulled them to sleep, and cats, with claws as well as teeth for weapons, can inflict a fair amount of damage. However, Olly and Ginny, although they struggled frantically, made no attempt to bite, never unsheathed their claws.

Siegfried put it briefly. 'These little things are scared stiff, but they're absolutely docile. I wonder how many wild cats are like this.'

I felt a little strange as I carried out the operations, looking down at the small sleeping forms. These were my cats yet it was the first time I was able to touch them as I wished, examine them closely, appreciate the beauty of their fur and colourings.

When they had come out of the anaesthetic, I took them home and when I released the two of them from the cage, they scampered up to their home in the log shed. As was usual following such minor operations, they showed no after effects, but they clearly had unpleasant memories of me. During the next few weeks they came close to Helen as she fed them but fled immediately at the sight of me. All my attempts to catch Ginny to remove the single little stitch in her spay incision were fruitless. That stitch remained for ever and I realised that Herriot had been cast firmly as the villain of the piece, the character who would grab you and bundle you into a wire cage if you gave him half a chance.

It soon became clear that things were going to stay that way because, as the months passed and Helen plied them with all manner of titbits and they grew into truly handsome, sleek cats, they would come arching along the wall top when she appeared at the back door, but I had only to poke my head from the door to send them streaking away out of sight. I was the chap to be avoided at all times and this rankled with me because I have always been fond of cats and I had become particularly attached to these two. The day finally arrived when Helen was able to stroke them gently as they ate and my chagrin deepened at the sight.

Usually they slept in the log shed but occasionally they disappeared to somewhere unknown and stayed away for a few days and we used to wonder if they had abandoned us or if something had happened to them. When they reappeared, Helen would shout to me in great relief, 'They're back, Jim, they're back!' They had become part of our lives.

Summer lengthened into autumn and when the bitter Yorkshire winter set in we marvelled at their hardiness. We used to feel terrible, looking at them from our warm kitchen as they sat out in the frost and snow, but no matter how harsh the weather, nothing would induce either of them to set foot inside the house. Warmth and comfort had no appeal for them.

When the weather was fine we had a lot of fun just watching them. We could see right up into the log shed from our kitchen, and it was fascinating to observe their happy relationship. They were such friends. Totally inseparable, they spent hours licking each other and rolling about together in gentle play and they never pushed each other out of the way when they were given their food. At nights we could see the two furry little forms curled close together in the straw.

Then there was a time when we thought everything had changed for ever. The cats did one of their disappearing acts and as day followed day we became more anxious. Each morning, Helen started her day with the cry of, 'Olly, Ginny' which always brought the two of them trotting down from their dwelling, but now they did not appear, and when a week passed and then two we had almost run out of hope.

When we came back from our half day in Brawton, Helen ran to the kitchen and looked out. The cats knew our habits and they would always be sitting waiting for her but the empty wall stretched away and the log shed was deserted. 'Do you think they've gone for good, Jim?' she said.

I shrugged. 'It's beginning to look like it. You remember what old Herbert said about that family of cats. Maybe they're nomads at heart – gone off to pastures new.'

Helen's face was doleful. 'I can't believe it. They seemed so happy here. Oh I hope nothing terrible has happened to them.' Sadly she began to put her shopping away and she was silent all evening. My attempts to cheer her up were half-hearted because I was wrapped in a blanket of misery myself.

Strangely, it was the very next morning when I heard Helen's usual cry, but this time it wasn't a happy one.

She ran into the sitting room. 'They're back, Jim,' she said breathlessly, 'but I think they're dying!'

'What? What do you mean?'

'Oh, they look awful! They're desperately ill – I'm sure they're dying.'

I hurried through to the kitchen with her and looked through the window. The cats were sitting there side by side on the wall a few feet away. A watery discharge ran from their eyes which were almost closed, more fluid poured from their nostrils and saliva drooled from their mouths. Their bodies shook from a continuous sneezing and coughing.

They were thin and scraggy, unrecognisable as the sleek creatures we knew so well and their appearance was made more pitiful by their situation in the teeth of a piercing east wind which tore at their fur and made their attempts to open their eyes even more painful.

Helen opened the back door. 'Olly, Ginny, what's happened to you?' she cried softly.

A remarkable thing then happened. At the sound of her voice, the cats hopped carefully from the wall and walked unhesitatingly through the door into the kitchen. It was the first time they had been under our roof.

'Look at that!' Helen exclaimed. 'I can't believe it. They must be really ill. But what is it, Jim? Have they been poisoned?'

I shook my head. 'No, they've got cat flu.'

'You can tell?'

'Oh yes, this is classical.'

'And will they die?'

I rubbed my chin. 'I don't think so.' I wanted to sound reassuring, but I wondered. Feline virus rhinotracheitis had a fairly low mortality rate, but bad cases can die and these cats were very bad indeed. 'Anyway, close the door, Helen, and I'll see if they'll let me examine them.'

But at the sight of the closing door, both cats bolted back outside.

'Open up again,' I cried and, after a moment's hesitation, the cats walked back into the kitchen.

I looked at them in astonishment. 'Would you believe it? They haven't come in here for shelter, they've come for help!'

And there was no doubt about it. The two of them sat there, side by side, waiting for us to do something for them.

'The question is,' I said, 'will they allow their *bête noire* to get near them? We'd better leave the back door open so they don't feel threatened.'

I approached inch by inch until I could put a hand on them, but they did not move. With a feeling that I was dreaming, I lifted each of them, limp and unresisting, and examined them.

Helen stroked them while I ran out to my car which held my stock of drugs and brought in what I'd need. I took their temperatures; they were both over 104, which was typical. Then I injected them with oxytetracycline, the antibiotic which I had always found best for treating the secondary bacterial infection which followed the initial virus attack. I also injected vitamins, cleaned away the pus and mucus from the eyes and nostrils with cotton wool and applied an antibiotic ointment. And all the time I marvelled that I was lifting and handling these yielding little bodies which I hadn't even been able to touch before apart from when they had been under the anaesthetic for the neutering ops.

When I had finished I couldn't bear the thought of turning them out into that cruel wind. I lifted them up and tucked them one under each arm.

'Helen,' I said, 'let's have another try. Will you just gently close the door.'

She took hold of the knob and began to push very slowly, but immediately both cats leaped like uncoiled springs from my arms and shot into the garden. We watched them as they trotted out of sight.

'Well, that's extraordinary,' I said. 'Ill as they are, they won't tolerate being shut in.'

Helen was on the verge of tears. 'But how will they stand it out there? They should be kept warm. I wonder if they'll stay now or will they leave us again?'

'I just don't know.' I looked at the empty garden. 'But we've got to realise they are in their natural environment. They're tough little things. I think they'll be back.'

I was right. Next morning they were outside the window, eyes closed against the wind, the fur on their faces streaked and stained with the copious discharge.

Again Helen opened the door and again they walked calmly inside and made no resistance as I repeated my treatment, injecting them, swabbing out eyes and nostrils, examining their mouths for ulcers, lifting them around like any long-standing household pets.

This happened every day for a week. The discharges became more purulent and their racking sneezing seemed no better; then, when I was losing hope, they started to eat a little food and, significantly, they weren't so keen to come into the house.

When I did get them inside, they were tense and unhappy as I handled them and finally I couldn't touch them at all. They were by no means cured, so I mixed oxytet soluble powder in their food and treated them that way.

The weather was even worse, with fine flakes of snow spinning in the wind, but the day came when they refused to come inside and we watched them through the window as they ate. But I had the satisfaction of knowing they were still getting the antibiotic with every mouthful.

As I carried on this long-range treatment, observing them daily from the kitchen, it was rewarding to see the sneezing abating, the discharges drying up and the cats gradually regaining their lost flesh.

It was a brisk sunny morning in March and I was watching Helen putting their breakfast on the wall. Olly and Ginny, sleek as seals, their faces clean and dry, their eyes bright, came arching along the wall, purring like outboard motors. They were in no hurry to eat; they were clearly happy just to see her.

As they passed to and fro, she ran her hand gently along their heads and backs. This was the kind of stroking they liked – not overdone, with them continually in motion.

I felt I had to get into the action and stepped from the open door.

'Ginny,' I said and held out a hand. 'Come here, Ginny.' The little creature stopped her promenade along the wall and regarded me from a safe distance, not with hostility but with all the old wariness. As I tried to move nearer to her, she skipped away out of reach.

'Okay,' I said, 'and I don't suppose it's any good trying with you either, Olly.' The black-and-white cat backed well away from my outstretched hand and gave me a non-committal gaze. I could see he agreed with me.

Mortified, I called out to the two of them. 'Hey, remember me?' It was clear by the look of them that they remembered me all right – but not in the way I hoped. I felt a stab of frustration. Despite my efforts I was back where I started.

Helen laughed. 'They're a funny pair, but don't they look

marvellous! They're a picture of health, as good as new. It says a lot for fresh air treatment.'

'It does indeed,' I said with a wry smile, 'but it also says something for having a resident veterinary surgeon.'

45

'Get back home to bed, James!' Siegfried was at his most imperious, chin jutting, arm outstretched, pointing to the door.

'No, I'm fine,' I said, 'honestly I am.'

'Well, you don't look so damn fine to me. About ready for Mallock's yard if you ask me. You're not fit to be out.'

His reference to the local knacker man was not inapposite. I had trailed into the surgery the day after one of my brucellosis attacks in the hope that a bit of work and exercise would make me feel better, but I knew that the weak, shivery object I had seen in my mirror didn't look much good for anything.

I dug my hands into my pockets and tried to stop shaking. 'I soon recover from these things, Siegfried, my temperature's normal and lying in bed gives me the willies. I'll be okay, I assure you.'

'James, maybe you'll be okay tomorrow but if you go out into the frozen country now and start stripping off you could drop down dead. I've got to be on my way now and I've no time to argue, but I *forbid* you to work! Understand? I tell you what. If you refuse to go home, you can go with Calum on his round. Just sit in the car with him – but don't do anything!' He lifted his medical bag and left the room at a half trot.

It didn't seem a bad idea. Better than lying in bed listening to the household noises going on through the closed door with the depressing feeling of being detached from the workaday world. I had always hated that.

I turned to our assistant. 'Is that all right, Calum?'

'Of course, Jim. I'll enjoy your company.'

I wasn't such bright company as I sat silently watching the drystone walls and the snow-covered hills roll past the car windows. When we arrived at the first farm, however, the gateway was blocked.

'We'll have to walk over a couple of fields, Jim,' Calum said. 'Perhaps you should stay here in the car.'

'No, I'll come with you.' I dragged myself out and we set off across the smooth unbroken blanket of white.

Even that short journey held something for my colleague. 'Look Jim, a fox has been along here. See his pad marks and the long trailing groove made by his brush. And those little holes – there are mice down there. The heat from their bodies melts the snow above them.' He identified the tracks of the various birds which had landed on the snow. They were just marks to me but a whole thrilling book to him.

The farmer, Edgar Stott, was waiting for us in the yard. Calum had never been to his farm and I introduced him. 'I'm not too grand today, so Mr Buchanan is going to see to your cow.'

Mr Stott was known as a 'clever bugger' among the local farmers. This didn't mean that they regarded him as intellectually superior, but rather as an aggressive know-all. In his own eyes, he was an outstanding wit and he did not endear himself to his neighbours by his propensity for taking people down a peg.

He was a big man and his bright little eyes in the fleshy face twinkled maliciously at Calum. 'Oh, we've got the reserve man on the job today. Vet wi' t'badger, eh? I've heard about you. We'll soon see how much ye know.'

In the byre, I sank down on a bale of straw, relishing the sweet bovine warmth. Mr Stott led Calum along the line of cows and pointed to a roan animal. 'Well, there she is. What d'ye make of her?'

Calum scratched the root of her tail and looked along the shaggy flank. 'Well now, what's the trouble, Mr Stott?'

'Ah, you're t'vitnery. I want *you* to tell *me*.'

My colleague smiled politely at the ancient joke. 'Let's put it another way. What are her symptoms? Is she off her food?'

'Aye.'

'Taking anything at all?'

'Just a bit.'

'How long has she been calved?'

'About a month.'

Calum took the temperature. Auscultated stomach and lungs. Pulled the head round and smelt the breath. Drew some milk on to his palm and smelt that, too, but he was clearly baffled. His enquiries about the animal's history were answered by grunts from Mr Stott and several times when Calum stood back and gazed blankly at the animal the farmer's mouth twisted in a sneer.

'Will you bring me a bucket of hot water, soap and a towel, please?' the young man asked.

He took off his shirt and thrust his arm first into the vagina, then deeply up into the rectum where I knew he was palpating the abdominal organs. Then he turned to the farmer who was standing, hands in pockets, observing him with sardonic interest.

'You know, this is very strange. Everything seems normal. Is there anything you haven't told me, Mr Stott?'

The big man hunched his shoulders and chuckled. 'Aye, there is summat I haven't told ye. There's nowt wrong wi' that beast.'

'Eh?'

'I said there's nowt wrong with 'er. She's as healthy as thee and me. I just wanted to see if you know owt about the job.' Then he burst into a roar of laughter and slapped his knee in glee.

As Calum, naked to the waist, his arm covered in faeces, looked back at him expressionlessly, the farmer tapped him on the shoulder.

'Now then, ah know you can take a joke, young man, Ha-ha-ha! There's nowt like a good laugh! Heh-heh-heh-heh!'

For several long seconds, Calum continued to stare at him, then his face relaxed slowly into a smile, and as he soaped and washed his arm in the bucket and pulled on his shirt, he began to giggle gently and finally he threw back his head and gave a great peal of mirth. 'Yes, you're right. Mr Stott! Ha-ha-ha! There's nowt like a good laugh. You're right, so right.'

The farmer led him along the byre. 'This is the cow you 'ave to see.'

As expected, he had already diagnosed the illness. Mr Stott knew everything. 'She's just got a touch o' slow fever.' This was the local name for acetonaemia, a metabolic disease easily cured. 'There's that sweet smell about 'er and she's losin' flesh.'

'Ah yes, Mr Stott, it sounds like it. I'll just check her over.' Still chuckling, he drew a few squirts from the udder, smelt the breath, took the temperature. All the time he kept murmuring, 'How funny, what a good joke,' then he began to whistle cheerfully. It was when he had his stethoscope on the stomach that the whistling slowed down and then stopped. He began to listen intently, grave-faced, moving from the left side of the cow to the right, then back again.

Finally he straightened up. 'Can you get me a spoon from the house, please.'

The grin faded from the farmer's face. 'A spoon? What the 'ell for? Is there summat wrong?'

'Oh, it's probably nothing. I don't want to worry you. Just get me the spoon.'

When the farmer returned, Calum recommenced his listening at the left side of the cow, only this time he kept tapping the lower ribs with the spoon.

'My God, it's there!' he exclaimed.

'What's there?' gasped the farmer. 'What are you talkin' about?'

'The tinkle.'

'The tinkle?'

'Yes, Mr Stott, it's the tinkling sound you hear in displacement of the abomasum.'

'Displacement . . . what the 'ell's that?'

'It is a condition where the fourth stomach or abomasum slips round from the right side to the left. I'm awfully sorry, but it's a very serious ailment.'

'But how about the sweet smell?'

'Well, yes, you do get that acetonaemia smell with a displacement. It's very easy to confuse the two things.'

'What's goin' to happen, then?'

Calum sighed. 'She'll have to undergo a very large operation. It requires two vets – one to open up the left side of the cow, the other to open the right. I'm afraid it's a very big job.'

'And it'll cost a lot of money, too, ah reckon!'

'Afraid so.'

The farmer took off his cap and began to churn his hair about. Then he swung round at me, slumped on my bale. 'Is all this I'm hearin' right? About this tinkle?'

'I'm sorry to have to tell you, Mr Stott, but it is,' I replied. 'That tinkling noise is classical. We get quite a lot of these cases now.'

He rounded on Calum again. 'Bloody 'ell! And will she be all right after the operation?'

The young man shrugged. 'Can't guarantee anything, I'm sorry to say. But most of them do quite well.'

'Most of 'em . . . and what if she doesn't have the operation?'

'She'll waste away and die. You can see she's losing flesh now. I'm really very sorry.'

The farmer stared, open mouthed and wordless, at the young man.

'I know how you feel, Mr Stott,' Calum said. 'A lot of farmers hate the idea of the big operation. It's a gory, messy business. You could send her in for slaughter if you like.'

'Send her in . . . ? She's a bloody good cow!'

'All right, then, let's go ahead with the job. Mr Herriot is quite ill and unfit to do anything, but I'll telephone Mr Farnon to come out with the equipment.'

The farmer, totally shattered, dropped down on my bale and his head sank on his chest. As he sat there, staring at the ground, Calum's face broke into a grin which almost reached his ears.

'It's okay, Mr Stott. I'm only kidding.'

'What?' the farmer gaped up at him uncomprehendingly.

'Only kidding. Just a little joke. Ha-ha! She's only got acetonaemia. I'll get some steroid from the car. A couple of shots and she'll be fine.'

As Mr Stott rose slowly from the bale, Calum wagged a finger at him.

'I know you like a joke. Ha-ha-ha-ha! As you say, there's nowt like a good laugh!'

46

As a cat lover, it irked me that my own cats couldn't stand the sight of me. Ginny and Olly were part of the family now. We were devoted to them and whenever we had a day out the first thing Helen did on our return was to open the back door and feed them. The cats knew this very well and were either sitting on the flat top of the wall, waiting for her, or ready to trot down from the log shed which was their home.

We had been to Brawton on our half-day and they were there as usual as Helen put out a dish of food and a bowl of milk for them on the wall.

'Olly, Ginny,' she murmured as she stroked the furry coats. The days had long gone when they refused to let her touch them. Now they rubbed against her hand in delight, arching and purring and, when they were eating, she ran her hand repeatedly along their backs. They were such gentle little animals, their wildness expressed only in fear, and now, with her, that fear had gone. My children and some from the village had won their confidence, too, and were allowed to give them a careful caress, but they drew the line at Herriot.

Like now, for instance, when I quietly followed Helen out and moved towards the wall. Immediately they left the food and retreated to a safe distance where they stood, still arching their backs but, as ever, out of reach. They regarded me without hostility but as I held out a hand they moved further away.

'Look at the little beggars!' I said. 'They still won't have anything to do with me.'

It was frustrating since, throughout my years in veterinary practice, cats had always intrigued me and I had found that this helped me in my dealings with them. I felt I could handle them more easily than most people because I liked them and they sensed it. I rather prided myself on my cat technique, a sort of feline bedside manner, and was in no doubt that I had an empathy with the entire species and that they all liked me. In fact, if the truth were told, I fancied myself as a cats' pin-up. Not so, ironically, with these two – the ones to whom I had become so deeply attached.

It was a bit hard, I thought, because I had doctored them and probably saved their lives when they had cat flu. Did they remember that, I wondered, but if they did it still didn't give me the right apparently to lay a finger on them. And, indeed, what they certainly did seem to remember was that it was I who had netted them and then shoved them into a cage before I neutered them. I had the feeling that whenever they saw me, it was that net and cage which was uppermost in their minds.

I could only hope that time would bring an understanding between us but, as it turned out, fate was to conspire against me for a long time still. Above all, there was the business of Olly's coat. Unlike his sister, he was a long-haired cat and as such was subject to constant tangling and knotting of his fur. If he had been an ordinary domesticated feline, I would have combed him out as soon as trouble arose but since I couldn't even get near him I was helpless. We had had him about two years when Helen called me to the kitchen.

'Just look at him!' she said. 'He's a dreadful sight!'

I peered through the window. Olly was indeed a bit of a scarecrow with his matted fur and dangling knots in cruel contrast with his sleek and beautiful little sister.

'I know, I know. But what can I do?' I was about to turn away when I noticed something. 'Wait a minute, there's a couple of horrible big lumps hanging below his neck. Take these scissors and have a go at them – a couple of quick snips and they'll be off.'

Helen gave me an anguished look. 'Oh, we've tried this before. I'm not a vet and anyway, he won't let me do that. He'll let me pet him, but this is something else.'

'I know that, but have a go. There's nothing to it, really.' I pushed a pair of curved scissors into her hand and began to call instructions through the window. 'Right now, get your fingers behind that big dangling mass. Fine, fine! Now up with your scissors and –'

But at the first gleam of steel, Olly was off and away up the hill. Helen turned to me in despair. 'It's no good, Jim, it's hopeless – he won't let me cut even one lump off and he's covered with them.'

I looked at the dishevelled little creature standing at a safe distance from us. 'Yes, you're right. I'll have to think of something.'

Thinking of something entailed doping Olly so that I could get at him, and my faithful nembutal capsules sprang immediately to mind. This oral anaesthetic had been a valued ally on countless occasions where I had to deal with unapproachable animals, but this was different. With the other cases, my patients had been behind closed doors but Olly was outside with all the wide countryside to roam in. I couldn't have him going to sleep somewhere out there where a fox or other predator might get him. I would have to watch him all the time.

It was a time for decisions, and I drew myself up. 'I'll have a go at him this Sunday,' I told Helen. 'It's usually a bit quieter and I'll ask Siegfried to stand in for me in an emergency.'

When the day arrived, Helen went out and placed two meals of chopped fish on the wall, one of them spiked with the contents of my nembutal capsule. I crouched behind the window; watching intently as she directed Olly to the correct portion, and holding my breath as he sniffed at it suspiciously. His hunger soon overcame his caution and he licked the bowl clean with evident relish.

Now we started the tricky part. If he decided to explore the fields as he often did I would have to be right behind him. I stole out of the house as he sauntered back up the slope to the open log shed and to my vast relief he settled down in his own particular indentation in the straw and began to wash himself.

As I peered through the bushes I was gratified to see that very soon he was having difficulty with his face, licking his hind paw then toppling over as he brought it up to his cheek.

I chuckled to myself. This was great. Another few minutes and I'd have him.

And so it turned out. Olly seemed to conclude that he was tired of falling over and it wouldn't be a bad idea to have a nap. After gazing drunkenly around him, he curled up in the straw.

I waited a short time, then, with all the stealth of an Indian brave on the trail, I crept from my hiding place and tiptoed to the shed. Olly wasn't flat out – I hadn't dared give him the full anaesthetic dose in case I had been unable to track him – but he was deeply sedated. I could pretty well do what I wanted with him.

As I knelt down and began to snip away with my scissors, he opened his eyes and made a feeble attempt to struggle, but it was no good and I worked my way quickly through the ravelled fur. I wasn't able to make a particularly tidy job because he was wriggling slightly all the time, but I clipped off all the huge unsightly knots which used to get caught in the bushes, and must have been horribly uncomfortable, and soon had a growing heap of black hair by my side.

I noticed that Olly wasn't only moving, he was watching me. Dazed as he was, he knew me all right and his eyes told me all. 'It's you again!' he was saying. 'I might have known!'

When I had finished, I lifted him into a cat cage and placed it on the straw. 'Sorry, old lad,' I said, 'but I can't let you go free till you've wakened up completely.'

Olly gave me a sleepy stare, but his sense of outrage was evident. 'So you've dumped me in here again. You don't change much, do you?'

By teatime he was fully recovered and I was able to release him. He looked so much better without the ugly tangles but he didn't seem impressed, and as I opened the cage he gave me a single disgusted look and sped away.

Helen was enchanted with my handiwork and she pointed eagerly at the two cats on the wall next morning. 'Doesn't he look smart! Oh, I'm so glad you managed to do him, it was really worrying me. And he must feel so much better.'

I felt a certain smug satisfaction as I looked through the window. Olly indeed was almost unrecognisable as the scruffy animal of yesterday and there was no doubt I had dramatically altered his life and relieved him of a constant discomfort, but my burgeoning bubble of self-esteem was pricked the instant I put my head round the back door. He had just started to enjoy his breakfast but at the sight of me he streaked away faster than ever before and disappeared far over the hill-top. Sadly, I turned back into the kitchen. Olly's opinion of me had dropped several more notches. Wearily I poured a cup of tea. It was a hard life.

47

The little dog stared straight ahead, immobile, as if glued to the kitchen table. He was trembling, apparently afraid even to move his head, and his eyes registered something akin to terror.

I had first seen him when Molly Minican, one of my neighbours in Hannerly, got him from Sister Rose's dog sanctuary a few months before and I had been instantly charmed by his shaggy mongrel appeal and his laughing-mouthed friendliness. And now this.

'When did Robbie start with this, Molly?' I asked.

The old lady put out a hand towards her pet, then drew back.

'Just found 'im this morning. He was running around, last night, right as a bobbin.' She turned a worried face to me. 'You know, he seems frightened you're going to touch 'im.'

'He really does,' I said. 'His whole body is rigid. It looks like an acute attack of rheumatism to me. Has he cried out in pain at all?'

The old lady shook her head. 'No, not a sound.'

'That's funny.' I ran my hand over the tense musculature of the little body and gently squeezed the neck. There was no response. 'He would have shown some sign of pain there with rheumatism. Let's see what his temperature says.'

It was like inserting the thermometer into a stuffed animal and I whistled softly as I saw the reading – 105.

'Well, we can forget about the rheumatism,' I said. 'The temperature is nearly always dead normal in those cases.'

I made a thorough examination of the little animal, palpating his abdomen, auscultating his heart and lungs. The heart was pounding, but that was almost certainly due to fear. In fact I couldn't find any abnormality.

'He must have picked up some infection, Molly,' I said. 'And with a fever like that it could possibly be his kidneys. Anyway, thank goodness we have antibiotics now. We can really do a bit of good in these conditions.'

As I gave Robbie his shot, I thought, not for the first time, that in a way it was a relief to find the high temperature. It gave us something to get at with our new drugs. A puzzling case with a normal temperature was inclined to make me feel a bit helpless, and at the moment I felt reasonably confident, even though I wasn't at all sure of my diagnosis.

'I'll leave these tablets for you. Give him one at midday, another at bedtime and another first thing in the morning. I'll have a look at him some time tomorrow.' I had the reassuring conviction that I was really blasting that temperature with the antibiotic. Robbie would be a lot better after twenty-four hours.

Molly seemed to think so too. 'Ah, we'll soon have 'im right.' She bent her white head over the dog and smiled. 'Silly feller. Worrying us like this.'

She was a spinster in her seventies, and had always struck me as the archetypal Yorkshire woman; self-contained and unfussy, but with a quiet humour which was never far away. I had been called when her last dog had been run over by a farm tractor and had arrived just as he was dying, and although it must have been a savage blow to a lone woman to lose her only companion, there had been no tears, just a fixed expression and a repeated slow stroking of the little body. Molly was strong.

She had taken my advice and visited Sister Rose's kennels where she found Robbie.

I lifted the dog from the table and put him down by his bed, but he just stood there and made no attempt to lie down. I felt another wave of bafflement as I looked at him.

I went over to the sink by the window to wash my hands and had to duck my head to see out into the garden. There was a rabbit there, sunning himself by a gnarled apple tree and when he spotted me through the glass he hopped away and disappeared through a hole in the ancient stone wall.

Everything about the tiny cottage was old; the low, beamed ceilings, the weathered stonework with its climbing ivy and clematis, the once red roof tiles which sagged dangerously above the two bedroom windows which could not have measured more than eighteen inches square.

I had to bend my head again under the door lintel as I took my leave, and I glanced back at Robbie, still standing motionless by the side of his bed. A little wooden dog.

Molly was in her garden when I visited next day.

'Well now, how's Robbie?' I asked, rather more breezily than I felt.

My spirits dropped as the old lady hesitated and then was clearly trying to find something encouraging to say.

'Maybe a little better . . . but not much.'

He wasn't a bit better, he was just the same, standing in the kitchen in the same attitude as the previous day. Still rigid, still trembling, and the frightened look in his eyes was replaced by a great lassitude.

I bent and stroked him. 'Can't he lie down at all?'

'Yes, but it's difficult for 'im. He's been in his bed for a few hours but when he gets out he's like this.'

I took the temperature. Still exactly 105. I hadn't even dented it with my antibiotic injection and tablets. With a feeling of bewilderment I repeated the injection, then I turned to Molly.

'I'd like to test his urine. When you carry him out to the garden to cock his leg, try to catch a little in a clean soup plate and put it in this bottle.'

Typically, Molly laughed. 'Aye, I'll try, but I might have a job.'

'Yes,' I said. 'It can be tricky, but I'm sure you'll manage. I'll only need very little.'

On the following day, Robbie was unchanged. Even the temperature was resolutely stuck on 105. The urine test was normal – no protein, nothing to indicate kidney trouble.

I switched to another antibiotic and took a blood sample which I sent to the investigation laboratory. The lab telephoned back that the sample was normal and after five daily visits and a negative X-ray examination the little dog had not improved.

I stood in the kitchen, looking down at my baffling patient. He was the picture of misery; utterly dejected, stiff and trembling. The grim reality was there before me. Unless I could pull something out of the bag, Robbie was going to die.

'I'll have to try something else, Molly,' I said. I had with me one of the new steroid drugs, dexamethasone, and I injected 1 cc.

'You must be sick of the sight of me, but I'll call tomorrow morning to see if this new stuff has done any good.'

Molly didn't wait until the next day. Her cottage was only about a hundred yards from my house and she was on my doorstep the same afternoon.

She was out of breath. 'There's a wonderful improvement, Mr Herriot!' she gasped. 'He's like another dog. I wish you'd come and see 'im!'

I was only too eager and practically trotted along the road. Robbie looked almost like the little dog I used to know so well. He was still stiff, but he could walk carefully over the kitchen floor and his tail gave a slow wag as he saw me. The trembling was gone and he had lost his terrified look.

My relief was tremendous. 'Has he eaten anything?'

'Yes, he had his nose in his bowl about two hours after you left.'

'Well, that's wonderful.' I took the temperature and it was 102 – on the way down at last. 'I'll still come tomorrow, because I think one more shot will put him absolutely right.'

It did indeed, and a week later it was good to see the little animal leaping around in his garden, playing with a stick. He was full of life, back to normal, and although it niggled me that I still had no idea what had ailed him, I was able to file away the whole episode comfortably in my mind as just another happy ending.

I was wrong. A month later, Molly arrived at my door, looking distressed. 'He's starting again, Mr Herriot!'

'What do you mean?'

'Same as before. Tremblin' and can't move!'

Once again, an injection of the steroid brought a rapid recovery, but it wasn't the end of the affair, it was only the beginning of a saga.

Over the next two years I fought a long battle with the mysterious condition. Robbie would be a normal, healthy looking animal for a few weeks, then the dreaded symptoms would suddenly reappear and Molly would rush along to my house, and when I opened the door she would be on the step, head on one side and an anxious half-smile on her face, saying, 'SOS, Mr Herriot, SOS.' Desperately worried though she was, she always tried to brighten the situation with a wry humour.

Each time it happened, I dashed to the cottage with my steroids. Sometimes the symptoms were very severe, being accompanied by gasping respiration, and I felt that I was saving the dog's life every time I treated him. I adopted various tactics along the way, the most successful being to supplement the injection with steroid tablets given regularly for a few days, then tailing off gradually before finally stopping. Then we would wait breathlessly until the next recurrence.

Sometimes nothing happened for many weeks and we relaxed, thinking we had won and the whole thing could be forgotten like a bad dream. Then Molly would be back again at my door, head on one side. 'SOS, Mr Herriot, SOS.'

It became part of our lives. Being a near neighbour I had always known Molly well, but now, during those frantic visits she talked about her life as I cradled a cup of tea in the kitchen by the tiny window with its trailing ivy and the branches of the apple tree beyond.

She had been in domestic service as a young girl and had lived in the cottage for over thirty years. She had been very ill some time ago and would have died but for a life-saving operation carried out in Brawton by the brilliant surgeon, Sir Charles Armitage.

Her face became radiant when she talked about Sir Charles. 'Eee, he's that clever and world famous, but he was so kind to me. I'm only a poor old body with no money, but I might 'ave been a queen. He couldn't do enough for me.'

There was another hero in her life – the actor, John Wayne. Whenever one of his films came to the little cinema in Darrowby, Molly would be there and when she discovered that I too was a Wayne fan, we had long discussions about his films. 'Oh, he's such a lovely man,' she would say, giggling at her own infatuation.

It was a warm friendship, but hanging over it at all times was the spectre of Robbie's recurring illnesses. I was at her cottage scores of times and of course I never charged her. She had only her old age pension and previously I had made a nominal charge, but now even that went out of the window. Often she pleaded with me to accept something, but it was obviously unthinkable. In return, she knitted little things for Helen and the children and gave us jars of her home-made tomato chutney.

When I look back over the years, that part of my life shines like a vivid thread running through the busy routine of my veterinary practice. Robbie's unique illness, Sir Charles Armitage, John Wayne and SOS.

At all times, I wondered at the little dog's forgiving nature. Every time I met him, I stuck a hypodermic needle into him. He must have felt like a pin cushion, but when he had recovered he always wagged his tail furiously when he saw me and rushed up, planting his paws on my legs and looking up at me in delight.

There came a time, however, when the attacks became more violent and more frequent. The little animal's distress on those occasions was pitiful to see and although I always managed to pull him round I was gradually having to face the grim fact that the battle was going to be a losing one.

The climax came at 3 a.m. one morning. I heard the bell ringing, pulled on a dressing-gown and went to the door. Molly was on the step again but this time she was unable to summon her half-humorous password of SOS.

'Will you come, Mr Herriot?' she gasped. 'Robbie's real bad.'

I didn't bother to dress, but grabbed my bag and hurried with her to the cottage. The little dog was in a terrible rigor, shaking, panting, hardly able to breathe. It was the worst attack yet.

'Will you put him to sleep, please,' Molly said quietly.

'You really want that?'

'Aye, it's the end of the road for 'im. I just know it. And I can't stand any more of it, Mr Herriot. I've not been too well myself, and it's getting me down.'

I knew she was right. As I injected the barbiturate into the vein and saw the little dog relax into his last repose, there was no doubt in my mind that I was doing the best thing in ending his suffering for ever.

As before, there were no tears. Just a quiet, 'Oh, Robbie, Robbie,' as she patted the shaggy little body.

I slumped into the kitchen chair where I had drunk so many cups of tea. Sitting there, in dressing-gown and slippers, I could hardly believe that the long struggle had ended this way.

'Molly,' I said after a minute, 'I'd really like to get to the bottom of this.'

She looked at me. 'You mean a post mortem?' She shook her head. 'No, no, nothing like that.'

There didn't seem to be anything I could do or say. I went out, leaving the mystery behind me, and as I walked through the moonlit garden, sick with failure and frustration, I reflected that it was a mystery which would never be solved.

I was soon swept along in the rush of my everyday work, but I found it difficult to put Robbie out of my mind. Inevitably, some patients of every vet die and, with dogs, heartache is always round the corner; their lives are too short. I knew I would not survive if I suffered along with the bereaved owners every time and I did my best to preserve a professional attitude. But it didn't always work and it didn't work with Robbie.

The association had gone on too long and the memories of

that little dog wouldn't go away. And what made it worse was that I had to pass Molly's cottage every day of my life, seeing her white head bobbing about in her garden where she used to play with Robbie. She looked very alone.

I had withheld my usual advice to 'get another dog', because the old lady's health was obviously failing and I knew she could not bring herself to start all over again.

Sadly, my fears were confirmed, and Molly died a few weeks after Robbie. That chapter was finally closed.

It was late afternoon, some time later that I came into the surgery and found Siegfried making up some medicine in the dispensary.

'Hullo, Siegfried,' I said, 'I've had a damned awful day.'

He put down the bottle he had filled. 'In what way, James?'

'Well, every damn thing seems to have gone wrong. Every case I revisited has got worse – none has improved – and a few people more or less suggested that I was a bloody awful vet.'

'Surely not. You're imagining things.'

'I don't think so. It started first thing this morning when I was examining Mrs Cowling's dog. It is a rather obscure case and I tried to spell out the various possibilities to her. She gave me a frosty look and said, "Well, the long and short of it is that you simply have no idea what is wrong with the animal!"'

'I shouldn't worry about that, James. She probably didn't mean anything.'

'You didn't see her face. But then I went out to see a ewe at George Grindley's. It was a pregnancy toxaemia and I was taking its temperature when, out of the blue, George said, "You know, you've never cured a single animal on my place. I hope you'll do better with this 'un."'

'But that's not true, James, I know it's not.'

'Maybe so, but he said it.' I ran my fingers through my hair. 'And after that I drove out to cleanse a cow at old Hawkin's. I'd just got out of the car when he looked at me under his brows and grunted, "Oh, it's you. My wife says it's always fatal when Mr Herriot comes." I must have looked a bit shattered because he patted me on the shoulder and said, "Mind you, she likes you as a man."'

'Oh dear. I'm sorry, James.'

'Thank you, Siegfried. I won't bore you any more, but it's been like that all day. And then right in the middle of it, I had to go through my own village and past poor old Molly Minican's cottage. There was an auctioneer there, selling off her furniture and her bits and pieces. There were all sorts of things piled up in her garden and it hit me again that her dog died without my having any idea what was wrong with him even though I treated him for two years. She knew I didn't know and she must have thought I was a dead loss. I think that was the lowest point of my hellish day.'

Siegfried spread his hands. 'Look, how many vets and doctors have lost patients without ever being sure of their diagnosis? You're not the only one. Anyway, we all have days like today, James, when nothing goes right. Every vet runs up against them now and then. You'll have a lot of good days to make up for it.'

I nodded good-bye and set off for home. My partner was trying to be kind, but I still felt low when I got to High Field and as I sat down at the tea table, Helen gave me a questioning look.

'What's the matter, Jim? You're very quiet.'

'Sorry, Helen, I'm afraid I won't be a barrel of laughs tonight.' I poured out my story.

'I thought it must be something to do with your work,' she said, 'but what's really getting you down is Molly Minican, isn't it?'

I nodded. 'That's right. She was a bit special. Seeing all her things lying in her garden brought everything back to me, and I don't like the thought that Molly died convinced I was a bit of a chump.'

'But she was always nice to you, Jim.'

'She was nice to everybody, me included. But I know that she must have felt that I had let her down. She's gone now, but I have this rotten feeling that in her heart she had a poor opinion of me and that's something I can never alter.'

Helen gave me a quizzical smile. 'I think I have something here that will make you feel better.' She left the room and I waited, mystified, until she came back with what looked like a framed picture under her arm.

'Peggy Ford in the village was at Molly's sale,' she said. 'She handed this in to me because it was hanging in the old lady's bedroom and she thought you'd be interested in it. Here, have a look.'

It wasn't a picture. It was a framed square of cardboard and across the top, in Molly's spidery writing, I read: 'My three favourite men.'

Underneath, gummed to the cardboard, were three photographs in a row. There was Sir Charles Armitage, John Wayne . . . and me.

48

It was the first time I had ever seen a man coming out of a house and *then* removing bicycle clips from his trouser legs.

I had been called to this cottage by a Mr Colwell to attend his dog and as I got out of the car I was surprised to see this man emerge, then, after looking back carefully, bend down to take off the clips. There was no sign of a bike anywhere.

'Excuse me,' I said, 'I hope you don't mind my asking, but why the clips?'

The man looked back again, grinned and spoke quietly. 'Now then, Mr Herriot, it's you, is it. I've just been in to read t'gas meter and I'm takin' precautions.'

'Precautions?'

'Aye, against the fleas.'

'Fleas!'

'Aye, that's right. They're canny folks, the Colwells, but the missus isn't ower particular and there's a lot of fleas in there.'

I stared at him. 'But . . . the clips . . . I still don't see . . .'

'Aye well,' said the man, laughing, 'they're to stop the fleas goin' up me legs inside me trousers.' He pocketed the clips and strode off round the corner to his next visit.

I stood by my car, chuckling to myself. Fleas up his legs! I'd never heard anything so daft. I had known that gas man for years and he'd always seemed perfectly normal, but clearly he suffered from an obsession. Like some people washing their hands all the time. Probably he put the clips on at every house. I went to the corner and looked along the row of cottages but he had disappeared.

It was incredible, the strange notions people got into their heads, but such whimsies had always fascinated me and a flea complex was something new. I just hoped the poor chap wasn't unhappy with a delusion like this, but I had heard him whistling cheerfully as he rounded the corner so I supposed it didn't bother him too much. I was still smiling as I walked back to my car and it was an expansive smile, because it was Thursday and this was my last visit before starting my half-day.

Though veterinary surgery was my life and I wouldn't have wanted to do anything else, the snag was that it never stopped – except on Thursday afternoons. On that special day I invariably felt lighthearted as soon as I awoke, knowing that by midday Helen and I would be off to Brawton, free as birds. A leisurely lunch at one of the town's splendid cafés then we would meet my pal, Gordon Rae the vet from Boroughbridge and his wife, Jean, fellow escapees from the telephone and the wellington boots. We would spend the afternoon shopping, followed by tea and the cinema. It doesn't sound much but to us it was a blessed relief.

The evening would be different this time since Helen had been given tickets for a concert by the Hallé Orchestra from the Miss Whitlings, pillars of the Darrowby Music Society. We would be returning home to change and then be making up a four with them for the concert. The conductor was my old hero, Sir John Barbirolli and the programme was mouth-watering. Coriolanus, Elgar Violin Concerto and Brahms' First.

I took a long contented breath as I knocked on the Colwells' door – in about an hour's time, we'd be off.

It was opened by the man of the house; sixtyish, collarless and unshaven, but with a welcoming smile.

'Come in, Mr 'erriot,' he cried, waving a courtly arm. 'I'm sorry we had to call you out, but we 'aven't no transport and our awd dog needs attention.'

'That's all right, Mr Colwell. I understand he's had a bump with a car?'

'Aye, he ran out in front of the post office van this mornin' and it sent him flyin'.' The smile vanished from his face and his eyes widened with anxiety. 'We hope it's nowt serious. Poor awd Roopy – we call 'im that because he's got a funny bark.'

The front door opened directly into the living room and the atmosphere was stuffier and more odoriferous than a cow byre. Dust lay thickly on the furniture and a colourful miscellany of newspapers, articles of clothing and food scraps littered the table and floor. Mrs Colwell was indeed not ower particular.

The lady herself appeared from the kitchen and greeted me with the same affability as her husband, but her eyes were red and swollen with weeping.

'Eee, Mr Herriot,' she quavered, 'we're that worried about Roopy. He's never ailed a thing all 'is life, but we're frightened we might lose 'im now.'

I looked at the dog stretched in a basket against the wall. He seemed to be a spaniel cross and he gazed at me with terrified eyes.

'Did he manage to walk inside after the accident?' I asked.

'Nay,' replied Mr Colwell. 'We had to carry 'im in.' He gulped. 'We think he might have a broken back.'

'Mmm, let's have a look.' I knelt by the basket and the Colwells knelt on either side of me. I pulled down Roopy's lower eyelid and saw a pink conjunctiva.

'He's a good colour. No sign there of internal injury.' I felt my way over all four legs, ribs and pelvis and found no fractures.

'Let's see if you can stand, old boy,' I said.

Gently I eased my hand underneath the dog's body and very carefully started to lift. He responded with a yowling protest which brought exclamations of anguish from his owners. 'Aw, poor awd Roopy!' 'Never mind, lad!' 'Oh, he's such a brave boy!' as they patted and caressed him.

I persevered and kept lifting until I had him standing shakily for a moment, then I let him down.

'Well, it seems he's got away with it,' I said. 'He's a bit bruised and you can see his pads are scuffed and sore, but I'm sure he's not seriously injured.'

Cries of joy went up from the Colwells and they redoubled their strokings and cooings while Roopy, his big spaniel eyes liquid and pathetic, gazed around him at each of us in turn. He was clearly milking the situation to its full.

The three of us got to our feet and I reached for my bag. 'I'm going to give him a couple of injections to relieve his discomfort and to help the sores on his pads.' I administered steroid and antibiotic and counted out some penicillin tablets. 'He's suffering from shock, too, but I think he's making the most of it.' I laughed and patted the shaggy head. 'You're an old soldier, Roopy.'

The Colwells joined in happily. 'Aye, you're right, Mr Herriot. He allus puts it on!' But again a tear stole down the lady's cheek. 'Eee, but it's such a relief to know we're not going to lose 'im.'

Then she quickly wiped her face with the back of her hand. 'We must celebrate with a cup o'tea. You've got time, Mr Herriot?'

Brawton beckoned but I couldn't say no. 'Right, thank you very much but it will have to be a quickie.'

The kettle was soon boiling and Mrs Colwell used both arms to make a sort of clearing in the table-top jungle where she deposited the cups. As I sipped my tea and looked at the friendly people laughing and gazing with love at their dog, I knew that the gas man had been right again. They were canny folks.

My departure had a triumphant quality as they ushered me out with repeated thanks and wavings of arms.

I shouted back as I boarded my car, 'Give me a ring in a couple of days and let me know how he's going on. I'm sure he'll be fine.'

I had only just driven round the corner when I felt a prickling round my ankles. Maybe those new socks were irritating me and I began to push them down. But the strange tingling and itching began to spread to my calves and I pulled in to the roadside and rolled up a trouser leg. My flesh was sprinkled with little black dots, but they were dots which hopped and jumped and bit, and they were working their way rapidly up my thighs. Oh my God, that gas man hadn't been so daft!

I wanted to get home with all speed but I got behind a couple of farm tractors with wide loads and was unable to overtake. By the time I reached High Field, the invasion had reached my chest and back and the maddening itch was setting me afire, making me wriggle around in my seat.

Helen was changing in readiness for Brawton and she turned in surprise as I galloped in to our bedroom.

'I have to get into the bath!' I shouted.

'Oh . . . had a dirty job?'

'No, I've got fleas!'

'*What!*'

'Fleas! Millions of them – they're all over me!'

'But . . . but . . . how . . .?'

'I'll tell you later. Please come and get my clothes and dump them in the washer. I'll need a complete change.'

In the bathroom I undressed and submerged myself, plunging my head repeatedly under the water. Helen came in and looked with horror at my heap of clothes with the agile insects leaping against the white of the shirt.

'Oooo . . . yuk-yuk-yuk!' she gasped as she grimaced and lifted each article by one corner and disappeared to the wash.

I felt as if I could have stayed in that bath for ever. The relief was enormous as I lay there, freed from the torture of the itch, watching in disbelief as the dark tormentors floated on the surface of the water. I wasn't going to take any chances. I emptied the bath and refilled it before having another long steep. I washed and scrubbed my hair again and again and when I finally climbed out and donned a completely new set of clothes I thanked heaven that my troubles were over. It was my first experience of such a thing and I hadn't realised how shattering it could be. I had often read about the suffering of people in foreign prisons lying on flea-ridden mattresses but I had never fully comprehended it until now.

When we at last set off for Brawton, it was difficult to recapture the carefree feeling which always settled on us each Thursday. The bizarre events of the morning were still too fresh in our minds. However, as we left the hills and began to bowl along the great plain of York with the familiar Thursday scenes rolling past the car windows, we began gradually to relax. Soon we would be at lunch, out of reach of our pressures, then, this evening, the particular joy of the Hallé Orchestra.

As a schoolboy in Glasgow I had actually met the legendary Barbirolli – it was before he was Sir John – and in rather odd circumstances. I was attending a special schools concert by the Scottish Orchestra in St Andrew's Hall. I went to the toilet in the interval and became aware that a white-tie and tailed figure was standing in the next stall to me. I looked up and was amazed and delighted to see that it was the great man himself. It was a strange place to meet, but he asked me how I was enjoying the music, what I had liked best and about myself. He was indeed the gracious, kindly man who became such a beloved figure throughout the world.

Since our meeting, I had followed his career through the years, from when he had succeeded Toscanini as conductor of the New York Philharmonic until now when he had been, since 1942, in charge of the great Hallé Orchestra. Over the years I had gone to his concerts whenever they were in reach and had watched him shrinking in size. He had always been small but now he was tiny and frail – but totally inspiring on the rostrum.

I was sharing these thoughts with Helen as our half-day euphoria mounted, and we were within a mile of Brawton when I stiffened in my seat and fell silent.

After a minute or so my wife looked at me. 'What's wrong? You've gone very quiet.'

I shifted position carefully. 'Oh, it's probably nothing, but I have a daft feeling that I've still got some fleas on me.'

'What! You can't have – not after two baths and a complete change! It's impossible!'

'I know it's impossible, but I tell you – I've got that same feeling.'

'Oh, it's just the after effects, Jim. Remember you were bitten all over.'

'I know, I know,' I grunted, 'but I'm pretty sure there's some fresh activity going on.'

She took my hand and smiled encouragingly. 'It's all in your mind. Try to think of something else.'

I did my best, but I was still wriggling when I mounted the stairs to Brown's café. The mingled cooking smells, the clatter of cutlery, the cheerful bustle and the welcoming smiles of the waitresses we knew so well had always sent my spirits soaring as though a great gong was signalling the beginning of our happy few hours, but today was different.

As we took our places and read through the good old-fashioned Yorkshire menu which had always delighted me – roast beef with Yorkshire pudding, plaice and chips, steak and kidney pie, steamed jam sponge, spotted dick and custard – my mind was churning and my smile was a fixed mask as I ordered.

Sipping my way through the delicious soup and toying with the meal, I was like a man in a bad dream as I tried to ignore the torture under my shirt.

Around the halfway stage, a couple threaded their way between the crowded tables and the man approached us.

'May we join you?' he asked politely. 'There's not a seat anywhere.'

'Of course,' I replied, digging up another smile. 'By all means.'

As they sat down it was easy to label them. A farmer and his wife out for the day like ourselves. They were in their fifties, with scrubbed, weathered faces and the man's bright tie and smart tweed jacket sat uneasily upon him. He reached a huge hand for the menu and studied it with his wife.

'Aye well,' he said, looking up at us. 'That were a good rain last night.'

That settled it, I thought as we nodded agreement. I didn't know them. Brawton was rather far for most of my farmers. They would probably be from Wharfedale.

My conjectures were cut short by Helen pressing her knee against mine. I turned to her and saw a look of horror on her face.

'There's one on your collar,' she muttered, then, 'Ooo, it's jumped!'

It had indeed jumped, right onto the middle of the white table cloth. As I sat helplessly, another one hopped out then another.

The farmer and his wife, who were clearly on the point of starting a friendly conversation, stared in amazement at the leaping objects. There was a terrible silence then the man spoke again.

'Ah, there's a table by the window, Eva,' he said, rising to his feet. 'That's where we usually sit. You'll excuse us, won't you.'

After they had gone we raced through our meal. I don't know how many more of the flitting creatures appeared on the table. I was too stunned to count and, looking back now, I have only the terrifying memory of the first few. We abandoned all idea of our dessert and instead of a happy discussion of the relative merits of ginger pudding and apple pie we called for our bill and fled.

We couldn't stay in Brawton to see Jean and Gordon. The bathroom at home was our only goal and, as I drove at top speed, images of the little terrors on that table cloth rose again and again in my mind. How could it possibly have happened? How had that second wave of fleas escaped all my precautions? To this day I have no answer, I only know it was so.

Back home, we repeated the morning's performance: the total submersion in the bath, Helen's finger-tip bearing away of my contaminated clothing and a complete change.

It was fortunate that I had reserved my 'good suit' for the concert because my limited wardrobe was running low. When I finally stood freshly arrayed and ready to go I turned despairingly to my wife. 'Surely I'll be all right this time.'

'Oh, you must be. There can't possibly be any of those things left now.'

I shifted gloomily under my fresh shirt. 'That's what we thought before.'

We had to pick up the Miss Whitlings, Harriet and Felicity, and we found them, as usual, bursting with vitality and good humour. They were in their late forties, large, busty ladies, and though some people might have called them fat, I had always considered them extremely comely and had been mystified that neither of them was married.

The journey back to Brawton passed quickly, aided by the non-stop conversation and, for me, the blissful knowledge that at last nothing was eating me alive. In the concert hall our two friends stationed themselves on either side of me, which I took as a compliment. In fact I was tightly squeezed between them because they both overflowed their seats to some extent.

As I drank in the familiar sounds of the concert hall, the orchestra tuning, the expectant buzz of conversation with my two attractive neighbours chattering on either side, I decided that, after my traumatic day, things had taken an upturn. Life was pretty good.

I joined in the wave of applause which greeted the slight figure of Barbirolli as he almost tiptoed across the platform. The people of Yorkshire loved him as much as anybody and the clapping went on and on. As he finally mounted the rostrum and raised his baton in the sudden hush, I settled back in happy anticipation.

It was just as the first majestic bars of Coriolanus sounded that I felt the prickle on my right shoulder blade. Oh, my God, no, it couldn't be. But the growing irritation was only too familiar. I tried to ignore it but, after a minute, I had to lean hard against the back of my seat to try to relieve the itch, and then, as it spread across my back, I had to execute the slightest of wriggles to transfer my weight the other way.

I realised suddenly and to my horror, that in my squashed-in situation even the slightest movement was transmitted instantly to one or other of my neighbours. As the maddening tickle mounted I wanted to scratch, throw myself about, fight the thing in every way, but that was unthinkable. I had to accept the frightening reality that for the next several hours I would have to sit still.

This involved a supreme effort of will on my part but I would have had to have been some sort of yogi to succeed. I did my best to concentrate on the music, but was forced to settle for short periods of inaction then a careful shifting of position, sometimes to brace my back against the seat or move my clothes against my skin by side-to-side shufflings.

I reckoned that there was only one flea at work now. After my experiences, I had become an authority on the species and I was positive that I could track his progress over my person. As Beethoven thundered around me, I had the feverish idea that I might trap him in the act and squash him and whenever I felt a fresh bite I tried to exert a fierce pressure against the hard wood and move slowly from side to side.

These manoeuvres inevitably involved encroachment on my partners' territory. I had expected during the evening to get to know the nice sisters better, to find out more about their personalities, but in fact I learned much more about their anatomies than anything else. Rounded arms, well-fleshed ribs, yielding hips – all were contacted and repeatedly explored in my helpless squirmings but, like the well-bred ladies that they were, neither of them showed any outward reactions to my incursions beyond an occasional clearing of the throat or sharp intake of breath. However, on two occasions, when I found my right knee deeply buried in the softness of Harriet's thigh, there was a definite withdrawal of the limb, and when my left elbow inadvertently but relentlessly nudged aside a weighty bosom I saw Felicity's eyebrows climb up her forehead.

I would rather say no more about that unhappy evening except that the pattern did not change. The divine Elgar Violin Concerto which, more than any other musical work, has the power to transport me to a perfect world, was only a background noise to my private battle. It was the same with the beloved Brahms' First Symphony. All I wanted was to get home.

During the interval and as we bade them goodnight at the end of the evening, there were a lot of fixed smiles and darting glances from the Miss Whitlings and the old saying about wanting the ground to swallow me was never so true.

And when it was all over and Helen and I were sitting on the edge of our bed going over the night's events I still felt terrible.

'My God, what a night!' I groaned, and as I dredged through my embarrassments with the sisters yet again Helen managed to keep a straight face but I could see that it was costing her dearly. Twitchings of the mouth, fierce frowns and an occasional sinking of her face in her hands betrayed her inner struggle.

At the end of my recital of woe, I threw out my hands in despair. 'And, do you know, Helen, I am convinced that all that agony I went throught tonight was caused by a single flea. Think of that! Just one flea!'

My wife suddenly dropped her chin on her chest, thrust out her lips and made a creditable attempt to sink her voice down a few octaves to basso-profundo pitch.

'A flea!' she intoned in true Chaliapin fashion. 'Ha-ha-ha-haaa, a flea!'

'Ah yes, very funny,' I replied, 'but Mussorgsky would never have put all the laughter in that song if he had suffered like me.'

Two days later Mr Colwell telephoned. 'Roopy's grand!' he cried in delight. 'Runnin' round, good as new, but 'e has a bit of broken nail sort of hangin' from his paw, and it's catchin' on things. I wish you'd come and cut it off.'

I didn't answer for a few seconds. 'You . . . you couldn't take it off yourself . . . just a little snip with scissors?'

'Nay, nay, I'm no good at that sort o' thing. I'd be right grateful if you'd drop in if you're out this way.'

'Right . . . right, Mr Colwell. I'll see you later this morning.'

'Helen,' I cried as I left the house, 'that was another call from the Colwells.'

'What!' she looked round the kitchen door in alarm.

'Yes . . . afraid so, but I'm calling first to see young Jack Arnold along the road.'

'Farmer Arnold's son?'

'Yes, that's right. The lad who does all that bicycle racing.'

'Why?'

'I'm going to borrow his clips.'

49

Sister Rose gently lifted the trembling dog on to the table. He was a tiny cross-bred terrier and he looked at me with terrified eyes.

'Poor little beggar,' I said, 'no wonder he's frightened. This is the one that was found on the road in Helvington, isn't it?'

Sister Rose nodded. 'Yes, running about aimlessly, looking for his owners. You've seen it all before.'

I had indeed. The desperate search for the people he had loved and trusted but who had dumped him and driven away. The dashing up, open-mouthed to somebody who looked familiar then turning away in bewilderment. To me it was an almost unbearable sight, evoking feelings of rage and pity which almost choked me.

'Never mind, old lad,' I said, stroking the shaggy head, 'there are better days ahead.'

There were always better days ahead for the abandoned dogs at Sister Rose's little animal sanctuary. It was amazing how soon her care and affection reassured and transformed the helpless creatures, and through the open door of the treatment room I could see the wagging tails and hear the joyous barking of the dogs in the row of wire-fronted pens.

I was here to do the usual duties. Check up on the health and condition of the new arrivals and give them their shots against distemper, hepatitis and leptospirosis, remove the stitches from the spay incisions (all bitches were spayed on arrival) and generally attend to any illness I might find.

'I see he's holding up a hind leg,' I said.

'Yes, he doesn't seem to be able to use that leg at all and I want you to have a look at it. I hope it's just a temporary thing.'

I examined the foot and claws. Normal. But as I felt my way up the leg, I soon found the cause of the trouble.

I turned to Sister Rose. 'He's had a fractured femur and it's never been set. The bone has formed a sort of callus but there's no real healing.'

'So this little thing had a broken leg and his owners just didn't bother about it?'

'That's right.' I ran my hand over the little body, feeling the jutting backbone, the almost fleshless ribs. 'He's emaciated too, just about skin and bone. This is a neglected dog if ever I saw one.'

'And I'll bet he's never had any affection either,' she said softly. 'Look how he trembles when we speak. He seems to be afraid of people.' She gave a long sigh. 'Ah well, we'll do what we can. How about that leg?'

'I'll have to X-ray it later today to see what can be done.' I gave the dog his inoculations and then Sister Rose carried him out and placed him in a pen on his own. 'By the way,' I said, 'what have you called this one?'

She smiled. 'I've called him Titch. Not a very elegant name, but he's so little.'

'Yes, I agree. Very suitable.' As I spoke, the thought recurred that finding names for her constant flow of rescued animals was only one of Sister Rose's problems. She was the radiologist at a big hospital but still found time to care for her ever-changing doggy family, and still was able to find the money by running events for her 'biscuit fund' and by dipping into her own pocket.

I was bandaging another dog's infected foot when I saw a man walking up and down the row of pens. He had his hands behind his back as he looked intently at the eager faces behind the wire.

'I see you've got a customer,' I said.

'I hope so. I like the look of him. He arrived just before you and he's making a very thorough search.'

As she spoke, the man half-turned to have a closer look. There was something familiar about that stocky frame.

'That's Rupe Nellist,' I exclaimed. 'I know him.'

A few years ago he had run a large grocery shop in Darrowby but he had expanded and opened another bigger business in the bustling town of Hargrove, thirty miles away, and had moved away to live there, but he was still a faithful client and had brought his dog to me regularly until it had died at the age of fifteen only a week ago.

I finished my bandaging and went out to him with Sister Rose.

'Hello, Rupe,' I said.

He turned in surprise. 'Now then, Mr Herriot. I didn't expect to see you.' His blunt-featured face, slightly pugnacious in repose, was attractive when he smiled. 'I've been miserable since I lost t'awd dog and I'm takin' your advice. I'm looking for another.'

'It's the only way, Rupe, and you've come to the right place. There are some lovely dogs here.'

'Aye, you're right.' He took off his trilby hat and smoothed back his hair. 'But I've had a heck of a job makin' up my mind. It sounds daft, but if I pick one out I'm goin' to feel sorry for all the other poor little blighters I'm leaving behind.'

Sister Rose laughed. 'A lot of people feel like that, Mr Nellist, but you needn't worry. I find good homes for all my dogs. I don't care how long I have to keep them – none is ever put to sleep. The only exceptions are in cases of extreme old age or incurable disease.'

'Aye, well, that's wonderful. I'll just have another stroll along here.' He recommenced his inspection of the pens, walking with a pronounced limp in his right leg, a relic of childhood polio.

Sister Rose hadn't been exaggerating when she said he was thorough. Up and down he went, talking to the animals, pushing a finger through the wire to tickle their noses. Many of the dogs were handsome specimens with a pedigree look about them – noble labradors, majestic golden retrievers, and a German shepherd which could have been a Crufts winner, and as I watched them all, tails wagging, leaping up at Rupe, I wondered as I often did how they could possibly have been abandoned. Each time he passed Titch's pen the little dog hopped along the other side of the wire on this three legs, keeping pace with him, looking up into his face.

Finally he stopped and gazed for a long time at the little creature. 'You know, I fancy that 'un,' he murmured.

'Really?' Sister Rose was surprised. 'He's only just arrived. We haven't had a chance to do anything for him. He's in a shocking state. Very lame, too.'

'Aye, I can see that. But let's have a look at 'im, will you?'

Sister Rose opened the door of the pen and Rupe Nellist reached in and lifted the little animal up until he was head high, gazing at him, eyeball to eyeball. 'Now, little feller,' he said softly, 'how would you like to come home wi' me?' The frightened eyes in the shaggy face regarded him for a few moments then the tail twitched and a pink tongue reached for his face.

The man smiled. 'I reckon this is a right good-natured little dog. We'll get on fine together.'

'You want him, then?' asked Sister Rose, wide-eyed.

'I do that. Right now.'

'Oh, I do wish we'd been able to get him straightened up for you first.'

'Don't worry. I'll do all that.' He put the dog down and pushed a note into the donation box. 'Thank ye, Sister, for letting me look round. What have you called this little bloke?'

'Titch, I'm afraid. Probably you'll want to change that.'

He laughed. 'Not at all. Come on, Titch.' He limped away toward his car with his new pet limping beside him. After a few steps he looked back with a grin. 'Walks like me, doesn't he? Same leg, too.'

*

I saw man and dog a fortnight later at my surgery when they came in for the booster inoculation. The difference in Titch was dramatic. He had filled out and, more striking still, the trembling and fear had gone.

'He's a different dog, Rupe,' I said. 'He looks as though he's had some good food at last, and he's happy, too.'

'Aye, by gum, he did eat for the first few days and he's settled down grand at home, too. My missus thinks the world of 'im.'

I noticed that as he spoke, the tiny animal's gaze was fixed unwaveringly on his new master. He was a shaggy little thing of baffling breeding, but his face had a scruffy appeal which was undeniably attractive and his eyes shone with devotion. Titch had found somebody else to love and this time I knew he wasn't going to be let down. Rupe Nellist was not a demonstrative man, but the way he looked at his new pet and gently stroked his head made it very clear that there was something in the little creature to which he responded deeply.

I took the opportunity to X-ray the lame leg and the picture was as I expected.

'It's too late to set the broken bone in plaster, Rupe,' I said. 'The only hope would be to plate the leg – bring the ends of the bone together and hold them there for a few weeks with a metal plate, and even then I couldn't guarantee he'd ever be sound. These things are best done at the time of the injury.'

'Yes, I understand that, but, you know, I'd give a lot to see the little feller goin' around on all four legs. He never puts that bad leg to the ground, and it upsets me. Think about it, and I'll do whatever you advise.'

Plating fractures was going deeper into orthopaedic surgery than I had ever done, but two things motivated me to have a go. Firstly, Rupe Nellist had a steadfast faith in my ability and, secondly, Calum Buchanan was determined to drag me into the modern world of small animal practice.

There was another thing, too. I kept hearing from people I knew who lived in Hargrove about Rupe's extraordinary affection for his new dog. It seemed that he took him everywhere with him, socially and in his work, showing him off proudly as if he was of the highest pedigree instead of, as most people would say, just a little mongrel. Rupe's business had continued to prosper with the opening of another large shop and he was active, too, on the town council and in local government. It caused some surprised comment that he actually took Titch into the council meetings with him, and had he not been a formidable personality, growing in power, he'd never have got away with it. There was no doubt about it, I'd have to try to fix that leg.

I found myself in a very familiar situation – having to perform an operation which I had never done, never even seen. I had received a good, scientific education at the veterinary college, but I had qualified at a time when a great wave of new drugs and procedures was sweeping over the profession and I was breathlessly trying to keep up with it all. All I could do was read up the new findings in our professional journals and this had enabled me to do a lot of bovine surgery such as Caesarean operations and rumenotomies which had never been performed in our district before. In my modest way, I was a pioneer in that field.

However, these things had been forced upon me, an unavoidable part of my life as a large animal practitioner. It had been only too easy to side-step the small animal surgery by sending our problem cases to the brilliant Granville Bennett, but it was time to face up to the fact that dog and cat work was going to occupy more and more of our lives. This was another revolution.

Calum was an enthusiastic advocate of the new ideas. He would tackle any kind of surgery with courage and determination, and he was enchanted at the opportunity to repair Titch's leg. And, unlike me, he had seen many of these orthopaedic operations done. The modern veterinary colleges had fine clinics where all the latest procedures were carried out – something undreamed of in my time.

We had to get in some new instruments and equipment but we were ready to start by the following Sunday morning. We picked that day because the practice would be quiet and we'd have more time.

I found, as with all new operations, that the actuality was ten times more difficult and frightening than I had expected from my reading. I seemed to spend an age, head to head with Calum, bending over Titch's sleeping form. Digging our way through the muscles down to the damaged bone, removing the partial callus and a seemingly endless mass of fibrous tissue, tying off the spurting blood vessels, freshening the ends of the bone, drilling, screwing in the plates which would hold the broken ends together. I was sweating and exhausted by the time the last skin suture was inserted and all that could be seen was the line of stitches. Thinking of what lay underneath, I breathed a silent prayer.

Over the next few weeks, Rupe Nellist kept bringing Titch in for examination. The wound had healed well with no reaction, but there was no attempt by the little dog to put the leg to the ground.

After two months we removed the plate. The bone had united beautifully, but Titch was still a three-legged dog.

'Doesn't he ever try to touch the ground with it?' I asked.

Rupe shook his head. 'Nay, he's as you see 'im. Never any different. Maybe he's been lame so long that he just holds the leg up out of habit?'

'Could be, but it's disappointing.'

'Never mind, Mr Herriot. You chaps have done your best and I'm grateful. And the little feller's grand in every other way.'

As he took his leave with his pet limping by his side, Calum turned to me with a wry smile. 'Ah well, some you lose.'

It was several months later when Calum read out a piece in the *Darrowby and Houlton Times*.

'Listen to this. "On Saturday there will be a civic reception for Rupert Nellist, newly elected Mayor of Hargrove, followed by an appearance outside the Town Hall."'

'Well, good old Rupe,' I said. 'He deserves it after all he's done for the town. I like that man.'

Calum nodded. 'So do I. And I wouldn't mind seeing him in his moment of glory. Do you think we could sneak through to Hargrove for half an hour?'

I looked at him thoughtfully. 'That would be nice, wouldn't it? And there's nothing much fixed for Saturday. I'll speak to Siegfried – I'm sure he'll hold the fort for us.'

Saturday morning found Calum and me among the crowd

standing in bright sunshine outside Hargrove Town Hall. At the top of the steps, several large pots of flowers had been placed on either side of the big doors and the multi-coloured blooms added to the festive air and the feeling of expectancy. A group of BBC men stood with their television cameras at the ready.

We hadn't long to wait. The doors swung open and as Rupe emerged, wearing his chain of office and with the Lady Mayoress by his side, a swelling cheer arose from the crowd. His popularity was reflected in the smiling faces and waving arms around us, then the sound increased suddenly in volume as Titch trotted out from behind his master. Everybody knew about Rupe's relationship with his dog.

However, the sound was as nothing compared to the great roar of laughter when Titch strolled to the front, cocked his leg, and relieved himself against one of the flower pots, a gesture which was to make him famous among TV audiences throughout the country.

Everybody was still laughing as the little procession came down the steps and began to pass through the crowd who opened up to make an avenue down which the Mayor and Mayoress walked, with Titch bringing up the rear.

It was a happy sight but Calum and I had eyes for only one thing.

Calum nudged me in the ribs. 'Do you see what I see?'

'I do,' I breathed, 'I certainly do.'

'He's sound. On four legs. Absolutely no signs of a limp.'

'Yes . . . great . . . marvellous!' The feeling of triumph made the sun shine more brightly.

We couldn't wait any longer, and as we got into the car, Calum turned to me. 'There was something else. When Titch was watering those flowers, did you notice anything?'

'Yes. He was cocking his good leg. All his weight was on the bad one.'

'Which means . . .' said Calum grinning.

'That he'll never be lame again.'

'That's right.' Calum settled behind the wheel and as he started the engine, he sighed contentedly. 'Ah well, some you win.'

50

Bob Stockdale was the sole survivor of the cataclysm which had struck the Lord Nelson Inn. In dirty wellington boots and flat cap, he sat there on a high stool at the end of the bar counter, seemingly oblivious of the endless torrent of piped music and the babel of voices from the jostling pack of smart young people.

I fought my way to the bar, collected a pint of bitter and, as I stood surveying the scene from a space against the wall, my thoughts drifted sadly back to the old days. A year ago the Lord Nelson was a typical Yorkshire country pub and I remembered an evening when I dropped in there with a friend from Glasgow, the city of my youth. There was just one big room then, rather like a large kitchen, with a log fire burning in a black cooking range at one end and a dozen farm men sitting on high-backed oak settles, their pints resting on tables of pitted wood. Those settles were a draught-proof refuge from the cold winds which whistled along the streets of the village outside and over the high pastures where those men spent their days.

The conversation never rose above a gentle murmur over which the ticking of a wall clock and the click of dominoes added to the atmosphere of rest and quiet.

'Gosh, it's peaceful in here,' my friend said. Wonderingly, he watched the proprietor, in shirt and braces, proceed unhurriedly down to the cellar and emerge with a long enamel jug from which he replenished the glasses, regulating the flow expertly to achieve the required head of froth.

'A bit different from West Nile Street,' I said.

He grinned. 'It certainly is. In fact, it's unbelievable. How does a place like this pay? Only a few chaps here, and they aren't drinking much.'

'I think it hardly pays at all. Maybe a few pounds a week, but the owner has a smallholding – there are cows, calves and pigs just through that wall – and he looks on this as a pleasant sideline.'

My friend took a pull at his glass, stretched out his legs and half closed his eyes. 'Anyway, I like it. You can relax here. It's lovely.'

It was indeed lovely and most of the pubs around Darrowby were still attractive, but as I looked at the modernised Lord Nelson I wondered how long they would stay that way.

When the new owner took over he didn't waste any time in starting his revolution. He wasn't a farmer, he was an experienced landlord and he could see rich possibilities in the old inn in the pretty village of Welsby tucked among the fells. The kitchen range disappeared and was replaced by a smart bar counter with a background of mirrors and gleaming bottles; the antique settles and tables were swept away, and horse brasses, hunting horns and sporting prints appeared on the walls. The end wall was knocked down and people ate in an elegant dining room where once I calved the cows and tended the pigs.

Two things happened almost at once; droves of young people swarmed out to Welsby in their cars from the big Yorkshire towns, and the old clientele melted away. I never knew where those farm men went, probably to pubs in the neighbouring villages – just Bob Stockdale stayed. I couldn't understand why, but he was a quiet man, a bit of a loner, and maybe he felt that he had sat in that room several nights a week for years and, despite all the changes, he didn't want to leave it. Anyway, whenever I called in, he was there, perched on the same stool, with his old bitch, Meg, tucked underneath. Welsby was part of the long long road up the dale which I had travelled a thousand times and when I had had a night call up there I sometimes dropped in for a beer. Tonight I had replaced a prolapsed uterus in a cow, and as I sipped at my glass I had the warm feeling of satisfaction after a successful operation.

I spotted a gap in the crush round the bar and pushed my way to Bob's side. 'Hello, Bob,' I said, 'can I top up your glass? It's getting a bit low.'

'Aye, thank ye, Mr Herriot. It's gettin' far down, right enough.' He drained the last few inches and pushed the glass across the counter.

He spoke slowly, articulating with care. It was nearing closing time and he would have been there a long time, quietly lowering the pints. He had reached a state of detachment from the world which I had seen before.

I looked down at Meg's nose protruding from between the legs of the stool and bent down to stroke the greying muzzle of the old bitch who was Bob's helper and friend. By day she brought the cows in for him, skirting eagerly around them, nipping at their heels if they strayed, and in the evenings they relaxed together.

I looked at the growing opacity in the friendly eyes. 'She's getting on a bit now, Bob.'

'Aye, she'll be ten come Easter, but she's still right active.'

'Oh yes, I've seen her at work. She'll go on for a long time yet.'

He nodded solemnly.

We talked for a few minutes. I had a great fellow feeling for men like Bob, the hardy farm workers who were part of my life – catching and holding the big beasts for me, sweating side by side with me at tough calvings and lambings. It was a pleasure to be able to meet them off the job and I could see that Bob was enjoying our reminiscing together. He smiled gently at the memories even though his speech was slurring and his eyes half closed.

I finished my drink and looked at my watch. 'Got to go now, Bob. Take care of yourself till I see you again.'

In reply he slid off the stool. 'Ah'm off 'ome, too.' He tacked his way carefully to the door, followed by Meg.

Outside in the summer dusk, he went over to his bicycle which was resting against the wall. I paused by my car. I had seen this ritual before and found it fascinating.

He pulled the bike from the wall and took some time about lining it up to his satisfaction, then he made an attempt to throw a wellingtoned leg over the saddle. He didn't make it first time and stood for a few seconds apparently breathing deeply, then with great care he got the bike into position before jerking his leg up again. Once more he missed and I thought for a moment that he was going to finish up, bike and all, on the ground, but he regained his balance and stood with bowed head, communing with himself. Then he squared his shoulders decisively, peered along cross bar and handlebars and this time with a convulsive leap he landed in the saddle.

For a tense period he sat there, moving only a few inches forward, feet working on the pedals, hands pulling the handlebars from side to side in his struggle to stay upright. Then at last he took off and began to move an inch at a time, almost imperceptibly along the road. After a few yards, he stopped and was stationary for several seconds keeping the bike vertical by some mystical means. I thought, not for the first time, that it was a pity that Bob had never entered for the annual slow bicycle race at Darrowby Gala. He would have carried the prize off every year.

Leaning on my car, I watched his progress. Old Meg, obviously familiar with the routine, stepped along patiently by his side, dropping on her chest whenever he carried out one of his miraculously balanced pauses. Bob's cottage was about a mile along the road and I wondered how long it would take him to get there. His erstwhile companions before the old pub was modernised were always adamant that he never ever fell off and I personally had never seen him come to grief. When man and dog finally disappeared in the growing darkness I got into my car and drove home.

As I said, I seemed to spend half my life on the road through Welsby, and I dropped into the Lord Nelson several times over the next few months. As always, I spotted Bob's flat cap perched incongruously among the modish jackets and dresses but one night as I peered through the crush I noticed something different.

I pushed my way to the corner of the bar. 'Hello, Bob. I see you haven't got Meg with you.'

He glanced down to the space under his stool, then took a sip at his glass before looking at me with a doleful expression. 'Nay . . . nay . . .' he murmured. 'Couldn't bring 'er.'

'Why not?'

He didn't reply for a few moments and when he spoke his voice was husky, almost inaudible. 'She's got cancer.'

'What!'

'Cancer. Meg's got cancer.'

'How do you know?'

'There's a big growth on 'er. It's been comin' on for a bit.'

'Why didn't you tell me?'

'You'd 'ave put her down. Ah don't want her put down yet.'

'But . . . but . . . you're jumping to conclusions, Bob. All growths aren't cancerous.'

'This 'un must be. It's a bloody great thing as big as a cricket ball.'

'And where is it?'

'Underneath 'er belly. Hangin' right down nearly to t'ground. It's awful.' He rubbed his eyes as though to blot out the memory. His face was a mask of misery.

I grasped his arm. 'Now, look, Bob, this sounds to me like a simple mammary tumour.'

'A what?'

'A growth on the bitch's udder. These things are very common and they're very often benign and quite harmless.'

'Oh not this 'un,' he quavered. 'It's a bloody big . . .' He demonstrated with his hands.

'Size doesn't matter. Come on, Bob, we'll go along to your house and have a look at it.'

'Nay . . . nay . . . Ah know what you'll do.' His eyes took on a hunted expression.

'I'll not do anything, I promise you.' I looked at my watch. 'It's nearly closing time. Let's go.'

He gave me a final despairing look, then got off his stool and made his careful way to the door.

Outside I watched the usual ceremony with the bike, but this time, at the third attempt at mounting, man and bike crashed to the ground. A bad sign. And on the interminable journey to the cottage Bob went down several times and as I looked at him, sprawled face down on top of his machine, I realised that the heart had gone out of him.

At the cottage, Bob's brother, Adam, looked up from his work on a hookey rug. Neither of the men had married and, though entirely different personalities, lived together in complete harmony. I hastened to Meg's basket and gently rolled the old bitch on to her side. It was indeed a huge tumour, but it was rock hard, confined to the skin and not attached to the mammary tissue.

'Look, Bob,' I said, 'I can get my fingers right behind it. I'm sure I can take it off with every chance of complete recovery.'

He dropped into a chair and Meg ambled across to greet him. He slowly stroked her ears. There was something pathetic about the waving tail, the open, panting mouth and the monstrous growth dangling almost to the floor.

There was no reply, and Adam broke in. 'You can see what 'e's like, Mr Herriot. I've been telling 'im for weeks to come to you but he takes no notice. I've lost patience with him.'

'How about it, Bob?' I said. 'Will you bring her to the surgery as soon as possible? The quicker it's done the better. You can't let her go on like this.'

He went on with his stroking for some time, then nodded his head. 'All right.'

'When?'

'Ah'll let ye know.'

Adam came in again. 'You see. He won't say, because I can tell you now that 'e never will bring her in to you. He's made up 'is mind that Meg's going to die.'

'That's daft, Bob,' I said. 'I tell you I'm pretty sure I can put her right. Will I take her away with me now? How about that?'

Still looking down, he shook his head vigorously. I decided on shock tactics.

'Well, let me do the operation now.'

He shot me a startled glance. 'What . . . right here?'

'Why not? It's not as big a job as you think. It doesn't involve any vital organs, and I always carry an operating kit in my car.'

'Good idea!' burst out Adam. 'It's the only way we'll get it done!'

'Just one thing,' I said, 'when did she last eat?'

'She had a few biscuits this morning,' Adam replied. 'But that's all. Bob always gives her her main meal last thing at night.'

'Fine, fine. She'll be just right for the anaesthetic.'

Bob seemed stupefied and he didn't say a word or make a move as Adam and I began to bustle about with our preparations. I had always been interested in the relationship between these two middle-aged brothers. They were opposites. Adam had never had an alcoholic drink in his life but seemed totally uncritical of Bob's beer-orientated lifestyle and when Bob was at the Lord Nelson he was usually attending night classes at the village school, rug-making being his latest interest. Adam wasn't a farm worker and was employed by the big dairy which collected the milk from the Dales farms. He was small and slightly built, finicky and fussy in his manner, unlike his burly, stolid brother.

After I had boiled the instruments, we lifted Meg on to the table and a quick injection of intravenous barbiturate sent the old bitch into deep anaesthesia. I made her fast on her back with bandages to the table legs and then all three of us scrubbed up at the kitchen sink. Bob, still wearing his cap, displayed a growing lack of enthusiasm and when I handed the brothers an artery forceps apiece and poised my scalpel he closed his eyes tightly.

My system with these tumours was to cut out an ellipse on the skin, then proceed by blunt dissection with my fingers. It looked a bit crude, but greatly reduced the amount of haemorrhage. I made my first incision and started to peel back the skin, and it was just at the moment when I had taken the forceps from the brothers and was clamping a couple of spurting vessels that Bob opened his eyes. He gave a hollow groan and tottered to an old horsehair sofa where he slumped and buried his head in his hands. His frail brother, however, was made of sterner stuff, and although he lost a little colour he set his lips firmly and gripped both the forceps on the vessels with a steady hand as I tied them off.

Once started, I went about my job with gusto, working my way with my fingers round the spherical growth, pushing back the adhering fascia from the skin. Some of these things almost popped out, and although this one wasn't quite as easy as that, I was doing fine. Soon I had the whole tumour in my hand except for a mass right at the bottom and I knew from experience that there would be a big vessel down there. 'Get ready with your forceps, Adam,' I said, tearing carefully at the tissue, but almost as I spoke a crimson jet fountained up into his face.

Bob chose this moment to uncover his eyes and after one appalled glance at his brother's blood-spattered spectacles he gave a strangled grunt and flopped onto his back on the sofa, pulling his cap over his eyes with a limp hand.

'Well done, Adam,' I said to the little man as he stood resolutely at his post, the forceps clamped on that final vessel while I ligated it and removed the tumour. 'We're about finished now. Just a few stitches to put in.' I inserted a row of nylon sutures and stood back, well satisfied.

'The old girl looks a lot better without that horrible thing,' I said and swept my hand across the unsullied abdomen. Unfortunately my fingers struck the tumour which was lying on the table and it fell to the floor with a bump and rolled towards the sofa.

Bob turned a startled face toward the source of the noise and his mouth fell open as he spotted the grisly object bowling in his direction. 'Oh, bloody 'ell,' he moaned, then turned his face to the wall.

There he stayed, immobile, while I helped his brother carry Meg over to her basket, scrub the table and generally clear up the debris.

When all signs of our operation had disappeared Adam took the kettle to the kitchen sink. 'I don't know about you, Mr Herriot, but I could do wi' a cup of tea.'

'I'd love one,' I said gratefully and dropped onto one of the oaken chairs.

Adam turned to the prone form on the sofa. 'How about you, Bob? Are you goin' to have a cup?'

Bob stirred, sat up and looked warily round the room. 'Nay . . . nay . . .' He got to his feet and went across to a cupboard from which he extracted a bottle of brown ale. He poured a glassful and took a long swallow, then he went over to the dog basket and peered in at the flat abdomen and the neat row of stitches. He crouched there for some minutes, stroking the sleeping animal and fondling her ears. Then he turned and looked at us and a slow smile of utter contentment spread over his face.

'Well,' he said, 'we did it.'

'Aye, Bob lad,' said his brother, smiling back at him. 'We did it.'

When I removed the stitches ten days later, I was able to reassure Bob that microscopic examination had shown the tumour to be benign and that his worries were over.

After that I didn't see him for nearly a month until, one evening, I spotted his cap above the crowd in the Lord Nelson. It was nearly closing time and as I pushed my way towards him he rose from his stool and Meg appeared from below and began to amble after him to the door. She looked younger and brighter without her disfiguring appendage. I watched the pair through the pub window, and once outside Meg flopped down with her nose on her paws waiting for her master to go through the time-honoured routine.

Bob seized his bike and gave it a good shake as though to let it know who was boss. He took only two efforts to get astride, and although he was poised there immobile, working the handlebars from side to side, there was an authoritative look about his movements and it wasn't long before he took off on his journey home. I watched man and dog until they were out of sight and although there were frequent pauses I could see that there was no danger of a catastrophe.

Bob wasn't going to fall off tonight. He was himself again.

51

Calum inserted the last stitch after one of his dextrous operations and looked down at the sleeping cat for a few seconds.

'Jim', he said, without raising his head, 'I'm afraid I'm going to leave you.'

'Oh.' My heart gave a lurch, and I couldn't think of anything else to say at that moment. Calum had been with us for two years and, like all young vets, there had to come a time when he wanted to branch out on his own. But there was only one thought in my mind – I didn't want him to go.

Receiving no further reply, Calum went on. 'Yes, I've had the chance of a job which I think will suit me.'

'Oh . . .' My restricted vocabulary was making me feel like an idiot. 'Well . . . I understand, of course, Calum. Where will you be going?' My brain was starting to work again and one certainty loomed large – it would be somewhere isolated, somewhere in the wilds. Most likely the north of Scotland . . . maybe in the Western Isles.

'Nova Scotia,' he replied.

'My God!' I realised suddenly that I didn't fully know him after all.

He laughed. 'I thought you'd say something like that. I've been in touch with a chap who runs a practice out there, and the prospect seems right for me. It covers a wide area of a rural district with some quite primitive conditions – a lot of the countryside is in its natural uncultivated state; unmade roads, rough farms, wonderful variety of wildlife. Some quite desolate country nearby, I understand.' A faraway look crept into his dark eyes as though he were glimpsing the promised land.

I began to laugh, too. 'Oh, hell, Calum, I'm sorry to be like this. It was a bit of a shock, in fact two shocks, but it does sound like your cup of tea and I hope you'll be very happy out there. What does Deirdre think about the idea?'

'Loves it. Can't wait to get started.'

'I don't doubt it. I think I hear Siegfried coming in. We'd better tell him.'

We met my partner in the passage. He looked a bit solemn as we gave him the news, then, like me, he put on a cheerful face and thumped Calum on the shoulder. 'I'm so glad you've found something you really want, my boy. I'm sure it will be the very thing for you and I wish you and Deirdre every happiness and success. But damn it, I'm going to miss you.'

He stopped suddenly and pointed wordlessly at an enormous feathered creature stalking past him. 'What . . . ? What . . . ?' In the darkness of the passage it looked as big as an ostrich.

The young man smiled happily. 'Just a heron. I picked it up a few days ago, down by the river. Wandering around, couldn't fly. Obviously damaged a wing, but seems to be improving.' As he spoke, the great bird spread its wings and flapped round the corner and out of sight. 'Ah, look. Soon be completely recovered.'

'I hope so . . . I do hope so.' Siegfried stared at him, then cocked an ear at the scrabbling of a couple of recently adopted tortoises on the tiles further along the passage. Then he grinned suddenly. 'Yes, I'm going to miss you all right.'

The few weeks before Calum's departure fled past and after he and Deirdre had gone, I had that empty feeling again as I went into the deserted flat. John Crooks and now Calum – they had become my friends and both had left a gap, but with Calum the change was even more traumatic. The silence in the absence of the menagerie was almost palpable and as I looked out of the window where he had demolished that cake on his first day, many things rose and lingered in my mind. 'Permission to eat, sir', 'I'll just put Deirdre up a tree', Herriot's duct and, most emotive of all, the picture of his rapt face and dark eyes as he squeezed 'Shenandoah' from my children's little concertina.

Calum had been an acutely interesting man during his stay in Darrowby, but it was nearly as interesting to follow his career after he had left. I received regular letters telling me about his growing practice among the dirt roads and untamed countryside of Nova Scotia. His bursting energy led him to start the first auction mart in the district and he was trying to develop small animal work. A sentence sticks in my mind, 'Doing quite a few cat spays – Herriot's duct much in evidence.' The letters often ended, 'Permission to fall out, sir' which pulled me back to the old days.

Training Border collies was another of his passions and he gave frequent public demonstrations of his skill, several generations of his dogs being descended from prize winning sheep dogs which he bought from a farmer friend during his stay in Darrowby. He bought a farm, too, in Cape Breton, as though he didn't have enough to occupy him.

I also was kept abreast of the regular arrival of his children, noting with growing wonder as they mounted up to six. He brought up all of them in his own image, to love the outdoors and the wild creatures which abounded, to scorn the soft things of life as he had always done, and to camp and back-pack in the forests and mountains.

Often as I read those letters from Calum, the thought recurred that at last he had found his ideal environment, but I was wrong.

Twenty years after he left Darrowby, I was treating a cow for his farmer friend, Alan Beech. Alan, who was holding the animal's nose, spoke to me over his shoulder. 'Have you heard the latest about Calum?'

'No, what's that?'

'He's leaving Nova Scotia.'

'Never!'

'It's right. And where d'you think he's going?'

A jumble of thoughts spun in my mind. At last, with the advance of middle age, he was finding it too rough and tough out there. Felt it necessary to take his family to somewhere which offered a more gentle life. Maybe he was coming back here.

'I've no idea.' I said, 'tell me.'

'Papua New Guinea.'

'What!'

'Absolutely right.' Alan's face broke into a wide grin. 'Would you believe it!'

'My God, from cold and snows to steamy heat. It could only be Calum! Maybe Nova Scotia was too soft and sophisticated for him?'

'That could be it. He doesn't seem satisfied there – wants a place where there's still a lot o' cannibals about from what I've heard. By heck, he's a rum feller!'

I'd heard that description of Calum a thousand times from the farmers around Darrowby and now it seemed to be more strikingly proven than ever. I looked up Papua New Guinea in the public library and read that it wasn't until 1930 that the first white man had made contact with the million inhabitants of the unexplored highlands where Calum had gone. It was a whole intact civilisation which had had no connection with the outside world.

I looked at pictures of fierce-looking, almost naked men with slivers of bone transfixing their nostrils and brandishing bows and arrows as they glared into the camera. These frightening people would be his neighbours and there was nothing more certain than that he would love them all, especially those wide-eyed little black children.

In due course, letters started to arrive from Mendi in the Southern Highlands. Calum, as expected, was utterly entranced by it all. The agriculture was Stone Age in character with pigs the only livestock, most of the settlements unchanged from when the first whites discovered them, and the primitive farmers, although a bit careless about keeping appointments when he tried to teach them animal husbandry, were charming chaps. Deirdre and he were already firm friends with all of them.

As the months and years passed, he was clearly absorbed in the development and improvement of the country. I learned how he introduced cattle, sheep and poultry into the local agriculture, educated the farmers and immersed himself in the life there with all his energy.

In 1988, his daughter, Sarah, wrote to me. She said: 'Dad still amazes me with his knowledge of the local vegetation and wild life. On his station farm he has 11 Border Collies, 2 pig dogs (labrador crosses), 2 water buffalo, 5 horses, many cattle, sheep, goats, an assortment of chickens, ducks, guinea fowl and a huge flock of homing pigeons.'

As I put down her letter I thought of Calum's little menagerie at Skeldale House. It had been only a rehearsal for this. The vet wi' t'badger would be happy now.

52

Months passed without any thawing of relations between me and our two wild cats and I noticed with growing apprehension that Olly's long coat was reverting to its previous disreputable state. The familiar knots and tangles were reappearing and within a year it was as bad as ever. It became more obvious every day that I had to do something about it. But could I trick him again? I had to try.

I made the same preparations, with Helen placing the nembutal-laden food on the wall, but this time Olly sniffed, licked, then walked away. We tried at his next meal time but he examined the food with deep suspicion and turned away from it. It was very clear that he sensed there was something afoot.

Hovering in my usual position at the kitchen window I turned to Helen. 'I'm going to have to try to catch him.'

'Catch him? With your net, do you mean?'

'No, no. That was all right when he was a kitten. I'd never get near him now.'

'How, then?'

I looked out at the scruffy black creature on the wall. 'Well, maybe I can hide behind you when you feed him and grab him and bung him into the cage. I could take him down to the surgery then, give him a general anaesthetic and make a proper job of him.'

'Grab him? And then fasten him in the cage?' Helen said incredulously. 'It sounds impossible to me.'

'Yes, I know, but I've grabbed a few cats in my time and I can move fast. If only I can keep hidden. We'll try tomorrow.'

My wife looked at me, wide-eyed. I could see that she had little faith.

Next morning she placed some delicious fresh chopped raw haddock on the wall. It was the cats' favourite. They were not particularly partial to cooked fish but this was irresistible. The open cage lay hidden from sight. The cats stalked along the wall, Ginny sleek and shining, Olly a pathetic sight with his ravelled hair and ugly knotted appendages dangling from his neck and body. Helen made her usual fuss of the two of them, then, as they descended happily on the food she returned to the kitchen where I was lurking.

'Right, now,' I said. 'I want you to walk out very slowly again and I am going to be tucked in behind you. When you go up to Olly he'll be concentrating on the fish and maybe won't notice me.'

Helen made no reply as I pressed myself into her back in close contact from head to toe.

'Okay, off we go.' I nudged her left leg with mine and we shuffled off through the door, moving as one.

'This is ridiculous,' Helen wailed. 'It's like a music hall act.'

Nuzzling the back of her neck I hissed into her ear. 'Quiet, just keep going.'

As we advanced on the wall, double-bodied, Helen reached out and stroked Olly's head, but he was too busy with the haddock to look up. He was there, chest-high, within a couple of feet of me. I'd never have a better chance. Shooting my hand round Helen, I seized him by the scruff of his neck, held him, a flurry of flailing black limbs, for a couple of seconds then pushed him into the cage. As I crashed the lid down, a desperate paw appeared at one end but I thrust it back and slotted home the steel rod. There was no escape now.

I lifted the cage on to the wall with Olly and me at eye level and I flinched as I met his accusing stare through the bars. 'Oh no, not again! I don't believe this!' it said. 'Is there no end to your treachery?'

In truth, I felt pretty bad. The poor cat, terrified as he was by my assault, had not tried to scratch or bite. It was like the other occasions – his only thought was to get away. I couldn't blame him for thinking the worst of me.

However, I told myself, the end result was going to be a fine handsome animal again. 'You won't know yourself, old chap,' I said to the petrified little creature, crouched in his cage on the car seat by my side as we drove to the surgery. 'I'm going to fix you up properly, this time. You're going to look great and feel great.'

Siegfried had offered to help me and when we got him on the table, a trembling Olly submitted to being handled and to the intravenous anaesthetic. As he lay sleeping peacefully, I started on the awful tangled fur with a fierce pleasure, snipping and trimming and then going over him with the electric clippers followed by a long combing until the last tiny knot was removed. I had only given him a make-shift hair-do before, but this was the full treatment.

Siegfried laughed when I held him up after I had finished. 'Looks ready to win any cat show,' he said.

I thought of his words next morning when the cats came to the wall for their breakfast. Ginny was always beautiful, but she was almost outshone by her brother as he strutted along, his smooth, lustrous fur gleaming in the sunshine.

Helen was enchanted at his appearance and kept running her hand along his back as though she couldn't believe the transformation. I, of course, was in my usual position, peeking furtively from the kitchen window. It was going to be a long time before I even dared to show myself to Olly.

*

It very soon became clear that my stock had fallen to new depths, because I had only to step out of the back door to send Olly scurrying away into the fields. The situation became so bad that I began to brood about it.

'Helen,' I said one morning, 'this thing with Olly is getting on my nerves. I wish there was something I could do about it.'

'There is, Jim,' she said. 'You'll really have to get to know him. And he'll have to get to know you.'

I gave her a glum look. 'I'm afraid if you asked him, he'd tell you that he knows me only too well.'

'Oh, I know, but when you think about it, over all the years that we've had these cats, they've hardly seen anything of you, except in an emergency. I've been the one to feed them, talk to them, pet them, day in day out. They know me and trust me.'

'That's right, but I just haven't had the time.'

'Of course you haven't. Your life is one long rush. You're no sooner in the house than you're out again.'

I nodded thoughtfully. She was so right. Over the years I had been attached to those cats, enjoyed the sight of them trotting down the slope for their food, playing in the long grass in the field, being fondled by Helen, but I was a comparative stranger to them. I felt a pang at the realisation that all that time had flashed past so quickly.

'Well, probably it's too late. Do you think there is anything I can do?'

'Yes,' she said. 'You have to start feeding them. You'll just have to find the time to do it. Oh, I know you can't do it always, but if there's the slightest chance, you'll have to get out there with their food.'

'So you think it's just a case of cupboard love with them?'

'Absolutely not. I'm sure you've seen me with them often enough. They won't look at their food until I've made a fuss of them for quite a long time. It's the attention and friendship they want most.'

'But I haven't a hope. They hate the sight of me.'

'You'll just have to persevere. It took me a long time to get their trust. Especially with Ginny. She's always been the more timid one. Even now if I move my hand too quickly, she's off.

Despite all that's happened, I think Olly might be your best hope – there's a big well of friendliness in that cat.'

'Right,' I said. 'Give me the food and milk. I'll start now.'

That was the beginning of one of the little sagas in my life. At every opportunity, I was the one who called them down, placed the food on the wall top and stood there waiting. At first I waited in vain. I could see the two of them watching me from the log shed – the black-and-white face and the yellow, gold and white one observing me from the straw beds – and for a long time they would never venture down until I had retreated into the house. Because of my irregular job, it was difficult to keep the new system going and sometimes when I had an early morning call they didn't get their breakfast on time, but it was on one of those occasions when breakfast was over an hour late that their hunger overcame their fear and they came down cautiously while I stood stock still by the wall. They ate quickly with nervous glances at me then scurried away. I smiled in satisfaction. It was the first breakthrough.

After that, there was a long period when I just stood there as they ate until they became used to me as part of the scenery. Then I tried a careful extension of a hand. To start with, they backed away at that but, as the days passed, I could see that my hand was becoming less and less of a threat and my hopes rose steadily. As Helen had prophesied, Ginny was the one who shied right away from me at the slightest movement, whereas Olly, after retreating, began to look at me with an appraising eye as though he might possibly be willing to forget the past and revise his opinion of me. With infinite patience, day by day, I managed to get my hand nearer and nearer to him and it was a memorable occasion when he at last stood still and allowed me to touch his cheek with a forefinger. As I gently stroked the fur, he regarded me with unmistakably friendly eyes before skipping away.

'Helen,' I said, looking round at the kitchen window, 'I've made it! We're going to be friends at last. It's a matter of time now till I'm stroking him as you do.' I was filled with an irrational pleasure and sense of fulfilment. It did seem a foolish reaction in a man who was dealing every day with animals of all kinds, but I was looking forward to years of friendship with that particular cat.

I was wrong. At that moment I could not know that Olly would be dead within forty-eight hours.

It was the following morning when Helen called to me from the back garden. She sounded distraught. 'Jim, come quickly! It's Olly!'

I rushed out to where she was standing near the top of the slope near the log shed. Ginny was there, but all I could see of Olly was a dark smudge on the grass.

Helen gripped my arm as I bent over him. 'What's happened to him?'

He was motionless, his legs extended stiffly, his back arched in a dreadful rigor, his eyes staring.

'I . . . I'm afraid he's gone. It looks like strychnine poisoning.' But as I spoke he moved slightly.

'Wait a minute!' I said. 'He's still alive, but only just.' I saw that the rigor had relaxed and I was able to flex his legs and lift him without any recurrence. 'This isn't strychnine. It's like it, but it isn't. It's something cerebral, maybe a stroke.'

Dry-mouthed, I carried him down to the house where he lay still, breathing almost imperceptibly.

Helen spoke through her tears. 'What can you do?'

'Get him to the surgery right away. We'll do everything we can.' I kissed her wet cheek and ran out to the car.

Siegfried and I sedated him because he had begun to make paddling movements with his limbs, then we injected him with steroids and antibiotics and put him on an intravenous drip. I looked at him as he lay in the big recovery cage, his paws twitching feebly. 'Nothing more we can do, is there?'

Siegfried shook his head and shrugged. He agreed with me about the diagnosis – stroke, seizure, cerebral haemorrhage, call it what you like, but certainly the brain. I could see that he had the same feeling of hopelessness as I had.

We attended Olly all that day and, during the afternoon, I thought for a brief period that he was improving, but by evening he was comatose again and he died during the night.

I brought him home and as I lifted him from the car, his smooth, tangle-free fur was like a mockery now that his life was ended. I buried him just behind the log shed a few feet from the straw bed where he had slept for so many years.

Vets are no different from other people when they lose a pet, and Helen and I were miserable. We hoped that the passage of time would dull our unhappiness, but we had another poignant factor to deal with. What about Ginny?

Those two cats had become a single entity in our lives and we never thought of one without the other. It was clear that to Ginny the world was incomplete without Olly. For several days she ate nothing. We called her repeatedly but she advanced only a few yards from the log house, looking around her in a puzzled way before turning back to her bed. For all of those years, she had never trotted down that slope on her own and over the next few weeks her bewilderment as she gazed about her continually, seeking and searching for her companion, was one of the most distressing things we had ever had to witness.

Helen fed her in her bed for several days and eventually managed to coax her on to the wall, but Ginny could scarcely put her head down to the food without peering this way and that, still waiting for Olly to come and share it.

'She's so lonely,' Helen said. 'We'll have to try to make a bigger fuss of her now than ever. I'll spend more time outside talking with her, but if only we could get her inside with us. That would be the answer, but I know it will never happen.'

I looked at the little creature, wondering if I'd ever get used to seeing only one cat on the wall, but Ginny sitting by the fireside or on Helen's knee was an impossible dream. 'Yes, you're right, but maybe I can do something. I'd just managed to make friends with Olly – I'm going to start on Ginny now.'

I knew I was taking on a long and maybe hopeless challenge because the tortoiseshell cat had always been the more timid of the two, but I pursued my purpose with resolution. At meal times and whenever I had the opportunity, I presented myself outside the back door, coaxing and wheedling, beckoning with my hand. For a long time, although she accepted the food from me, she would not let me near her. Then, maybe because she needed companionship so desperately that she felt she might as well even resort to me, the day came when she did not back away but allowed me to touch her cheek with my finger as I had done with Olly.

After that, progress was slow but steady. From touching I moved week by week to stroking her cheek then to gently rubbing her ears, until finally I could run my hand the length of her body and tickle the root of her tail. From then on, undreamed of familiarities gradually unfolded until she would not look at her food until she had paced up and down the wall top, again and again, arching herself in delight against my hand and brushing my shoulders with her body. Among these daily courtesies one of her favourite ploys was to press her nose against mine and stand there for several moments looking into my eyes.

It was one morning several months later that Ginny and I were in this posture – she on the wall, touching noses with me, gazing into my eyes, drinking me in as though she thought I was rather wonderful and couldn't quite get enough of me – when I heard a sound from behind me.

'I was just watching the veterinary surgeon at work,' Helen said softly.

'Happy work, too,' I said, not moving from my position, looking deeply into the green eyes, alight with friendship, fixed on mine a few inches away. 'I'll have you know that this is one of my greatest triumphs.'